LIBRARY OF FILM AND TELEVISION PRACTICE

THE WORK OF THE FILM DIRECTOR
A. J. Reynertson

THE WORK OF THE SCIENCE FILM MAKER
Alex Strasser

THE WORK OF THE INDUSTRIAL FILM MAKER
John Burder

THE WORK OF THE TELEVISION JOURNALIST
Robert Tyrell

THE WORK OF THE MOTION PICTURE CAMERAMAN
Freddie Young and Paul Petzold

FILMING FOR TELEVISION
A. Arthur Englander and Paul Petzold

Filming for Television

A. ARTHUR ENGLANDER
PAUL PETZOLD

Preface by
Kenneth Clark

FOCAL PRESS
London & New York

ISBN 0 240 50961 7

First published 1976

Text set in 11/12 pt Photon Baskerville, printed by photolithography, and bound in Great Britain at The Pitman Press, Bath

Contents

Preface

BY LORD CLARK OF SALTWOOD, CH, KCB

ALL THE PERFORMING arts involve the collaboration of two or three people. The stage actor requires a director, and usually comes to grief if he tries to direct himself. In television the performer is also dependent on a director, but in addition he needs an expert cameraman, in whom he has complete confidence. In making the series called *Civilisation* I had the great good fortune to have a cameraman and master of lighting who was generally accepted as the most experienced and skilful in the country. Tubby Englander was, if he will forgive me for employing a word which may sound too formal, the doyen of cameramen. When I began work on *Civilisation* I had already made over fifty programmes; but most of these had been studio productions. The whole of *Civilisation* was taken in the appropriate locations, and these were naturally of very varying kinds; huge buildings, small interiors, wide landscapes, rowing boats, every sort of unexpected circumstance. I had chosen these locations without thought of the difficulties they might present to a cameraman, and in the event I was seldom made conscious that there had been any difficulty. At precisely the moment indicated to me I walked up to the spot I had chosen, and did my first "take" without a qualm. If it was not always a success that was because I had not yet realized how my words would sound under these particular conditions. In my experience the third "take" is nearly always the best. After that the performance tends to become mechanical, and after about seven "takes" fatigue or boredom become apparent. I am told that professional actors sometimes do as many as twenty "takes"—a great waste of time and film stock. Perhaps they have not had the same confidence in their cameraman that I had.

The two most difficult locations that Tubby Englander had to face were the Sistine Chapel and Napoleon's tomb in the Invalides. They both involved vast problems of lighting. The Sistine ceiling, being so far away, required and absorbed an incredible quantity of light, the huge, dark *Last Judgement* only a little less. I had to come in through the screen that divides the Chapel, and somehow contrive that my commentary on the episodes on the ceiling were in correct sequence. And all the time I had to be lit in harmony with my august surroundings. We were at it till well after midnight. I have sometimes been asked what is the secret of success in television. The answer is "patience", and this applies to the cameraman as well as to the performer. A curious footnote: the Sistine Chapel is extremely noisy. When one visits it as a tourist all outside noise is drowned by competitive, multi-lingual bellowing of the guides. But when it is closed to the public one realises that the left wall is beside the steep road that runs up towards the Vatican gallery, and cars and motor-bicycles roar up it till after midnight, so that a sound problem—that most boring bugbear of location television—was added to the difficulty of lighting. The interior of the Invalides was even more difficult to light, and Tubby, perhaps mistakenly, thought it was necessary to light almost the whole church. The well of the actual tomb would probably have been enough. He spent at least seven hours on the job, and fortunately my presence was not required till about an hour before the exhausted lighting crew were ready. The resulting sequence lasted fifty seconds, and the illuminated chapel was just visible for about three. Such is the price of perfectionism.

There is no doubt that Tubby Englander is a perfectionist. On location he was always immaculately dressed, his dark suits contrasting oddly with the conventionally unconventional garments of the crew (although his brilliant assistant cameraman, Ken MacMillan was also a great dandy). Like Hercule Poirot, the smallest spot of dust offended him, and he used to flick one off my suit before almost every shot. He also carried a neat little comb and small hairbrush to deal with any of my hairs which the breeze had displaced.

I ought to add that the name of "Tubby" (like so many nicknames) is entirely misleading. No one less Tubby can be imagined. He looks like a figure from a Moghul miniature, one of those elegant, silent men whose presence in India must have been almost as foreign to the original inhabitants as that of the English. His love of perfection made him a somewhat solitary man, and my wife and I were proud that he should have accepted us as friends. The years spent in filming *Civilisation* were amongst the happiest in my life, and much of that happiness I owe to my directors and my crew. But I feel that I owe a special debt to Tubby for the example he set me of perfect expertise, and the confidence he inspired in me.

Introduction

"We don't ask you to make films—we defy you to!"

THAT AGE-OLD statement of frustration is still applicable today, and one of the aims of this book is to offer solutions for technical problems that arise when filming for television. Problems stem from several causes, because film is used in many contexts in television, ranging from short inserts to complete programmes. The cameraman is presented with many different types of situation in a wide variety of programmes. Yet in all these situations, including drama, because of time, economics and weather, he is liable to find himself operating in areas over which he has little control. He is presented with a given set of circumstances and, however unfavourable they may be, he must do the best he can.

To be efficient, a cameraman must always maintain speed and mobility, good image definition and correct exposure. Time is the most expensive factor in film production. As a cameraman I know, and there are other technicians who know likewise, that the day of the "Rembrandt" has been over for quite a while. It is now the era of "bread and butter" filming. When the jam does come along, as inevitably it does, it is all the more sweet for being rare.

Any cameraman can cover every eventuality, real or imagined, on a production by ordering up vast quantities of hardware (with the crews to operate them). Any director and, indeed, even a ten year old child can, if given unlimited time and supplies of raw stock, produce sufficient film material to be edited into a thirty minute programme. But if a cameraman and director really work together and fully understand each other's problems, they can keep crews and equipment to a minimum, conserve filmstock by maintaining a low shooting ratio and so help reduce the cost of a production without impairing the quality of the result. These are very much today's facts of life, or they should be, otherwise the industry will begin to wither away as others before it have done.

There was no particular reason why I went into the film industry in 1931. The family fortunes were at a low ebb because things had gone wrong with my father's business during the slump. At that time we were living in Surbiton, where I was born, but my parents decided to move into London, where my mother would open a guest house. I was just 15, and had to find a job. Our new home was at Brondesbury, not far from Cricklewood, where my mother remembered there was a film studio—Stolls Picture Productions. The cameraman there, Desmond Dickenson, was a very faint acquaintance of my brother. My mother wrote to him and much to everyone's surprise, a letter came back inviting me to an interview for a trainee job on a new production.

The film was *Lloyd of the CID*. It was made by Universal and was a 13-part serial, each part being six reels. So I was "permanently" employed in the film industry—until the bottom fell out of it, as it usually did every twelve months! My start was sheer luck. I had simply wanted a job but here I was as trainee cameraman, doing the number board, fetching the tea and getting D.D. his morning sherry—an early acquaintance with the close relationship between the film industry and the trappings of high life.

Eventually, I was to become disenchanted with feature films—the waste of time and effort—but at the outbreak of war I was working for Warner Brothers. As is the case of many people who might have been first assistant or second operator at that time, I did a couple of years in the infantry and was then transferred by the War Office to Wembley Studios where the AKS (Army Kinematograph Service) was starting up. We made military information, instructional and secret films and during this period I became Freddie Young's operator and later a junior cameraman. My four years experience in this "forcing ground", where mistakes were made and corrected in army time, gave me knowledge and experience worth ten years training in the film industry!

I did not go back into the feature film industry after the war, and had no reason to regret it because I was able to join a documentary company, called Basic Films, that had already been formed by three other people. I was with them from 1946 until 1950, when I left the company and worked freelance for a while. In 1951, I joined the Ministry of Works to make industrial and construction films. I did the scriptwriting, the camerawork, etc. almost single-handed, which was very interesting. However, because of economic measures introduced by a new government, that department was closed down.

I then managed to get a British and European agency for an American television newsreel company called Spot News. Besides being European representative for them, I was to make 15-minute documentaries myself. This brought me in contact with the BBC for the first time, inasmuch as I negotiated an agreement for the exchange of their newsreel material and the material I had shot for the American company. It was a useful agreement and the prospects were bright—but the American company closed down after about two months!

So it was back to freelancing again but before I really got going on anything substantial, the BBC gave me a call to ask if I would join them for a month. That was in 1952 and I stayed with them until 1976. At the time the BBC was not keen on employing "outside" film people because they did not agree with their attitudes to filming. At this stage of television, the BBC did not like the classical set-piece approach used by the feature film industry. The basic objection was the slow speed at which feature film people were trained to work and their demands for particular types of equipment. For a television company there was a difference in approach between a film studio technician and his documentary equivalent. Television companies preferred documentary technicians because they were themselves doing a considerable amount of documentary and newsreel work.

Today, we work even more quickly in television than twenty years ago because we now have much lighter equipment—for 16 mm instead of 35 mm filming. Twenty years ago TV technicians worked with standard film industry hardware but without the film industry time standards or their crews. Salaries were much lower, too, so feature film industry staff were not particularly anxious to work in television. The documentary field, however, was no better paid than television, so the first BBC technicians came from documentary origins or were trained by the Corporation itself. In 1946–47 the BBC had taken back the people who had worked for them before the war (they were obliged to do that anyway) and began to train a few of them in order to service the TV film department which made television newsreels. These were part-news, part-magazine programmes which appeared twice a week.

The film department did not really begin to grow in size until 1955–56, and only then did the really skilled technicians start to come into the BBC. Those who had worked in the industry and were fully trained technicians certainly had the advantage and tended to be given virtual *carte blanche* and very interesting jobs to do. One advantage to belonging to the BBC at this time was that you were not just an employee but were actually helping to build it up. This was a very good period. From the early 50s to 1960 everyone there was helping to create the organization and training people off-the-cuff. When we moved from Alexandra Palace to Lime Grove it was the first time that we had proper studios in which to do film sequences. The five or six cameramen then active were very conscious of telling directors how to use film (how scenes would cut or how to shoot them to cut) and most of the directors were prepared to listen.

Although British television was the first to return to broadcasting after the war, there was no filmed content. This did not appear until about 1950. For drama, which was mostly live in those days, filmed content simply provided a breathing space to allow time for changes of scenery or costume down on the studio floor. It tended to consist of shots of people coming down stairs, going through doors, getting into cars, driving off and arriving at another place from which there would then be a cut to further studio action. It was very primitive. Sequences, as such, were not really thought of.

By the end of the 1960s the production powers within the Corporation became disembodied—departments grew and "empires" within departments established themselves as the administrative side expanded. In the film industry there had always been pressures between the technician and the administrator. Up to the war the technician's viewpoint had usually been paramount—he was always able to get his way, against the administrators. After the war the administrator gained ascendency and took control over the technicians. It was the effect of the war, no doubt. They always used to say that there were nine people back at base in order to keep one man (in their case a technician) in the field. Soon, this effect started to appear in the industry in general.

With the advent of independent television (ITV) in 1964 great emphasis was placed on achieving and maintaining the numerical superiority of the viewing audience. Because of that the production process had to become slightly akin to that of a factory. Programmes came to conform much more to a set pattern, often seeming almost computerized. Naturally the technician's views carried even less weight from that time forward. He helped to build the machine which the administration has since taken over. But we have to set against this the inescapable fact that, with the old order, productions like *Civilisation* did not, and could not exist. Someone thought of it, it happened and was a success.

Civilisation was a justification, if I needed one, for my rather fortuitous entry into the film industry. Every single thing that I have learned and remembered from the very early days seemed to have been of use on this production. I was involved in it for nearly two years and did nothing else in that time. When I had finished a shooting stint I immediately went on to the next pre-production planning stage with the two directors. In the whole project I did 3500 set-ups (shots) and I never had to refuse what a director asked. This was only because in tackling various types of problems I was able to draw on experience that I had accumulated since I began as a cameraman. For example, I was asked to do a long shot of the dark interiors of Chartres cathedral. If I could turn the camera motor slowly and carry out the movements slowly, if I could avoid having people in the shot, the available lights would barely give enough illumination to make the shot possible. Yet I knew subconsciously that all the shots would work out. I am not religious but I had a strange feeling when working on *Civilisation* that something was backing me up. There was a reason for *Civilisation* and I had the feeling that I was not on my own, something was giving added strength. I do not think I could do it again. For instance, if I were to go back to the roccoco church at Ottobeuren with the number of lights that I had then, I do not think I could manage it; it would not come out that way, I am sure. For me as an individual, something like *Civilisation* will never happen again.

Filmed by A. Arthur Englander

1952	Her People Rejoiced (Coronation Films)	Series of pre-Coronation films. 1st BBC filmed documentary.
1953	Communism in S.E. Asia (Chester Wilmot)	Political documentary series.
1955	World Communism (Christopher Mayhew)	Political documentary series.
1956/62	Act of Faith (Rebuilding Coventry Cathedral)	Documentary. First BBC TV.
	Hungarian Revolution	Panorama—political background. (Dir. Charles Wheeler).
	Iceland Expedition (B.S.E.S.)	British Schools Exploring Society. Shot, scripted, directed, narration, by A. A.
1958	Quatermass and the Pit	Drama serial.
	Europe in Slippers (George Mikes)	Pilot programme in conjunction with author. Dir. Script.
1959	The Cry Goes Up	Religious programme. Shooting, script. and direction.
	Maigret	Thriller serial.
1961	Anna Karenina	Drama.
1962	Anna Christie	Drama (based on play by Eugene O'Neill).
1963	Stalingrad	Historical drama.
	Remembering Summer (Compton Mackenzie)	Women's programme.
1964	Count of Monte Christo	Drama serial.
1965	Hereward the Wake	Drama serial.
1966	Royal Palaces	Art feature.
1967/68	Civilisation	Arts feature series.
1969	Rembrandt	Historical documentary.
	Spoils of Poynton	Classical drama, based on novel.
1970	Ross	Historical drama (Rattigan).
	Bernard Berenson (K. Clark)	Arts feature.
	Paul Temple	Thriller series.
1971	History of America	Historical documentary (A. Cook).
1972	The Long Chase	Thriller series.
	A Lasting Joy	Literary feature.
	Lord Peter Wimsey	Drama (based on D. Sayers novel).
	Colditz	Adventure series.
1973	Inflation in Germany (1920's)	Documentary.
	Terracotta Horse	Children's drama.
	The Pallisers	Drama.
1974	Colditz	Adventure series (whole prod.).
	Fall of Eagles	Historical drama.
	Late Call	Drama.
	Last of the Summer Wine	Comedy series.
	Death of Charles Bravo	Drama.
1975	You're on Your Own	Thriller series.
	Madame Bovary	Drama.
	Boston Symphony Orchestra (Great Orchestras)	Arts feature.
	Claude Monet	Arts feature.
	Friend or Foe	Stories around the world.
	The Prince and the Pauper	Children's feature.

1

The Beginnings

SHORTLY AFTER THE WAR a very small nucleus of ex-army, naval and RAF cameramen who had been trained for combat camera work joined the BBC, together with a few ex-film industry cameramen who had worked for the Corporation immediately before the war. These people combined to form the film department at the BBC . In those early days they were chiefly concerned with making newsreels for magazine programmes as at that time no filming was done for other television programmes.

It was not until much later that the BBC began to film sequences which were to be edited into live or drama programmes. Documentary production had not really started because the facilities were not available. The documentary side of the BBC began its development, in fact, with the political type of production containing 75–80 per cent filmed material. This material was interlaced with live sequences of the anchor man in the studio together with a couple of experts who had international or local knowledge of the area or subject concerned. They would discuss the subject and question each other while the programme alternated between the studio and the filmed material. It was a fairly standardized style of production.

For the early television newsreel type programmes, however, individual cameramen were sent out to make their own short documentary contributions. Later, in 1953, those who had proved successful in this direction in addition to doing the usual newsreel material (and these included two ex-feature film people) were separated into the so-called Film Documentary and Sequences Department—a unit set up to deal with all sequences and larger documentaries as well as drama inserts. Other film cameramen stayed on in newsreel production.

The nucleus of the new department originally consisted of only three cameramen who were really quite hard pressed with the work load. This department made the first TV documentary films for television. All three members of the team had been trained in the film industry before the war and had developed their skills either in the industry or in the services during the war, and perhaps worked in documentary or education films for industry and government in the post-war period. So there must have been considerable influence from the original Grierson documentary idea.

The Modern Department

The department soon grew in size and more cameramen were taken on to handle the greater quantity of film material required. It is now known as the Film Department and handles a greater diversity of work than ever before. But it is, and always has been, a servicing department. It has never instigated programmes itself. All the other departments come to the film department for film effort, and it is only recently that entire productions have in fact been made on film. Until two or three years ago, the average amount of film content in any production was between 10 and 25 per cent. The remainder was VTR. There is now, however, very much greater film content in the ordinary programmes, and some complete programmes are made on film. Many series productions such as *Z Cars* and *Barlow at Large* occasionally make a single episode entirely on film.

Function

Everyone likes to use film these days. They like the mobility of the film medium. Perhaps they also like being film directors! There is, after all, a romantic tradition in this, from both the artistic and the power-structure viewpoint. But undoubtedly the mobility is the main factor because it offers so much more scope and has a considerable bearing on the economics of some types of production.

In a large corporation which has had enormous capital expenditure on all types of equipment, it is quite possible that some equipment may be idle at any particular time. The BBC has tried to curtail this wastage by re-applying its resources. For example, outside broadcast equipment, normally reserved for covering sporting events, parades, etc. might be brought into play to shoot whole drama productions directly on to videotape. The production is planned for one location and all the equipment is deployed and used as if it were in the studio. The producer switches from one camera to another in the same way as if he were in the studio gallery. It is a method that requires considerable organization, and shooting is limited to the chosen location. Some people claim that it works, others say it doesn't.

There is no question, however, about the mobility. You cannot move heavy OB equipment about in the same way as film equipment, which can be packed and ready for work in another location half an hour later. It is very easy for a film unit to work in two or three locations in a day. With outside broadcast equipment there are cables, generators, heavy cameras and vehicles to transport. The film camera unit also requires minimal staffing—so there are fewer people to move about. Moreover, the film can be freely cut and edited, whereas this is a more limited and time-consuming practice with VTR. All in all, the film unit is the most mobile and flexible medium available. The wholly-filmed BBC productions might be shot in the film studio, outside, or on some distant location— possibly in a foreign country.

Staffing

Despite the considerable changes in equipment used by the film side of television over the years, the staffing, in terms of numbers per active production unit, has remained more or less the same. Television film crews are generally smaller than those in the feature film industry where it is normal to work on 35 mm, but larger than those of many independent commercial concerns working on 16 mm.

In the days when the BBC worked on 35 mm, for nearly all productions except drama, there was a two or three man unit. On drama there might be one extra person. But otherwise there would be a cameraman, his assistant and a sound recordist—in effect a combined sound and camera unit. On some productions, such as topical or political programmes there would be only two men to a unit, the cameraman and the sound recordist, who usually helped each other to carry heavy equipment or with other awkward jobs where another pair of hands was needed. With drama, on the other hand, the cameraman would always have an assistant and with really complicated productions the sound recordist might also have an assistant.

With the introduction of 16 mm for black and white productions the crew sizes were increased so that both the cameraman and the sound man almost always had their own assistants, making units of four. Additionally, if there was to be heavy tracking equipment or a crane, there was also a film assistant general—the grip from the film studio.

Since that time the crews have been increased further to a basic five—two camera, two sound, one grip, with the possibility of adding a further assistant to the camera side if the cameraman feels that the job is big enough for him to concentrate fully on the lighting and allow his assistant to operate. In that case the extra man is there to help the assistant on the camera. So the maximum crew would then be six.

Not counting the news side, there are now more than fifty film camera units in the BBC. These each consist of a cameraman plus an assistant. There are about thirty two-man sound recordist units.

The size of the crew assigned to a particular job is dictated to some extent by the kind of production involved. Sometimes on very small jobs, for instance, cameramen work without assistants. But generally these days the total one-man-band situation for camerawork is so rare that one can say that it has virtually ceased to exist.

Some cameramen prefer to operate the camera themselves. They can feel much more in contact with the physical areas that they are lighting, and therefore it is easier to light what they know will be covered and to suit the way in which it is to be done.

Others prefer not (or even refuse) to operate the camera themselves, so this is done by an assistant who works as an acting cameraman. This method of working requires an extra assistant to be available to pull focus, etc. for the assistant working as an operator. This larger crew must, however, be justified by the production and the arrangement is entirely at the discretion of the cameraman. On smaller programmes the cameraman must do his own operating, or allow his assistant to operate while he pulls focus and puts the number board in.

The sort of remote location programme that was covered by one man many years ago would today involve a cameraman, an assistant and a sound recordist with either a director or a reporter. The reporter in that case has a director-type role. This is really the old role of the political commentator. It is usual with this type of job to send out the younger and more agile cameramen. The newsreel type of job is covered by a news department in the BBC but if there is a magazine programme to be shot in a place where there is known danger, then the units are made up from volunteers, and the Corporation prefers not to send married men. There is never a shortage of volunteers. In the BBC the individual always has the right to refuse to do a job on a production if he thinks he is in personal danger. The same applies to a cameraman in charge of others who might be doing a dangerous shot. This is understood within the Corporation. A case in point is where cameramen are to be sent to battlefields or danger areas where there is civil commotion of some kind. All technicians who go to such places are volunteers. If a cameraman is put on a job filming in submarines, in confined areas, or high places he can refuse. Apart from the human aspect the most obvious disadvantages in sending someone to do filming under duress is that his results are unlikely to be first class. A cameraman could invite his assistant to do a shot he did not wish to do.

If you are filming drama it is normally preferable to do your own operating. Somehow it is easier to light and rehearse with reference to the view through the camera. So the camera viewfinder is constantly being looked through to check progress with setting up the shot or to observe actor movement. You see the artist in the context of the lighting you have done—as a whole. This is not quite the same thing as watching the action from outside the camera. Although the camera viewfinder gives only a very small picture you can see lighting more cohesively through the camera in the confines of the screen (bordered by black) rather as you would see it on the television set. You might first light it to look as you think it should look, and then look through the camera to make final adjustments, i.e.: darkening or lightening certain areas.

Cameraman and Assistant

In the feature film industry the roles of cameraman and assistant and indeed all other members of the technical side are strictly compartmented. The working arrangement with the director is also cut-and-dried. The hierarchy in television is much looser, and there is a far greater overlap of activities and even interchange of roles on the part of everyone concerned. For a cameraman the responsibilities are greater, because he has to operate the camera and take charge of the sound crew, electricians and many of the arrangements made for them. It is a semi-paternal role.

The nearest equivalent to the film cameraman in the electronic studio is the technical manager (TM), the chief technician in the studio. He is responsible for planning the lighting and putting it into operation. He is administratively responsible for all the camera and sound crews. He has an assistant who helps with lighting and some planning. Like the film cameraman his job is both creative and slightly administrative.

The film cameraman is responsible for the whole technical crew when on location abroad. At home this applies to a lesser extent because here there are plenty of administrative back-ups. The artists are the responsibility of the director or the production staff.

The provision and transport of equipment is taken care of by film operations managers back at the film studio (but in conjunction with the director and cameraman) who deal with specific types of production. They, in fact, organize the allocation of equipment, personnel, the editing and finally the production of a show print.

The director tends to be checking on the camera operator's work much more than on the lighting, which he leaves entirely to the cameraman except for particular instances such as opinions on mood of lighting or dramatic effect. In non-dramatic productions where there is no actor movement to be controlled, the director becomes far more preoccupied with the movement of the camera. Initially, his contact is with the cameraman. He might tell the cameraman what he wants, who agrees or otherwise that he is able to do it. Thereafter, if the director asks for particular shots, i.e.: a pan from A to B, the cameraman would do just that.

Or, in another case he might say that he cannot cope with that shot because of the lighting facilities or available positions for lighting equipment, but he could pan from A to C with the particular facilities, and then cut in to B.

The cameraman is concerned to get the director's ideas on film in a way that is both practicable and convincing visually.

The assistant's responsibilities are confined to the function of the camera. He must make sure that it is operative. He loads the magazine, focuses the camera, inserts filters, checks and cleans the gate between shots, etc. (In certain cases such as shooting topical or news material, however, the task of focusing the camera is left to the cameraman, as he can do this more practicably by looking through the eyepiece while he is filming.)

At the BBC, assistants are assigned to cameramen not for productions, as in feature film work, but for a period of time regardless of the productions they may be involved in. They work together initially for a trial period and, if everything goes well they may continue to work together for twelve or eighteen months. A similar system is operated in the sound, electrical and grips departments. Each department has an operations head with overall authority. Obviously at the basis of the working relationship is the question of whether the cameraman thinks the assistant is good at his job and does what ought to be done and what is asked of him. A cameraman can request a particular assistant. It is slightly more than a matter of good teamwork where a cameraman and his assistant are concerned because much of the time you are forced to live very much in one another's pockets. You live, work and eat together on location. If at any stage either person feels that you are not getting on together or you have had the halcyon days and it is time for a change, one or both goes to the film camera manager and asks for the change to be made.

If there is a clash of personalities a change can be effected very quickly.

A person remains as an assistant until there is an opportunity for promotion. The BBC is rather like the army or civil service as far as promotion is concerned. You fill a newly-created post or a dead man's shoes.

Occasionally staff are hired in excess of establishment on a temporary basis for holiday relief work on short time contract to maintain the same work force numerically. If and when a vacancy occurs the job is advertised and an interview board reviews the applicants who have been shortlisted. Certain jobs within the Corporation must be advertised outside as well as internally. People already within the organization get preferential treatment. Staff are hired from outside the Corporation throughout the year but the productivity at the BBC is not affected much by seasonal change.

Working with an Operator

In a documentary production you normally do your own operating but if you have great areas to light it is really too much for one man to handle both camera and lighting. The operating on *Civilisation* was done by the assistant although this practice was still rather unusual in 1969–70. But it allowed more time to concentrate on the lighting. We had the previous experience of the programme *The Royal Palaces* which involved filming much the same type of material—large interiors, works of art, general exterior views—with similar types of problem that these can bring. The operator on *Civilisation*, Ken MacMillan, had worked as operator on *The Royal Palaces* and this series had proved beyond doubt that with such a large scale undertaking it is too much of a strain on the camerman to both operate and handle the complex setting up and lighting problems for sequences in large interiors. Ken MacMillan did the operating throughout the *Civilisation* series and we worked in three to four month stints. The series was planned to allow for recceing by the director and the cameraman so we did this and other preparatory work between shooting periods, while the remainder of the crew returned to England. Despite the wide scope of the series we did not use a second camera unit on *Civilisation*, and indeed that approach is still normally reserved for drama productions. If you are using a second camera it is advisable to look through both cameras while lighting and before taking a shot.

In having someone else operate the camera you do surrender certain advantages. Some cameramen like to light according to how they are going to operate the camera. You may find, for example, that the amount of lighting equipment at your disposal is going to make it difficult to light a given area. In this situation you can light a particular area and restrict the camera movement to that zone. The area chosen would not exclude any part required by the director for his radius of action or other intentions. This type of approach is far easier if you are operating yourself. You can place restrictions on yourself but not very easily on an operator. Another factor against having an operator is the rather time-consuming process of having to explain everything to him in words before he can carry out the movements physically.

If the production calls for the simultaneous use of two cameras, as in some drama, then the second camera is operated by your personal assistant who already knows the way you work, what you are doing and the kind of results you want. Although you have to check the second camera for each shot you would have more confidence in your assistant than another technician just brought in for the production. So, as a rule, in the BBC it is always the assistant who operates the second camera. Obviously, with a reflex camera you have to take it for granted that he is operating in the right way because you cannot watch the shot through the viewfinder. But if you watch the operator and the camera, although you are not looking through it you can judge if the camera is moving in the right way because you are visualizing what the operator is seeing. Multiple viewfinders are a nuisance and are largely used as a means of interfering with the cameraman's knowhow.

Other Staff

The continuity girl fills in continuity sheets after each shot, which then go to the editor to help him in assembling the scene. She takes down details of what goes on in the shot, how the artist moved and what he did, and she indicates the shots the director wants to print, and details of the sound to be transferred. (The remaining material is not printed or transferred.) She also enters the timing of the shots. This she does with a stopwatch rather than working from the footage figures because the footage on the camera is measured from the time the camera is switched on to the time it is switched off. A stopwatch would be used from the time the director says "Action" and "Cut"—a much more accurate timing. In the BBC the continuity girl is called a production secretary. She is, in effect, the director's secretary.

The crew is supported by floor managers (FMs) who, on location jobs, are frequently supplied with walkie-talkie sets to help with short range out-of-sight management of actors, props, scenery, etc.

Before going out on location the schedule for the production is planned by the production assistant (PA) in conjunction with the director. He arranges the calls for the actors, make-up and wardrobe, sees to transport and officially applies to the film department for any special film equipment that may be needed. These needs would already have been determined by the cameraman on a reconnaissance trip to the location. The PA organizes both the film and the live side of a production and to some extent co-ordinates them. His role is very important and in the film industry he would be a combination of production manager, assistant director and assistant producer. The production assistants in television are, in effect, assistants to the director.

Organization/Training

During the war some cameramen were lucky enough to find themselves in the Army Kinematograph Service (AKS), together with people like Freddie Young, Carol Reed and Roy Baker. The AKS made instructional, military and some documentary films so the training received by all those in the unit was magnificent. It was a forcing ground for cameramen.

There is a parallel in the working methods of the AKS and television today in that cameramen were, as now, presented with a *fait accompli* in terms of planning, and simply had to go ahead with what they were given and obtain the best results they could. The British documentary industry immediately before the war was so small that most of the people in the AKS were ex-feature film staff. They were obtaining a first taste and first test of the factors involved in television production. So they did not come to television unprepared. Naturally, at that time no one knew that this would be the way things would turn out.

The AKS was a very pleasant situation. If you made any mistakes it was not vital and you were not going to be fired! You were allowed to make your errors, but you made them only once, and you were learning all the time. That is the sort of training that the film industry, and especially the television film industry, lacks today. It is doubtful that these conditions could be reproduced in a modern film school. The circumstances of wartime provided an artificial situation but a very beneficial one.

The problem of insufficient training today is one which television producers are well aware of. It leads to certain cameramen becoming "typecast". Some BBC producers select the in cameraman because of his previous work and consequently some cameramen come to be known for the certain types of work at which they are particularly good.

An assistant cameraman in film production before the war could spend ten years on that job before he could expect to work as even a third or second operator. Today, a lot of people are needed to produce the volume of material consumed by the television networks. Consequently, most newcomers to the creative side have dissimilar backgrounds from those who have been there for upwards of 20 years and came from the film industry. Since 1950 or so, few, if any, have come from that source and it is probably a bad thing, but unavoidable. It means that many television film technicians are not what the ex-film industry people would call properly trained. That is, they have not been trained in the formal sense with the solid basic grounding that the film industry provides. They were thrown into television at the deep end. After a short technical training they are sent out into the field. No one has time when working for television to give much attention and advice to the novice. This is, however, less of a problem on the electronic side where the greater theory and mechanics involved can be taught, instead of acquired by constant practice. It would certainly be an advantage to broadcasting if more young people entering television were recruited from the film industry, because filming is a very particular art.

After the war the old hierarchical staffing system disintegrated when television began to overtake the film industry in popularity. Because of the lower salaries offered few people went from the feature film industry to television, and television production staff did not like the methods employed in the film world. There was, in fact, a degree of mutual distrust between the television and film industries on account of the great difference in attitude towards the economics. There was also the importance of improvisation in television and readiness on the part of those involved to accept a given set of circumstances without having all the best equipment and facilities made available for the asking, as in feature films.

The television administration was more prepared, however, to accept a *documentary* film technician because they knew that he was accustomed, indeed forced, to use his initiative more of the time. He, too, had to accept unalterable circumstances under which to work. He, too, was used to lower salaries paid in television. The feature film technician would not have accepted employment with the BBC. A few documentary technicians did.

In pre-war America and until the beginning of the decline of the film industry, people were paid what they were considered to be worth. There were 40- or 50-year-olds who had 25 or 30 years experience as camera assistants. Because they were paid according to their worth they did not have to seek promotion in order to earn more money. In England (and on the Continent) if you wanted financial advancement you had to change your job and had to become a very good operator or, if an operator, a cameraman. In the US you could earn more money as a first class operator than as a second class cameraman. Experience was valued.

Due again to the large output of material required for television, promotion must be rapid. Assistants, after a basic training, can have as little as eighteen months to two years operational experience before they are promoted to being a cameraman. So there is a wide variety of standards of work in the BBC—some people lacking even the quite basic knowledge for the job.

Maintaining Standards

Theory does not really play a major part in the production of a film or any filmed programme. It is essential to work with the equipment for a time, experience all the situations and make your mistakes. The quickest way to learn, without a doubt, is to make the mistakes, because you only make them once. You dare not make them again, because so much money is at stake! In television you are, of course, working with a much smaller final picture area than with cinema films. The medium itself is smaller and you can get away with many defects on that screen which you never could on the cinema screen. Whether or not your mistakes are tolerable in the medium depends to some extent on individual opinion. In filming for television you never stop learning, even after twenty or thirty years experience. It is a good habit to go and see the rushes of the previous day's work, if possible, albeit with fear and trepidation! Provided you, as a cameraman, are ready to accept an attitude of self criticism then you are winning the battle. It is all very well to have the director or producer say your work is marvellous but you know very well when it is not, or when you could have done better. The moment you are prepared to accept consoling criticism, eulogising your poorer efforts, and believe it, that is the end of your awareness and conscience as an artist-technician.

We have unfortunately now reached a stage when the minimum of a proper training is only too obvious. This can be seen on some filmed television programmes, not only in the way the production is running, but in the camerawork and camera operating also. You see material which, to be kind, is not quite sharp. You see unintentionally overexposed and badly shot footage, and hear sound which should never have been allowed to go on the air. Because the television machine is a monster that has to be fed with vast quantities of material there is virtually no possibility of doing retakes for shots which are unsuccessful unless it is immediately following the first attempt.

At 9.30 a.m. when the previous day's work is viewed as rushes, many cameramen at the BBC not yet actually engaged on any job, take an opportunity to see some of the other people's material being run through. This is where some of the most ghastly mistakes can be seen. At this point cameramen have been known to gasp in amazement and horror and then leave the projection theatre by the nearest exit that leads to fresh air!

2

Programme Quality and Organization

AFTER THE INTRODUCTION of independent television in Britain, the BBC had to achieve good enough audience viewing figures to justify the renewal of their charter. The Corporation believed that if they obtained 40 per cent of the possible audience they were doing quite well, bearing in mind the higher quality content of their programmes. In fact, they are getting nearer 50 per cent. In general, the BBC is producing more good quality programmes than any other station at home or abroad and in drama productions particularly, it offers a very wide choice. Its expertise is recognized even by the U.S. television networks. They buy quite a lot of foreign material, especially British. *Civilisation* and *America* are examples.

Since the BBC obtained its second channel, the scope for individual artistic expression in the material produced, and the coverage of areas of minority interest has greatly widened, this despite the fact that the Corporation is in direct competition with commercial television to gain a good share of the viewing public. Audience ratings are considered to be of major importance both for the public service and for the commercial sector, a fact that militates strongly against good quality and high intelligence level in the average programme fare. It also makes companies wary of the unusual, the experimental, the specialized or the more complex in subject matter and treatment. The fact that minority interests are still well catered for must be of lasting credit to the television industry.

JOINT PRODUCTION

At times it does not matter to the BBC that they are getting only two or three million viewers for a programme they envisage as of minority interest. But all television companies are constantly searching for material for the majority viewer. Some programmes come between these two rigid categories or, if they appear regularly, tend to develop in one direction or the other. *Civilisation*, again, is a case in point. At the outset this was envisaged as a minority interest programme entirely different from anything done before. Nevertheless, it was hoped that it would catch some extra audience as it went out each week.

An educational programme in the best sense of that word, *Civilisation* soon showed that it was also of enormous general interest. Time-Life Inc. came to hear of it and, after seeing a couple of rough-cut episodes, decided to take a share in the financing. From that moment onwards, funds were almost unlimited for us in the field. For example, if we wanted to go somewhere for a location or needed extra lighting or a crane, we could order it up without hesitation and there was never any problem about it. Such favourable working conditions gave us much greater confidence and flexiblity. As an example of the difference made by the extra financing, I can quote the case when, as cameraman, I went on a recce to the United States with Michael Gill and Peter Montagnon, joint directors of the series. We spent three weeks touring Virginia looking at the locations and subjects we were later going to photograph. To go so far afield on such a trip was unique in my experience and we could not have done it without the Time-Life backing. Normally the producer and director (the same man in this case) would have gone, but not the cameraman.

By that time, however, the film team was well into the production. But none of the material was reshot. This was unnecessary as we did not make the series in one episode at a time. For example, the material we shot on a trip to Rome, Florence, Padua and Mantua was envisaged as adequate for three or four programmes. When it was realized that something was missed that would do for another programme, it could be covered while we were in the area. But we did no re-shooting. In fact, one of the remarkable things about that production was that we worked the whole way through it with no retakes at all, either for technical or any other reasons. Something like 250,000 ft of film was shot over a period of two years and out of that we lost one 400 ft roll, in the processing. Normally one has to expect a certain amount of loss due to the various hazards of location filming, processing, etc. But, in proportion, this was no loss at all.

Commercial television companies in Britain take a somewhat different approach. They make a planned series of productions in their film studios, using film technicians. The methods used are fairly similar to film production for cinema distribution but on a more commercially conscious basis and with tighter schedules. Many of these productions are designed principally for sale abroad, but might be shown on independent television in Britain as well. Some are joint productions with foreign television companies, as indeed are some BBC products.

The BBC tends to attract such co-operation for certain types of production, particularly the better quality material and the results of this policy are reflected in its programmes. The Corporation has immense accumulated knowhow in the production and combined film and general production field. It was the first broadcasting organization to start the regular transmission of television programmes, in 1936, and was also first to re-start after the interruption of the war.

It surprised us all the same, that the BBC were asked to produce, of all things, the *America* series. It would be hard to imagine anyone based in Britain going to France to commission a film on the history of Great Britain or the British Empire. This shows some quality of integrity; the project was entrusted entirely to the BBC in planning and detail. There was no attempt by the American side of the organizational body to influence the content one way or another, other than small details of editing, etc. A similar situation prevailed in the case of the *Civilisation* series—the project was left entirely to the BBC to plan, write and organize and it was the beginning of UK/US joint production work for television. Although the earlier production *The Royal Palaces* was sold to US television after it had been made *Civilisation* was the first to achieve co-production stakes during the shooting.

Forerunners of *Civilisation* were the black-and-white series *The Glory That Was Greece* and *The Glory That Was Rome* presented by Sir Mortimer Wheeler, whose personality was an important factor as always with these programmes, in gaining and holding attention. *Civilisation* was presented by Sir Kenneth (now Lord) Clark, whose personality is not exactly magnetic and the bias was there for some people. I liked him and his approach to the subject.

The presenter in such programmes is rather like the barker in a circus—getting your attention and drawing you in to see what he has to show. In this case, the director/producer was very much in on the final writing of the script (written by Clark) and the layout of each programme, guiding Clark as to which sections he would prefer to have in the programme. If Clark disagreed there was room for discussion. Directors usually have a hand in the script, and in this particular instance it was useful because the director, Michael Gill, knew a fair amount about art history. He also produced the whole series. The other director was Peter Montagnon, who also tends to specialize in that subject area.

Michael Gill also produced the *America* series, of which I shot two programmes. In its complete form the filming for this went on for over two years. The main cameraman on that (there were four involved altogether) had been my operator on *Civilisation*, Ken MacMillan, who did about six programmes. Two other camermen did two and three each. It was split up because travelling around America for long periods is not quite the same thing as being in Europe. When working in Europe you can do a shorter stint—you can work, say, 4–5 weeks, and then come back home and rest for a couple of weeks before returning, which is what we did on *Civilisation*. We had only one very long stint (about 9 weeks). But working in the USA with the exhausting and lengthy travel involved, would have produced personal and work problems on the two programmes that I did. We drove ourselves over 12,000 miles, and worked in 14 states to produce material for two entire programmes of the *America* series. I should not like to have done the whole 13 episodes.

We did one or two sequences in Indian reservations and the graveyard of Custer's Last Stand—interesting in a macabre way. I think I knew for the first time what a second class citizen looks like—the expressions on some of the Indian's faces—utter apathy. I felt in filming them, the same way as I do if I am asked to film anyone with a deformity—I am intruding on their grief or personal misfortune and I do not and never have liked it. You tend to encounter this with topical programmes. The moment some directors see someone who cannot walk properly, they immediately order the camera to film them in close-up. There was an instance recently when I was filming for the *History of Europe* in Paris. I was on a rostrum during the armistice parade around the Arc de Triomphe with the *ancien combatants*, and the woman director I was with kept saying: "You must get that one", "Look at that one over there" and so on. I was rather unhappy with this.

Shortcomings of Foreign Co-productions

Co-productions or production of television features for foreign markets have obvious financial benefits for a television company—the greater finances at its disposal which affect the expansiveness of the treatment as well as the security of the project as a whole. While the result should be better in quality there are also shortcomings for which the addition of lavish sets, special technical facilities, etc. do not make amends.

Foreign productions often have to cater for more than one type of audience, thus the emphasis of a given documentary or play may be at odds with what the foreign sponsor requires or feels his audience will demand. In the case of fiction, producing this way can result in the film having different endings according to the market. Then the latter part of the drama must be written, directed (and perhaps costumed) and shot twice over adding greatly to the production cost and thereby reducing the proportion of the film benefiting from foreign sponsorship while at the same time absorbing further work effort and entailing extra expense for the producing company on material that will not be used by it. The extra cost of catering for foreign requirements can outweigh the financial advantage of such jointly financed operations.

Films imported from abroad also produce problems. Censorship standards vary from one country to another and in certain films scenes must be removed to be acceptable to the domestic audience. Moreover television films received from the North American commercial television companies are often supplied complete with advertisements spaced through them which have to be cut out.

3

A Television Film Studio

THE STUDIOS used by the BBC for film production are those built at Ealing in the early and mid-1930s for the feature film industry. It was from these studios that the celebrated series of Ealing Comedies came. These included *Kind Hearts and Coronets, Whisky Galore* and *The Ladykillers*. Ealing was the last feature studio to run a continuous production programme with full time staffing before the wind of change brought on by television swept through the film industry and totally altered the economic conditions under which such films had been made. It is pleasant to recall that although the small screen ultimately resulted in the closing down of numerous studios, it is through the same agency and the purchase of the Ealing Studios by the BBC that films continue to be made at Ealing, thus maintaining an historic link with an important era of British film history.

The Ealing Studios were built on a relatively modest scale when compared with other studios in Britain or the USA. This fact, together with their close proximity to central London, make them particularly suited to television film production. The adaptability of such studios within the relatively limited budgets of many television productions and the convenience for artists who might have to travel from the live studios at Shepherd's Bush, or to theatres in London's West End, made them a most attractive choice for the BBC.

There are three studios at Ealing, and like some television studios elsewhere, two of these studios can be run together to form a larger working space if required.

Stage 2 which was the first to be built, has overall dimensions of 125 × 75 ft. The setting area is 98·5 × 60 ft. This studio is equipped with a tank which can be covered by flooring for normal operation. The tank measures 25 × 20 ft and is 7 ft 8 in deep.

Stage 3A, which was built a few years later, is smaller at an overall 70 × 83 ft with a setting area of 57·5 × 62 ft. Stage 3B built at the same time is of similar dimensions, with a setting area of 57·5 × 61 ft. This, however, is equipped with a tank of similar depth to that on Stage 2 but larger in proportion to the studio floor area at 36 × 20 ft. It holds 4500 gallons and can be heated. By opening doors between stages 3A and 3B extra working area becomes available.

The studio tanks have many uses. They can, of course, be used for water scenes such as bathing pools or the sides of ships. When used dry they can provide greater working heights than the studios can normally allow. For *Quatermass and the Pit* the tank in Studio 2 was used. (This was also the studio used for *Colditz* (see p. 161). The scenes represented the discovery of a mysterious rocket buried in the earth on a construction site. For this purpose the rocket was placed in the tank which was then filled with loose soil. People on the site were seen digging down to it. In subsequent scenes where the rocket had been dug out, the earth was removed to show the rocket and the set above. These scenes were all shot inside the tank. After a while the rocket was brought up to ground level and the whole set was, in effect, transferred to that position.

There are storage tanks for stages 2 and 3A measuring 40 × 17 × 6 ft and 30 × 15 × 7 ft (the latter, however, is not suitable for film use). Gas, water, steam and hot water are available on all stages, and the weight loading for tanks and ducting is 130 lb. per sq. ft. Most kinds of "mess" can be coped with on all stages.

There are two schools of thought as to how a film studio should be rigged for lighting. Some would like to see it rigged in exactly the same way as the television studio with its very complex electronic equipment—dimmers, memory banks, etc., whereby one set is blacked out and another is lit at the flick of a switch. Such sophisticated lighting control is unnecessary in filming because of the difference in filming methods and it would be much slower to work with. The film studios at Ealing have a series of permanent catwalk gantries at a fixed level from the floor. The set is put in under a pattern of gantries for flown lights which can be raised or lowered manually. Occasionally, to light a corner or somewhere that is inaccessible and must be lit from the top, a small lamp can be mounted on a bracket on the top of the set or on a high lamp stand. The old-fashioned method of cradles following the top of the set is never used.

The gantries, or lighting bridges, in the Ealing studios have a minimum height of 14 ft and a maximum of 22 ft. Power for lighting comes from a 110v DC supply generated by the studio's own power plant. There is an extra 60 amp AC supply for such things as special effects fog or cookers.

All stages have facilities for normal back projection with either still or moving plates. Stage 2 has front axial projection as well.

There are only two production offices (with phones), three rooms for make-up purposes and two single and five double dressing rooms, each with their own lavatory and bath, six dressing rooms for four persons and three for twelve persons with showers available.

This studio can cope with almost all demands made on it, given sufficient prior notice, and makes its own arrangements with the other service departments of the Corporation whenever there are special requirements.

The statistics quoted above apply, of course, to studies which were not designed for television production but for feature work. If a new studio were to be constructed from scratch no doubt the statistical data for it would look very different on paper. Nevertheless, it is perhaps further evidence of the adaptability of television film production itself that it has been possible for a major television organization such as the BBC to make such a studio serve, with relatively small modification, for the larger part of its interior film work over the past fifteen years.

4

Going on Location

THERE ARE SEVERAL distinct advantages with filming on location, interior or exterior, when working with a reasonably mobile film unit. The first is economic. It is obviously far less expensive to use existing locations, provided they are suitable and do not require too much modification to be appropriate to the film. In topical productions this is of no importance. It is mainly in drama productions, particularly costume pieces that extensive changes are made to signboards, street surfaces, street furniture and so on.

With most television productions, however, the core of what is real remains the same. And this is its strength, because the increasing sophistication of television and film and the improvements in image quality make the difference between what is real and what is mocked up, however well, become increasingly apparent. What is real looks and feels real. The same applies in cinema feature films, where actual locations are being increasingly used in place of elaborately contrived sets on the studio lot.

There is also a genuine atmosphere present when on a location as opposed to the studio set. The things that one sees and the places where one works have atmospheres of their own. For the most part, however, that applies to *exterior* locations. Interior locations can, in fact, be interiors anywhere, or can be built, in the studio or elsewhere. For a studio set you might be informed that it is supposed to be a certain place. But on location there is no hiding the fact of where you are and you can feel that. Some of that mood is bound to find its way into your approach to the filming.

The feeling of reality is particularly important with children's programmes, where situations are presented which are obviously real rather than those which could be real but have all been built in a studio. When you are dealing with children's programmes it is much better to see the characters moving about in freedom with plenty of space around them, rather than in confined areas which would put limitations on children—and on their imagination. Children tend to run around. You need a sense of freedom, and to be in the country if possible. A strong point about the programme *Terracotta Horse* discussed later, was the ample space that the Moroccan backdrop provided for the action. Set-ups in rooms with two-person conversation tend to make rather dull children's television.

In planning, the decision to shoot on indoor locations is determined by many factors—the cost of studio work, and constructions, studio availability, etc. For most occasions these days it is more economical to use real rooms and houses rather than the studio. This does create the real atmosphere although there are certain difficulties in filming, lighting and action, moving the camera around and shifting equipment. But they are positive difficulties because they all help to create the illusion—which illusion is more real than if you do it in the studio.

RECONNOITRING

The practice of reconnoitring locations before starting a production was strengthened in the BBC when a time and motion study found it to be justifiable in purely economic terms. While detailed planning is taking place on a recce, it demands only the time of those involved on the recce as opposed to the artists, crew and equipment hire time if planning is left to the shooting stage. Now, all major productions are given sufficient recce time.

In the BBC, most productions try to set aside enough recce time for the cameraman to take part. Recceing is valuable because besides saving time and money, you know roughly what is going to happen before you get on to a location. A cameraman knows in advance what he is going to do on the production because he will have had time to think about it beforehand. He has already visualized where he is going to put the tracks for the tracking shot, and how he is going to light the scene if the weather is a little dull, or where the filler could be placed if the weather is normal. He has visualized some of the shots in advance, where the hardware is to be moved during the day, what angles will be involved, any close-ups, backgrounds, etc. He might have warned himself that there are certain features he must miss—television aerials, poles, etc. It is a subconscious process, in effect. The cameraman is forewarned by the recce and has time to think out his actions.

Most recces are one or two day jobs and you fit what you can into that time. Sometimes it takes only a couple of hours. After that, you return to the studio and put in your requirements to each particular department—lighting to the electrical department, the tracking facilities, extra lenses or special filters to the camera department. You also make known any information useful to others pertaining to that location. It is a fairly informal routine. The equipment is sometimes available for checking over fully, but usually is collected either on the previous afternoon or the morning of departure.

The production department at the BBC initially finds the locations. There is a department which has a log of past locations. But most of the research is done simply by going out in a car and looking.

For non-drama productions all filming is done by prior arrangement, even on exterior locations. Sometimes it is important not only to obtain permission but to make sure that no one is missed out along the chain of the official heirarchy. This is particularly important when planning productions in Germany and France these days. Damage to paintwork and the fabric of buildings is a very important consideration in an industry whose activities depend so much on the indulgence of private individuals who place their property at the disposal of television crews. The cameraman has to make sure that no damage is done. On a project such as *Civilisation* the importance of this remark can easily be imagined! During that production scaffolding was frequently erected but this was done by officials belonging to the institution concerned such as the art gallery, museum or church. This had to be paid for, and the payments made for use of the buildings or works or art concerned varied between quite high fees and use without charge. The famous sites tended to be those which charged the higher, indeed occasionally excessively high, fees.

The location for a television film may be determined by the question of accessibility, where, for example, it would be essential to use lights. It is sometimes necessary to compromise with the director on the matter of locations. In some situations if there is much rainfall you may not be able even to get the heavy equipment, such as the service vehicles containing tracking dollies, etc., over soft ground. A Land Rover can be used as a shuttle service but this is time-consuming. In this event it is advisable to have a tractor standing by to pull out any vehicles that may become bogged down.

The main importance of the recce to a cameraman is the practical side (to determine the equipment needed, tracks, lights and the accessibility). It is well if, at the same time, you can see how you might set up some of the shots. It is handy if a shooting script is available, which indicates certain types of shot. The director might have written down his intentions, and if he is not actually present, the production assistant can indicate approximately positions on the working area where, for example, tracking shots are intended. The cameraman can note what extra packing or levelling-up equipment he is likely to need. The grip would be informed so that he brings all necessary ancillary equipment.

The more you can keep to one base the more economical and

efficient it is, especially with night exteriors, because you do not spend much time travelling. With all the equipment, lighting, generators, cabling, props, etc. it is hardly practical to move to another area. It would take two or three hours to pack up, move, and unpack. So night exteriors should be confined to one place if possible. In fact, the less you move from one location to another for night or day sequences the quicker and cheaper is the filming.

Sometimes the designer comes on the recce with the cameraman and others. This would be, for example, to modify the scene in some way, such as to disguise non-period features on a period farm house or make alterations to suit the context of action, such as putting up a flat or blocking up a window, putting up curtains or making a mock doorway. He is also there to check on the suitability of the design and architecture of that particular location. If necessary, he then sends down one or two pieces with the construction staff to the location.

Occasionally a sound man is allocated to the recce, but this also depends upon availability. He is not often needed, however, unless there will be difficulties with recording, such as dialogue sequences in an industrial area where there is excessive extraneous noise, or in a large enclosed area where there is too much reverberation. Sometimes the cameraman takes an electrician with him, especially if it is to be a night sequence. The electrician knows where he can place the generator and how much cabling he needs—the finer details of setting up lighting. Otherwise the cameraman has to take the responsibility for these matters upon himself. These days alternators and generators are well sound proofed. You can film within 50 ft but normally you have them further away. For night sequences you have to take into account the fact that the generator does make some noise and diesel smell, and should therefore not be very close to any houses.

Recceing for night sequences is more complicated than for day. With daylight you are only adding to what is already there, titivating, as it were, the conditions that exist. With night sequences you are starting from scratch and, of course, it involves more lighting. Whereas with day shooting you can work with an alternator and, say, ten kilowatts worth of light, with a night set up you have to start with a generator and arc lights. In the latter case you have to get within 300 ft of the site. It is just possible to do a night exterior with an alternator and a 10 K incandescent lamp. On *Fall of Eagles* (see also page 114), a night exterior railway sequence at Welshpool was done with only an alternator, a 10 K and two multi-beam lights. The factor governing this was economics. It was not worth taking a generator and arcs right across the country just to do some rather short exterior shots. So an alternator was used, together with the normal type of inky lighting carried for daylight shooting. This was sufficient for the shots we had to do and the area we were covering (that had all been decided and agreed with the director on the recce). In this case only half a railway carriage was being shown together with the immediate area around it. If the whole carriage was to be included plus a platform and people milling around—i.e.: if the area of cover was increased by 50 per cent, then an arc would have to be used. It would be necessary to tell the director that if a smaller area in certain cases is sufficient, then it would be possible to work without a generator for that sequence, which might have cost the production an extra £500.

For the *Fall of Eagles* railway carriage sequence, a recce was carried out. The ordinary day shooting equipment was ordered up—a couple of six lights, four small quartz units and incidentals but also a 10 k and a 6 ft rostrum for the one night sequence. No Molevator was ordered to get the 10 k right up in the air because this would have required an extra electrician and transport which would naturally be charged to the production. Union regulations have to be borne in mind constantly in Britain. As the 10 k was to be used only during the night sequence and not during the day, union rules did not demand the extra electrician.

Union rules apart, however, it is quicker, easier and more sensible to work with minimum lighting equipment. The small alternator truck can carry some lights inside and avoids the need for another vehicle. The lighting is entirely the responsibility of the cameraman and he has complete freedom as to how it is done beyond any specific requirements mentioned in the script, such as a flash of lightning.

WEATHER AND SEASON

When working on location for the BBC, we have to shoot almost regardless of the weather or time of year (see page 53). But it is advisable to think of these factors in advance while on a recce. *Fall of Eagles* was shot in Wales in early spring although it was supposed to be midsummer in Bavaria. Fortunately there was sunshine, but we had to restrict our shots in such a way that it could not be seen that the trees were not in leaf. Where possible, evergreens and conifers were included in the backgrounds. But we could not do many long shots. Snow in such scenes, of course, would put one at a definite disadvantage!

Very occasionally, conditions make it impossible to shoot certain sequences demanded by the script. It is difficult to simulate storm sequences in good weather, and in the event of bright sunshine, it would normally be necessary to postpone such a sequence. It is virtually impossible to pull together two sequences taken in widely differing actual weather conditions even if the weather sequence is simulated. If there is no sunshine, and you want it, you can create it. But the trouble is that if you have it, you cannot lose it. For close ups, and perhaps medium shots, gauzes can be used to reduce the brilliance, but nothing will cut down the sunshine in a long shot.

Recce Problems: An Example

The BBC production *Late Call* was a four-part drama serial about a retired couple and their relationships with their grown up children, how they coped with them living in their home, and the domestic conflict between young and old. The recce was at a place called Tidgewick, near Buckingham. Two situations were represented, one about 1960 and the other a flashback situation of the mother when she was a girl of 10 or 11 in 1906. In the flashback sequences, the mother and her friend are seen as children running through fields and streams getting themselves dirty and spoiling their dresses—and being caught by their parents and then chastised. In the 1960 sequence, the mother is seen running through farmland again and rescuing a young girl in a storm. A tree under which the girl had been sheltering is struck by lightning and the mother pulls the young girl away from the tree just before that moment.

For shooting in such a situation, there must be sufficient lighting to compensate for any possible (unwanted) bad weather, which you invariably get at some stage. The alternator would need to be placed within a workable range of the locations where the shooting is to be done. These could be in open fields and by streams, so that the unit would in fact be a long way from any hard standing or roads where one would normally place the alternator or generator.

This is a very important aspect to be taken into account during a recce. If the terrain is such that you cannot bring an alternator or generator into range, there is only one alternative—you have to make do with battery lights with their far smaller output. Voltage drop limits the length of cable from the generator to about 500 ft. With colour, you cannot accept a drop of more than about 10 volts otherwise the colour quality is likely to suffer because the light source starts to redden.

The real problem would be if the weather was very good when a storm sequence with lightning was to be done. To emulate lightning as in the case above, there must be arc lights, which require a generator to supply their 110v DC. Lightning on this film was simulated by using two brutes, and shutters. The shutter is a small metal venetian blind which fits over the front of a brute and can be operated manually. To obtain a flash of lightning the shutter is quickly opened and then closed. In this case two brutes were called for. They had to work simultaneously which, as it cannot be done mechanically, must be done manually.

For the rain effect, the local fire brigade might pump water high into the air over the location. They need to draw the water for this from a hydrant or other suitable source. In this case it was from a stream which was more than 300 yards away. With soft ground neither a fire engine nor a generator could be very easily brought close enough.

Such are the potential difficulties that have to be foreseen on a recce. Even so, the atmosphere may be very different on the day of shooting from that seen when the recce was carried out.

If the weather were impossible for a particular sequence, you might work on different parts of the same script in nearby locations (say, within half a mile) provided there is the scope. Often, the BBC plans for shooting to embrace a number of locations within a relatively small radius, for convenience. So in many instances this is a practicable expedient.

Organization

On location you do not have the same structure in television as in feature films: director, assistant director, producer, assistant producer, continuity girl, etc. The assistant director on feature films is the man who whips up enthusiasm and keeps the unit and everything else going at a good pace. In television this formal job does not exist and the task should, in theory, devolve on the production assistant, who is directly responsible to the director and works with him. In fact, when you are filming for television it usually falls to the cameraman to set and maintain the pace, as work proceeds from shot to shot. This is appropriate because the camera crew are "on the go" all day long, unlike, say, the sound department, who depend upon the cameraman to first establish his shot. The director, too, is dependent upon the cameraman being ready. Nothing can happen until then.

In the BBC, technical people are organized in such a way that when working away from the studio they are, in fact, doing very long hours. For instance, we are at the studio at 7.00 a.m., we go out on location at 8.00 a.m. and we finish on location at 6.00 p.m. This is followed by an hour's drive back to the studio and then the clearing up, filling in camera sheets and getting the film stock sent off to the laboratories.

Pre-Production Conferences

A broad difference between television and feature film work is that the cameraman has very little pre-planning time for the small slots of production time on which he is employed. Often, when you start on a new production you have hardly made contact with anyone concerned. You may not even be working for more than a day or two on that programme before moving on to the next. So any ideas you may have for the camera work are distinctly *ad hoc* and worked out at the moment of shooting. An idea may come to you at that point, or you have a quick word with the director about his or your ideas, and then you shoot.

It is very rare in television to have a full pre-production conference unless it is a large production. For such a production the cameraman might be presented with most of the scripts beforehand, which he reads. These are, to all intents and purposes, the shooting scripts. But the half day's conference that follows might only be for those concerned to discuss their administration problems and some production aspects that look troublesome. The cameraman, having read his scripts, might be asked if anything in them suggests a need for extra equipment, or anything that might present an undue problem where lighting or personnel is concerned, that can be solved before going on location. In the case of television productions, this is probably the only practicable way to work. Where a cameraman is in continuous employment elsewhere, he can hardly be called in to take a hand in planning the shooting scripts.

The factors of main concern at the pre-production conference of a large television production, from the filming point of view, are the need for, or the availability of, ancillary equipment—cranes, dolleys, tracks or extra lighting for a big day sequence, for example. A warning to the cameraman that there will be several night sequences implies the use of arcs, generators and the problem of siting generators in a residential district, and the question of sound track noise being picked up from it. Also discussed are arrangements for recces at the various locations, questions of costumes (colours, etc. where anything such as a predominance of white or black in the costume might affect the cameraman's side of things) and whether they can be changed if necessary.

Apart from lighting and personnel, you must discuss the transport required for artists, technicians, equipment and properties as well as the catering arrangements. Make-up and wardrobe people are also present at the conference. There might be several vehicles for the equipment and a complicated schedule due to the requirement for properties and customs, border controls, etc. for part of a production only. The fitting together of these different commitments is a highly organized operation which must also take into account the cost of hiring the vehicles used.

Whatever is agreed with the cameraman (and the filming is always done first) has also to be acceptable to the electronic (studio) production technicians, who are also present at the conference. To this extent the cameraman and the TM (technical manager) work together. If it is a large production they try to get the technical manager to come and watch the filming. By the conference stage rough plans for the interior sets have already been prepared.

Production Costs

Costs are charged internally in the BBC from one department to another. Each piece of equipment used is charged to the production in the same way as the services of each individual. Vehicles used by the film department however, are charged as if a part of the camera "crew", except in the case of special vehicles such as camera cars needed in the filming which are separately charged to the production. Such vehicles would be hired from outside film hire firms. Lighting is charged as a flat rate regardless of the number size or type of units involved. Most of this equipment is hired. The processing has been worked out in such a way that over a period of 12 months the film department, which is paying the real cost of the hiring of lighting, etc., recovers the full amount by means of a flat rate charge. It would be very difficult to charge a department pro rata for every piece of lighting equipment used, because of the great difference in charges to be expected from each production. Drama productions might involve expensive night exteriors, another production might be quite cheap to light.

The flat rate charge is a fairer system.

Television studio production has a "built-in" overhead cost. If you are in the studio for a day, there is a flat rate cost against which the film unit cost is very small by comparison. If a production requires studio, film and outside broadcast (OB) facilities, this makes for expensive administration. One of the main objectives in employing OB in a film role is to absorb heavily captilized and otherwise unemployed OB units into the overall economic stituation rather than have them lying idle. So, although it costs more to use OB in this role, it is cheaper for the Corporation to use them.

If you do not go on a reconnoitre with the PA or director, you cannot guide them as to the type of equipment that you are likely to need. Consequently they are likely to order up some that you will never use, and even omit an item that would have been useful. The PA and director tend to guess what is needed; sometimes equipment is ordered simply because it seems to be the thing to do to have it. Cranes and large dollies may often be ordered for this reason.

On one particular production the equipment had already been ordered, because it was a case of taking over a job that was intended for another cameraman. The equipment had been ordered by the PA and the director. Two items that had been ordered were a side clamp to mount the camera on a moving car where there would be a sound sequence of the driver and a passenger (side by side) and also a bonnet clamp which would enable the camera to shoot two people through the windscreen. The side clamp attached to a side door positions the camera to look through a side window either from the driver's or the passenger's side. Neither of these mountings was used because there were no dialogue or even sound shots of the car moving. In the sequence as filmed a hand-held shot from the back seat looked through the windscreen from the inside with the driver on the right hand side of the frame. The shots previously intended just did not materialize on the day of production.

The use of certain hardware implies a need for other items. Having ordered equipment to clamp the camera on to the sides of a car, you would need equivalent lighting equipment for this type of approach. Consequently, taking the type of location in to account, you would in this case order clamp-on lighting. Absence of one item may render the others useless. If you have time before you start on a particular production you try to get all your equipment together and test it, making sure that it is appropriate for the particular purpose you have in mind and that everything fits, and the lenses are sharp etc. Normally, in film production, and to a certain extent in the early days of television when the equipment was less sophisticated (there are so many bits and pieces which join you or you are asked to bring with you these days) whenever you started a production all your equipment was available to you the moment you wanted it because nothing much was hired. Today, in television, you are not often able to interest yourself in a production or the equipment it involves more than 24 hours before it is due to start. You are lucky to have that much time because you may finish one production the night before and start the following day on the next.

VEHICLES, CAMERAS, ETC.

In the BBC, the camera crew drive themselves—cameraman and assistant in one car, sound recordist and assistant in another. One or two electricians with the minimum equipment necessary travel in a third car. About one per cent of the vehicles have a roof platform for use as a location rostrum. This is dangerous to use as a moving platform. The camera cars generally used in the BBC are intended simply for transport. The only special vehicle in the Corporation is a rather old Citroen Deux Chevaux which is superb for tracking, used either as a tracking car (being driven) or sometimes pushed as a dolley. In this vehicle the tripod-mounted camera needs no extra stabilization.

The BBC does not have a proper tracking vehicle like the standard feature film tracking car with platforms of various heights on top, side, front or behind with safety bars, etc. When it is essential to have such a vehicle it is hired. If a low angle vehicle-mounted shot were to be done, a special low level vehicle would be used but if it were a silent shot in which the camera did not have to be manned from behind, we would fix a special low level mounting on the conventional car. The hiring policy for special vehicles preserves them from the depredations of misuse in a large corporation.

The chances are that a fair amount of the equipment used on each production will be hired. This is, in fact, the most practical way to supply 52 crews with what they need. Each BBC cameraman, however, has his own personal camera which goes with him wherever he goes, and he is responsible for it, though it is owned by the Corporation. There is an element of choice in cameras rather in the same way as that laid down by Henry Ford: "You can have any colour you like, as long as it's black". The choice is between the 16 mm Arriflex and the Eclair models. Tracking equipment, jibs, cranes, etc. are hired and also much of the lighting except that in the studio, though a few arcs used there may be on hire.

5

Drama Production

MOST TELEVISION PRODUCTIONS start with a script. There are two types of script writer: the first is a writer who is established within the department, someone who is known to be a competent writer and has been working for a long time for television, like N. J. Crisp, who has written for the BBC dama department for many years. He produces a script—a first draft—which is quite well advanced, but nowhere near a synopsis, which is split into left and right hand columns. The left contains all the stage instructions, and all the dialogue is on the right hand side. A script writer of great experience writes such a script from scratch, including what he considers to be telecine sequences (filmed parts) and what the filming will entail.

The other type of writer, the unestablished writer, will produce nothing more or less than a synopsis which is turned into a first draft script by the producer. In the same way that a producer procures an advanced first draft, so he makes a first draft of the synopsis of the second kind of writer. The producer then writes in the script where he considers a telecine section is required.

The director, who by that time has been chosen for the production, reads this draft and then produces a more advanced second form in which any telecine sections are elaborated upon (or obliterated as irrelevant to the plot, as the case may be). Thus, they build upon the script to produce the final draft version which tells the cameraman allocated to the production what and where the telecine sections are that he is expected to contribute.

THE FILM CONTRIBUTION

Telecine content is determined by feasibility. It mainly consists of backgrounds that cannot be produced satisfactorily in the studio. On exteriors for a classical drama involving the usual settings of such productions—big homes, horses, landscape, etc.—then telecine film work is called for. A switch from television to film treatment would be determined by a change in approach, deletions or tightening up of the story or shift of emphasis to another part of the story which signals a different medium. Film is also used to tighten up the plot generally (as it offers greater scope and control in that area) to improve the flow of the story or advance the action by omitting sections that do not add anything, or even detract. To give a studio production a broader canvas, to make it more photographically attractive or to increase the pace, a particular section might be taken out into the open. For example, in a four-way conversation, the actors, instead of being seated round a table could be put in the garden, a car or a carriage or elsewhere, making it more alive and adding a sense of freedom to the scene. The fact is, that with good editing and many changes of angle you can speed up and increase the interest in dialogue. On film, you can have a very much greater variation in size of reaction shots, shots which quicken the conversation. With a three-camera studio set up you can alter shots while running all three cameras, but with film you may have ten different shots which can be cut into a rhythm and so avoid a drag in the dialogue. It does not mean that film is very often introduced to a production for that reason. Usually it is for much more mundane and simple causes. Also, with studio space being so limited, with perhaps four or five sets in position at a time, using film and taking one set out of the studio or moving to a real location, relieves pressure on the studio.

THE STUDIO

A studio is allocated to a production not necessarily on account of the size but because of what is available. Consequently the designer, knowing that he will have to fit his set into studio X will sometimes have to cut here and there to make everything fit. This is, of course, planned. The same pressures do not apply in the film studio, even though at Ealing there are only one large and two small studios (see page 35).

ADVANCE PLANNING

A drama production department has to plan six months ahead knowing, for instance, that they will be producing six dramas in the three months following. They indent for so much film effort that far ahead without knowing exactly what is needed (they do not even have scripts). When it comes to producing the work they might have three dramas to do in one month and three weeks filming reserved. Perhaps one of the three plays does not need film at all. Another may need a week or two of filming, thus leaving two weeks of film effort to be expended on the third, which, however, may not need so much filming. So that can be cancelled and given over to someone else. The cost is also cancelled provided it is within a certain period.

It is not very frequent for the film department to overrun in time. In the present circumstances this eventually represents an extra degree of flexibility because film studio time would usually be available, whereas in the television studio it is not. If they overrun time in the television studio it must be for a very particular purpose (a technical breakdown) or there would be harsh words! The time given to cover the production required in filming is not unfair. But some people are quite naturally slower workers than others. Some people are almost always behind schedule. The producer knows who are the slower directors and who are the quicker cameramen, and will tend to pair them up by asking for such a cameraman to keep the thing going. But it is also a question of availability. In general the requirement comes in to the film department about two months ahead of its being done, the occasional big production three months ahead, and the day to day work requests come in literally overnight.

Staff and Artists

The producer chooses his director. The director chooses the cameraman or does not make a choice, as the case may be. There are certain good working teams in the BBC, which is inevitable, and beneficial to the production. With television artists you do not get the prima donna attitude to turning up for work. Illness usually means a rearrangement of schedule so that you have to shoot round the parts involving that person. This presents complications for the cameraman. An occasional problem when working with an artist, and which is also a source of strain, is where he or she is due to make a theatrical appearance on the same day. It is often a question of shooting all his or her material together, not necessarily in the most practical order from other aspects. In the remaining shots close-ups, for example, must be close enough to exclude the missing artist (if you did not have time to do the reverse shot while he is there). Stand-ins are never used in BBC television work—only doubles for certain trick work.

If possible you can juggle the schedule about to suit the weather but the main snag with that is artist availability. The payment made to artists depends on how many and which days they are to be engaged in filming. If they are in a series it is quite common for them not to be available for film on particular days of a certain episode. But they might be available for a couple of hours perhaps on another day. This is a highly geared operation and can put a considerable strain on the artist, much more so than when working on location for feature films. In a programme like the *Paul Temple* series which goes on weeks or months or longer, the filming might be three episodes ahead of the one they are rehearsing to transmit. The artist has to try and remember perhaps three or four different scripts at any one time. So it is not unusual to have to work with artists who have already been under some mental stress before they appear for the filmed sequences. If possible, the schedules are changed around to give them a rest but this is not always feasible. So this aspect of strain is a particular feature of part-filmed productions. The crew, of course, may be fresh from doing nothing or something different. Even the director is replaced for the filmed sequence as these are usually multi-director productions. A series may have three or four directors but they interchange between episodes and so they have time to think about and develop their side of the production. But the main artists are engaged more or less the whole way through the series.

Invariably on part-film productions the filming is done before the telerecording side, so that, in effect, the inserts are produced before the sequences into which they are to be fitted. These days the rehearsal for the filming is done just before the filming takes place. Then, immediately after filming, the artists go into the rehearsal room and thoroughly rehearse the entire programme. The filmed sections are therefore established beyond change and the production can be fitted round them. Nevertheless the way the filmed sections are done is largely dictated by the studio side of the production. So, even though you might have ideal weather one day and poor conditions when you are to do the filming, you have to fit in with the studio requirements.

The Cameraman's Contribution

It is an old adage that you are never certain of any shot until you see it yourself on the screen. You might be quite content with your own lighting and camera operation on a shot but you can never be certain. There are so many more variables after you have taken the shot, over which you have no control. You cannot necessarily even be sure that a take you thought was the best of, say, three *was* in fact the best. There are certain aspects—movements, timings, that you are not quite conscious of at the time because you were concentrating on something else, which, in the cold light of day (or rather the projection theatre) do not prove to be as good as those on another take. Technically one take may be better, but another is chosen by the director because he prefers the performance when technically it is acceptable anyway. If it is technically poor he will reject it regardless of the performance. An experienced cameraman can judge the technical aspects of lighting and camera movement more or less without fail on each shot he takes.

When working on drama productions, many a cameraman, once the shot is actually being taken, pays as much attention to the artists as to the technical side. If he realizes that a particular take is absolutely first class for performance but the camera movement is slightly out or the lighting vaguely unsatisfactory he should never ask for a retake. The performance is just as important, if not more important, than the camera technique in this. It is the artist's performance rather than the cameraman's that the audience is looking at. He must go out of his way not to disturb the performances of the artists or their future performances of their future shots.

Continuity with Weather on TV Schedules

It is an amazing fact that, with a small quantity of lighting equipment and, by, for example, cutting in to a close shot instead of using a medium shot in a particular instance, it is possible to disguise the different weather conditions that might prevail from shot to shot. But it is a little tricky if you have shot, say, two thirds of the sequence in dull weather and then it suddenly starts to rain and there is no hope of continuing that sequence. It is just about possible for dry and wet shots to be cut together and yet the difference to pass unnoticed on the small screen of a television set, though that small screen is getting a little larger these days and the definition is still improving. So perhaps before long such breaks in continuity will be intolerable.

But today, even in the weather conditions found in England, the BBC film team are out filming every day and there are perhaps only three or four days in the year lost because you are rained off or there is an exceptionally heavy downpour. Once the lenses or filter on the camera begin to steam up then filming has to be called off. As yet, the television film crews do not have any special equipment for dealing with these conditions such as the revolving screen (adapted from ship windshields) used in feature films. But this would only be needed for an actual rain and spray sequence. Such heavy rainfall would normally rule out filming.

Television scripts do, on the other hand, offer a degree of flexibility for weather conditions and can offer scope for *ad-hoc* changes of plan. It is possible to alter a schedule and turn a particular part into a rain sequence if it happens to be raining that day.

In filming for television you have to accept a series of unalterable circumstances and you have to do the best you can. Perfectionism through numerous retakes is out of the question. Good work under these conditions can sometimes prove almost impossible but with the aid of the laboratories and commonsense, measures like cutting down the scale of the shot, etc., usable material can usually be produced.

BUDGETING FOR SERIALS

In costing a drama series, an overall figure is set aside for each instalment, but deficits or surpluses from individual instalments can be transferred across to others so that at the end of the production the overall budget is maintained. A daily running total is available and if the production is running over cost the producer may ask the director to cut cost on future work. One of the most expensive items in a budget is artists' fees. If a production is running too high, the number of people involved may be reduced or the number of location overheads (i.e.: locations used) and the amount of overtime reduced. This would involve changes to the script. If the cuts were very substantial the script might be referred to the script writer but if cuts were only to be on a day-to-day basis by cutting out or cutting down a small sequence, the script writer would not be consulted. The onus is on the director.

For studio productions plans of the set are drawn up. For exterior shooting the cameraman would have seen the situation for himself on a recce to the location. Only very small alterations, if any, would be made to the set and these would be made known before shooting is due to begin.

Studio plans are provided for the cameraman and these are the same as the ones used by the construction department. They show the whole studio with the set placed within it in the exact position, showing the amount of space available behind and in front of it. No camera placements are shown and, in fact, no camera plans are drawn for filming in studios. The plan just shows proportions, the shape and size of a set and where the windows or certain props are placed. As cameraman, you know from the plan where the lighting gantries are in relation to the position of the set in the studio, so that you can visualize your lighting and, if necessary, make your arrangements for bringing in extra lights. You decide the power and type of lighting which you will need in advance of the actual filming, but camera sitings and movements within the space available are not worked out until you are actually on the set with the director and artist.

The plan also shows an elevation of the set, with the sections, say, windows or other features, which allow or demand any special treatment such as lighting or camera position. These too are designed previously for the constructors but there is much that the cameraman can glean from them.

There is a considerable difference between the problems of building sets for filming and building them for work in the TV studio. In the TV studio, the floor space is often crammed with sets and the artists and production team move from one to the other. In the film studio, if they are small sets you can have two or three in the same studio, but you never have more than one large set for studio filming. If, say, two other small sets were needed, they would be built in another studio, so you would move from one studio to another to complete the filming.

BBC sets are made at Television Centre and transported up to the film studios. With them come the painters and chippies (carpenters), and once built, if it is a big production, only one painter and one chippy would remain on standby to make any alterations needed during the filming or in case something goes wrong or needs repairing or patching up.

In BBC television there is very rarely any particular co-ordination between the designer and the director or the film cameraman. So television stage sets are not designed for convenience of lighting. As the cameraman is presented with a plan of the set a week or two before he is due to use it, he has some idea what it is to look like and what it consists of, but does not know much about it apart from this. With normal productions the set will probably be put up in the live (television) studio and used for other sequences. So it will be designed around the live production rather than the filmed part, which is ancillary. In fact, the film department of the BBC is a servicing rather than an originating department. Therefore, there is limited time set aside for working on a production apart from the actual shooting. The cameraman may have scanned the script, especially for the filmed sequences, to get some idea of what is to happen. But if he happens to be working on several productions simultaneously, he can only give a limited amount of time to this. There are times when he will arrive at the studio having only half read the script.

Preparing the Shot

The first thing to do when reaching the studio is to discuss with the director the ideas and aims behind the work that needs to be done. You start lighting for the first set ups. Ideally, you should be given the extreme long shot of the set first so that you can light for that. Once you have done that, any other shots or sequences will fall in quite easily, even automatically, with the existing set up. The worst thing is to be asked to start with lighting a medium shot or a couple of close-ups because artists or props are not available. To light such shots and then go back and light a long shot is mechanically wrong because the medium shots or close-ups are out of any general context. It is very much more difficult to work this way round because there are problems with matching the continuity so that the key lights come from the right place and the overall lighting densities are the same. If you work from the long shot you have already set your key lights and you know where everything is, or should be, for the shots that follow. It may be that if a long shot

1

2

3

The set construction follows architects' plans drawn for the purpose. These elevation features on the set correspond to plan numbers opposite. They give some idea of the style of the set and give a scale reference to the cameraman which is occasionally useful for advance planning.

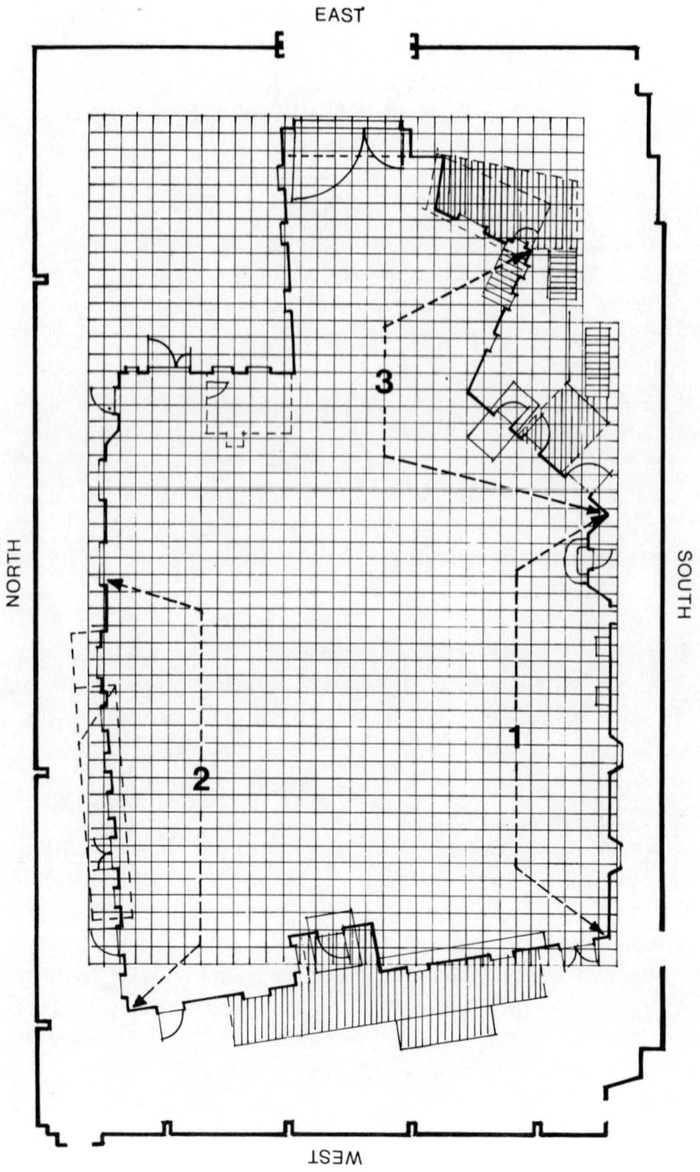

Plan view of castle courtyard set for *Colditz* constructed at Ealing studio for production of this series. The plan is of assistance to the cameraman in planning lighting and selecting camera operating areas within the set.

follows a close-up, the key light cannot be placed in the same position for a realistic effect.

There should be a shooting schedule for the production in which the shot order is laid down and it should be planned to start on long shot. The schedule is lighting planned for time.

You have a script, plan and shooting schedule. The schedule is not taken too seriously as it is only a rough guide. You do the best you can to keep up with it, even overtaking it on occasions. It is, in fact, more of a guide for the other departments—make-up, props, etc.—than for the technical crews, who work continuously in any case. It is, however, the responsibility of the cameraman to keep up the working pace in the studio in drama productions, just as much when working, for example, on location for a documentary. He is usually prepared before the others for each shot. Without this impetus, it is possible to arrive at a situation where everyone is ready to work but thinks they are waiting for others and because no one says anything, nothing happens. This is one of those rather odd situations that happens in filming for television because you do not have an assistant director on the studio floor who sets the pace and keeps up the pressure. This is another of the cameraman's unofficial jobs.

The director tends to concentrate on his artists—the acting, the lines and the rehearsals. Once the director has decided what he wants in the shot, he should leave the cameraman to organize it—lights, set-up, camera.

The cameraman then confirms that he is ready to shoot and the director returns to rehearse.

While the cameraman is lighting, the director may have pulled the artists out of the set and be rehearsing them. Or he might rehearse the artists on the set while the cameraman is doing his lighting. This happens frequently and, in fact, makes it quite difficult for a cameraman because he tends to light "air", i.e.: he is visualizing where the artists will be without them actually being there, and how they will be placed in this or that particular part of the set. He must do his lighting without the stand-ins or artists. This television practice is quite different from that used in feature films because of the time and money factors. It is not difficult to light air. But if you begin to light a person who moves away by the time the gaffer has put a light on, this is very confusing. To light air you have to measure the light instead of the reflection from the artist. It is not until you have had one or two rehearsals that you see whether what you imagined and planned is working out or not.

In the first rehearsal the cameraman memorizes all the alterations that he wants to make, or he might ask the gaffer electrician to make certain changes as the rehearsal proceeds. You can see the lighting through the camera better on close-ups or medium close shots, but, in general, you look through the camera to see the action and put your head over the top to look at the lighting.

It is often better to shoot certain extra shots out of the director's intended working sequence in order to avoid moving lights and then having to re-set them in the existing arrangement later on. For instance, it is often quicker to shoot a close-up at the same angle before a following shot at a different one which would entail shifting lights.

If the cameraman does his own operating he sees it much more easily from the director's and editor's viewpoints and also from that of the viewer. If he is watching the scene through the camera, he is automatically thinking about other shots, closer or wider, for example, in order to stress a particular point or to keep the movement flowing smoothly, which it would not if the sequence just consisted of a series of long shots jumping mechanically from one to the next.

Often, when operating in a drama, the cameraman is the only person who actually sees what the shot is doing. The director is imagining and visualizing how the sequence of shots is being constructed and how it is developing. If he has faith in the cameraman he will not worry about this, but the cameraman is looking through the camera all the time, and he is not only physically and immediately involved in that particular shot but he is also thinking how it is going to come out in the context of the film and what is needed—such as a couple of close-ups. Often enough you need close-ups to stress a particular point—a line of dialogue, a reaction in the face, which is not visible except in close-up, or perhaps from an angle where both eyes are visible or possibly in a tighter shot than the one before.

The cameraman must think constantly of the editing aspects of the drama material he is shooting. Can it be cut into a sequence as it stands? Will it work smoothly? Are any extra shots needed, or cutaways? Are the shots held for long enough at the end after the action? A good cameraman is thinking all the time about cuts from one shot to the next almost like editing in the camera. If, for instance, you come to the end of a shot you have to think whether or not the editors can cut at that point or if the shot should be run on a little more. Or, if you are to pan at the end of a shot the editor might have to cut on the end of a pan which would be bad, so instead of panning you remain static and let the artist walk out of shot. The process of thinking in terms of an editing pattern becomes automatic so that you do not consciously think of it at all. You merely take the required action at the time it is called for.

You always have at least one rehearsal before you shoot. While this is going on you would be watching the lighting, for the most part through the camera as you "operate". The director is not concerned with what the cameraman is doing unless he has a special "mechanical" rehearsal for himself. Usually, however, when you are working in that type of production, the director and you, the cameraman, are *en rapport*. In certain problematical instances, the director may try to eliminate a cameraman's difficulty by looking through the camera and altering the actor's movement to suit the shot. The cameraman would ask the director to do this.

REHEARSALS

At the BBC, most filming is pre-rehearsed. This is quite a recent practice. The artists and director go into rehearsal rooms the week before shooting to rehearse all movements, lines, settings, etc. for the forthcoming filming. They know the plan of the set because it is marked out on the rehearsal room floor. This is where the director actually works out the movements. He works with an imagined camera viewpoint and often uses a director's viewfinder to help him visualize it within the limits of a film frame. (He always plans live work in advance of film work on "mixed" productions.) The artists have the equivalent of four or five rehearsals of each particular scene in the film studio. So they are probably work-and-movement-perfect by the time of shooting.

REHEARSALS ON FILM

When the scene you are shooting involves artists (as opposed to static shots or sequences concerned with scenery or mechanical subject matter, for example) you never shoot without rehearsals. But there are no separate rehearsals for camera, sound and artist. You all rehearse together. A very good working method, and many directors agree to it, is to have one complete rehearsal and then follow with a rehearsal on film, which you shoot. Time and again, that is the best take. If the rehearsal on film works, that is it. If not, you shoot again. Where artists are concerned, it is on the last rehearsal, where you are shooting, that they and everyone else is at their best—probably the second or third time they have gone through the action. After that everyone becomes so conscious of what they have to do to improve on the previous take that the whole routine begins to look a little contrived. The artists like this method because, if it is only a rehearsal, they do not worry so much if it goes wrong. This goes for the cameraman too! The virtue of this approach is mainly the psychological advantage.

We can get away with only one rehearsal before shooting when working in the film studio or on location only because the artists have been so adequately rehearsed before coming to the set. It is only a matter of the cameraman being able to run through it once to see that it all works. This practice resulted from the McKinsey time-and-motion study that was carried out in the Corporation in about 1969, though in fact the method had been proposed by a number of people before that time.

One of the advantages of having a cameraman operate his own camera is that he can tell what might be acceptable in terms of both performance and camerawork because he knows from experience what shortcomings one can or cannot get away with on the small screen without it appearaing below the acceptable standard. If he operates the camera himself during the shot he can see exactly what happens as it is filmed. If the assistant works the camera, the result can only be checked on the rushes, when it is too late to take the shot again.

The director often asks the artist if he is satisfied with the shot, and, if he is not, it is taken again. The artist is quite at liberty to say that he is not.

In feature films, even when you have taken a good shot you take another "just in case". But in television there are not usually many saving takes. This, of course, varies with the director or producer but is, nevertheless, generally true. It is possible to shoot through drama productions for day after day with only one take per shot. If anything were to go wrong in the processing the chances are that "main" and "saving" shots would be passing through the bath one after the other and probably the same problem would affect both. So a saving shot may not act as a saver anyway.

Matching with Live Production

Occasionally the cameraman can find time to see the artist's rehearsals in advance. Many cameramen at the BBC like to see the live sections of the production being done, which, in fact, takes place *after* they have done their part. It is helpful to a cameraman because live shooting is a slightly different medium and it is interesting to see how the live studio technicians deal with their own particular problems. They also have problems which are almost the same as your own. It is interesting, for example, to watch the lighting for different angles, how it is planned so that the key light suddenly becomes the back light and *vice versa*.

Because of the problems of matching the material the tendency is not to have filmed scenes cut in to the same sequence in the live studio. Each sequence is kept separate. For instance, you might have a long shot of people walking across a farmyard and leaving through a gate, passing out of shot. At one time you could have cut to a studio shot of the people coming along by the side of the farmyard, still purporting to be an exterior but in fact built in the studio. Such a match was almost impossible to achieve effectively. You cannot match a real exterior to an interior-exterior. Today complete exterior sequences on film cut to complete sequences in the studio are not directly related. You do not cut from exterior film to "exterior" studio. You go from exterior film to interior studio or *vice versa*. But you do not mix media for the same location. Such a match would be very risky.

As the cameraman shoots his contribution to the production, even short inserts, before the live section, any visual matching must be done in the live studio.

Sometimes, however, it happens that a set is brought into the film studio and part of the live sequence has to be done on that same set, because the artist was only available for live studio work. In that case the technical manager from the live studio comes to the film studio to watch the filming in the context of the work to be carried out live. He could point out, for example, that a key light position cannot be reproduced in the live studio, and he and the cameraman would work out a compromise solution to enable the lighting to be matched. But transplanting a set in this way is not very common these days.

The live set is brought in to the film studio not only because the main artists would be filmed in the film studio on this particular set. There can be occasions when there is another, smaller, sequence involving minor artists on this same set using the same lighting as the live studio. It is much quicker and more efficient to be able to shoot that sequence in the film studio and then insert it into the live sequences of the main programme. This is therefore done on film rather than by breaking everything down and putting the sequences in, in a live context in the live studio. That is because of the time that it would take in the live studio to do this particular sequence—time that would be better spent concentrating on the main sequences with the principal artists in the main studio. These would be scenes involving only minor artists who probably do not appear again, but also requiring the use of the whole set, which is then shifted. So there must be visual continuity of lighting and you are forced into problems of matching the media. Even so, the filming is always done first.

The main reason why filming is done before the main production is that artists have to be booked for a particular period of time. They have also to be booked for the rehearsals of the main production. If you rehearsed the main production and recorded it, there would be no guarantee that the artists would be available for the filming, or that it would be possible to schedule the filming to start immediately after the end of the main production. The filming usually represents the smaller part of the production and may take place in a location in any part of the country. Naturally, actors find it easier to come to a studio, which would be in a city, where, for example, they are at the same time appearing in a theatrical production. The difficulty in obtaining actors for location work means that this must be done first, taking advantage of the availability of actors as and when possible. This is general practice even with studio filming—all filming is done before the main rehearsals and the recording.

In terms of normal desirable working procedure that approach is actually the wrong way round because you are doing the minor portion first. Actors in the studio have time to meet, discuss the programme in hand, get to know one another and get familiar with one another's working methods. On film, however, they do not really have such an opportunity. But a good director, knowing that he is going filming, will get all his artists together and rehearse them in the filming sequences in advance, perhaps a day before filming starts. This pays off in terms of economics as well as artistically when the filming is done.

Once the filming is finished the actors go into rehearsal for a week, a fortnight or ten days perhaps, for the main part of the production. They go straight from rehearsal into the studio, where they might have one full day rehearsing with the cameras, plotting it out, etc. The next day they record.

6

The Director and His Style of Work

THE TERMS director and producer, which in television were once reversed for their respective roles, now correspond with those used in the feature film industry, although a producer tends to take overall responsibility for productions running in a series. They are very much concerned with economics. Originally television was in this respect closely related to the stage—there was even a slight anti-film feeling in television circles in the early days, whereas today it is uncomfortably close!

The question of the treatment for a series or programme, i.e. decisions to use film, OB, or other means of recording, is a producer's decision, based on the money and equipment available. In the BBC this is no concern of the cameraman. A policy is suggested to the director and he works it out with the producer on the basis of this. There may be pressure from higher up to use equipment that was lying idle though not, of course, to the detriment of the production.

The working relationship between the director and the cameraman is of fundamental importance in any film making activity. It is a two-way partnership. But the role of the cameraman varies according to the personality and experience of the director with whom he is working. A certain director may require very little of the cameraman—merely to record on film with the best technical quality the scenes which he creates in front of the camera. At the opposite end of the scale, a director of limited experience might virtually place himself in the cameraman's hands, not only for the filming but in respect of planning the scene, management of the artist and even approach to the sequence as a whole.

EXPERIENCE

There is, of course, nothing to be said against working with a director of limited experience—everyone must start somewhere. But a director needs the respect of artists and technicians. They must have confidence in him. He should never assume the attitude that he "knows it all" and then follow up with instructions which betray total non-comprehension of the medium. Lack of judgement or confidence is not concealed for long. Many actors working in television have long experience both of this and films. They will sense what is amiss almost as soon as work starts. So will the technical staff.

On the other hand, a director who comes to the cameraman and asks his advice will surely get all the support he needs in order to see the production through. This way, he will have both the technicians and the artists on his side.

His Function and Working Relationships

A cameraman working for television has greater freedom than his opposite number in the feature industry. He is constantly seeking easier and quicker ways of doing things. He also has greater responsibility beyond the actual photography, for the crew and the way they behave and much of the organizing involved in shooting films. In a way, his job is like a military one—the officer in charge of a unit. He has a certain amount of privilege.

This situation may have arisen because the TV director is not basically a film director. He is neither a hundred per cent conversant with film techniques, nor does he expect the cameraman to be fully conversant with electronic TV technique. So they rely on each other to a certain extent for a particular section of a composite production. Such a production is not a cut and dried affair, as it would be with one consisting only of filmed material. The director relies on the cameraman to give him what he wants not only in film terms but also bearing in mind that the filmed section must eventually be combined with live studio material, which is usually the basic content. It is really a mental exercise to gain the same sort of approach in the filming to that in the studio material.

Most TV directors spend far more of their time working with electronic methods than film. Their training and experience would be on electronic and the techniques are somewhat different. A director might come to filming first, which is no problem provided he brings with him a spirit of co-operation and an open mind. It is no crime not to know something. None of us know everything. But if he is willing to accept advice from someone who is supposed to know and in whom he can have confidence, it works very well. In this way the director can gain confidence and greater knowledge of what to do with film, how best to use it, how good or otherwise any particular shot might be.

Where shooting is concerned, lining up, shooting sequences, etc. working with film is not very different from shooting in a television studio. Directors have to adjust to the fact that they are not seeing the pictures on several screens while the scene is shot, as only one person can look through the film camera—i.e., the man operating it. For this reason also they must have confidence in the cameraman. The cameraman must make sure that he really is *en rapport* with the director and fully understands what he is talking about.

This is one of the greatest problems in filming for TV. Often, the director and the cameraman think each knows what the other is talking about. When it comes to viewing the rushes, often enough neither has understood what the other has been saying. The cameraman, to cover himself, as well as to give satisfaction to the director, should always let the director look through the camera, at least at the beginning and end of shots so that he has a rough idea of what he is going to get. He should be entitled to check whether what he has asked for is what he is going to get at the beginning and the end of a shot even if it is not possible for him to see it during the shooting.

With the old Michell 35 mm camera with its extra side viewfinder you could have a rehearsal with the camerman operating the camera and the director watching through the other finder. The reflex camera has deprived the director of this view, but they are trying to retrieve it with the electronic viewfinder—something that the camera operator does not like very much for obvious reasons! Consequently it has had very bad field reports! Many directors would long to have it because this would put them back in the gallery as if they were controlling the shots on a group of electronic cameras. But the camera operator does not want to be told in the middle of a shot what someone else thinks is the right composition. Film cameramen know about making compensation for movement, when to pan left or right, when to tilt up, how much headroom to give. This is one of the fundamental differences between the film cameraman and his electronic equivalent who is basically under orders from the studio gallery all the time. In this context, cameraman is a really confusing term.

In relative terms the television cameraman is a tool on the end of a control line. He is always at the command of the voice that comes through the headphones and is not often called on to use his own initiative. For a film cameraman there is nothing worse than to be whispered instructions or tapped on the arm in the middle of a shot. This happens with some directors on topical or "talks" programmes. The cameraman might be in the middle of a shot and knowing exactly what he is going to do when suddenly he hears a voice in his ear saying, "Don't pan right, pan left." This is where the fighting starts, because he is visually and mentally concentrating on what he is doing and he has already anticipated his next move by watching what is going on in front of him.

One of the problems of working with a director who is ambitious to "make films" is that he makes it difficult for a cameraman to concentrate properly on the job. The cameraman may be told to do things which he knows are wrong and he has to stop and explain why. There may then be a risk of some argument but the cameraman is instinctively aware when a director does not really know what he is talking about. Such directors will not give an inch because they take it to be a sign of weakness.

When working on "home" locations a total breakdown in co-operation between the cameraman and director can be resolved by a phone call to the head office of the department. But every cameraman prays that this will never happen to him while he is on location abroad where the main objective is to keep the production going. In practice it very rarely happens at all that a cameraman will ask for a substitute to be sent out to replace himself.

In the working relationship between a cameraman and a director differences in age are immaterial. But there is obviously the possibility that a young director might think of an older cameraman as one who has "seen it all" and is cynical about any efforts to be imaginative. A cameraman, on the other hand, might bring to the task preconceptions that force him to prove himself.

The BBC attracts a large number of young people from university, some of whom bring with them a measure of artistic and intellectual conceit that makes them impervious to advice on practical details. The problem is that the director pays the piper and if he really wants to call a certain tune, he must have it, however cacophonous.

Explaining why something technical will not work can be difficult in some cases. Moreover, in filming for television the team cannot afford the time for arguments. Some directors will show quite clearly that they do not wish to understand why they cannot do something. The only answer to the utterly intractible person is to do what they want—the responsibility is theirs. All directors will, of course, understand such basic factors as depth of field. But the kind of question that is likely to cause argument might concern cutting or movement, changing the eye-line, etc. Many women feel that in order to be as good as a man at a job they must be better.

For the cameraman, when he works with the director all he wants is confidence in that person, to feel that they know what they are doing and are asking him to do something in which he believes. The cameraman can and would step in with suggestions if the director is really uncertain about what to do, and with some directors the onus might quite frequently be on the cameraman to find the solution to a problem. But he does not have the time to debate the issue for long. A cameraman is in a very strong position both with directors who are uncertain and those who definitely do not know what they want.

Some differences in opinion are lost to time. You, the cameraman, may have slightly modified the director's requirements for practical reasons so that by the time he or she views it on the screen, the small difference is forgotten. It is possible to save the director from his own mistakes, and this is very common practice among some cameramen at the BBC. These questions are mainly in the field of camera manipulation—tracking in or out at a certain point of panning over to another person at a certain point. In one case you might be asked to pan off someone on to someone else and then the other person comes into shot, whereas it might have been much neater in the circumstances to follow the first person as he moves over to the other, keeping him in frame.

Another example is where a director asks for a specific size of shot, which is impractical because the subject is not a trained artist but a man doing his job. The amount of movement he is going to make would cause the corresponding camera movement to be far too untidy. In a slightly wider shot you would be able to cope with all the subject movement without shifting the camera about too much. You can do these modifications as long as you do not make the result obvious to the director and you do not spoil the effect the director was trying to obtain. It must be your own personal compromise, as it were, and should be a process of rationalization making the film slightly more logical or viewable—not altering the intention. Cameramen develop a sixth sense about what will or will not work because they are looking through a camera nearly every day of the year.

Directors' Style and Approach

The question of style from the filming point of view hardly arises with a television director. You come across directors who have a very good way of doing a normal routine which can make it appear entirely different. But individualism does not flourish in the way that it has done in the world of the cinema.

There are some directors who really can draw a cameraman out of himself. They make him think and do much more than usual. How this comes about is difficult to understand. It may be because they are on the same wavelength and suddenly find they are thinking in the same way. Personality has something to do with it.

From the cameraman's viewpoint a "good" director is someone who triggers a response rather than has a particular method of doing things—although his methods are sure to be sound. Directors who are unquestionably good often differ very widely in their approach to things.

Rudolf Cartier, a veteran Austrian director, who has done much work in television, was an ex-UFA assistant director. He always tried to do the most with his television productions. He "thought big", which meant that he would work on an enormous scale—if he could. And he knew that was what his audience wanted. Whereas other directors would make do with a small area, he would have what, for television, was an enormous set, and a crowd of 150—again, a large number for a TV production. For the BBC he did *Stalingrad* and *The Cross of Iron*. Working with him was working on an entirely different plane and his horizons seemed almost limitless. The things one did with the lighting were against all basic principles and in most cases would be against the judgement of an experienced cameraman. But one did them quite willingly because of the confidence of the man and, consequently, confidence in onself. He was sure that these things would work, as indeed they did.

Cartier never looked through the camera, but would just ask for a particular shot or for this or that to happen and then go away. When viewing the rushes next morning he would see what he had been given and, nineteen times out of twenty, it was exactly what he wanted—this was probably a matter of mutual sympathy and instinctively knowing just what he was after. One problem with this "grand style" approach, however, was that there was never enough set to get the real long shot that Cartier wanted. The first time of working on this problem, one might be terrified by the prospect of what might happen. We would take the camera right to the end of the studio and a third of the picture would be off the set with gantries, lights and other studio fittings clearly visible. We used to fill that area with smoke or cloud or fog coming up from the Thames or the Volga or the Prippet Marshes (*Stalingrad*). There was not enough money available in fact to build larger sets. On one of his productions, *Quatermass and the Pit*, we produced some remarkable results, but it was all on a shoe-string budget.

The railway sequences, day and night, in *Anna Karenina* were done on the privately-owned Bluebell Line in the south of England. In some shots steam trains were to go over the camera which was to be positioned on the track. There was an inspection pit between the rails and it involved going into this with the camera and with a tarpaulin over the top as a protection from the hot steam, ash and sparks that came from the engine. When crouched down with the 35 mm Cameflex, the clearance was about 6–12 in. above head level—and the instructions were to stay put whatever happened. The train started up in the distance and then came nearer and nearer. Suddenly one felt an idiot, as there was really no reason to be there at all. The camera could have been left down there on its own. When the locomotive was coming near it felt like the end and the last moments needed the strongest resolution not to get up and try and scramble out. The train went over and all was well, and it was, in fact, quite a nice shot. Then Cartier said he wanted the train to go a little faster. The shot was repeated three times in all, by which time one could feel completely inured to the whole thing.

If a director and his cameraman have full confidence in one another, neither interferes with the work of the other. In other words the director, as in the case of Rudolf Cartier, does not look through the camera because he has confidence and he allows the cameraman to get on with his work. With this mutual confidence, a director feels more free to do the unusual, adventurous or even outlandish things because he knows that he is going to get the image. He is also left with more time to concentrate on the direction of artists. There are regrettably few directors who are both self assured and have this level of ability.

Philip Dudley is a much younger director than Rudolf Cartier. He, too, does not interfere with the cameraman but says what he wants. Occasionally he will look through the camera to check one or two things but in general, provided he has sufficient confidence in the cameraman, he will not come anywhere near the camera unless asked.

Philip Dudley is an entirely different type of director from Cartier. Whereas Cartier is an established, traditional type of drama director, Dudley is much lighter and a much more modern director. Peter Cregeen, also of a much younger generation, is an excellent director and very independent of mind. When we worked together on the *Colditz* series, he had to be asked to look through the camera on some shots to be sure that he was being given what he wanted.

Philip Dudley has a modern approach inasmuch as he favours hand-held shooting and hand-held movements and the slightly drawn out camera movement that involves a long running time, and might turn through 360 degrees. He is also a great believer in making shots develop and having a shot in length, not having to break it down in order to slow it down with cuts. He will make a single shot last two and a half minutes if necessary, developing all the time, still remaining concentrated in the main movement or plot in which the artists are involved. Perhaps he feels that this is the most visual way to handle some shots and, where television time and budgets are concerned, the quickest and most efficient way of getting a large amount of cut footage on the screen in the shortest time. There is an old joke in the industry concerning directors who shoot take after take after take—"Right, print takes 1 and 75". Some people are far too pedantic and want everything perfect every time. But you cannot afford to work at this rate or you would have only one good shot a week.

A typical instance of this kind of shot development, which is a great asset to television production, was used, for example, in the *Colditz* series. The scene starts with a full long shot showing the whole of the castle courtyard with the doors in the background. Through these doors come some vehicles, which drive into the courtyard and go over to one side where crowds of people are greeting them. As this happens the camera moves down and in so that when the jeep comes to a standstill and is surrounded with prisoners, the camera is still moving forward and arrives at a close-up of a particular individual who is talking to somebody out of screen. At a given point the person who is out of screen comes in closer to the person who is talking so the camera comes back a little to a very tight two-shot, still favouring the original speaker. As the shot continues the camera starts to creep round (tracking) so that it develops to a complementary over-the-shoulder shot of the second person who begins to speak. Meanwhile, as the shot proceeds other people continue to move around. Thus, in this scene, the action continues and the dialogue is unbroken. A large portion of the plot is developed and as much as two or three minutes of dialogue are covered which will remain as they stand in the final version. The shot is forever developing, and is much more interesting than the conventional long shot-cut, medium shot-cut, over-the-shoulder, etc. routine. It is also more satisfying because with this method it is possible to achieve some very pleasant compositions.

Philip Dudley's hand-held approach is usually relevant to the action and circumstances, but it remains a fact that with most hand-held attempts, if the camera had been put down on a tripod and the artists moved in a slightly different way, the whole shot could probably be done with a pan and zoom. One of the favourite tricks, for example, with hand-held work is applied to a person getting into a parked vehicle such as a car or lorry. The driver, perhaps, comes out of a building and walks over to the lorry in order to get in and drive off. With the hand-held shot you start by shooting from the back of the lorry looking forward, and the man comes in to view. He comes towards you, by which time you have panned over a little to the right and the lorry begins to come into frame, right. As he advances you begin to move backwards, so including more of the lorry. When he reaches the back of the lorry he comes round it and you are moving with him, walking with the camera. He then turns his back on you and walks towards the driving door to get in. You follow him to the driving cab, he gets in and drives off and you pan to follow the lorry driving away.

This is a standard hand-held shot that is seen time and again on television screens. It could be done quite easily by setting the camera on a tripod and shooting over the bonnet of the car with the driver coming towards you, and not having him go round the back of the lorry (for which there is in any case no need). Instead, he comes round the front and the camera pans with him into the cab. He then drives off and the camera pans with him. The shot is neater, whereas the previous example was a case of a contrived hand-held shot done for its own sake without much justification. There are, of course, many instances when the only way you can do something is with a hand-held track—for instance, where no track is available due to lack of foresight or limited finance or, because of lack of space, where the dolly could not be accommodated in the working area. In another situation you may start with plenty of room at the beginning of the track but end in a very tight position where not even a tripod could hold a camera and only a hand-held shot will do. In another case you may wish to follow a subject around in a very small room. This may be more effectively done with the camera hand-held. If the director wants a shot hand-held you do it—though it is sometimes worth questioning why, if it doesn't seem warranted.

It is as well to place yourself near the director when he is talking to his artists or discussing various points with them—telling them what the set-up is to be, or how he is going to shoot it. He does not have to explain the shots again to you and you already know the approach he will take. This saves time and puts you in the picture more quickly than if you were to wait for him to explain. It also helps in any general work because as he is talking, the next shots can be visualized and because you know in advance how these shots are going to take place within a sequence it is possible to work out how it should be lit.

7

Equipment in Practical Use

IN THE DAYS when 35 mm was still the standard format for television filming most ancillary camera equipment and lenses remained the same and very few things had changed since the war. But when 16 mm and colour came in, the equipment started to change inasmuch as the zoom lens now really came into its own. This was probably the greatest single technical innovation in TV filming equipment. Every 16 mm camera used for television was based on the camera-plus-zoom as a complete unit so that, in theory, you worked with only the one lens. However, the disadvantages of the zoom lens were quite considerable.

First, there was the relative lack of definition compared with a prime lens. Another factor was the much smaller maximum aperture of these lenses. Whereas cameramen had been used to working with maximum apertures of T2 or *f*2 they were now faced with using only one lens with a maximum aperture of T3·5 or 3·2. This was a considerable drawback, especially in the United Kingdom where the daylight conditions are less favourable than elsewhere. In bad light in Britain, you may often be shooting at T2 or T2·8 so that if your only lens has an aperture of T3·5 you are definitely forcing the film into the region of underexposure.

Mobility was also affected to some extent. A great advantage of using the film camera and unit is its mobility, with its very light equipment—including the minimum quantity of light you have to carry about with you. Returning to a T3·5 lens (the maximum aperture of an earlier generation of prime lenses) meant that more lighting had to be carried, more men and, consequently, more vehicles to move them about in.

Looking back over the past couple of decades, it seems as if the major changes in television outlook or policy were brought about by changes in equipment rather than the other way about.

Development of the Zoom Lens

The zoom lens was in use during the 35 mm period but was not thought of as a permanent fixture. A zoom shot (using the zoom action) might be conceived and then developed as a zoom but basically the set-ups were visualized with the prime lenses in mind and the zoom only mounted on the camera for a particular shot or effect. Zoom lenses in their early stages of development did not, of course, deliver an image with quality to match that of fixed focal length lenses. In fact, when the changeover to colour came about (not necessarily in the BBC), cameramen were still using the same lenses as for monochrome. There were certain lenses which were not colour corrected so that they tended to be inaccurate in focus owing to chromatic aberration and in some cases did not give the correct colour rendering (some colours would not focus when others would). This was overcome over a period of a year or so when new suitable replacement lenses became available.

At present the BBC is using Zeiss zoom lenses which in their latest form are beginning to give a result in definition comparable with that of a prime lens. One has only to guard against mixing film showing the superb definition of lenses like the Zeiss 10:1 with that shot with ordinary lenses, such as when you are using two cameras. The material will not cut together satisfactorily without the difference in quality and definition becoming immediately noticeable. In a two camera set up, therefore, the cameras must be fitted with lenses of equal quality. But the prime lens still has the advantage in image quality over existing zoom lenses and, more important, the benefit of larger working apertures such as T2 or T1·4. There are many situations where you work at T2 in television filming. (The Zeiss zoom is a 10:1 T3·2.) These are, in fact, the two most important considerations for a television cameraman.

Admittedly, a wide aperture lens is likely to have a large front glass and be cumbersome as a result. But it would still be an advantage to have further improvements in this direction. Depth of field, even when working at these apertures, is not generally an active consideration. It is relatively easy to manufacture a prime lens of, say, 12·5 mm (normal) focal length with a maximum aperture of *f*1·4 or wider and still retain good quality. This is naturally out of the question with zoom lenses. The basic zoom ratio at present is 10:1, as in the Angenieux 12·5–125 or the Zeiss 10–100. The latter seems preferable because you tend to find in practice that the lens is most often needed at the wide angle end of the range and you are likely, in a typical day's work, to use it between 10–25 mm for the most part. If you are shooting with the Arriflex BL you have to use the zoom lens most of the time because the design is based on the blimped zoom lens construction. Thus, the whole camera is sound proofed with its zoom lens. Prime lenses are available which fit inside the blimp, but with the Zeiss 10–100 zoom the definition is so good that you may as well have the convenience of the immediate choice of an infinite number of focal lengths. You do not have to waste time changing lenses.

Wide-Angle Shots

For extreme wide angle shots prime lenses can be fitted. For example, all BBC Arriflex BLs are equipped with a 10 mm wide angle lens, and, although the Zeiss 10:1 zoom has a minimum focal length of 10 mm also, the angle of view of the prime lens is, in fact, just a few degrees wider. In critical situations this is an advantage. Another advantage is the greater aperture of the prime lens, T1·8, as opposed to the T3·3 on the zoom.

There is also an 8 mm prime lens for the Arriflex BL. In 35 mm terms this would be the equivalent of about 16 mm. In the widest angle available for a 35 mm camera was generally about 18 mm so the 8 mm gave the 16 mm format a considerable advantage. But an overriding problem with extreme wide angles is the distortion they introduce and the 10 mm lens is as wide as one would normally wish to use.

Wider angle lenses give noticeable barrel distortion, but the extent to which this need influence the way you handle the shot depends on the circumstances of the scene. With a particular shot in close-up or a tight two shot in, say, a drawing room drama, you would avoid using a 10 mm lens and you may have to take the shot from further away with a 12·5 mm. If, on the other hand, you are in a moving car and taking a shot of the driver from the passenger seat next to him, you might have to use a 10 mm lens because any longer focal length would give too large a head in the screen area. You could put up with a little distortion in these circumstances, however, because a moving background and the vibration of the car and usually the nature of the scene itself draws attention away from this aspect.

In a static interview situation where the viewers are also studying the face, such distortion would be completely unacceptable. There is, however, a tendency for some directors nowadays to demand "anti-technical" effects from technicians in an attempt to put on the screen things which are technically outrageous. These may be in direct conflict with the known rules of what you should or should not do to achieve an acceptable image. The question of whether the result is acceptable or not seems to be a purely subjective one. Many people are pleased in some way with this approach—to others it seems to conflict with basic precepts or may seem pointless or even ugly. Experienced technicians usually aim to work well enough within the familiar limitations of the medium to give a reasonable standard of quality.

Cine lenses, although used so much at full aperture, are not designed for best performance at that stop. T2 lenses are sometimes stated as giving optimum results at T3·5 or T4. If, as a cameraman, you have strong feelings about a particular demand put upon you, you have to explain to the director the various reasons why something should not be done, would not work or would not be as satisfying or as good as if it were done in a slightly different way, which might be a compromise between the two. But if you are overruled then there is nothing for it but to warn him that if he does not like it, it is his own fault. But he usually likes it—on principle! There has to be plenty of give and take for television work.

Zoom or Prime Lens

Whether one uses zoom or prime lenses depends on the type of production. In some productions a zoom lens removes a lot of the work—topical productions and documentaries for example. These entail much more "grabbing" of shots, and often make it difficult for you to get into the position you want. The zoom lens, however, allows you to adjust the framing slightly to make the picture fit.

Many people who were brought up on working with prime lenses tend still to think in terms of lenses of fixed focal lengths when working with a zoom, as if it were a set of prime lenses. Many cameramen prided themselves in their ability, when lining up a shot visually, to ask for a "tight two here" or "a loose three over there" and "put a 40 mm on the camera and shoot from here". The resulting image framing was nearly always exactly right. With the advent of the zoom lens this small personal skill has gone.

(A "tight" two-shot is the term used for a shot of two people very closely framed, leaving little space around it. The term "loose" is often given for the converse meaning, such as a "loose three"—three people framed with space around them. The tightness of a shot is often determined by the degree of concentration required on the particular artists in a given situation.)

The zoom lens is very quick and easy to use but it has a dangerous tendency to make the cameraman lazy. It is so much easier to alter the focal length of a zoom lens than to pick up the camera and tripod and place it so that, say, a 25 mm lens gives you the picture you want.

The attitude of just dropping the camera into any position and zooming to fit ignores the question of perspective. With the zoom there is a strong temptation to forget about perspective altogether. With prime lenses you think in terms of the right distance for a focal length to give a certain perspective. Some cameramen are concerned only with fitting the picture to the subject—a kind of mental indolence that is symptomatic of working with a zoom lens. Rather than pick up the camera and tripod and move it a few feet to the left and a few feet towards the subject, they just zoom to get the people about the right size.

Cameramen who were trained or gained their early experience with prime-lens cameras learned or could learn about the effect of each lens in terms of perspective, depth of field, angle of view, etc. This is much more difficult for people whose only considerable experience is on zooms. Moreover, the zoom lens encourages some directors to spend more time behind the camera looking through it than the cameraman—playing with the zoom, which seems to fascinate them. Often, when a director asks a cameraman if he may look through the camera, his hand is moving the zoom bar before his eye has reached the eyepiece. He never sees the shot that the cameraman was going to give him but confidently tells the cameraman that the framing isn't really what he had in mind! One director has been known to sit in a chair looking through the camera for ten minutes doing nothing else but wearing out the zoom! Back at the studio, the zoom had to go into the workshops because it was juddering and had "hard bits" on the travel. The zoom was not really invented as a substitute for a tracking shot but it gives a good punch shot to make a directional point.

T Stops, *f* Stops and Exposure

It has long been the practice for lens manufacturers to graduate movie lenses in T stops rather than the *f* stops used for still photography. T stops take account of the absorption factor of the many glass to air surfaces inside the lens, and provide an indication of the actual light transmission ability of the lens as a whole, hence the letter "T". The T stop does not, however, indicate the ratio of the focal length to the diameter of the effective aperture as the *f* stop does. Therefore it does not indicate the depth of field obtained at any setting.

Some telephoto lenses are graduated in *f* stops, not T stops. In these cases you have to take into account the light loss due to the number of lens-to-air surfaces. The latest multi-coated lenses have reduced this loss by increasing the light transmission efficiency of the lens.

When you use a telephoto lens you magnify the picture and the exposure area. In effect, you are concentrating more on a particular feature and the exposure should be based on that selected area. You have to make allowances for the brightness of the actual area you are photographing plus the difference of say, half a stop which must be taken into account if the aperture is being read in *f* stops rather than T stops. This is because the transmission loss due to the glass-to-air surfaces in the lens is reckoned to be half a stop. It is, in fact, something which you come to know by experience with a particular lens. This factor does not have to be taken into account with most zoom lenses which are almost always calibrated in both T and *f* stops.

8

Film Materials and Working with Colour

WITHOUT A DOUBT the single most significant change in television filming in the last two decades or so was the move from 35 mm to 16 mm film stock as the standard working material. This came about with the advent of colour. The 16 mm format was not taken very seriously before that and was used only for the occasional production. The main reason for moving over completely to 16 mm was the high cost of colour material compared with black and white. At the BBC, some series were still being shot in 35 mm, i.e. *Civilisation*, and latterly all the *Paul Temple* series. In this case the reason was partly political and partly economic. The *Paul Temple* series was partially financed by German TV who insisted on 35 mm, not just because of the better quality obtained but because it was easier to dub on this format and insert subtitles which were necessary for them to distribute these films throughout Europe.

Normally, the BBC works in 16 mm unless the foreign TV company requires any special conditions. Most distribution these days between television companies is either in 16 mm or videotape, so even if shot in 35 mm, 16 mm copies would still have to be made for this purpose. Certainly all countries with television are as technically advanced as one another and no country has an "advantage" or technical secrets in that sense. In the USA 16 mm is the standard format for TV, though there are some special film series made for television by the big film companies on 35 mm. In the USA and most of Europe, television filming is in colour. The BBC still do a few black and white productions for education programmes where the budget is modest and colour is unnecessary, as, for example, where the object is to teach mathematics.

For a television cameraman the great difference in cost between colour and black and white is in the filmstock and processing. Colour negative plus processing runs to something like five or six times the cost of black and white. Lighting and wardrobe requirements are pretty much the same. The camera crews in the BBC are certainly made aware of the costs of material involved on particular productions and they may be instructed not to overshoot. But it is the production staff who are the final arbiters of how much film stock will be used and the crew are given a budgeted allowance based on an estimated shooting ratio. Certain productions overshoot considerably whereas others come home on a very low ratio. In fact, one tends to associate shooting ratios not only with particular productions but also with the particular people working on them. With "talking head" programmes involving many interviews, the shooting ratio is likely to be quite astronomical, as can be easily understood. Some people have been known to work to a 30 : 1 ratio. Today, television has replaced the feature film industry as the main consumer of film stock and likewise for the processing laboratories.

EQUIPMENT AND FILM STOCK

With 16 mm film stock you have more screen time for weight. Work with 35 mm equipment was based on the use of 400 ft film rolls. With the changeover to 16 mm, the 400 ft roll was retained but in 16 mm it gives 2½ times greater time/footage, but weighs only about one third as much. Of course, the camera and its equipment, tripods, etc. also weigh much less than those used for 35 mm. Consequently, freight charges are less than half when taking 16 mm equipment on foreign locations.

At the time 16 mm was introduced, very few cameramen were happy about it, not so much because of the quality of camera or lenses but because of the lack of quality with the "small" format. It was the same film emulsion as that used for 35 mm so the grain size when the image was enlarged to viewing proportions, was much greater. Since that time there has been a considerable improvement in the quality of the optics and, until recently, only marginal improvements in the film stock.

Another problem with the introduction of 16 mm black and white arose when we found that the material returned from the laboratories was giving very peculiar results—not all being the fault of the cameraman. One problem was that at that time 16 mm was still considered to be an amateur format and, as such, despite what everyone said, was being treated to some extent as an amateur medium. There was then still a far greater quantity of 35 mm going through the laboratories.

However, with the advent of colour we gained some advantage. Because of the much greater accuracy of temperature and time control, we started to get a more stable result from processing houses. This was a great asset to the cameraman who now had a proper standard to work to for exposure and quality. So, to that extent, the introduction of 16 mm which made the use of colour an economic proposition eventually turned out to the cameraman's advantage.

Although productions for the BBC are normally shot on 16 mm there are occasions when, because of some special trick required, a part might be shot on a 35 mm camera which had the necessary facilities. In that case it would be reduced to 16 mm afterwards. Or you could VTR the material separately and then put them together for the programme, though this would involve more equipment than usual, i.e. two telecines.

All film material used for broadcasting is recorded on VTR and mixed with original electronic material. The film can then be thrown away. (Most of the original film material produced by the BBC is in fact destroyed.) If, however, it is a complete film, the programme goes out on the air direct from a telecine machine.

In 1973, Kodak introduced a fine grain 16 mm colour negative stock of the same speed as the existing 64/100 ASA material, but with finer grain which approaches 35 mm Eastmancolor quality. The 7247 stock has better definition than the previous film but this also means that there is less working latitude when it comes to focus. As film stock improves this becomes inevitable. You have to be more careful in splitting focus. If there is any question of compromise with "spreading" the sharp area between two features (or people) one must be completely sharp in preference to the other.

This film reclaims the advantage of good image quality lost in the changeover from 35 mm to 16 mm formats. Of course, it is only where two formats are seen side by side that the difference is really marked. Normally you do not refer one to the other in practice so the comparison would not be made directly. An interesting comparison between the old and new stocks was inadvertently made on a production called *Late Call*. For this, some tests were done to achieve strong effects on the screen to imply flashbacks in certain sequences. All the flashbacks involved two small children. The "present day" sequences showed these as old people who had retired. Tests were done using colour filters (for monochrome) so that a total saturation in one colour over the picture was achieved. Others used a combination of diffusion discs and star filters, and anything which would make people realize that the scenes were not the "present day" ones. We decided to use the strongest star filter on all these scenes which gives a soft, low-contrast colour effect. This would give a sufficient difference between real and flashback on both colour and black and white TV receivers. You always have to make sure that the result is going to come up well on black and white. The testing was done on the old stock. When it came to doing the actual shooting the new stock was being used, and it was so good that it cancelled out all the effects achieved in the test! So this high definition stock had to be degraded for a week's work to obtain the necessary effect.

Despite improvements in optics and film stock, television

techniques have advanced at such a pace that when you compare 16 mm with electronic images (i.e. direct VTR) the difference is very striking—the film image is definitely inferior. There are one or two electronic aids to help improve the film transmission quality in such situations, and these facilities are fitted to telecine machines.

Even with the best optics and film material however, you are still very conscious of the need to gain maximum definition and refrain from doing anything that may interfere with it. Hence, one tends to avoid any unnecessary filters, and one never uses diffusion gauzes or discs. This is inherent in the system of filming for television. The film camera is in competition with live cameras, where definition is almost too good, although there is unlikely to be a direct cut from one shot to the other. So one does not diffuse the close shots taken of ageing actresses in the manner of some feature film cameramen. No vanity photography is practised in television filming, even in drama.

NEGATIVE TRANSMISSION

At one stage, negative transmission was thought to be an answer to the need for better definition from filmed programme content but this practice has been largely discontinued. In any case the improvement was not as great as many people had expected.

Negative transmission involved transmitting the original camera negative and electronically reversing the picture to a positive. There are, however, serious problems. It is very difficult to make a join in a negative that does not transmit badly in a positive form. Dirt and blemishes are troublesome, too, because it is not easy to keep the film clean as it is put through on a telecine. There is also the risk of the film transport failing for some reason, such as a broken join, resulting in a pile-up of film in the mechanism, and almost certainly some damage being done to it. This means that somewhere there should be a standby print or an internegative. The back-up material (i.e. a positive) could be running simultaneously through another telecine in sync with the first, so that if anything went amiss it would be possible to switch straight over without loss or interruption to the programme.

At the moment there is not the electronic control over the negative image for taking corrective measures that you have in the laboratory by using the full printing latitude. You cannot adjust the colour balance from scene to scene with electronics as you can with laboratory methods. Whenever we were shooting material which might be negative transmitted we were asked to tend towards overexposure rather than underexposure. This was a question of colour saturation. If it was slightly overexposed, by, say, one stop, the negative would still yield full colour with a little extra printing light. With an underexposed negative, however, the colour content would be lost and it is, of course, impossible to put colour in which is not there already. So for negative transmission, the original camera exposure has to be more exact.

One of the things that governed, or rather limited, the type of sequence that could be handled in this way was the preference for a continuously shot sequence, without any basic cuts. There was also to be as little change in quality as possible (the whole production would be shot for negative transmission). It required two telecines for dissolves, mixes or fades and for this there had to be A and B rolls, one on each telecine. There was also the question of grading, which had to be done on the telecine machines. This meant running the negative back and forth at least a couple of times in the telecine, which, in turn, meant more wear to the film.

The three main programmes that did have negative transmission in them at the start were *Holiday 73, Dad's Army* and *Panorama*.

Although the factor of speed in operation (camera to screen) with negative transmission is important in topical and newsreel programmes, in drama and other normal productions it is not. Rushes are normally viewed in black and white and this has been the case for negative transmission also.

NEGATIVE/POSITIVE

The reason why we always use the negative/positive system for all but topical and news programmes, and why cameramen prefer it, is because it allows more control than reversal material. There is more exposure latitude in the negative in shooting and correction latitude in printing than with reversal film. So there is, as it were, "cover" at both ends. And as one is working so often under relatively poor conditions, bad weather, small locations and small rooms that do not allow the proper lighting or enough of it, such extra flexibility in exposure is well justified. Often you cannot control your image density on the film sufficiently because, for instance, lights used too close because of cramped surroundings vary too much in intensity over a short distance to get consistent effects with a moving subject. The negative/positive system provides the only efficient corrective. This was also the case when we used to shoot in black and white.

REVERSAL MATERIAL

The BBC uses reversal colour film (Ektachrome) for virtually all news material and for certain topical programmes—any programme in which the filmed sequences or clips will only be wanted for that one programme and can then be discarded. So the question of videotaping does not normally come in to it. The main disadvantage of using reversal stock in the camera is the lack of exposure latitude. There is no scope for improving the results in printing or processing—virtually no control, in fact. One always tries, in the course of normal filming, to be absolutely accurate where exposure is concerned but there are conditions where you cannot be accurate and you have to rely on the latitude of exposure in the film stock to obtain usable results. With reversal material this is impossible. Switching from using negative to reversal is apt to be troublesome for a cameraman because at the back of his mind all the time is the knowledge that exposures must be much more accurate. A further disadvantage with reversal material is that you have only your original copy unless you use internegs and then you lose quality, which must be avoided.

Rushes

In the BBC, rushes of colour filming are normally printed up for viewing in black and white. There is a small allowable quota printed in colour each day—roughly 10 per cent. There is really little point in printing up 10 per cent in colour because when viewing the rough or first or second cuts, it is most distracting, even shattering, to watch a sequence in monochrome which is suddenly interrupted by a colour shot. It is better to print entirely in black and white where the terms of reference for judgement remain the same.

It must always be borne in mind that large numbers of viewers have black and white sets. So it is essential to get a good monochrome picture as well as a good colour picture. If you have a well exposed negative on colour or monochrome, it will come out well on both types of set. So you must take care with exposures. These days even when most film is shot in colour, a properly exposed colour negative will always reproduce well in black and white. Borderline errors tend to be emphasized when the colour original is seen in black and white.

Some people in the BBC still shoot a grey scale to check the colour rendering at the beginning of a reel or shot, and it indicates that it is correctly printed. But as the rushes are usually in black and white, you do not need to check the printed quality of a rush print.

When the film goes to the cutting room to be edited the first part that is taken off is the grey scale with the number boards. So the grey scale is never used. The cutting is done in black and white and no colour is seen until the first answer print is produced from the cut negative.

Even if you were to see colour rushes, they would all be printed at the same printer light intensity and with a uniform colour pack, completely unbalanced, often with very poor colour. The general standard of black and white printing as supplied to the BBC, is also poor and is often done on non-standard printing stock. At other times the black and white print might be superb. The rushes of any film are, of course, invalidated by very poor quality printing.

A cameraman does, in fact, think very consciously in terms of colour when he works with it. The first priority is, of course, to make the film *in colour* so colour considerations come first.

Lighting and Contrast

It is easier to photograph in colour than black and white because the colours give you a natural separation between different points of the subject. It is not necessary to light different parts of scenes to different levels in order to separate them artificially in tone. Half the battle in photographing it is therefore already won. In lighting for colour there is much more emphasis on getting the correct exposure than in separation and moulding—the reverse of working with black and white.

When we started working with colour film in television, many cameramen found that because they were still lighting as if for black and white, the backlight tended to be too strong for a realistic effect in colour. Backlight is most important to gain separation and contour in black and white; coming from behind the object, is rims it and acts as an outline. Backlight is quite important in colour work also because it gives the moulding and contour necessary. You cannot leave the differences in colour to do all the work—this would produce a dull image. The backlight might be from above and directly behind or from a three-quarter viewpoint (three-quarter backlight). Backlighting in the studio replaces that element of lighting from that direction in nature. The sky, pavement or other surroundings reflect light from the sun—all round the subject. One is not immediately aware of it when looking at a typical studio lighting set up but this back and filler lighting is there nevertheless.

In the days of black and white filming, a picture with more than 50 per cent of bright area would lead to automatic underexposure on a telecine, so that the remaining part of the picture might become a silhouette. Faces against sky backgrounds would lose all detail. If, however, the composition was arranged so that the bright area occupied no more than 40 per cent of the picture area, there was less risk of losing detail in the picture. A similar effect happens with colour although not to the same extent because, with colour, there are not the extremes of contrast.

Obviously, even with colour one tries to avoid shooting against sky backgrounds if detail is needed in the subject. You make sure that there is plenty of light on the subject so that the difference in brightness between the background and the subject is not more than two to two and a half stops. If, in a subsequent shot, say the reverse shot, the subject were seen against a solid background of trees, you would have to remove the fill light. But this would make a rather unsatisfactory kind of cut. The cut would be to another view closer or further away from the subject and in either case a greater non-white area would be seen. The first shot might be three-quarter length, followed by a close-up or long shot, either of which would overcome the likelihood of any direct comparison between the density of areas in the two shots. Large dark areas do not produce so much trouble this way.

Quality

Where colour is concerned, most cameramen probably favour a natural or pastel colouring in a scene rather than fierce or garish colour. It pleases the eye. Not surprisingly, some cameramen and directors, particularly in the field of light entertainment, actually prefer loud colours. In drama, however, natural colour should be the rule. Some of the classical drama sets used by the BBC are dressed with the most beautiful selection and combintions of colour. If you have a situation where the colours in the set are too garish for the general theme, or a supporting artist's clothes draw attention away from the principals, some alteration should be made.

The field of the arts film can put this problem in reverse. On *Civilisation* one of the problems was that the brightness of colour on certain works of art was very much lower than that experienced in real life—there was particular trouble with the paintings of Franz Hals. Great care was taken with this series to make sure that the colours were as accurate as possible. Two art researchers familiar with the works, who sat in on the viewing of the answer prints checked that the colour printing being produced was all acceptable from their point of view. This is always a problem with films concerned with that kind of subject matter. Many people would not know what the correct colour should be. Hence the printer needs guidance. But colour memory is notoriously unreliable. The results obtained with *Civilisation* justfied the cost of reprinting, checking, etc.

Colour in the Set

Before the introduction of colour filming, the sets used to be produced sometimes in the most curious shades and colours, not necessarily bearing any relation to the true colours—but they came out in the proper shades of grey. With today's sets the colours you see are the true colours. If you have the wrong blending (ill matched colours) it usually shows up very obviously on television. For example, with a number of well matched colours it is only necessary to alter one very slightly before they begin to clash instead of harmonize. The colours must be correct.

On interior/exterior studio shots, the colours must be absolutely accurate. If, for instance, all the colours are natural enough except for an over-red brick wall, it will upset the balance of the whole scene. Two dresses, a brilliant red and bright yellow, would not be admitted to the scene side by side except for effect, as the shock to the eye is not what one is used to. Some of the dresses, drapes, carpets and tapestries in the period classical series on television are beautifully blended. There has been a tendency in recent times to use very subtle colours. The sets of Hampton Court Palace for the BBC production *The Six Wives of Henry VIII* with the beautiful woodwork and the flash of colour gave superb effects.

If you feel that the colours in a set are wrong or too strident, you can discuss the problem with the art director. Once the lighting is switched on the set takes on an entirely different hue. But you might suspect in advance if this is likely to be troublesome. Over-bright colour can be sprayed down or repainted. Or perhaps something can be added, such as a piece of ivy, to break up the colour a little. Bright clothes can be a problem, where you get cross reflections on a two-shot, for instance, with the clothes of one person reflecting on to the face of another. You can avoid this by altering the direction of your key light. But normally, the designer chooses colours for a set knowing how the colours are likely to come out. The lighting should not be unsympathetic to this. If it is a night set you tend to light with a slight bias towards the blue because it is a "cold" situation.

You have some control over the colours with the lighting. For example, if the background colour is too insistent you can put less light on it. If the background colour reflects on to the artist you can increase the distance between them and/or reduce the background lighting a little. You can redirect the lighting for the same purpose. You can also place colour filters in front of the lights (with wire, papers or silks to reduce the intensity) but these measures are more likely to be taken for light entertainment or comedy programmes than straight drama. You can fade or change over the colours. If you drew back curtains for interior (night) lighting to reveal daylight, the lighting keys would change direction as well as colour. This is much easier in the television studios because any light on the set has a built-in dimming facility controlled from a dimmer bank.

To summarize, then, colour control can be by:

light direction,
light intensity,

light filtering,
manipulation of artists.

As a last resort, if the error is an overall one, it can be compensated in the laboratory in printing and grading. If skin tone is too pink or blue it can be corrected, provided that the change does not noticeably affect other colours in the scene. If, on exteriors, the 85 filter is accidentally omitted (this is needed with Eastmancolor—an interior-balanced 3200K stock—the 85 filter puts it up to 5600, for daylight), the result is a heavy blue cast. The laboratories can just about pull that back to normal. Colour can be further modified in transmission if the answer print comes up slightly out of balance from the telecine.

Matching Shots in Colour

In the studio there is little problem because you have full control when matching shots in colour. If the light intensities are kept the same so is the colour balance. You check with a meter all the time. With an interior type set up you work at a fixed level of light intensity all the time unless there is a particular shot in which you want extra depth of field or something for which you need to overlight. Then the power of the light is stepped up in proportion. A normal lighting on a set might, for example, be T4 for all shots. This means that you use 200 foot-candles for your key light. If you want more depth of field on a deep two-shot, you consult a set of depth of field tables, and see that for this particular lighting you need to light for T8 which means increasing your key light to 800 foot-candles. Background light, kickers, backlights, etc. are raised in proportion. The contrast increases a little, unless the filler light is increased by the same amount. The new, more powerful, lights are substituted for others with the same spot or flood settings. This takes a little time as results must match the previous shots perfectly. After the shot the original lamps are replaced. This can be planned beforehand by placing lamps in approximately the same position. One should keep a constant check with a meter.

Effects and Colour

Camera effects, today as always, are successful when the producer and cameraman have rightly judged what they can get away with—what the medium will accept before the effect no longer "stands up". The added dimension of realism provided by colour has not seriously depleted the stock of visual devices that can be summoned to convince the viewer that he is seeing what you are implying rather than actually showing him.

Effects such as those used in *Stalingrad* (page 69) are just as possible now as they were in 1963 when the BBC was using 35 mm monochrome material. The quality was good enough for the camera to be as perceptive of the rough edges and disguises that were present in these scenes as with modern equipment and materials. You can still work out effects as broad as these today with 16 mm equipment—the differences in the medium are not really related to it—except that, with colour, you could not build one vast set as we did then and split it in to sixteen different locations.

Today you would have to change your colour blendings. You could not get away with using the same foreground and background from one scene to another and at the same time expect the audience to believe that it was an entirely different place. You would have to build more into the scene, and you would need more props.

The *Stalingrad* set was supposed to represent different locations at different times of the year. Whereas in monochrome it was basically a matter of getting your impressions with a series of gradations from black to white, in colour you would need much greater detail. You expect something very much more specific and the proper colours.

9

Processing, Rushes and Picture Quality

THE TELEVISION film cameraman has only the minimum control over his finished product unless he is working in the studio, where he has easier access to the rushes and contact with people handling later stages of the process. But television filming being what it is, for the most part he is likely to be working away from base, shipping the rushes back to the studio. They are viewed by a member of the film department, the Film Operations Manager (FOM). If possible, the cameraman phones in to the studio half way through the morning. The FOM can give him a report on the rushes from the previous day's work, saying how they are printing—if they are scratched, if they look all right, if the action is satisfactory. In fact, the cameraman is really only seeking information from him on technicalities and his judgement varies according to his experience in various areas of film activity—topical programmes, drama, etc. The only way for a cameraman to be certain about what he is achieving is to see his own work. Often he cannot see his rushes even when he returns from a location, either because they are already being edited and are therefore not available, or because he is immediately sent out on another production.

The cameraman is unlikedly to see the show copy, the answer print or transmission copy, so the editor is given most of the control. He views the answer print and orders new sequences or reprinting where he thinks it is called for. The cameraman has no say at all in this, and consequently there is no feedback to him as there would be for a cameraman in feature films. Indeed, he is not likely to learn by his results at all unless he happens to see the programme on television. Unfortunately, the less experienced people working in television conditions like these are learning very little from what they produce. This is a situation that one has to live with in the BBC. At best, if a cameraman does see rushes he will see them only in black and white. On the other hand there are some cameramen who are not even interested in seeing their rushes and some assistants who resist the opportunity. But, as everyone knows, the only way to learn the job is to see rushes. A cameraman should make sure that his assistant is not only a good one but that he is going to do what he is told *and* he is going to look at the rushes.

On long productions where most of the rushes are not viewed by the cameraman, he should at least see those that he can at the *beginning* and not half way through the job. The benefits are that you can see your mistakes very clearly. These may be mistakes that other people cannot see. For example, you might be going through a phase when you are giving slightly wrong headroom to your shots or you are not composing quite properly. The shots may look all right but might not be quite "falling into shape" although the mistakes are not of a kind serious enough to justify retakes. If there had been a bad mistake you would have been notified by the FOM.

Viewing rushes enables you to keep your work up to standard. When abroad you send rushes back to base whenever you can.

Location Rushes

Rushes are sent out to a remote location only when a director specifically asks for them. This might perhaps be once a week but certainly not every day. That is not because he is working on any particular type of production but possibly because he may wish to check on the artist's performance. It is, however, usually a larger type of production which allows sufficient budget to hire a projector and facilities for viewing film on location. On a large production working to a tight transmission schedule the editor might be on the location doing the editing there, synching up rushes and breaking down the material for a rough cut version which can then be seen on location. This is possible only if there are proper facilities available in the area, to wit: a 16 mm projector and a place to view the rushes, or if the editor comes to the location with a portable projector or portable editing machine that can be set up in a hotel room. But this consumes an editor's time and is unusual because normally, as soon as the rushes are returned to the studio, the editor is already working on them and keeping up to date, getting them into a rough cut form ready for the director to see when he returns.

A disadvantage in viewing rushes locally on location is that the projection conditions are unfamiliar. At the studio, where the viewing conditions, projector light, etc., are known quantities it is much easier to make an accurate assessment of quality, gleaning enough from what you see to make mental comparisons. But on location the rushes are sometimes seen under very curious conditions. You may think you have underexposed when in fact it is only the projector light which is inadequate. It is very difficult, at least for the first few days, to judge what you are seeing on a moviola or in a strange cinema. It can be more of an annoyance than a help. The studio reports, however, are a good guide.

The producer, who is back at base, views the rushes with the FOM. There are occasions when a little material is sent out to the cameraman because of a specific problem. If, for instance, there were some doubt about certain rushes or a couple of shots which they thought he should retake, then they would be sent out. Sometimes, for matching a shot or sequence the editing department might send a few frames of the print through the post. This enables the cameraman to re-establish a shot or match the continuity (determining who is standing where or what they are wearing) for an extra shot to be cut into the sequence. An alteration to the sequence might come from the director on location, or, as happens quite often on all-film serials, the editor working on a rough cut in London might send a cable stating that an episode is likely to be two or three minutes underrunning, and requesting more material. The director might extend some existing sequences or send a request for the scriptwriter to prepare and despatch additional dialogue, sequences or situations.

The editor does not order up extra material unless absolutely essential, because by the time the request comes through the unit will probably be on another location.

On *Civilisation* we sent all the material back and, as a guideline, worked using the reports sent out from the laboratory, when necessary. No material was returned to us for viewing on site. But telegrams would be sent saying, "O.K.", "half a stop more", etc. where necessary. On returning, we saw all the rushes, which had not been touched while we were away.

For that production the time factor was not critical.

Liaison with Laboratories

When trainee cameramen pass through the BBC school they are given full information about technical control at the laboratories. But they do not go "on site" to see it all happening and there is very little contact between cameramen and laboratories, other than where the cameraman is doing some special effect or has a requirement out of the ordinary. The reason for this is the lack of time and the need for the cameraman to be available at the studio. In working for television this knowledge is not really essential. Most of the shots have to be done in any case under prevailing conditions, regardless of either the weather or circumstances pertaining to a particular location. You cannot do much to alter these, so you tend to shoot "according to the book".

You cannot, in practice, specify particular development

requirements, etc., when it is more or less essential to pass the material through the standard production facilities at the laboratory—otherwise it will not necessarily be available for the morning's viewing. Also, with the schedule provided for so many television productions it would be too late to make corrections or modifications as the team would be disbanded by that time. In the normal course of events all the cameraman would ask of the laboratory would be for them to "save" a particular sequence which had been wrongly exposed. But with colour there are very few measures for "saving" material that can be carried out by a laboratory.

The use of a negative/positive film stock system means that there is almost total control over the resultant print. Any corrections or alterations can be carried out in the printing, provided the starting point is a correctly exposed camera negative.

In colour, the laboratory can resort to using an almost infinite number of filter combinations for any adjustments necessary to produce a correctly balanced colour print from the negative. With reversal colour film stock the degree of colour balancing and control is severely limited.

VTR

With material which is subsequently to be VTR'd, the most important thing to bear in mind is that you have a properly exposed negative. The laboratory, editors, etc. can then do anything they want in the way of producing effects they may want from it.

An occasional badly exposed negative produced perforce by circumstances beyond your control is understandable. But one should never deliberately produce poorly exposed material for whatever reason, and then expect it to be successfully VTR'd. This puts an unnecessary burden on the VTR people. They need a reasonably good quality negative or positive in order to get good quality results and to be able to match the filmed VTR with the live studio television—which these days is very high quality. When film is VTR'd it is rather like duplicating the negative. But when the live studio material is VTR'd you are, in effect, producing the original negative, as you are VTRing direct, not through a film negative. When you are VTRing a film the result is degraded by one stage.

Sometimes the film content is VTR'd separately and then physically cut into the live recorded VTR or fitted in to live VTRing as it is done—cueing it in or out as with ordinary telecine, when shooting on the floor.

OB units can wire back pictures and sound simultaneously to the studio. But on drama they usually VTR it on location.

Camera Report

The cameraman makes up a report sheet at the end of the day which authorises the laboratory to process the material and charge it against the production. The sheet contains the name of the production and its job number, the type and batch number of the film stock used; the strip number of each particular roll in each magazine.

Each magazine number is marked on the sheet with the relevant scene numbers that go on that roll, and all the scene numbers shot that day, the numbers of takes of each scene and their footages, and the takes that you want printed are circled. Each roll is then given the magazine and strip number, and you also indicate the type of shots on the roll (i.e. day interior sync, or exterior mute) against each particular scene. Due warning must be given to the laboratories if there are any technical points you wish to raise, such as that the lighting conditions were bad or that this roll was underexposed but should be treated as normal. If you were using any special effects such as fog or dusk rather than night or day or you want an early morning effect, you enter on the sheet that this particular shot should be printed for dusk or evening and the lab makes a slight alteration in the rush print.

There is not much point in going into too much detail about special treatments, because rushes are normally printed at one light. The camera sheet is not used in making the final print but the editor knows when the first answer print is delivered whether it is too light, dark, etc. He has a copy of the camera sheet though this is mainly supplied to him so that he can check which scene numbers have been printed, etc. The cameraman must rely to a great extent on the editor to see that such things as dawn and dusk effects are carried out because, after shooting, it is probably the last that the cameraman will see of the material until it is transmitted—if he sees it at home.

Laboratory Report

You read the laboratory negative report sheet before viewing the rushes. So you have your alibis all sorted out! You sometimes find that the negative report sheet indicates that a particular sequence is printed light but the negative is satisfactory. The lab sheet comments on basic technical facts like scratches, exposure, focus, hair in gate, etc.

The rushes are black and white because of the expense and wastage of printing such reference material in colour, unless it is particularly required for a special scene. All rushes are printed at the same "light" or exposure, so any error in camera exposure would be clearly visible at that stage. The printer has a range of the equivalent of 4–5 *f*-stops adjustment. But in actual fact one tries to hit the middle position with

TELEVISION FILM DEPARTMENT SEQ Nº 38249

CAMERA REPORT

To LABORATORY

To: ______ Labs. (Rushes to F.O.M. C. Brown AT TFS/LG/TC/KH/AP/WG)

Production: Further Education Date: 14-12-75

Sub Title: Carry on Learning Episode No. —

Project No.: 2088-9823 Cameraman (Stockholder): W. Jones

Camera: BL.17. Camera Assistant: A. Smith

Remarks: Please print Rolls 1, 3, & 5 in Colour. Variable exposures Roll 2 & 3.

Tick applicable sections	35mm	16mm	Neg.	Rev.	Stripe	Colour	Type	Batch No.
		X	X			X	Eastman 7247	154/11-1

PRINT CIRCLED TAKES

Roll No.	Scene No.	1	2	3	4	5	6	Mag. No.	Int. Ext.	Day Night	Mute Sync.	Strip No.	Remarks	Total
	1	(100)							I	D	S		Roll 1	
	2	60	20	(60)									Mag No 2 — Strip 8	
	3	(60)												380
	4	40	(40)											
	5	(120)							E	D	M		Roll 2	
	6	80	(80)										Mag No 3 — Strip 8	400
	7	40	40	(40)	RUN OUT.									
	8	20	(60)						E	D	S		Roll 3	
	9	(90)	(70)										Mag No 1 — Strip 32	
	10	20	(20)	HAIR IN GATE TAKE 1.										390
	11	(60)												
	12	50												
	12	X	(70)						I	D	M		Roll 4	
	13	140	(120)										Mag No 3 — Strip 19	395
	14	(65)												
	15	(100)	(100)						I	D	S		Roll 5	
	16	(50)	50	(50)									Mag No 2 — Strip 8	350
														1915

STOCK B/F: 2,400
RECEIPTS: 3,600.
TOTAL: 6,000
USED: 1915
WASTE (to Stock Stores): 85
STOCK C/F: 4,000.

Signature: W. Jones.

For costing purposes only		
Footage	Colour Rushes	B/Sheet Ref.
	Processing List	Invoice Amount

F/342

Camera report sheet which accompanies the rolls of exposed film to the laboratory. Circled footage figures are takes to be printed. The batch number and the strip number are taken from the negative tin when loading the camera magazine. Conditions such as day/night mute/sync are shown. Remarks column: magazine number etc, are a check in case of possible technical faults. Total column: indicates footage exposed per roll.

FILM LABORATORIES LTD. A 62870

Production THE LONG CHASE Date 11.8.72

Cameraman A ENGLANDER Sheet No. 67234-35

FORM 41

SCENE	TAKE	REMARKS	SCENE	TAKE	REMARKS
	#124	30·30·30		#125	34-34·36
826	X	26·26·26	841	X	30·30·30
827	X	32·32·32	842	+	34·34·34
829	X		843	⊗	Slightly overexp
830	+	Variable Exp.	844	X	OOK.
831	+				
832	+	OOK		#126	30·30·30
834	X		845	X	
835	+		846		Variable Exp
836	X		847		
837	X		848		OOK.
838	+		849		
839	+		850.		
840	X				

Laboratory contact for the above work is Mr. ______________

Laboratory rushes report sheet which accompanies the rushes to the projection theatre for viewing. Made out by the laboratory viewer who sees the material immediately after processing. Scene column: slate numbers; Take column: roll number (top), marks indicate that the slate has been checked as printed by the viewer; Remarks column: figures indicate high/low printer light settings to print on roll 124–126, remark draws attention to variable exposure throughout roll. e.g.: Shot 843 slightly overexposed. OOK = Otherwise OK.

exposure all the time, which leaves lattitude either way for balance control. If the exposure is on a marginal point one should (on neg.) try to overexpose a little to over-saturate, rather than do the opposite. In any case, Eastmancolor responds better to overexposure than to underexposure. The great advantages of the more recent Eastman 7247 negative stock are the increased definition and finer grain structure which, combined with the optical quality of the 10:1 Zeiss zoom lens give a screen image comparable with that from 35 mm only a few years ago.

It is not necessary to ask for speed to be "pushed" in development. As soon as modifications of this kind are made there is likely to be trouble with the grain, and there is enough trouble anyway with definition. Processing time changes can only give an advance in speed equivalent to one stop. In any case, Eastmancolor has enormous latitude and can be underexposed by two stops and still give good results. The speed for the film quoted by the manufacturer errs on the side favouring the cameraman so there is more exposure latitude available to him than is immediately apparent.

10

Shot Planning

WHEN THE CAMERAMAN sets up for a shot he has several considerations in mind. He must think about the lighting character and brightness in relation to the scene, the camera position in relation to artists and the lighting he has provided, and any particular camera movements that may be involved. Behind these technical considerations are the two most important factors—how he can give the director what he wants in terms of film, and how to provide the editor with footage that fits together without gaps or unnecessary duplication, either of which would cause a waste of his time and effort. Both these aspects have a direct bearing on the question of where to cut in a filmed scene.

VISUALIZING AND BUILDING UP SCENES

Basically, when approaching a scene you try to visualize the effect the director is aiming for, as explained by him, or to visualize an effect which is complementary to the mood and character of the scene. You then build it up from that point. Perhaps the effect you want cannot be obtained in the time available or the physical dimensions of the set, because, for instance, the lamps may not be placed in particular positions. In that case you alter it to obtain almost the effect that was visualized in the first place—the point from which the building up process, or development started. In other words, you visualize the scene as it will be and then amend or improve it with ideas of better things.

THE MASTER SHOT APPROACH

Despite the close proximity, within one organization, of the traditional film camera technique and the essentially multi-camera electronic method of recording a production, there has been remarkably little cross-fertilization between these two very different approaches, although, of course, one can use multi-camera techniques with film just as one can adopt certain film practices with electronic equipment.

For years in drama productions, television film cameramen have followed the feature film principle of providing a master shot of a long piece of relevant action so that there is always something to cut away to or from. The cut-ins, close-ups and two-shots are then covered according to how you think you need them. This applies to exterior or interior work. If you have taken a master shot, you know exactly how that scene is played and you know more easily what cut-ins you want and how they ought to cut. Also, if you run into trouble with continuity, or light problems (where the sun goes or it starts to rain), the editor can cut to the master shot and then back to another shot to disguise the shortcomings of the material. It is an old technique, and though despised by some, it is a safeguard. And, after all, one does not have to use it.

The master might be a long running shot and could involve some camera movement. The maximum might be the whole length of a 400 ft magazine, i.e. 11 minutes. Such a shot is, however, very unusual, because a shot of that length would probably be the only one, involving various camera movements with changes of viewpoint, reverse shots and possibly close-ups. The disadvantage of this method for television filming becomes apparent if it takes longer to light and line up because of its complexity than if it were done in separate shots. So, although you have 10 minutes of "already cut footage" the man hours required to achieve it may not make it worthwhile.

A normal master shot would probably be about $2\frac{3}{4}$ minutes, running through the complete action (in long shot). Then you would cut and re-line up. You might make the master shot end on a track in to close-up, for example. But then you would need other shots to cut in to the master. Such a shot is worked out from a shooting script provided for the cameraman at the outset and discussed with the director. Producers, too, these days are quite familiar with the fact that you can overcome a technical problem by cutting from one shot to another.

If you have a continuous shot showing the entire action (in this particular type of sequence) without departing from it, the viewer will believe what he is seeing more readily than if you do it in a series of cuts from one shot to another. It is a matter of having real continuity of action. This factor is not only a matter of the individual conditioning of a technician—audiences have been watching films long enough to know that there are technical dodges to avoid such effects. Consequently, for them, the "straight" treatment carries more conviction.

Editing Pattern

In shooting any sequence consisting of several separate shots, one always thinks in terms of an editing pattern. This might not be the *right* one, but it gives the editor material that he can use without difficulty and which fits together in a logical way when it is assembled by him.

Some directors tend to forget about the editor and omit such things as overlaps where the editor may want to cut. Instead they should be keeping the dialogue or acting going, or starting the dialogue further back in order to make the overlap if the editor should want it.

The editor usually prefers to cut on a movement rather than a static subject. But if one shot involves a movement you must have the artist move in the shot that follows. If the subject is static he must be static at the beginning of the next shot. If you have a static shot that ends in a movement and this is followed by a static shot, the editor is confined to making his cut before the movement begins in the first shot. If a close-up insert is to be introduced in a shot involving first a static position and then movement, it must end on movement in order to avoid forcing the editor to cut this qualifying or detailing shot in to the static portion of the main shot and then having the movement after the end of the insert instead of cutting back from the moving end of the insert to the movement concluding the main shot. A cut on the movement is much smoother and more slick. It is important to try to keep things moving. The responsibility for providing elbow room for the editor often enough devolves on the cameraman himself.

It is, perhaps, a good idea if you never stop the camera when the director says "cut" but always let it run on a fraction, say, four seconds, before stopping. Some directors tend, in any case, to give the word to cut far too soon, when the action has hardly finished. This would be an embarrassment to the editor by leaving him very little material with which to cut smoothly or indeed to have much choice in the matter at all.

There are many directors who not only want to cut too soon, but also start their action too soon, almost before the number board is out of picture, and before everything has "settled down". Again, this gives the editor little to work with and the cameraman no chance of balancing himself and settling in before taking the shot. But the main problem is that of cutting too soon and the danger that the artist may not have quite finished delivering his lines before the director shouts "cut". The editor may hardly be able to get his scissors in to the gap between!

Most directors must have a concept of how they want a particular sequence edited and, indeed, they are in a position to have the editors do what they want.

Overlaps in Drama and Topical Material

With drama, you tend to run in to the shot, i.e. run the camera before the action really gets under way, and cut the shot fairly decisively at the end. You overlap the shot at the beginning in each case and end fairly specifically. But with ordinary topical or documentary programmes there is not much overlap. You do, however, concentrate on overlap when you shoot a "commentary-with-vision" sequence, i.e. where the commentator is seen in shot. Such sequences may appear at intervals through a programme as they did for example in *Civilisation*. The other technique, where the voice is heard when the commentator is not seen, is known as "commentary-over" or "voice-over", or sometimes "commentary-out-of-vision". You would overlap at the beginning of a sentence if you were cutting from, say, a MS to CU or MS to LS or CU to LS, in order to give the editor latitude in making his cut so that he does not have to cut at a particular point. He can cut in the middle of a sentence if he wants to; it is really a question of obtaining a smooth flow or words or action.

With drama, you should not run the camera for very much more than the actual shot that you know you are going to use. The director knows much more clearly what part of the shot he is going to use than he does in topical productions, for example, so extra material after the shot only confuses the editor and wastes his time. At the beginning you give an overlap, a run-in in order to get the words and action to overlap properly and allow space for the editor to make a cut without necessarily cutting dead on a particular word or given situation. In drama, the end of a shot is more "final", as it were, than the beginning. You need the beginning of a shot to be flexible in order to allow the editor to find a point where it butts in properly on the end of the previous shot. That shot will end on dialogue or action and will butt into the beginning of the next shot on which you will get overlap—rather like headers and sleepers in bricklaying or like overlapping boards.

Timing

Timing does not take into account the run up of the camera, the clapper board and the time it takes the director to call "action!" At that word the continuity girl presses the button of the stop watch. The moment he calls "cut" she presses it again, so that only the action is timed. The irrelevant material at the beginning is not timed. Thus, the director and production staff can tell exactly how much *cut* footage has been shot. For example, of 1200 ft shot they know that they have, say, 600 ft, or, of half an hour's running time there is 15 minutes of cut footage shot on that particular day.

Sync Sound Cuts

There are special problems in shooting and cutting where sync sound is involved. This is not only because artists may forget their lines in mid-shot, or not really know them, but because of interference from extraneous noises from aircraft passing overhead, or cars from nearby, and the difficulty of cutting a shot containing such a sound in to a sequence without it. If a close-up which, though shot ten minutes later than the main shot, is supposed to follow directly after the first, the sound would break off abruptly when going from one shot to the next. So in such a case there is the additional need to lay an aircraft noise over the second shot to match the first. These days the extraneous noise factor is very significant, especially if you are working on historical drama where such sounds are totally inappropriate.

Reshooting and Matching for Cuts

The accumulation of experiences is mentally recorded. Every technician has a "filing system" in his mind by means of which he remembers a certain effect or result he obtained in a particular way. The complications for the cameraman in matching shots are that he must remember how he lit a particular scene a fortnight later when the artist returns to the studio. As many such "new" and "old" parts may be directly joined together in the final assembly, it is essential to match their lighting. To get it *exactly* the same is difficult. This applies equally to retakes shot over a period of time.

In some ways re-shooting material (due to loss of stock in processing or transit, for example) is more of a problem than working on the original because in re-shooting, a cameraman instinctively tries to remember what he did the previous time and may have some difficulty in recalling it accurately. You have to think *why* you did something, as well as *how*, in order to do it again. There is so much in photography and camera operation that is subconscious that it is a great strain to try and repeat what you have done, especially on long and complicated shots. This is, after all, not the normal process but a reversal of it. Sometimes you try to work from basics again, but usually you try to remember the shot and repeat it, though it is not necessarily the best approach. If, on the other hand, you can still see the effects of your work—the lighting contrast, modelling, etc.—and you find that it is not very good—you should definitely start again from scratch. Although you have the same set-up, lens, aperture, etc., you may move your lighting to improve it. You should only attempt to repeat the very good work.

11

Camera Movement

THERE IS A SCHOOL of thought in film direction that seems to demand that you must not let anything be static. It is almost as if they are saying that you must not let the audience see what is going on but you have to move everything all the time. Film is, of course, a moving medium recording moving images rather than static ones but this premise is easily misinterpreted. Indeed, in such a purposeful movement, as when you are moving the camera with people who are dictating that movement, then one movement is even cancelling out the other. But if you start to move the camera round two stationary people there can hardly ever be a reason for it. If the camera is the voyeur and the two people remain in the middle of a room, talking, it takes a relatively long time to move the camera round to point the other way (i.e. the diametrically opposed direction) to get the second person's point of view. The most effective way to speed up the action and dialogue is by cutting (which is often treated as old-fashioned) and not by drooling round with the camera, especially with a hand-held movement, which, in itself, is visually uneven and in many cases disturbing.

PURPOSE

There is one question that every untrained and unprejudiced cameraman should ask himself at the outset of his career in filming for television. If he were sitting in his own home watching the relatively small picture on a television screen, would he want to see the picture jumping up and down and moving round and round or would he want to see well composed, pleasant shots and quick cutting in order to make the fast moving sections of a drama plot incisive? Alternatively, would he prefer to see the image jumping about and the plot taking a long time to develop because the camera is moving, rather than have instant development by cutting? Which would be the more restful, mentally and visually, in something which is supposed to be entertainment?

Surely, in most instances, the visually and mentally restful is what we should aim for. Too many productions are made for the benefit of the technicians rather than the audience. Too many productions are made for the benefit of the director. Too many film sequences are made for the kudos of the cameraman, because, in both instances, it is thought to enhance their technical standing.

Let us look more closely at the typical instance of arbitrary camera movement just given above. This was a hand-held shot moving around two static people in conversation. The main centre of interest there is the expression on the face, assuming that the people really are stationary. Because the subjects are stationary, motion is produced by moving the camera purely for the sake of getting movement in the scene. This movement is really uncalled for. The camera is acting independently, as if it were a separate entity or a third person, and the director may be striving to avoid a stationary set-up on the screen although there is nothing wrong with a stationary situation.

With a director who understands how to use a camera in a positive way (page 70) the camera would be stationary at this point. Or he might have arranged things so that the artists are moving as they talk and the camera is going from one to the other or from place to place. The director uses the camera in such a way that its movement is being *originated by the movement of an artist from A to B*, or whatever. The camera might follow. Unnecessary camera action is boring. This is easily demonstrated in a close-up of a person seen over the shoulder of the man he is addressing. You move the camera round through 180 degrees so that you have a reverse shot. But all the time you spend moving round is dead time, in fact. And it is a dead picture because you are only moving the camera across in order to get another framing. This can be done very much quicker by cutting and the above movement is not interesting or necessary, nor does it help reinforce the situation dramatically.

In the shot cited previously, the camera might have moved from one over the shoulder shot to another while the artists were moving, but this would be as a part of the developing action and not a selfconscious camera movement to "make up" for inactivity.

It is a good rule of thumb that applies to zoom shots as well as tracks that you should never move your camera or move your zoom lens unless you have some sort of motivation—something in the background, or your foreground artists moving. Otherwise the camera movement is usually obtrusive. Everyone is aware of the mechanical movement of the camera. The movement of a character in a shot would perhaps make you widen the shot in order to allow the viewer to see the reason for it. Really you should strive to cover up mechanical movements of the camera.

It is not difficult to envisage a situation which would be covered most successfully by having the artists move in order to avoid a cut, and thus save having to set up the camera in a different position and make a satisfactory join between the two shots in editing. Or, again, it may save moving the camera during the shot, which might in some cases call for some kind of rolling camera support.

Suppose there are two people in MS talking and moving towards camera, stopping in close shot framed just above the waist. The director now wants to cut in to a closer shot. But if, instead of stopping where they first stopped, they were to come closer to camera so that they finish up on a two shot, this would obviate the need for another cut. They would move *themselves* to the close-up position rather than staying in medium close-up, from which the *camera* would have to move to a close-up. The whole effect is more smooth and natural. This may be something that the director has not foreseen when positioning actors in relation to the camera. The cameraman may be able to suggest that the actors be brought forward and perhaps turned round so that he ends with an over-the-shoulder close-up on A. This means that there is only one cut to do—an over-shoulder close-up on B. By this approach he has eliminated one cut and speeded up the whole filming process.

Panning and Tracking

Any cameraman should know at what speed he should pan for a particular shot. If it is a POV (point of view) shot, he should pan at a rate corresponding to the natural rate at which a person looking around would scan the horizon. There is, however, the problem of "stagger"—a strobing effect arising from panning the scene at the wrong rate. "Stagger" arises because the moving picture is a series of still frames, and between each frame the camera has moved a little. With a variable opening shutter camera, if the shutter is opened a little the stagger is reduced. At one time all cameras had this facility and the range of shutter openings was usually about 175 degrees–0, though on more modern cameras the range is from about 220 degrees–0. If you normally worked at 170 or 175 degrees there was still some opening available beyond this, which you could use either if you had a very quick pan for some action or to give more exposure on night exteriors. If you were travelling along in a train or car shooting a back projection plate (page 212), you could open up the shutter in order to reduce the stagger slightly in the hedgerow. Conversely, if you closed the shutter down, there would be more stagger because the frame was exposed within the 90 degrees of open shutter, leaving 270 degrees closed. Therefore, the image was blacked out for a longer period while the camera moved.

The Arriflex BL camera has no adjustable shutter. The Eclair has a variable shutter which is not, however, adjustable during the shot, only beforehand. Likewise the Cameflex.

Full Circle Pans

Occasionally, as with a scene in *Colditz*, a 365-degree pan is called for. In this case we were panning the camera from a position in the centre of the large courtyard with people moving around. The shot involved two artists walking and talking as they proceeded round the courtyard wall. This meant that at certain points they were further away from the camera than at others and a slight zoom movement was used to keep them at the same magnification the whole time. These magnifications were determined by looking through the viewfinder at various points beforehand and chalking marks against the datum line on the lens barrel to represent the zoom lens movements at particular points of the shot. This was done with adhesive tape. The assistant judged the zoom adjustments while watching the action as the camera turned round. The *Colditz* shot was in fact one and a half complete turns and was further complicated by points where the actors stopped and, while they carried out bits of action, the camera view had to widen to accommodate them. When they moved on, the camera had to zoom back again to a tight two shot (MCU) to continue following them round. Making this sort of adjustment successfully requires a sort of sixth sense from an assistant—a good one has that.

In this way the director was able to shoot about three minutes of dialogue in about ten minutes actual time—which made an interesting shot and was a great time saver. It was a "day" shot and required 16 brutes to provide illumination over so large an area. Surprisingly, it did not take long to light although it was quite elaborate. The light did not have to be particularly even because in a shot around a courtyard or anywhere at 360 degrees there are bound to be some areas of shadow, etc. The gantries were quite high and the mattebox-sunshade kept the lights that would appear as "strong" lighting or flare at certain angles, out of the lens. The zoom was set between 25–32 mm and the mattebox bellows were at maximum extension. The camera battery hung below the tripod and there were no sound sync leads to get in the way as we were using crystal sync.

Long ago, on BBC Newsreel, we filmed Roger Bannister's record breaking four-minute mile at Iffley Road, Oxford University Sports Ground. For this we set up the camera on a 6 ft rostrum in the centre of the track. Bannister, paced by Chris Chataway and Chris Brasher, would be going round the track four times, so before we started we wound the cables up round the camera so that during the shot the camera and cables unwound during the four minute continuous take. This provided a completely unobstructed pan movement.

TRACKING

Tracking, crane and hand-held shots may be grouped together as having certain functions by which an effect is achieved which cannot be done with a conventionally static camera.

Tracking is useful in certain drama sequences. For example, a shot may develop in such a way that by gradually moving the camera the expression or actions of one person may be seen in reaction to another who was previously favoured by the camera angle chosen for the start of the shot. Thus action and reaction are registered in one continuous movement which, as well as showing the people from a different angle may also widen or concentrate the view. Another use for tracking is in following a moving subject while maintaining a constant or near-constant camera-to-subject distance.

Tracking, however, like most specialized techniques has come to be such a commonplace part of the director's artillery that it is often employed arbitrarily in scenes which gain nothing visually from this treatment. In drama for instance, it is much easier to keep up the tempo and patterning of a sequence by cutting from shot to shot than to use any of the camera movements—tracking, craning or zooming—all of which take time and tend to interrupt the flow of things by dictating the speed of events.

Tracking also involves extra preparation, although modern equipment has reduced this to such a degree that it is now possible to lay quite a long track, say, 40–50 ft, in a matter of minutes—no special underlay being called for. It is essential in most tracking shots to have the camera move in an absolutely level direction, otherwise the image drifts and leans to one or other side as the camera moves along. Formerly, this levelling up required long and patient adjustment to the track. But today with the right track, and using a bowl head (a cup shaped friction head which fits into a bowl at the bottom for levelling), the track need only be levelled up laterally (i.e. left to right). As long as the rails of the track are at equal heights and therefore parallel in height all the way along, you can compensate for differences in height at the ends of the track with the bowl adjustment on the tripod head, even on a 100 ft track. The bowl adjustment incorporates a level indicator. If you were to try and compensate for the slope in such a situation, without using a friction head and merely by adjusting the camera, the track would probably have to be built up to 6 ft at one end, which would obviously be an unnecessary expense and waste of time and effort. Thus, with this method, it is quite easy to track on a sloping surface and still achieve remarkably uniform framing from one end of the shot to the other, even if it is a matter of correcting a drop of as much as 3 ft by use of tilt on the bowl head.

The slope-correcting method has obvious advantages for tracking shots outdoors, where the ground is almost invariably uneven, as opposed to the studio where you have a flat working surface. The head is locked in the tilt position and and a mean is taken of the overall slope over which you are tracking.

In practice, however, with many shots it is not too important to maintain an absolutely level view as the loss of perpendiculars would only be noticeable with certain static subjects. A small deficiency would not be noticeable in a shot where the viewer's attention was concentrated on the central part of a scene or activity or in the centre of the field of view. In such a case the lack of levelness must not show in the background either. The centre of the picture is least likely to show a deficiency of this kind; the nearer the subject is to the edge of the frame, the more prone it is to show untrue levelling. Hence, subjects which have definite geometrical outlines such as buildings must be shot only from tracks which have been very accurately lined up otherwise the failings are only too obvious. When following ordinary moving subjects, however, especially people, the discrepancies would not be too apparent. Assessment of how much inexactness is acceptable is like so many other techniques in camera work, purely a matter of visual judgement.

With tracking shots you must be prepared for the change in perspective as the shot develops. The artist might come a little closer to you or move further away. As in any other shot you retain a free hand to take account of movement. If you can lock off one of the directions of movement you must be very certain that things are not going to alter during the shot in such a way that you cannot follow with the camera. The grip who does the tracking must be careful to start and end the track in a smooth movement or a camera on a free head will tip up or down or jerk left or right.

The camera crane, a most versatile camera mounting, allows a more elaborate type of visual coverage in a scene than a tracking dolly. It can track, and move in a crabwise or oblique fashion and also move the camera vertically up or down, either to find a position or for an effect during a shot. Like the tracking dolly, it has to be lined up and levelled before taking a shot.

The crane may be used either as a special effect or as a mobile rostrum simply providing a high stationary viewpoint over a scene. It could be advantageous for situations where a number of shots are needed from different levels and positions that would otherwise require the erection of several rostrums, a time-consuming process. It might provide a point of view (POV) shot for characters supposed to be high on a building, for instance, but in the normal case of things a shot from such a high viewpoint is unnatural. It is not the normal view obtained by a standing person, and the perspective effect dwarfs the proportions of the contents of the scene. Nevertheless many directors feel tempted to use the crane for such shots, however inappropriate. There is, after all, a certain distinction attached to the use of such an elaborate and expensive piece of equipment.

A crane shot has great visual force. It can make a big show of an ordinary situation. But the fact is that a camera viewpoint floating down through the air tends to give the impression that the viewer is falling into the scene. An imaginative use of the crane was in *Stalingrad*, where the effect was employed to simulate an aircraft taking off, as seen from the plane itself.

Cranes, like all elaborate devices, are expensive to hire and use in films. The same strictures apply in relation to the speed of movement of a crane compared with the pace of a film.

An example of where a pan shot would have served as well as one from a crane may be quoted from a courtyard scene in the *Colditz* series. In this particular case, however, the circumstances were such that it was reasonable to use the crane because it had been needed for the previous shot and the camera was therefore already in position on it, and the crane was in the right location for the one that followed.

The crane was above normal head height looking over the crowd at a group in the centre. A jeep enters the courtyard in the background (covered by the crane shot) and comes forward through the crowd and into the foreground and so, round to the left, the camera from a wide shot moves obliquely sideways following the jeep and stops on a close four-shot nearby. For this shot the camera lens had to be zoomed, focus pulled and the camera panned to maintain a near parallel position as well as the boom swung across according to pre-set marks on the central pillar—all at the right moments, a relatively complicated manoeuvre yet which did not involve raising or lowering the boom—the chief advantage of the crane.

When it comes to production costs such a shot would not, on its own, justify the great expense of hiring a crane.

However, if there is a crane in the studio, the director may be determined to use that facility on a shot where crane movements are not really called for, do not improve it and where a single pan would do as well. In some cases the use of the crane may prove a complicated effort for the crew. Yet a simple tripod-mounted camera movement can achieve exactly the same result. Furthermore, when the camera is trotting along there is often an implication that the observer himself is moving or that there is something that the camera (or he) is on, that is moving. In some cases the sideways camera movement that can be done on the crane imply a certain kind or degree of movement which is foreign to the situation. This is perhaps different from the type of camera movement used, for example, in the sequence just described where the camera suddenly rises high into the air over the crowd as they converge on a single person in a spontaneous reaction. Here one can accept the movement as subjective—one does not fly and so one does not relate this to normal traction. It is a dramatic shot, pure and simple, and seems quite acceptable. With obvious tracking you do feel you are moving or being moved. The only purpose of a tracking or crabbing shot (which should be unobtrusive) is to make sure that your principal artists are not being obscured by one another in such a way that you cannot see or hear them properly. Such a complicated shot takes time, and time is a very expensive thing these days—a factor which is not always taken into account.

A Practical Problem Solved with a Crane

In a difficult situation where other kinds of camera movement have some distinct disadvantage the crane could provide a useful expedient. The problems encountered with the lighting on certain scenes in the television production *Fall of Eagles* are described on page 158. But another problem, indeed the main problem, concerned the camera movement. On *Fall of Eagles* the camerawork took into account the availability of a Nike crane. In the event, this factor was very significant.

The whole set was surrounded by a white cyclorama sky backing. The top of this sky backing could only be at the bottom of the gantry because you cannot take such a backing above the rail you intend to use for lights. This meant that the sky backing was only about two feet higher than the actors when they were on the top superstructure. However, the camera, which was on the lower deck with the artists before they walked up the companionway to the superstructure, could not be panned up very far to follow them without shooting off the set (i.e. off the backing) and so including the gantry in shot.

Alternatively, if the camera was craned up with the artists to keep slightly above them and so be on the backing at the top, then it was off the set at the bottom. Beyond the side rail which ran round the deck were studio floor and lights, so that as the camera went up it could not be tipped up (because it would be off the set at the top) and it could not tip down (because it would be off the set at deck level). Consequently, the camera had to be absolutely square on to the artists all the time. As they were constantly running up and down stairs and the camera was tracking forward also—all at high speed—it was sometimes sheer chance whether the off-set area was included or not. As luck would have it, it worked out. Some of the operating could not be of the highest order; the most important thing was to keep on the set. So sometimes the artists touched the top of the camera frame (although their heads were not cut) and sometimes they were off centre because the camera could not be panned left or right off the set into lights, etc. But as the action was so rapid these shortcomings would probably not be noticed.

Working under these conditions is very trying. Cartier wanted an expansive treatment but it was not his fault that the set was in the wrong studio. With day material the zoom was used to make sure that the lens angle covered the set once it had arrived at the high or low position on the set. Once out of the "danger area" the shot could be framed as normal. The zoom lens was used to close in to a tighter shot as the camera rose towards the more cramped conditions of the superstructure. The assistant could adjust the focal length in order to arrive at the correct lens angle at the end of the movement. These shots were rehearsed.

Much of the skill in this type of shot is in the crane operating. With the electrically driven crane, one person runs it back and forth, another operates the swing, and a third the jib—in accordance with chalk marks. So the whole is a pre-measured shot. You aim to make the fewest adjustments yourself so that you have everything working smoothly and you can concentrate on your framing. There were rehearsals on film with only a few of these complicated shots. You can have too much rehearsal on shots like these.

HAND-HELD SHOTS

There are cross influences between television and the cinema. Feature films show obvious influences from television—rapid cutting, closely grouped subjects, hand-held camera work and other techniques. In large scale features, hand holding is largely confined to shots where some camera movement is actually to be seen on the screen, such as the subjective viewpoint of a person represented by the camera. Some feature directors have tended to adopt the hand holding technique for flexibility in certain "straight" shots but have lost quality in doing so. With the small screen, television has much greater use for hand held shots, but even here the method has been abused and hopelessly overplayed. It became the vogue with tele-verité to hand-hold nearly every shot and though undoubtedly successful in particular instances, like everything novel that works well on occasions, it was taken up by many television directors as The Way to Make Better Films.

If there is a real reason to justify a subjective camera approach then, provided it is done well, it will certainly do the job. But you have to remember that with most straightforward programmes being watched by the ordinary viewer at home, if the picture starts to jump about, as inevitably it does, he is going to find it disturbing and feel like switching off. If, however, such things are used intelligently and sparingly they work practically all the time. Some directors ask for a hand-held shot yet cannot explain why, or say that they do not want to waste time putting the tripod down—even though it is quicker to set up a tripod than prepare for a hand-held shot!

There was a craze not so long ago for doing hand-held interviews. This is complete nonsense. Everything is bobbing up and down, yet it is a static situation. Often, towards the end of the interview, the cameraman gets so tired that his arms begin to give out and the headroom becomes less and less. At any minute you know the subject is going to be cut off at the eyes!

Hand-held walking shots are sometimes used if the ground is too impossibly uneven for anything else. This might be shoulder holding or holding the camera in front, depending on its design and accessories. Some people can do hand-held walking shots very well. Even so, they do not give the same quality of image as a tracking shot.

Hand-held "tracking" with a moving subject gives far more acceptable results than when tracking along and on to, a still object. This is quite simply because in the first case everything in the picture is on the move. This applies, for example, to sequences shot, with or without dialogue, inside a car. Obviously in this case there is no space for a tripod, though the camera can be supported by brackets which are hung or clamped on the side or front of the car.

EXECUTING CAMERA MOVEMENTS

The governing factor in achieving good camera movements is that the operator must feel that his own body is perfectly balanced *at all times*. If he is not correctly balanced it is very difficult for him to operate smoothly and effectively. How he actually holds the pan bar is immaterial. He should be balanced in such a way that he can follow an artist or subject without a pause to get himself into a position to make the movement. Normally he can work out the balance for the whole movement during the rehearsals, and find the optimum position of balance from which to execute the shot.

In some cases he may be completely off balance at the start of the shot but move in to correct balance for the remainder of it, in effect "unwinding" himself in order to be balanced *through* the shot. It is in the unfolding of the shot where balance is most important.

In another case a cameraman can start off balance and, following the subject, reach a position where the next movement will unbalance him if he does not shift his body. He may have to lock off the pan and tilt, shift his body position and then unlock. This has to be done at great speed and sometimes the locking off is done by the assistant, having been rehearsed beforehand. If it is done correctly the shot remains steady and no one would notice it. It becomes necessary to lock off the camera because it is impossible to shift one's balance without accidentally moving the camera, even slightly. Good balance, this time with the weight of the camera taken into account, is also the essential ingredient in hand-held and walking shots.

With pan shots which follow people, all movement in the scene should ideally stop and start at the same time. That is to say, one should avoid having the camera continue to move after the artists have stopped. This draws attention to the camera. Ideally the camera and subject should move simultaneously as if locked together—a matter of timing.

The camera movements are timed to coincide properly with the action during the rehearsal. However, you have to be prepared to alter your rehearsed movements and yet still have them work properly. This could occur when an artist makes a movement during the take that differs from that rehearsed beforehand. If, for example, you see in rehearsal that the artist moves from one place to another with a pause between to pick up a cigarette, you still have to be subconsciously aware during the actual take that he may take the cigarette *en passant*. You should never accept the rehearsal as an exact representation of what is going to happen in the take, only as a rough plan.

If the artist moves unexpectedly beyond the range of the shooting area you can see the limiting factor—lights (flare from these can be seen in the viewfinder), mike or edge of set—coming up in the area outside the picture area. So, while up to a point you can make alterations to take account of the unexpected, there is no danger of exceeding the limits.

Zoom Shots

Zoom shots do not involve camera movement as such, but they are sometimes used as a substitute for tracking, although the effect is quite different. When combined with actual camera movement such as tracking or panning the relatively crude magnifying effect of a zoom becomes partially disguised.

There are two kinds of zoom shot which, in the BBC, we call the "light entertainment" zoom and the "drama" zoom, respectively. With the first you must zoom straight in or out regardless of what is suggested by the subject or scene. But the drama zoom is governed by the tensions within the scene and what is going on in it. You very rarely use instant zoom in drama, only fast zooms occasionally.

A zoom shot is controlled according to roughly the same basis as a pan. The zoom follows the movement of the artist or subject. When that movement ceases one does not normally want to see the zoom continuing independently and then coming to a halt a moment later. Moreover, if the camera is also panning, the zoom takes place *during* the pan, which largely disguises the presence of the zoom in the shot. Ideally, again, artist, pan and zoom should all move together. A zoom continuing after it should have stopped is, if anything, a worse effect than a pan movement doing the same thing.

The zoom should be smooth, definite and without jerks. The worst effect is to zoom in on a subject, stop and then make a final small adjustment to the correct position. If the cameraman or assistant makes a mistake, they should leave it and not try to adjust the position to the desired framing. It is better to be slightly wrong in the magnification than to try and correct it by a further adjustment. For fast zoom shots the assistant should use marks on the lens so that he can move the zoom bar to exactly the right spot at a given time as predetermined in the rehearsal. This makes it far easier for the zoom to arrive at the correct framing for that part of the scene and the camera movement and zoom to stop simultaneously.

Shooting on a Moving Platform

When operating the camera on a mobile platform such as a boat, car or train, the first and foremost objective is to secure such a rigid connection between the camera and that platform, as to eliminate all possibility of gratuitous camera movement. In such a shot only the background should move. The foreground should be stationary on the screen as if the camera were almost a part of the structure. The image should not move about the screen because of the annoyance this causes in viewing and the loss of informational value in the picture generally. Such camera movement would disguise the natural movement of people in the scene as they respond to the motion of the vehicle, whereas if the camera is rigid, the effect of this motion is set at a maximum. The use of camera stabilizers is wholly inappropriate to this type of treatment.

If the moving platform is being used as a substitute dolly or tracking device for views external to the vehicle only, it may be necessary to "iron out the bumps" with a stabilizer. In this case one is not trying to convey too much of a feeling of travel in the vehicle and the main priority is obtaining a steady image on the screen of the view around, which after all forms the whole picture. It would be quite inappropriate in most ordinary situations to have the entire screen image moving vigorously about. It might only be done as a special effect, for example, in drama, representing a person's aberrant subjective view, supposing, for example, that he were intoxicated.

Boat Sequence

A typical boat sequence involving a small boat and therefore much movement, was one that we shot for the historical series *Fall of Eagles*.

This series contained a scene in which Lenin and his wife were rowing around a lake (supposedly in Switzerland but, in fact, shot at a reservoir in Wales) awaiting the call back to Russia to take part in the revolution. In this particular sequence, after an initial long shot showing the boat on the lake, the camera had to go in to the boat to obtain close-ups of both Lenin and his wife. But by the time this part was to be filmed, quite a strong wind was blowing and the waves on the lake were quite large. In these conditions the rowing boat would have been tossed around, and the background in the shots would have moved rather unpleasantly. Moreover, it would have been uncomfortable not only for the artists but also for the cameraman trying to work in that small boat with a tripod. To overcome this problem, the boat was tethered by one end to the bank of the lake.

The camera was in the boat with Lenin in the rowing seat and showing the mountains, cliffs, water, trees, etc. behind him. Lenin pretended to row, but with feathered oars so that there was little pull. While the scene was shot, the assistants pulled on the tethering yards turning the bow of the boat round a little to the left or right so that the background was seen to be moving very slightly as he rowed. The same effect was used for the shots of Lenin's wife who was sitting in the other end of the boat. But this time, having tethered the bow and set up the camera at the opposite end, we made sure that a different section of background was used. Together with the different direction of looks, one person looking camera left and the other camera right, the two shots were perfectly convincing. Medium shots were also taken of the boat arriving at the side of the lake and Lenin being greeted by one of his friends, who came running along screaming that the revolution had started in Russia and then waded into the water to reach them. Lenin and his wife stood up in the boat and a cross cutting sequence was introduced at the point to reinforce the drama of those moments in the film.

Owing to the considerable movement with this type of sequence, the camera was put on a baby tripod which was screwed down to the base of the boat so that whatever else happened, the boat and the camera would not move in relation to one another but only in terms of the surroundings. Because of the movement in the boat, it was easier and more efficient to have to cope with only one type of movement. We therefore tried to keep one of the tripod head movements locked off most of the time. In this situation the tilt is the more capricious so that was locked off and only the pan was used. Lenin's movements were not very great and it was possible to gauge the mean headroom for him. The means of holding the tripod was simple: a stage screw was put in to the base of the boat with ropes and a Spanish windlass. A Spanish windlass is, in its simplest form, rope which is threaded several times between the underneath of the tripod head and a stage screw put in the floor. There is a certain amount of play on these strands of rope, and you insert a piece of wood or similar object between them and twine it round to tighten the rope, thus pulling the tripod hard down on to the floor. The piece of wood can be locked behind a tripod leg.

With this set-up only the background, and the person to a lesser extent, appear to be moving which gives a good impression of being on board a boat. This is the technique recommended for all such scenes.

Some people imagine that because you are in a boat you need to use a gimbal head. If you use a gimbal head, the artists and the boat move but the background remains steady because the gimbal is compensating for any movement away from the norm, as if the camera were not present in the boat but was on solid ground. Consequently the sense of movement is eliminated from the resulting scene because the wrong things are moving. Moreover, the gimbal, which is a heavily weighted piece of equipment, could not be used in a small boat without going through the bottom! Such a head might, however, be used to reduce movement to a viewable scale when filming on a medium sized boat in a very rough sea. But in sequences involving small boats the camera should always be solidly mounted on the boat itself so that everything moves in unison but independently from the horizon or background.

Train Sequence

A train sequence is rather more straightforward than filming in a small boat. But you cannot work in any moving vehicle with a free head because every jolt has its effect on the picture. So, for a train sequence, in a real moving train, you lock up all the movements and then make yourself ready at a moment's notice to unlock something. You may, for instance, have to release the pan, make a slight movement to follow an artist and immediately lock it up again. A practical method in train sequences where you are filming two seated artists is to lock the pan movement and keep the tilt free. Being seated together the amount of movement they are likely to make left or right while talking to each other is probably negligable so you can afford to lock the pan and concentrate on the up and down movement. If they talk to another person they might lean forward to look at them which would involve a slight tilt movement. You can stabilize the camera tripod mounted on a moving vehicle by pulling the pan bar hard down on your shoulder and, in effect, doing the tilt movements by raising or lowering your body.

The *Fall of Eagles* series also involved a sequence on a train. It was filmed on a private railway in England using some authentic rolling stock preserved from the last century. This train sequence was filmed inside the coaches while the train was in motion. The sequence might have been *easier* to shoot in the studio but we would not have obtained the same effect. The train itself was, and looked, really authentic and this was reinforced by the degree of proper movement that could be seen in the sequence.

The camera tripod was lashed to the floor with a Spanish windlass, and, despite the fact that we were working in an old coach, we had obtained permission to put the requisite stage screw into the wooden floor. You would not do this to parquet flooring, which in any case would probably come up with the stage screw! You can use the Spanish windlass on any moving vehicle. It will prevent movement or the risk of the camera being knocked over. If the camera is mounted on the back or top of a camera car it is always tied down in such a fashion. It also gives you something to hang on to.

Car Sequence

The filming treatment of car sequences is discussed elsewhere. Here we are concerned with the methods of mounting the camera whether or not the cameraman is also present.

Most often, car interior scenes are shot hand held inside the car with the cameraman sitting in the front seat. He can brace himself to some extent against the seat itself to obtain steadiness, or, rather, more direct contact with the movement of the vehicle. Some movement due to hand holding the camera in a car is certainly acceptable in the circumstances.

There is less movement when the camera is held by special brackets and clamps mounted on the car itself, because everything except the occupants moves together. The background will be moving in any case.

The brackets which hold a camera on the side or front of a car are attached to it by limpet mounts. The disadvantages of these brackets are that you cannot look through the camera while shooting and the camera has to be switched on and off by a sound man who is usually positioned down behind the rear seat. As you have no direct control, you have to take a chance on the framing and exposure—the latter, of course, being liable to change once the car is under way. The director can only hope that the dialogue is well enough delivered, though he can, of course, play the recording back afterwards to provide an immediate check.

The side mount for the camera is a double hook arrangement that hangs on to the door frame with the window wound down and a limpet sucker or two attached to the door underneath. The whole assembly is quite rigid and takes a tripod head on which the camera is then mounted. You line up the camera on the driver or other character to be filmed. The only worry apart from this is that there is some very valuable equipment travelling along with no one to hold it, though probably nothing has ever been lost in this way.

When the camera is mounted on the front of the car to film back through the windscreen, some people have the windscreen taken out to avoid strong reflections from its surface which can obliterate the subject. Unfortunately it always looks as if the windscreen has been removed as the picture lacks that "something else" between you and the characters inside. You *can* shoot through a windscreen but the problem nowadays is that windscreens are laminated and if you use a pola screen on the camera to reduce the windscreen reflections in the normal way, a strong pattern from the lamination appears, which you cannot remove from the picture. The only other way to take out reflections is to set up a rigid shield (made from wood, covered, perhaps, with black velvet) covering the area from the top of the windscreen forward to the camera position which is never very close to the screen. This blocks off the reflections from the sky, trees, etc. which, more often than not, are much too obtrusive. This does not darken the subject significantly because there is generally still a certain amount of light coming in from around this area. In any case, you need to use lights as well.

Latterly, we have developed this principle to allow a more natural effect of controlled reflections in the windscreen but not obliterating the artist behind. Instead of the solid shield, the use of ·3, ·6, or ·9 ND acetate sheet allows a degree of reflection which makes for a much more natural effect.

A BBC series called *The Long Chase*, which was about two children driving a car from Devon all the way up to Inverness and being chased by goodies and baddies—a kid's whodunit—involved a large quantity of car filming with both non-sync sound and dialogue. Because of this, we, together with the special effects departments at Ealing, developed a device which would effectively solve the lighting and reflection problems for these sequences. The device was basically a long trough or bridge over the bonnet of the car which was fitted on to the top of the two wings. On this bridge were two upright supports that held a roof piece reaching from the top of the car in the front over to the camera. That removed all the reflections in the windscreen. The camera and three or four tungsten halogen battery lights (with dichroic filters) were mounted on this bridge.

These lamps were fitted on to various arms, mounted on the bridge, that could be raised or lowered and taken to the right or left of the bridge. There was also a battery light fitted in the back of the car to provide some backlight. We shot sync sound sequences with this arrangement. There were no light reflections whatsoever from the battery lights because the windscreen was slightly raked back. The lighting was fairly hard, one lamp was the key light, the others moulders and kickers. The same car was used for internal shots and also for shots of the car moving along the road, so it was necessary to remove and replace the mounting at various points in the journey. Being, as it was, a sequence of this kind, it was impossible to use the feature film approach of grouping all shots of a kind together. So the mounting had to be designed for quick removal or setting up which, in fact, took only minutes by the time we had had some practice with it.

The need for this device originated from production conferences following our reading of the script. Other mountings that have been devised by the Special Facilities engineers are brackets for slinging a camera underneath a car and underwater camera housings.

To use this type of solid mounting where you cannot look though the viewfinder while shooting, you line up the camera to allow for actor movement and warn the actors that they should try and keep in a certain position and not move out of picture, say, to the left. The zoom lens can be adjusted to get the desired framing from the fixed camera position. The equipment we used for *The Long Chase* was so rigid that it was possible to fill the frame with the driver's head when he was travelling along a subsidiary road at some 40–45 m.p.h., and still obtain a very steady picture.

This type of set-up would have to be used on any car the film unit was presented with. Unlike a feature film cameraman, you have no say in selection of the vehicle. You simply have to adapt your technique to the one provided, large or small, roomy or cramped. You should have a good road but locations are governed by what the script calls for. If you had a poor surface, you could help matters by letting the tyres down slightly, although with modern suspensions you are usually better off with normal tyre pressures.

The speed of the vehicle is very important and rather a tricky problem because according to which side of the road you are on, and which side of the road you are filming, and the type of background and whether you are filming side, back or front, your speeds have to be altered. If you are going sideways you want to travel a little slower than if you were filming with the camera facing backwards or forwards because the sides will be closer to the camera and to your subject. You would have two distances. If you were photographing the driver from the passenger seat, the side background would be further away from you than if you were where the driver should be, photographing the passenger, still going in the same direction.

So, if you are photographing the driver, you should go faster than if you are photographing the passenger in order to give the impression that the car is travelling at a constant speed. The difference in speed would be a question of, say, 7 m.p.h. Now with backward or forward facing shots you would want to go faster still to give a real indication of the speed because the background is so far away and the sides do not come in until they, too, are a long way off. You could afford 15 m.p.h. increase for shots from the back or front assuming an average speed of, say, 40–45 m.p.h. This, of course, applies where there are hedges, bridges or any other objects close to the side of the road and would not be necessary in shots taken of the car crossing completely open landscape.

This question of matching speeds and the different angles that one takes is very important indeed when it comes to matching back projection plates. This is discussed more fully on page 203.

12

Composition

PICTURE COMPOSITION must be the area of filming technique about which cameramen are least willing to talk. It is generally accepted that the feeling for a well composed picture is something with which a person is born. Either that, or he does not have it at all. The actual teaching of formal composition beyond a few basic rules seems to be a futile exercise. If a person does not have the sense of design and function that goes into arranging a subject in the viewfinder then there is little reason why he should be in control of a camera. One should assume that people without this sense of composition never have any ambition to become cameramen and never, in fact, do so.

Cameramen tend to visualize compositions within an imaginary 3 × 4 format, and somehow this fixed frame proportion becomes imprinted on the mind. Some cameramen use a director's viewfinder to help them find the composition they want. Others do not find it necessary. Sometimes a cameraman sees a composition that cries out to be "framed up" even if it is at a great distance. In fact, if you are a hardened cameraman, even when you are not working, when perhaps you are on holiday and are just walking along, you are constantly seeing shots. Subconsciously they are all within that 3 × 4 format. This makes it very much easier when you are working. If the director asks for a shot, you automatically switch on this subconscious 3 × 4 framing. If you mentally select a certain focal length of lens and go to a position, you can automatically visualize almost exactly what the framing will be and how much of the scene the picture area will include. This happens after some years of experience. Alternatively, you can walk back from a shot and then state where the camera should go to frame it.

Composition for Television

Although there must be much in common between composition in films intended for the cinema and those destined for television showing, particular techniques are applied in television work to compensate for the fact that the image is magnified to only 1/200th part of the viewing area of a large cinema screen. Therefore, with television filming, as opposed to filming for the screen, when composing the picture you make a point of cutting out all the "air" in your compositions. This makes the most of the comparatively small screen size and gives a slightly larger scale of subject representation. Provided that in all cases you take into account the space needed for the action then space at the sides, bottom, etc. is not, in general, necessary. So the composition of two-shots, for example, is slightly tighter than those shot in cinema feature films.

You cannot effectively photograph wide open views with tiny figures seen in the distance because such detail is lost on a television screen. Although there is always a call for an extreme long shot to show the location, the general idea is to "keep in" on the subject as much as you dare. The main risk is getting a cut off in the transmitted image when viewed on a badly adjusted TV set. A television picture can tolerate a little cutting on the sides of the frame but not if it is the top of someone's head, although such a composition becomes ugly anyway.

In close work, you should always work with a free unlocked camera head to be prepared for following any unexpected subject movement. The closer the camera is to a subject, the less depth of field there is to work within. But for close shots the camera is not necessarily physically close. If you want more depth you adjust it on the lens accordingly; you go closer to the subject and use a wider angle setting (or lens) or move further away and use a longer focus setting.

With very tight shots you may have to ask an artist not to move away from another so far, or so sharply, to give you time to pull the camera away and so take in the move. Normally, a television film cameraman discusses the movements with the artist, not, as with feature films, via the director, a practice which would delay production.

Camera viewfinders are marked in such a way that when you are framing up you can work to full screen size or frame up to normal screen size which would be the headroom that you would want to give, bearing in mind that it is going to be projected on to a normal screen. Or there is television screen size which gives you even more headroom, side room and bottom room. (The whole format is either larger or smaller.) But the most important factor is headroom—the top. This must be correct for good composition. Only when you have a shot where, for example, the subjects are concerned with something on a table, do you have to worry about the bottom area. There is actually no "correct" measurement for headroom—it is simply a matter of knowing.

For television transmission, the headroom would be the norm for cinema projection plus a little extra, i.e. a very liberal cinema headroom. The camera viewfinder gives a liberal TV screen area whereas with

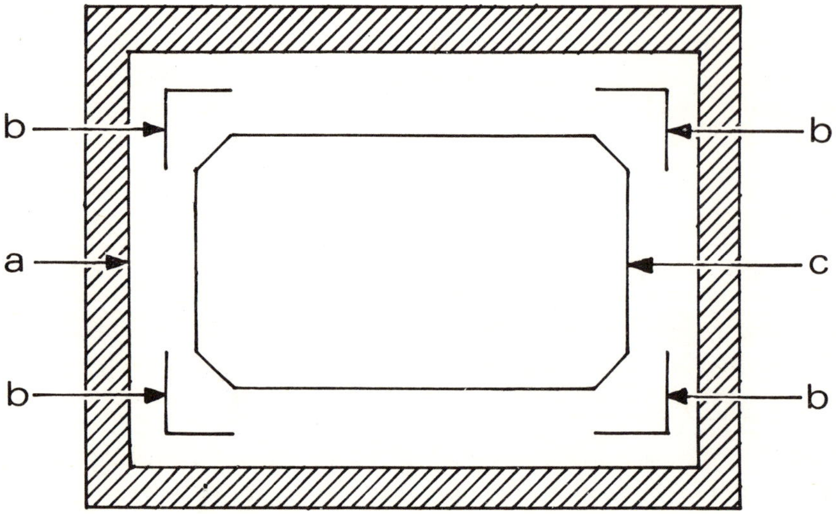

Markings for a camera viewfinder. It could indicate three picture formats as a guide to the cameraman: (a) is the picture actually being included on the negative (e.g.: 10.21 × 7.42 mm); (b) is the area which is transmitted from telecine (BBC: 9.35 × 7.01 mm); (c) on some cameras shows an area regarded as 'safe' for important action or for titles; this takes account of wrong adjustment on receivers which may exclude parts of the picture area transmitted. Parts of the scene falling in the shaded area outside (a) are not photographed. Some cameramen prefer to work without such markings.

a cinema screen you work with a fixed area. The problem with the masking effect of the television screen is that it varies from one set to another, according to how it has been lined up. Although a picture looks right on the screen in the transmitting station, it may not be elsewhere. So you have to allow for this in filming. The material shot for TV could, of course, be used in a cinema without being too far out.

There are times when the composition allows you to give more generous headroom than normal. For example, on exterior work, a good cloud formation could provide interest in that area—it may even make the picture.

Classical rules of portraiture lay down that the subject's head must "sit on enough shoulder" in the picture. But today this sort of outlook is overruled. In fact, one of the most fashionable approaches to talking head shots is to use a part-face close-up which might be called a "television close-up" and is very ugly. A head-and-shoulder shot cuts at a more or less ideal point. The rule is, if it *looks* right, it *is* right. The practice of shooting ultra close-ups of part of a face as interview routine is an abomination. It is quite unreal and one does not see people like that, subjectively or otherwise. Moreover, it is not often used successfully as an effect, even in drama productions. A big head or eyes in close-up have been used frequently in feature work. But in television interviews one is concerned with the personality and expression of the subject, not with dramatic effects. In the context of a television interview such a close-up, if anything, draw attention to the medium rather than the subject and the restricted view of the subject which serves only to emphasize the limits of the frame.

Drama: Composition and Movement

If you are filming drama, the main interest is in the actors—where they are going and what they are doing. So, if it is a moving shot, you start off and end with a good composition. What happens in between is less controllable as you have to follow the artist and keep him in picture—as the saying is: "point the camera where the money is". It is not difficult to start with a static set-up. You can rehearse the shot and check the end composition in the shot and you can adjust it accordingly, by moving in or out or by shifting props, etc.

A first principle in filming drama is to avoid, if possible, influencing or restricting the movement of an actor in any way—nor his rate of movement. An actor's movements are necessary to him. You can usually sense an artist's movement just before it happens, which enables you to follow him. You can often tell from the rehearsal if an artist is likely to make unpredictable movements. Judging this is largely a matter of practice. The most important thing for a cameraman when filming drama is to try not to impose any restrictions on the artist, or, at least impose the minimum restrictions. You must not tell him that he cannot do this, that or the other. He should only intervene at all if the movements are so very violent that the actor cannot be adequately followed by the camera. The artist is just as important, or more important, than the cameraman. In the final result the camera and artist should appear almost to be linked together.

The most difficult action to cover with the camera is following people getting up and sitting down. It is a sudden movement over a relatively large area and to cover it adequately you have to be a fraction ahead of that movement. If you are in difficulties it sometimes helps if you suggest to the artist that he does not get up or sit down quickly. This also depends on how tightly you have them framed in the viewfinder; in a looser shot the artist has more room to move before you yourself decide he is moving. If it is a waist shot, the headroom is fairly generous and allows you time to react. But you would get an idea of the amount of movement required in a rehearsal.

Vertical movements are more difficult to follow than those in a lateral direction. Because of the shape of the screen, there is more room at the sides to absorb subject movement. Nor is lateral shift so noticeable because the subject and the camera tend to be moving on that axis during the whole film. If the artist is moving laterally, you should always give him more room in the direction in which he is moving than the direction from which he comes, rather than placing him in the centre of the picture. So the camera should always be ahead of him, which, although pictorially more attractive is also better from a practical point of view. The old adage is "you must always see where the artist is going"—i.e. the space he is moving in to.

In filming drama, beyond the need to just keep the subjects in the picture, you are also filming in sympathy with the actors. The type of camera movement you use tends to reflect the action and the emotion behind it. With musical programmes, for instance, there is a particular way to pan. You cannot pan at any speed. You determine how to pan as you hear the music. This gives you the feeling for the right type of camera movement. The BBC uses very little post-sync dubbing. If, however, you are doing a period film and you are never free of extraneous modern or unwanted noises, the scenes would be post synchronized. In such cases all the sound tracks are treated as guide tracks.

In filming with guide tracks there is all the more reason why the microphone should stay well away from the picture area! The worst consequences of wrong microphone placing would be if, during a dialogue scene, the microphone were quite clearly visible hopping across from one speaker to another and back again. This has happened in more than one cinema production. But television, unlike the cinema is not so subject to the risk of the projectionist racking the frame up or down to include areas of the image not intended by the cameraman to be included. The viewfinder on the Arriflex BL camera shows the area covered clearly as well as a border "dead ground" area around that. You can therefore see any approaching influence or object before it enters the actual picture area. You should not have a microphone visible even in that outer area. Some cameramen may find, moreover, that if they can see things moving, out of the frame area, it is a distraction from what is going on within it and reduces their concentration.

Before any shot the sound man asks for a height at which to position the microphone. He then places it and the cameraman tells him if it is too low there and likely to be in the picture. As a cameraman, you should never have the microphone near to the frame line because you do not necessarily know what the artist is going to do. He may suddenly jump up or move off to the left or right. You should also have the tripod head free (unlocked) all the time so that you can move with the artist if necessary. There must not be the constriction of seeing a microphone in the area out of frame when you may want to use it.

Choice of Lens

Directors occasionally seek to use the distorting effect of a wide angle lens for some dramatic impact that they feel it has. Others fear that such a lens may introduce distortion where they least want it. But unless a subject is within two feet of a 10 mm lens, for example, the degree of distortion in a static frame is negligible. Any distortion that you have with wide angle lenses does not begin to show until you move the camera during the shot and when you pan. Barrel distortion then becomes noticeable. In situations where the camera is stationary and the artists do not move too much the distortion is not really visible. Only when the artist comes very close to the camera does it show. With wider angle lenses the distortion is mainly visible at the sides rather than the centre.

The main objection to distortion with wide angle lenses is the effect on faces. Any other distortion is not really so noticeable because you are normally looking at the centre of the screen where, in drama productions, your artists are or where the subject is in other types of production. When you move the camera the bending of objects or walls, doors, etc. on the edge of the screen can be disturbing.

In most cases it would be wise for the director to leave the matter of avoiding distortion to the cameraman. Last minute demands can have unfortunate consequences. On one particular production we had a set of hired prime lenses which were not delivered until the morning when we left for the location. Lenses should always seat properly and should be scaled correctly for your particular camera; in this case there was no chance to test them, (one has to take a lot on spec. these days). Fortunately, these lenses proved saitsfactory. When we were on location however, the director insisted on using a 12 mm lens for certain scenes instead of the 10 mm that we had with us. He believed that a 10 mm would cause too much distortion. Although he had been told that this was not the case, he said he felt more confident with a 12 mm because he had used one before. So an extra lens was specially sent from London. The people at the BBC were very quick to act, and despite the remoteness of the location, the lens arrived an hour and a half before we were ready to shoot on a night sequence. All material shot with this lens subsequently proved to be slightly out of focus because the lens was wrongly seating.

Sometimes defocus is less noticeable in colour prints than in monochrome. So, following the provision of black and white rushes, the out of focus material shot with the 12 mm lens on this production was printed in colour to see if the defocus was as bad as it looked at first.

Directors do have their own shibboleths. But it should not be necessary for a director to argue elementary technical points with a very experienced cameraman.

CAMERAMAN'S JUDGEMENT

There are ways of operating a camera that apply to the particular scene you are photographing; there is a mood that dictates a move. As a cameraman, you have a particular way of covering that scene, which you do not want another person to interfere with. For instance, in a scene where one person comes up to another and attacks him, the camerman is governed by the speed of movement of the two people or the one person. But if, at the same time, the camera is tracking as it follows the movement, there is a definite move which governs the speed of the track. There is also a definite way of composing such a shot in the frame, especially in the final position, in order to be able to see the action. The composition is the visual formation of the shot to the camerman's eyes. He is the most experienced person with the camera on the set, knows what he wants, what the camera can do and he knows, or thinks he knows, what the director wants.

The cameraman's idea of speed of the track, and the mood that is being dictated by the dialogue of the whole of the preceding scene is extremely important. He knows even the speed at which he wants people to move. He can tell if the actors are moving so quickly that they are going against the mood of the scene and, if it happens, this can be pointed out to the director. The movement might compel the cameraman to stop too suddenly or start a movement too abruptly, or some other problem. His judgement in these circumstances is really to do with having a "feel" for a scene. Yet, there are many cameramen who think camera operation is merely a question of moving from A to B. They could hardly be further from the truth. Sometimes in a drama production the mood changes more than once within a scene and the camera must react accordingly.

This type of work requires enormous concentration on the part of the cameraman, and there is nothing more disturbing to him than to have that concentration broken while the shot is in progress. Of all times, this is the one requiring the most concentration on that little rectangle of picture seen through the camera. Occasionally a cameraman has to give cues to the assistant while he is operating. The slightest touch breaks this concentration, so no one should ever talk to a cameraman during a shot. The worst thing a director can do is to give a cameraman a cue by a punch in the ribs!

ELECTRONIC CAMERA MONITORING

If you have electronic "keyhole" cameras whereby the director and anyone else who is standing around can see what you are "getting", there is a great danger of the director questioning your framing or composition not only in the middle of the shot, but also when lining up and working out the composition in rehearsal, or, if it is a static shot, when simply lining up. Most directors in television have been "brought up" in the gallery of a TV studio and are used to looking at several television screens simultaneously and giving instructions to the technicians on the floor. In the middle of a shot, even when recording, they will talk to the cameraman on the floor and tell him to pan left or right, tilt up or down, which does not leave much for the operator to do. This operator has no control over his own movements and is always at the mercy of the director. There is much more to film camerawork than this. The film cameraman knows a great deal more about operating and composition than the director. The electronic monitoring system also opens up the possibility of interference from the production assistant, or secretary. It removes from the camera operator the authority that he has been given through the training that he has gained from experience.

Another situation that can arise is that if the shot rehearsal does not work someone looking at a monitoring screen can easily attribute it to the wrong causes.

Unless you have a multi-camera set-up there is no point in using an electronic viewfinder. The director should know what the camera is getting at any time. He knows the lens being used, the area covered, etc. He would only have to sit in a chair underneath the camera as all the old-fashioned directors used to, from which position they knew what was going on and what was being covered by the camera. Multi-camera set-ups are rarely used in television filming. At most, there may be two cameras for a couple of shots on a production. This is usually for a shot that cannot be repeated satisfactorily.

13

Daytime Exteriors: Exposure, Control and Contrast

THERE IS MUCH arbitrary thinking and action where exposure technique is concerned. For example, there are certain factors which one subconsciously takes into account, such as a previous experience which suggests that you should modify the exposure in some way from that indicated by the meter. The latitude of negative film stock allows + or − one stop before quality begins to be affected. For most of the time there is no reason why the exposure should not be absolutely accurate, where, for instance, you can take direct readings off the subject or foot candle readings of the light, assuming that you are filming on negative. Reversal material does not allow such latitude and, because you are rarely working under perfect conditions, the BBC and many other companies in the television and film industry shoot on negative only. The latitude offered by negative material is essential and it supports the requirements for speed and mobility in filming for television.

EXPOSURE WITH DISTANT SUBJECTS

/The normal approach here is to take a reading in the immediate surroundings as if the subject were at medium range, and then look through the camera at the shot about to be taken and mentally assess whether there should be any difference, in terms of reflected light, between the subject being photographed and those which provided the basis of the reflected light exposure assessment. The difference might be a stop, or half a stop, according to the colour of the far subject compared with that nearby. One would also take into account the effect on exposure of using the telephoto lens—sometimes half a stop more, or less, than the reading indicated. For example, a T8 reading obtained from nearby would become T11 if the subject seen through the camera is a white rock, with half a stop extra to take into account the effect of the lens.

Exposure Adjustments During Shot

Pulling aperture during the shot is a very useful means of control. Most cameras do not provide a shutter that can be adjusted during a shot. There are in any case disadvantages. If the shutter is closed down too far there is a tendency to produce a very "choppy" image. The manually operated shutter usually offers the approximate equivalent of one and a half stops before the shutter becomes unreliable in that way. If the cameraman and his assistant are well co-ordinated and the cameraman gives the right instructions about where to open or close during a pan shot the results are remarkable. These stop pulls cannot be seen on the screen. The cameraman speaks his requirements as he films and a good assistant responds accordingly. All this is rehearsed beforehand.

It is always possible to do this effect and the factor of depth of field does not affect it. The assistant may have to be quite adept at working with both hands, pulling focus with one and pulling stops with the other. Only too often the rings have to be moved in opposite directions to one another.

When panning from a light to a dark area a definite pull stop can be given to the assistant to compensate for exposure differences. Often, he has to pull aperture simultaneously with the panning movement. He can be given the various stops and shown the positions or points where the planned alterations will be called for. He has to judge the positioning or area covered sitting or standing in his position at right angles to the camera. He is not looking through the camera. Any drastic errors made by the assistant while shooting are immediately noticeable when seen through the viewfinder.

Colour Bias in Shadow Areas

If Eastman stock is underexposed in shadow areas it tends to take on a blue-green tinge. This is noticeable on the print. It is, of course, avoided in shooting by simply putting more light into the shadows—incandescent light in the studio and blued incandescents outside, or a reflector.

Checking Cloud Movements Through a Pan Glass

If the camera is lined up ready to take the shot, yet the sun is constantly going in and out because of drifting clouds, it is a good idea to check cloud movement through a pan glass, possibly holding over the longer shots for a period when there should be uninterrupted sunlight. The difference in light levels between a sunlit scene and one where the sun is temporarily obscured by cloud requires approximately one stop adjustment on the lens. A particularly dark cloud may demand one and a half stops adjustment. One approach to the problem of obscured sunlight involves giving the assistant carte-blanche to change the aperture during the shot to compensate for the changes in light level. The stop can be operated to cope with this situation without it being obvious, though, of course, where sunlight appears or disappears in a scene there is inevitably a visual change. But the shot can still be perfectly acceptable without needing a cut, or disturbing the action. In any case, it is natural in everyday scenes for the sun to go in and out. You avoid situations where this happens purely as a matter of convenience as far as exposure is concerned. But if it does happen then the changes are made.

Balance with Sun In and Out in Same Sequence

If you have a two-shot, and you know that you are going to cut close-ups into the two-shot, if you shoot in sun-in, or sun-out situations then the close-ups must obviously also be sun-in or sun-out to match. If, on the other hand, the people in the two-shot walk out of frame and then walk into another shot (area or set-up) that might be somewhere else, even a few yards away, you do not have to be so meticulous with the quality of the light for matching. It is essential in this case that the actors actually walk out of shot and the scene is not cut before that point. You can get away with some extremes by this method but the effect can be reduced at the laboratory stage in printing. Also, one can conceive a situation where one shot following another in approximately the same location could, ostensibly, be taken from the shadow side of the subject, thus excusing a sunlit scene which follows one in shadow, i.e. the second is a shot favouring the sunlit side. You never show the juxtaposition of those two locations' backgrounds. In television, unless there is a downpour of rain you have to get through a day's work, so that you have to make the most of your opportunities. Most jobs have to be done on the day allotted.

But, whatever the natural hazards, the basic attitude to these problems should still be to leave the minimum necessary corrections to the printer. You should get what you can with the camera. So, whatever you want must be on the negative. If you then want effects afterwards these can be done in the laboratory. This is the easiest way to work.

Contrast in the Image

In the early days of telecine there was a very rigid stipulation that film material produced for television could not be even fractionally contrasty—an ambiguous statement, for how contrasty is contrasty? It is not, and was not then, actually measured with a foot candle meter, for example. It was a visual assessment.

But to be on the safe side many cameramen tended to flatten the contrast a little with frontal fill light if there was any risk of excess contrast in the scene.

But with modern telecine and the ability of the laboratories to produce (with the various printing stocks now available) a wide variety of results, you aim to give them a negative which is normal by cinematic standards, i.e. a negative suitable for producing show prints for screening in a cinema. Although laboratories have sufficient control to make a print of the required contrast for television, if the print is of the wrong contrast this can be corrected to some extent at the telecine stage. So today, what with the cameraman, the laboratory and the telecine, there should be fewer difficulties in obtaining correct results.

Contrast in the Subject

On exteriors, if the subject is of extremely high contrast, a ·3 or ·6 neutral density filter can be placed on the camera to soften the picture slightly. The denser the neutral density filter the greater the softening. The greater the neutral density the larger aperture you have to use on the camera which, in turn, will slightly soften the contrast. The combination of these two adds up to a significant effect. When filming in hot climates and bright sunlit conditions the neutral density filter is in any case essential to avoid stopping the lens down too far. In such a situation with only the Wratten 85 filter (for exteriors in colour) in use, it might be necessary to stop down to T22 or 32. But with an 85 N6 which is a filter combining the effect of the Wratten 85 and the ·6 neutral density, you can open up the lens a further two stops.

One way of reducing the contrast in a scene where that contrast is excessive is with the aid of reflectors. They have distinct advantages. They are portable, cheap and operate independently of any power source, though they do need favourable conditions in order to make a useful contribution—preferably bright sunlight.

Not very much light is obtained by reflection from a blue sky. The most pronounced effect comes from reflecting from white cloud.

Reflections of impure colour, even where it occurs naturally in the scene, can cause problems. Blue sky reflecting off water or concrete gives a blue-tinged reflection. Sometimes, if an artist is wearing a coloured garment on a day exterior, or with a high intensity key light, the colour of the garment reflects upwards giving a colour tinge on the neck, underneath the chin. It cannot be avoided but it is rather obtrustive in certain shots.

Standard reflectors consist of a flat surface of varying dimensions covered in different types of reflective material like silver paper, dull or bright, or bright or dull aluminium paint. They have different reflecting abilities and characteristics. One type gives a soft reflection over a wide area, and the other (of equivalent size) gives a hard, sharp reflection over a smaller area. The second is like a light. The first gives a bright reflection with no form to the light, not casting a shadow. The strong reflector, usually a polished metallic foil surface casts a shadow so care must be taken in using it. The soft reflector gives an overall filler effect.

Whether you use a bright or dull reflector depends how far it has to be from the artist in order to reflect the sun on to them. If the reflector has to be close to the artist, you use the dull surface. If it is a long way off, you use the brighter one. The type of surface is purely arbitrary—but you must not use a surface that reflects a coloured light. Because you are reflecting the sun you get a smallish reflection covering a relatively small area. The reflection from a dull surface is more soft and diffuse but it covers a larger area, though it is less bright.

If you look at the sun it is not a very large area. A diffusing reflector seems to be reflecting a larger area because the punch of the sun when it reaches the subject is less and there is a large portion of soft reflection outside the area of the sun from the clouds or the sky. On a hard reflector the "hard" spot of the sun swamps everything else because it is so hard and sharp. When you use the softer area the whole effect is smoothed out with a soft reflection from the larger area.

We use two reflectors for close-ups, with dull white plastic paint, and gloss white paint. The gloss gives a brighter and slightly harder light than the other. These are used mainly to put a little white light in the eyes in close-ups—the light point that makes the eyes come alive. Again, it is up to the individual as to what type of reflector he uses. The main consideration is that it must be white light. You cannot, as in the days of black and white photography, use gold paper, bright or dull, to give a softer light compared with silver paper. The gold bias would, of course, show up in colour.

You can use reflectors efficiently only in close-ups. For long shots, with a very hard reflector you could pick out the side of a tree, for example. But you can always tell when reflectors are being used, and it looks very phoney. This is not so true of close-ups. The reflector can be toned down, either by placing it further away or covering it with gauze. As it is withdrawn it is reduced in effect like a lamp.

Practicality of Reflectors and Battery Lights

Reflectors are mainly for convenience. If you already have lights on location, then you can afford to have large solid reflectors in frames which go on to lighting stands because there are enough electricians to handle them and the stands and transportation are available.

On large productions abroad the larger reflectors can be used if there are technicians to handle them. In television the largest used are about 3 ft square. The small, personal wooden reflectors are about 2 ft square. One man can hold them and they fold for transport. Cloth reflectors may be aluminized. In bright conditions the finest reflector for close-up is a white cloth, say, calico.

If you use cloth it should be either mounted on a metal frame or held by two people.

On a small location you are confined to using small reflectors. Their best application is for close-ups or a tight two-shot. Lights are always preferable, but reflectors are a useful expedient if no alternator or generator is available, or no battery light. On a two-shot in sunlight or very bright light, the reflector can be used to reduce contrast. But if the available light is dull, you cannot use a reflector because there is no light to reflect—nothing even from the sky. So, with a two-shot, you use a battery light to act as a key, because on a tight two-shot the battery light can be brought close enough to give a key shadow.

On a *Z Cars* sequence, for example, the overall exposure was barely T2 or T2·8. On a close shot, however, a battery light would have given a hard key and skill have been in balance with the background. For lighting in general shots, a 6-light was used to brighten up the existing light (which was at quite a low level) in the foreground, Particularly on the artists. The existing light then was a normal English "soft light"! There was no shadow but it was quite bright. A kicker was used on a three-quarter back light to separate the artists from the background. We worked with these two lamps for much of the time. When the sun came out, the 6-light became a filler to reduce the contrast a little, the sun being the key light.

Exposure Balancing

One tricky sequence we had to do when filming the *Terracotta Horse* entailed shooting in the congested, high, narrow streets of the Medina in Fez, among the stalls and local manufacturers, with the constant movement to and fro of donkeys carrying heavy packs. We had to shoot dialogue sequences of our two groups of actors following each other through the Medina. It was impossible to use a tripod, so everything had to be hand held. Light and reflectors could not be used either, because lights would attract too much attention. We did not want people looking at the cameras as they walked past (a particular problem in an Arab country). We had to accept existing lighting conditions, which varied from almost pitch darkness to brilliant shafts of light coming down from the slatted rooftops carrying awnings just over the alleyway. And the sequence had to be shot quickly and sharply without any rehearsals. It was a question of dashing into position, getting the artists to approach you very quickly or you approaching them equally quickly and retain the flow of the local inhabitants to keep it looking as natural as possible. Once or twice we were able to hide in an alleyway and place the artists in the main stream of people passing through, so that it looked natural. But the main problem here was the question of exposure. Although I could take a reading in a couple of areas, in most cases, according to the exposure meter, there was not enough light. But when we panned round there was quite a high level of light, so the camera assistant had to know where to alter the aperture setting during the shot. This is rather tricky when you are operating a hand-held camera, because the slightest movement or pull on a lens, even when following focus, is likely to upset your balance and pull your framing off a little, especially in the middle of a pan. If, on the other hand, it is a walking shot, the fact that you are moving disguises movements due to the assistant touching the lens. As there were no rehearsals we had to "rehearse on film" for every shot. The results worked out quite well, despite the wide range of exposure required. Alterations of exposure during a shot are disguised by camera or subject movement or a changing situation.

In other sequences the reflector was used for group shots and the battery light for single close-ups. The battery light, for the intensity that one needs, covers only the face of one person. This would be used either in very bad lighting conditions where you want to put a fraction of extra light in the face or eyes. It is only a fraction at any time. The other situation in which a battery light is useful is in brilliant sunshine for a three-quarter front or a half-front or even a bad light to soften out the shadow a little. The battery light was used on every close-up except where the sun was more or less fully frontal to the subject's face. The reflector was used on groups mainly as a kicker (a three-quarter backlight) in brilliant sunshine, or as a similar light on a single person, though the advantage of the reflector is the spread it will allow. We used a wooden reflector (3 ft × 2 ft) covered with silver paper, bright on one side, dull on the other, and placed on a knuckle arm.

With weak sun or no sun but a bright sky, you use the bright side of the reflector. In brilliant sunshine you use the dull side to avoid too harsh illumination. The trouble with reflectors is that you have a tremendous "punch" of light over a small area. So that to get any considerable spread of light you must take the reflector back a long way. The whole art with exterior work with additional light, from reflectors or lamps, is to keep people unaware of the fact that lights are being used. So the light from reflectors or battery light must be minimal, i.e. just doing the job. An exterior shot should never look obviously lit, with a front light, for instance. You can flood or spot a battery light a little, for example, to modify this. But the best method is to keep the battery light fully flooded all the time to give the maximum area and then adjust the intensity by adjusting the lamp/subject distance. With a reflector you need sun or bright sky. The distance that you take your reflector away from the artists is governed by the strength of the sun. One basically uses the reflector in support of the existing light (i.e. a kicker) not to put light in places where it is missing in the particular situation, such as a shadow area in an exterior. The battery light would not, in any case, be very effective, unless there was a particular point in the story justifying or explaining the presence of the light, to pick out a person or an object.

Moving subjects in existing light situations can be allowed to be lit by the actual presence or lack of light in the scene. Reflectors and battery lights are best used on static situations or set-ups where you are dwelling on a subject for long enough for the lack of detail in shadow areas to become objectionable. Otherwise, let it pass because the latitude of the film material, printing process, etc. copes with the problem entirely. Even in the tropics, the fact that the sun is high, and has extra intensity, does not prevent the colour stock from coping with the situation.

The meter will give the base and you can work to a half stop difference by visual assessment. There should be no variation due to climate or local conditions. You can expose a stop either way of the "correct" exposure and yet still be within acceptable limits of exposure latitude.

14

Lighting

LIGHTING IS THE SECOND most important individual skill that a cameraman needs after that of operating the camera itself. In a sense it is more so. Although the job of handling a camera can be transferred to another person, lighting the scene is inescapably the responsibility of the cameraman. He cannot pass the job on to his assistant, neither can the director "take over" the lighting in a difficult situation. No one but the cameraman is able to make the necessary technical decisions and none but he has the judgement in the handling of lights to ensure that the image presented to the camera is as good as it can be. Lighting is the most complex part of the cameraman's job and it presents a fresh problem with every new situation. It is here also that experience and a "feel" for the handling of lights counts. The lighting has much to do with the distinction of the production as a whole and although the ordinary viewer may not be conscious of it, good lighting accounts for much of the pleasure of viewing the well filmed television image.

FILM AND TELEVISION LIGHTING COMPARED

The tendency in filming always has been and still is, to light each particular shot separately. For live television and outside broadcasting, on the other hand, the lighting is arranged for several different shots to be taken consecutively. So a particular shot can start off being lit correctly but as that shot develops into a different area it is not necessarily lit as you would want because the position of lights is governed by the camera positions of the previous shot. So, for television, you have to light for all shots together, which means that there are inevitable compromises. The resources of lighting equipment must be spread out over the whole job which limits the amount of lighting you can bring to bear for a particular shot. This leads, in the case of outside broadcasting, to carrying more equipment to do a certain job. This is one of the reasons why OB is less mobile.

With filming, however, the standard method is to arrange a particular lighting scheme for each individual shot. The same lights may be used in a subsequent shot, and consequently relatively little lighting equipment is needed—no more than to cover the exigencies of the most demanding separate set-up. Often the actual equipment needed can be of quite modest specifications. These factors added together with the reduced transport and labour needed to handle them contribute largely towards the mobility and economy of the television film unit.

Another factor is that the versatility of the equipment—the wide aperture lenses and fast film, plus some residual measures for certain scenes—allows the cameraman to make do with less light than that required for television cameras. Indeed, it may be counted a blessing that the camera is so capable of making use of the existing light in many scenes. The feeling of naturalness that this imparts would tend to be reduced if powerful film lighting were brought in.

Visualizing and Planning the Lighting

If you are working in a studio and are presented with a built set, first of all you need to know whether the scene is supposed to represent night or day. You then visualize what this set would look like if it were a real room or a real exterior, taking into consideration where the main source of illumination would come from in such a case. For example, in a daylight interior scene, the main illumination would come from the direction of the windows, whereas for a "night" sequence the light would come from the "practical" lamps or room lighting. If you were filming a built exterior set, like a street or farm, the lighting could be coming from the sun or the moon—and this would be determined either to suit yourself or the particular story or plot which is to be acted out in it.

You always try to make your lighting appear as convincing and natural as possible so that the set then has a chance of looking as real as it can. It would, in fact, be worthwhile when you are walking about at night or by day to look closely at the lighting in your surroundings just to see how this or that feature appears in natural conditions—and store up the information so that you can reproduce the effect with lights when you need it.

When you first plan the lighting of your set you do not necessarily know what shots are going to take place in it. You might form an awkward lighting plan for youself, but in this case you can always rush in a change in the lamp arrangement up on the rail—once you have started shooting. You begin by lighting the set for the master shot, as we have seen. You try to use that basic lighting on the set for subsequent shots and only alter the lighting on your artists.

A shot following, made from another direction, might show a part of the background which is well lit for the master shot but, say, too full of shadows for this angle. The lighting would have to be altered to suit the new shot. The difference between the lightings would not be noticeable, unless you have seen a specific feature in the master shot such as a shadow across a wall, which, in the shot following (from a different angle) must remain there. You can still alter the lighting on the artists. But basically you are lighting each shot separately, if not differently. This is a difference between lighting for filming and that for television. In the TV studio the lighting is set for all angles and the camera can move around in many directions. It is enormously complicated, especially nowadays that lights are, in fact, controlled during the shooting so that, in effect, there are separate lighting set-ups. This is really an extension of the system they had before, which is a far cry from the individual "illusion" of the special camera set-up. You do try to retain the basic lighting throughout for the sake of speed. You do not set up your master shot lighting to take care of shots to follow for different angles. You set it up merely to establish a lighting situation (i.e. the conditions under which the scene is supposed to be taking place). It is, however, usually a wide angle shot and takes in most of the set, and will, in fact, be suitable for most other shots from other angles, basically at least. But you do make small alterations. All the time you are making alterations to the lighting on your artists because they are seen from a certain angle and you want the key light to come from a particular angle. When you turn to another person you cannot use this key light so you alter it again.

Key, Kickers and Fillers

The main source of lighting in the scene is the "key" light. This is not, as in still photography, just a light set arbitrarily for the best modelling on the subject, but ideally a light representing the supposed main source of light in the scene—the window, "practicals", sun or moon. As such, it should be placed as near as possible to the angle of the visible light source, such as the window. Often, however, because of the action or direction of shooting you have to compromise with this ideal. The key light may tally with the known or visible light source in the set, but from the camera angle chosen give no modelling, even no light, on the main subject. You, therefore, have to use a "kicker" light.

The kicker works in combination with the key but it follows the direction and angle of the visible known key source. The kicker is actually of lower intensity than the key you are using to model the subject's face, for instance, but strikes the subject at a fairly acute angle and therefore *looks* very much bright than the key. Thus, it simulates the visible main source of light without interfering with the modelling from the key. The scene looks real because although the subject has dimension in depth (due to modelling from the key), it also seems to belong in its surroundings because it is responding to the "natural" light of the location. In daylight scenes at least, indoors or out, the actual main source of light is the sun, which is normally *high* in the sky. Therefore, even in a room lit by window light the key light should come from a high angle. This also gives you the best chance of good modelling. (This does not, of course, apply to "effect" lighting which is another problem entirely.)

So the key light is the simulation of your main source of illumination, if possible, and the kicker can help you to keep your lighting orientation. But the kicker can also be the equivalent of a "backlight" or can be used in conjunction with backlights—all of which help to give a separation of your subject from the background, and a pleasant outlining of the artists.

After the key light has been set, the kickers and backlights are used for the completion of the overall modelling of the scene and to give a pleasing and natural look.

As the key light is the main source of light, giving the primary modelling, its intensity also determines the basic exposure.

There must be only *one* shadow in the scene. This will come from the key. The main sources of secondary shadows are a key light which is not higher than the subject or a "filler" that is bright enough to produce another shadow within the key light area.

The "filler" light is simply an illumination that fills or softens the "shadow areas" created by, or rather left by, the key and kicker lights. It serves to reduce or regulate the contrast of the lighting so that it is suitable to be photographed. The filler must never be strong enough to produce its own shadow. It is normally a diffused light source from a wide diameter unit.

The key modelling lighting for a scene must be established from the outset. It helps you to visualize the set as a whole as if lit for a master shot, even if that master shot is never in fact going to be taken. This establishes, at least in your mind's eye, the strength and direction of all other lights for shots that follow.

PLANNING LIGHTING FOR A SEQUENCE

After you have seen a plan of the set, read the script and talked to the director, you place your lights for the effect you think you want. A very important factor is that you must be ready to do reverse shots and have lighting in the right positions only needing to be switched on—in effect, 360-degree lighting.

The television productions *Colditz* (discussed in greater detail elsewhere) and *Rembrandt* were typical examples with continuous

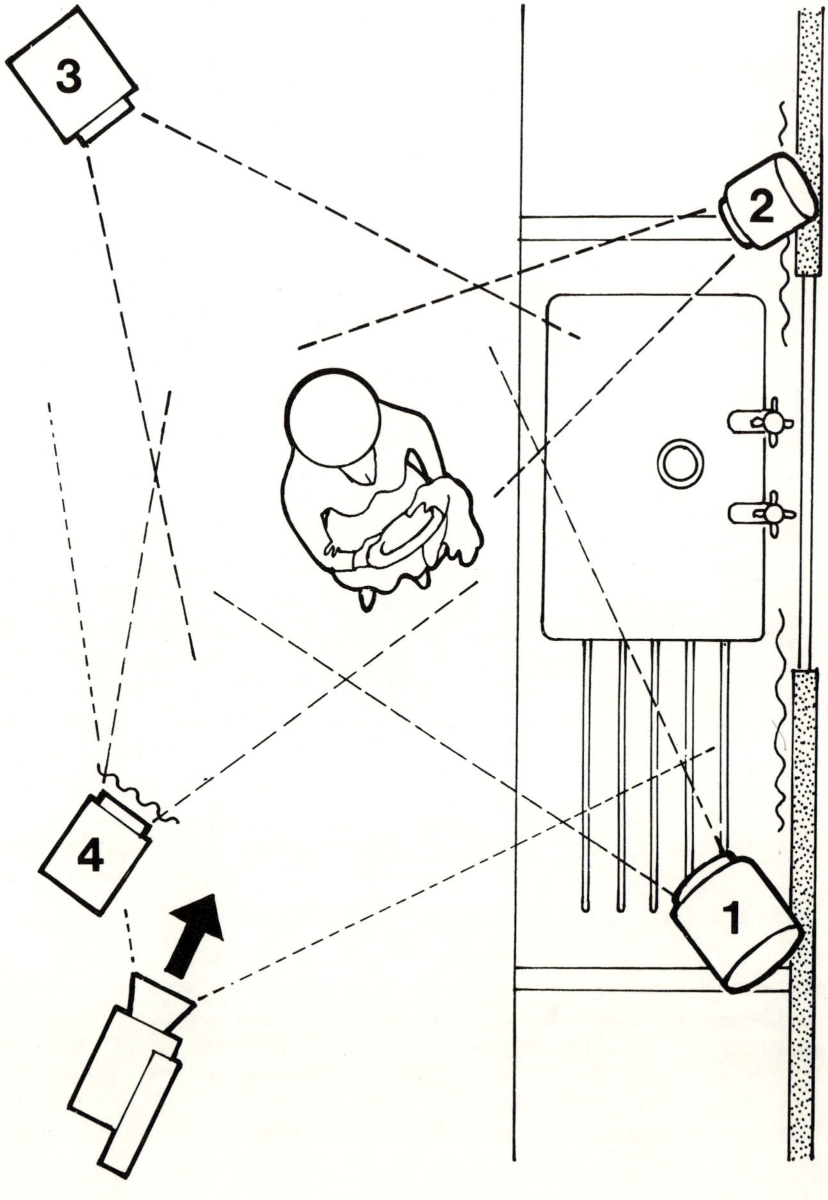

Camera set up with key, filler, back and kicker lighting. 1, Key establishes the basic light level and models the subject. 2, Kicker (placed high, and therefore out of shot) follows direction of known visible light source. 3, Backlight separates the subject more distinctly from the background. 4, Filler light softens the shadow area created by the key.

backgrounds, where the whole set had lighting rigged for immediate filming in any direction, switched on and adjusted as required for each shot.

One pitfall that must be avoided is to say to yourself that you cannot do a particular shot because no "arc has been rigged for this or that angle", or some such argument, and so persuade yourself into rigging one—thereby wasting half an hour. You must be sure to have the right quantity of light available no matter which way you are looking. This is part of the mental visualization process that must take place when looking at the plan and working out key lights, backlighting, etc. Most of this lighting would be rigged (i.e. hanging from the gantries) as one normally tries to avoid cluttering up the floor with lighting units on very high stands. If the director then suddenly comes up with an unexpected requirement, there is a certain amount of lighting available on the floor which could be brought in to answer those requirements.

You have always to remember with any situation that you have to light the subject from behind as well as in front to gain the all-round lighting that you get in nature. (This is a requirement separate and distinct from the need for the reverse shot lighting mentioned above.) Without paying attention to these peripheral lighting factors the subject and image is inclined to look "dead". The degree of balance between these varies according to the mood to be evoked or the set or situation in which the sequence is to take place. Personal artistic preferences also tend to influence the way a cameraman lights a scene—other than effect lighting, of course. There is a saying in the film industry that if you ask twelve cameramen the same question you will get fifteen different answers. Cameramen and photography are very individualistic. Eventually most cameramen come to the same end result—a viewable image that few people can fault. But they arrive there by different routes, especially with lighting, where there are more variables.

Number and Kinds of Lights

In the studio, the fewer lamps you have to use the more quickly and efficiently you can work, because it takes a shorter time to rearrange the lighting when changing from one shot to the next. Large numbers of arcs in the studio means that they have to be trimmed and moved, and so you become less mobile even within the relatively restricted studio area. So, if you can obtain an intermediate aperture, yet using only a minimum of lights you can still work quickly and efficiently.

You assess the set before shooting and light to the foot candles required. The size of the set is a critical factor. With a large set, and the action widely spaced, the large working space enables you to use arcs, which cover a wide area yet give a high intensity. On a small set, on the other hand, you cannot use arcs. They are far too bright for a small area and any subject movement tends to find places where the subject becomes "burned out" in the arc light. So, for small sets, you have to use a 10K or a 5K incandescent lamp. In effect, then, your working conditions depend on the type of set and the equipment that you can use on it—taking into account the time/effectiveness of that equipment. The production moves at the speed of the cameraman; his work is the determining factor. But the lighting aspect never comes into anyone's mind except that of the cameraman. The designer designs the set to suit the story, actor movement and the designer's own personal ideas—including the size of the set.

Arcs do not necessarily mean slower production, but the larger the set the more lights you need and men to operate them, which causes a certain slowing down of the work rate. Large equipment also takes up more space and there are always things in the way. With a large set the director often brings in a crane to move about and so gain the full benefit of the size and construction of the set.

For all interior-exteriors, whatever size, you use arcs as your key light because only an arc light can represent the sun, with its hard, sharp shadow. Sometimes you use more than one arc, according to the size of the set. In a small "interior" set when the arc "sunlight" comes through a window, for example, you could substitute it with a quartz light which gives a hard shadow. Many of the mobile lighting units used nowadays (especially for exteriors) are the quartz types, because of their lighter weight and ease of handling. So for real exteriors, arcs are nowadays used only occasionally. With the normal drama-type production involving possibly half a dozen actors you would not use arcs at all. But they are often used for filming night exteriors.

With *Civilisation* (in which arc lights were never used) we started to use quartz lights about a third of the way through the production. Up to that point we had been relying on Colour Tran. The quartz lights were a boon because of their high power/weight ratio. A 750 quartz weighing about 2 lb. can equal the output of a 1000 watt pup (and sometimes a 2K). This speeds up the electrician's work and consequently you do not need so many electricians to handle lighting for a given power unit.

Finding the Place where Light Falls

If a lamp is positioned to light a specific area it is often difficult to check that it is hitting exactly the right spot if a number of other lights are also present and the general level of illumination is high. The centre of the area covered by the spotlight can be determined quite easily by placing yourself in front of it and looking straight into the lens or open front of the lamp through a dark glass such as a pan glass (used originally to check degrees of contrast but now largely discarded) and moving your position until the filament or carbon points of the lamp appear to be exactly centred. This gives the exact centre of the light cone and thus the point at which it should strike the subject or surface. This is a particularly useful method for recentering lights which have been re-aligned during a production.

CONDITIONS ON THE SET

One basic difficulty with a high, fixed gantry for lighting in the studio is related to the small average size of the three- or four-walled sets used. If the set is large, lights on a high gantry can cover the forward part of the set quite adequately. But with small sets the angle of light from this position is too acute so that the light is shooting straight down into the set rather than slanting across it. The only way to light in this situation would be to position the lamps looking over the top of the walls of the set, which is difficult because normally the lamp stands do not extend high enough, say, ten feet or more, so wall clamps or brackets are used, allowing the lamp to hang from the top of the set wall.

Sets are constructed on a stage in such a way that, in the constructor's opinion, the lighting should be able to reach into the set from the gantries. So the sets are built under the gantries, and thus, there is an even greater tendency to tip the lights downwards into the set. Consequently you tend to be confined to toplighting rather than back or side lighting. Cradles could be slung from the gantries but nowadays they are not in fashion for television filming. In the large interior *Colditz* set, there was a catwalk gantry bisecting the set and lining its edges. This allowed light into the set at a reasonably flat angle, rather than from on top of it. The side gantries were used to light the central area and the central, bisecting gantries to light the sides.

SHADOWS

As stated earlier, whenever you are lighting you try to obtain only one shadow. When an artist is walking near a wall, where multiple shadows are picked up very easily, you make sure that the particular section which will be seen in the shot is lit with only one key light. Shadows from steeply angled spots are thrown on to the floor and are those which you are least likely to see. If, as is often the case, they are dark and also the subject is for the most part being seen in medium shot, these shadows are excluded from the picture.

Some cameramen like to show floor space rather than avoid it, especially if it is a special feature of the set, as in *Colditz* where the courtyard of moulded cobbles gave a feeling of reality to the rest of the set. There can be problems with a flat surface such as an unrendered or unprepared floor. For one thing, it does not look very real in certain circumstances, particularly with revealing camera angles. Also a flat floor tends to show up every shadow very clearly. There were, for example, many problems for the technicians working on the first *Colditz* series where the floor was flat and not given a cobbled surface. Because of the complexity of the lighting, in long shots people walking around were seen surrounded by multiple shadows—star shadows, in effect. The camera crew tended to keep the camera view as clear of the floor as possible. In situations like this you have to try and avoid showing the surface and be very much more careful with how you light the large area. There may, indeed, have been multiple shadows on the moulded floor for the second *Colditz* series but one can afford this risk with such a broken surface because shadows are less obtrusive.

The only instance where you have to be very particular with floor shadows is with interior exterior night shots, as in the case of the night sequences in the courtyard of Colditz Castle. You must have only one shadow (from the moon) which is, in fact, your key light. A single arc only must provide the detail outline or balance in lit and unlit areas that you need to convey the right impression. This would, of course, have to be very carefully placed, and might be supported by *very* soft filler to reveal a few details here and there. The single brute gives the deep long shadow effect of a night shot.

A "must" in prewar lighting for film was the rule never to throw shadows of people on to the wall. Some technicians used to go through the most elaborate gyrations to prevent it, even if the artist was practically hugging the wall, or going in and out of doors. All key lights and most others were placed high to lose the shadow of a person. The reason why the shadow of a person on the door or wall looks "wrong" is really quite obvious. If someone is walking along, your eye is always on that person. But the moment you see a shadow, even for a fleeting second, the eye leaves the person, goes to the shadow and then returns to the subject. It is almost as if you have seen another person, and spoils your concentration.

Nowadays in film studio material shot for television you can often see shadows of people at almost their own height, going across the wall or door on the shot. For some reason cameramen will not put their key light high enough to make the shadow fall below the subject, an area which is probably out of shot.

You may, for example, have a situation where people are sitting in chairs or at desks and cannot be moved away from the wall because there is not enough space. Even when lit properly, a little shadow might be visible on the wall behind, either right or left of screen. You should either shift the key over a little more to put the shadow out of shot, or

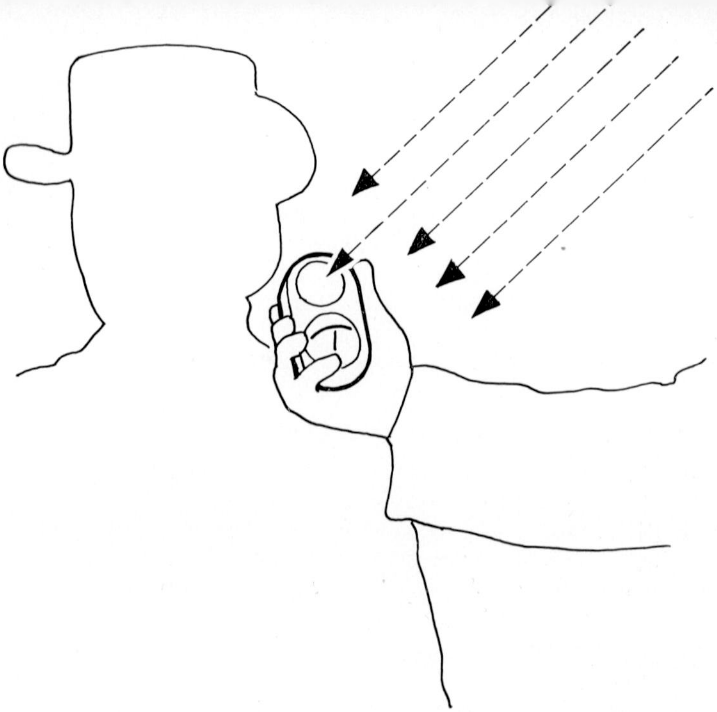

Determining exposure. Episode from *Paul Temple* programme filmed in Hamburg. This was a typical dull day situation. Before putting in a key light you find out how much light is coming from the sky, taking a ft. candle reading, e.g.: 50 ft. candle falling on the artist's face from the sky. For exposure, 120 ft. candles is desired, so the key light must be 70 ft. candles (which, combined with the overall light gives 120). The advantage of this method is that you do not accidentally over-light the artist, because the overall light falling on artist and background is equal. Therefore, when you add light to the artist the separation in light level between them does not make the additional light seem artificial.

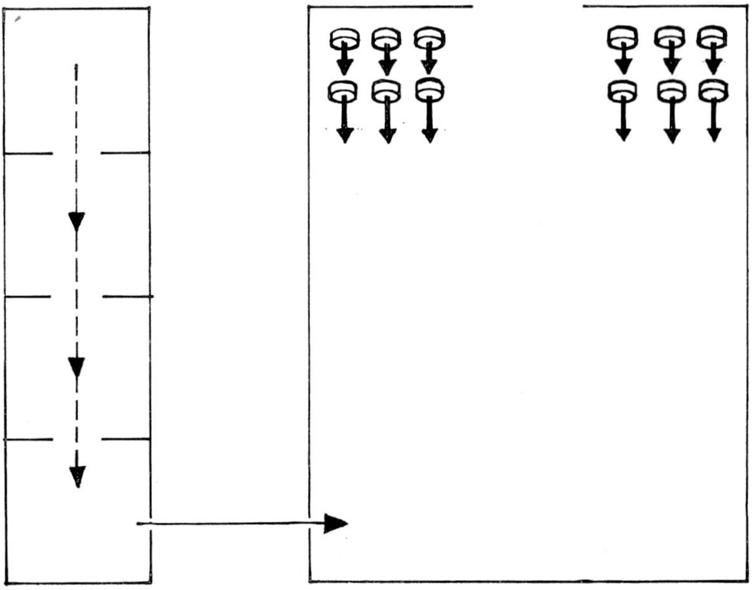

Royal Palaces. A long tracking shot passed through three rooms and ended in a fourth. The rooms were surrounded by mirrors. They offered a high risk of reflection and flare. To avoid this, and to get sufficient illumination, lightweight lighting units were ranked near floor level at one end of each room. These lit the ceilings, chandeliers and far ends of the rooms.

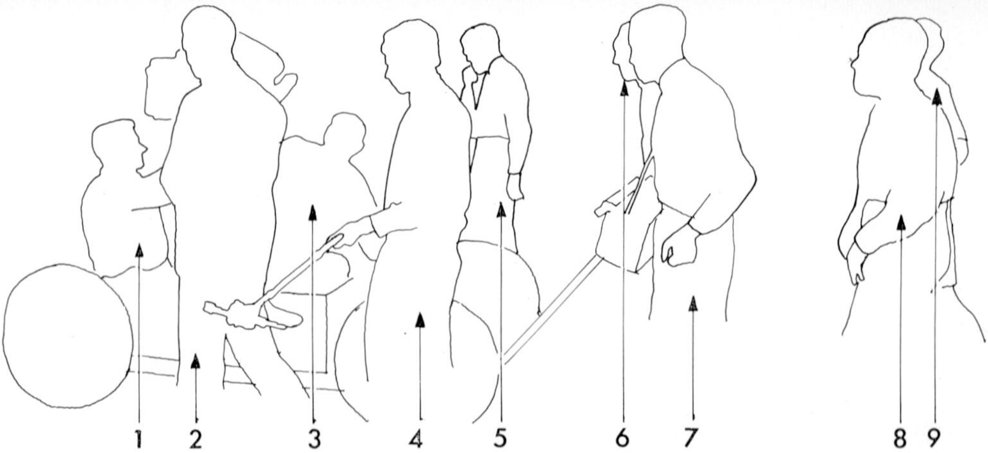

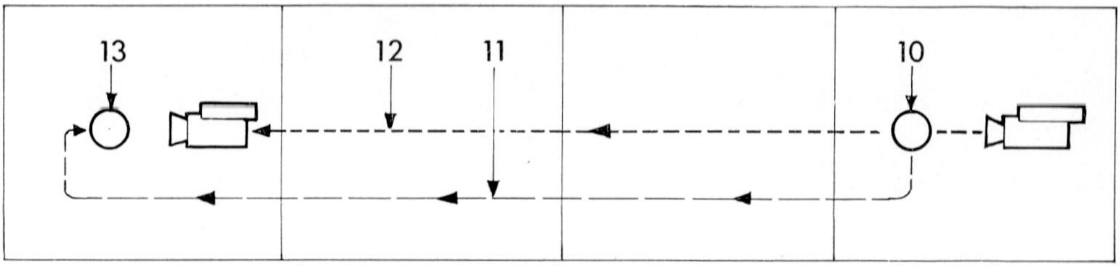

Royal Palaces. Tracking shot through four rooms in which Lord Clark speaks throughout. The individuals are: 1, Camera assistant (pulling focus). 2, Lord Clark. 3, Camera operator. 4, Sound assistant. 5, Director. 6, Dolly pusher (grip). 7, Sound recordist. 8, Cameraman. 9, Production assistant. The shot started with Lord Clark standing and speaking in front of the camera at 10. He continued to speak while walking 11, beside the camera 12, and reappeared in shot at 13 in the last room.

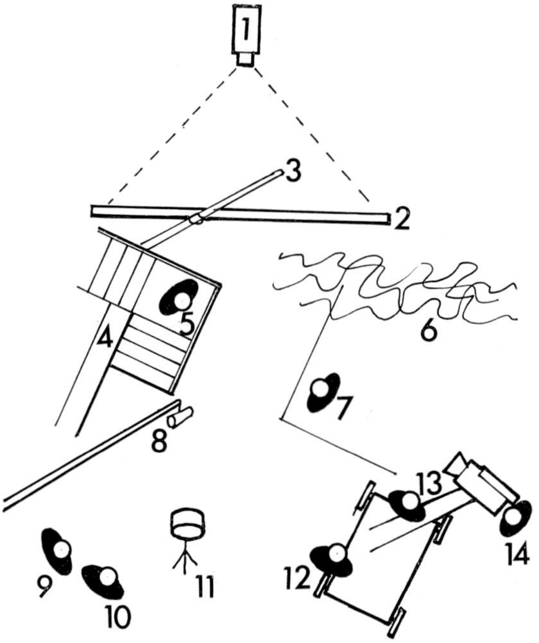

Back projection in the studio. *Maigret* 1964. 1, Projector. 2, Back projection screen. 3, Part of built set in front of screen (mast and stays). 4, Keyside wall. 5, Maigret. 6, Sea mist (smoke floated in). 7, Artist. 8, Microphone. 9, Continuity girl. 10, Director. 11, Lamp: (500 W) filler. 12, Dolly pusher (grip). 13, Camera assistant. 14, Cameraman.

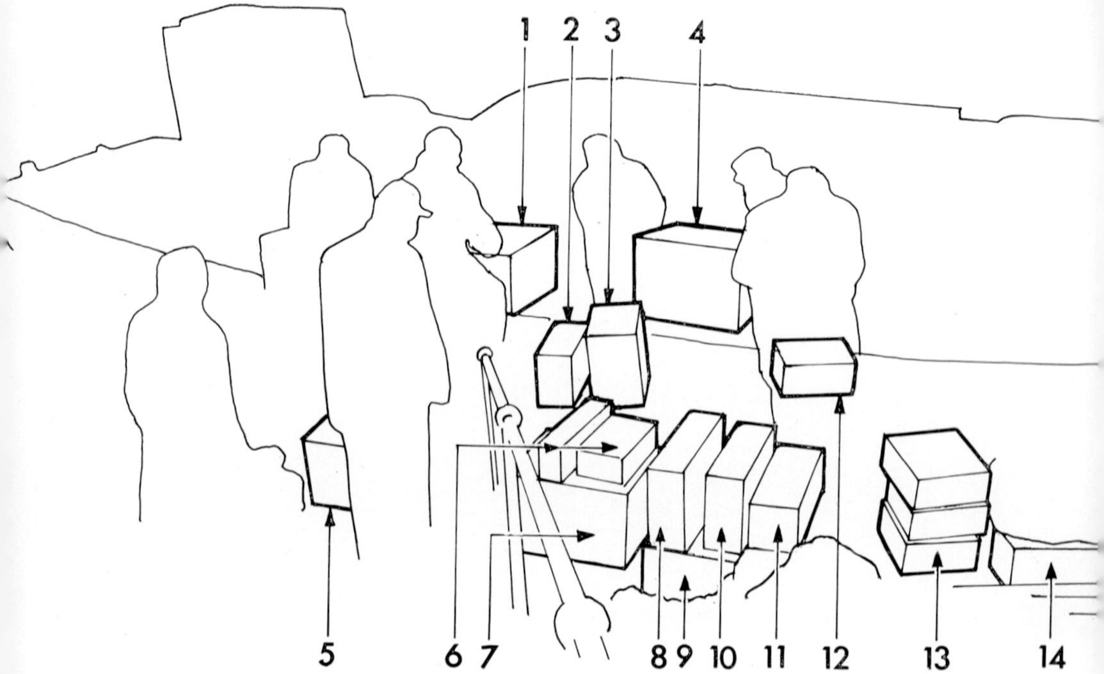

Civilization. Embarking for Iona. Lighting was taken as a separate boatload. Contents of the cases: 1, Teleprompt. 2, Sound accessories. 3, Film magazines (4 × 400 ft.). 4, Camera and blimp. 5, Film magazine (4 × 400 ft.). 6, Camera battery (24 V). 7, Camera accessories. 8, Sound accessories. 9, Camera 'coffin' containing baby tripod, hi hat, small geared head. 10, Sound accessories. 11, Camera case. 12, Batteries (24 V). 13, Three empty boxes or 'biscuits' for standing on when using high camera positions. 14, Camera accessories.

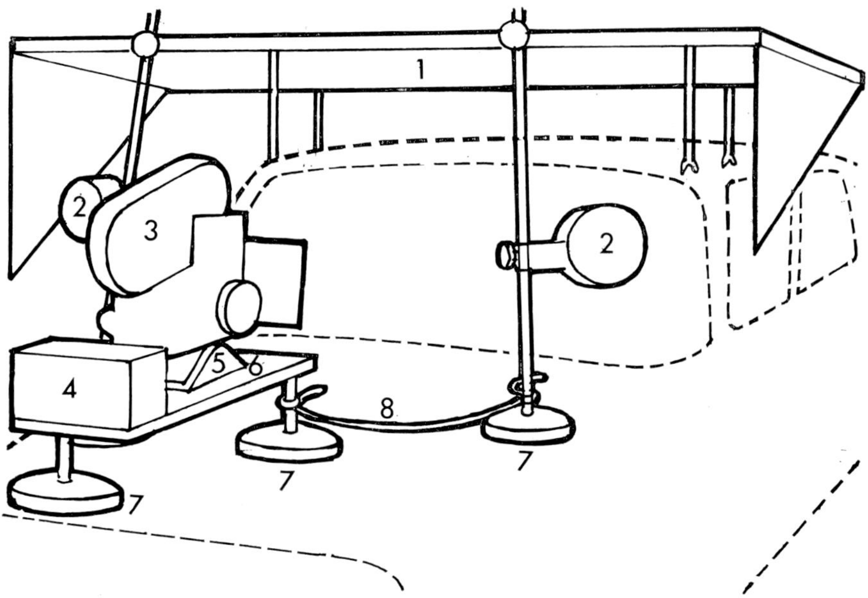

Mobile camera set up for filming through the windscreen of a car. 1, ND acetate sheet top. 2, Tungsten halogen (iodine quartz) lights. 3, Camera magazine, blimped. 4, Camera battery. 5, Geared head base. 6, Rigid camera platform. 7, Support suckers. 8, safety line.

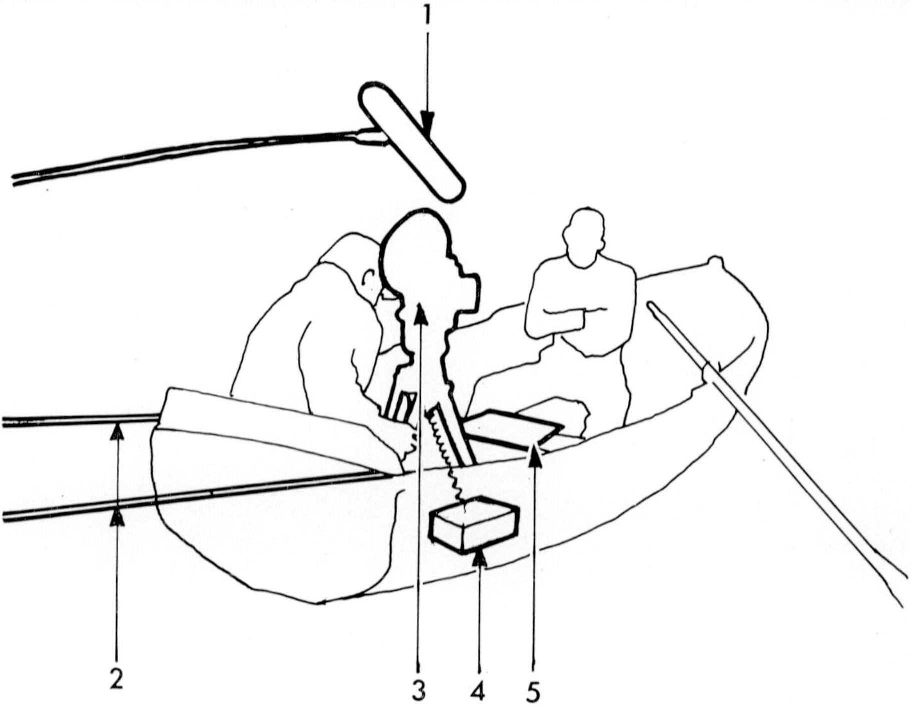

Fall of Eagles. Scene in which Lenin (Patrick Stewart) is seen 'rowing' on the lake. Filmed in Wales. Owing to the turbulence of the water the boat was tethered to the shore and Lenin 'rowed' with feathered oars. 1, Sound boom with gun microphone. 2, Lines to shore. 3, Camera with friction head on tripod, rigid with boat. 4, Battery box with 12 V camera battery. 5, Clapper board, worked by artist.

Tea with Lenin. Cameraman A. A. Englander and actor Patrick Stewart discuss some points arising from the morning's filming on *Fall of Eagles*.

close in slightly on the subject to exclude the shadow from the picture and leave a clear wall behind the subject. Or you can try and nigger it off the background with a French flag and make a straight line shadow which looks as if it is a part of the set.

LIGHTING CONTRAST

When you increase the lighting level, by stepping up the key light, the contrast rises and you have to increase the filler light to restore the balance. There are times when you have difficulty in getting filler light into certain areas away from the camera. It is easy to put filler on your foreground artists. It is more difficult to get filler into the parts of the background which are still in picture. This is because the background filler lighting must not include sharp shadows. Such lighting normally originates from diffused light sources such as floods, which lose power rapidly with distance because their light beam is not focused but spread over a wide area. Consequently you often cannot position these lamps close enough to the background area. This means that you must use a spotlight which, because it focuses the beam of light, maintains the lighting power over a much greater distance. These lamps can be used from further back or higher up than normal, to flood in to the background area. This way you get whatever intensity you need but you do not get the same quality of lighting because the spotlight, even with diffusion, still has a certain harshness about it. You can diffuse it with gelatine gauzes and other diffusers, but it is, nevertheless, not quite the same as floodlighting.

So the difficulty when lighting to a higher key is to get the overall balance exactly the same as before, so that when you cut from one shot to the other the alteration in contrast ratio in the background is not noticeable. There is a marginal difference in contrast range in certain areas whatever you do but as you are concentrating on the foreground, you do not notice unless something suddenly happens in the background and focus is thrown on to it—or you attention is drawn by that event. This aspect of lighting should be considered as more of a bother than an actual problem but it is another thing that the cameraman has to think about.

In normal circumstances outdoors where you are working with no sun and totally unmodelled lighting you have some additional light sources to provide an effect of key lighting with shadows. This must, of course, be balanced out in accordance with the amount of light present in the background so that the separate lighting does not become so pronounced as to appear artificial in the picture. For example, you take a reading of a flatly illuminated subject with a reflected light meter which indicates a setting of T2·8. You have to bear in mind when adding key light to illuminate the foreground area, with people perhaps, that the background which dictates the light level to be added, does not allow you to illuminate the foreground to the equivalent of T5·6 or even T4. You have to take the view that you are building up lighting for T2·8 plus just a fraction more, up to the level of T3·2 possibly. A shadow on the face or faces (where shadows are most pronounced) will be visible but will not indicate that you have used a light. The difference between T3·2 and T2·8 is negligible technically, but visible in the picture. It is better to underlight this effect than overdo it. Unfortunately shots unbalanced by fill light do appear only too often on television—with foreground and background completely unmatched. If the foreground were flat and were lit with a little extra light, the modelling would also be very acceptable on black and white. If no ordinary lights are available, a small battery light might provide the same effect on close-ups.

With colour you can afford to have much more flat lighting than you could with black and white film, because colours make their own separations. As long as each particular colour is illuminated you get the effect of not being "flat" in photographic terms—though in black and white it would be merely a series of greys with never a black or a white tone in the picture. In colour, the alternation of the different colours breaks up the subject into distinct areas. But you have to allow for the fact that the films you shoot are going to be seen on some black and white receivers.

Exposure

The cameraman sometimes does things which may be technically very accomplished and look marvellous on the screen, but he also has to take into account how much of the picture the audience in the home is going to see on a possibly not very well tuned set. Will they appreciate the great technical achievement of the cameraman, the laboratories and the VTR controllers? Someone living 150 miles from the nearest transmitter and on the end of a long chain of boosters will not receive the most specially contrived pictures as even a good image. Therefore, the factors determining the best picture are those that make a good picture in average receiving conditions, rather than the most pleasing results on monitor screens in television stations. The old adage that whatever you want must be in the negative still applies. If you have a properly exposed negative, the services that follow can do whatever they like with it. They can turn night into day, day into night. Proper exposure means enough exposure in the right places. The laboratory can cut or increase highlights or shadows. The main factors in exposing the negative properly are exposure level, lighting balance and also angle of key light, according to what the scene happens to be. The placing of the key light and lighting balance (contrast) have already been discussed; we can now consider exposure.

One method of approach to light measurement is to use two types of meter, one for interior and one for exterior use. The "interior" one is a foot candle meter and measures the key light to the required intensity which is based on the speed of the film being used. Having adjusted the key light to the right intensity all the other lighting can be based around that key. There is often no need to measure any light other than the key light. But the backlighting can be checked occasionally with the meter and set at not more than about half the power of the key light. There is, however, no fixed ratio of back light to key light; it is a visual thing. You just make sure with the meter that it has not gone higher than it appears to the eye. With backings and back walls in interiors you can measure the amount of light that falls on them to be one third of the key light. But this varies, when judged by eye, according to the colour of the background. If it is a very light colour compared with the key lit area you do not want it to be even as much as a third of the key light. But, apart from the key light, all the other readings are really only assurances that the illumination is not too high or too low compared with the key. They should all be within a range of about one third of the key light for backgrounds and one-half to two-thirds of the key light intensity for backlighting. All other lights are balanced by eye.

The advantage of using a meter for every shot is that you can check that the key light is always of the same brightness. It ensures that exposure is consistent from shot to shot, and you are therefore supplying the laboratory with material which is completely evenly exposed all the way through. This can be done easily with a foot candle meter because it reads directly the amount of light falling on a particular object or area. You place the foot candle meter in the subject position and measure the key light from there.

If you are filming a genuine exterior scene you are likely to be exposing at an aperture setting of T8 and T11. At such stops the depth of field is quite considerable and most things in the frame will be seen in sharp focus.

When you are lighting an "exterior" set built in the studio, in order to retain a feeling of realism you light to as high a key as possible which, in turn, enables you to stop the camera down to an aperture giving sufficient depth of field to match the genuine exterior scenes. It is, however, impracticable in a studio to try to light to T11. On the other hand, a normal studio working aperture of T2·8 would not give nearly enough depth effect to match properly with the outdoor scenes.

On such interior-exterior scenes therefore, one aims to light at a level that is going to prove most convenient yet gain the required effect. One might aim for a minimum of T5·6 for this situation. But it also depends to some extent on the type of set and action within it that is planned for the sequence. For example, if a character is to run right across the field you will have to light an enormous area at one time. For this you need more light than normal. Furthermore, in interior-exteriors you also want to match contrast.

For exteriors, you can use a Weston Master-type reflected light meter. But a foot candle meter would be more convenient for exterior night sequences and also in a situation where there were people inside a vehicle and you were lighting from the outside to balance up with the exterior. In other words, you might have two people sitting in a car and lights coming in through the windscreen to represent the daylight coming in at a realistic height. So you would direct light through the windscreen. And, knowing what exterior value would be set for the view seen through the car, you would adjust the amount of light coming through the windscreen—and for that purpose a foot candle meter would be very handy again, working on the basis of the speed of the film.

Using Eastmancolor negative film, the daylight ASA value is 64 and 100 ASA tungsten. For T2·8 you need a 100 foot candles with 100 ASA. If you use that value on exteriors, you have to open up the lens a fraction more to make allowances for the 85 B filter which is on the camera lens for filming exteriors. If you are lighting two people in the car scene you might know, for example, that the exposure value for those two people is T5·6. It would be appropriate to have the people inside the car slightly less bright than the exterior background in order to preserve the natural balance of subject and background. Consequently, you would light them for the value of T4·5 and stop the lens down to T5·6 which would give a fractionally underexposed interior, in relation to the exterior of the car. But the degree of underexposure would be so very nearly negligible that they would, in fact, appear to be in balance. Probably only under those conditions would you find much use for a foot candle meter on day exteriors. On normal exteriors, you are governed by the existing light as far as setting a T stop is concerned.

On interiors you decide to what stop you are going to light when you go on to a set. The main factor governing that is personal convenience. It is probably a good idea not to use too many lights. If you work with a minimum amount of light it is more under your control and you can work more quickly and be more mobile.

When we go on to the set, except under very special circumstances, we use the zoom lens because at the BBC we use BL cameras for general film work and this has a zoom lens which is, as it were, one piece with the camera. This zoom lens is a T3·3 so at all times you can reckon to have light to at least T4. That then would be the general day interior key light level (for working in the studio, under artificial light). If you start with the assumption that you are going to use the zoom lens then you are well able to handle any possible request to switch to another lens without needing any extra lighting because the zoom lens has the smallest maximum aperture. A prime lens of, say, T2 can reasily be stopped down to the basic working aperture of T4 that was, up to that point, the stop being used on the zoom. Normally you choose the T stop for flexibility unless you have some special shot or sequence in which you must get two extremes of the depth of field sharp.

There is a problem with the very small apertures such as those beyond T16. It is hard to believe that these very small apertures are really correct. You get more reliable results if you use the aperture control to, say, T11, and then thereafter use a neutral density filter. Working at such apertures would not apply in Britain, of course, where the daylight is rarely strong enough, but there are many parts of the world where it would be the case although with 64 ASA colour material, you need very strong, perhaps desert, light to have to stop down beyond about T11. The neutral density filter is satisfactory for minor adjustments but it begins to affect definition if a stronger disc is used than 0·6. The image is, in effect, slightly softened and working with 16 mm such things have to be taken into consideration. Stopping down the lens also increases the contrast, but this effect is mainly visible in black and white. In colour you have a great range of colour densities which disguise the difference.

If you only use the Wratten 85 filter, as one normally would with colour, you would probably have to stop down to, say, T32 or 22 at least. If you use an 85 N6—a combination of the ·6 neutral density filter and the Wratten 85, you can immediately open the lens by two stops—say T11. Opening up gives slightly less contrast, the ND filter gives slightly less contrast also. Combined, they have a considerable effect.

Some cameras have an adjustable shutter which is a helpful adjunct when you want to alter exposure. The Arriflex BL does not have one. But today there is far less need for it. At one time the cameraman used to do his own fades and dissolves in the camera. Or, if he altered the camera speed through necessity, or for fast or slow filmed effects, he could close the shutter down instead of stopping down the aperture, or he could do both together. Or, again, with black and white he could make any adjustments to the exposure that were called for, by adjusting the shutter and thus not affecting the contrast so much by an aperture adjustment, i.e. when not stopping down he could compensate at least partially by closing the shutter to give the desired lack of exposure. Alternatively, he could open the shutter to give more exposure on night exteriors. But as an adjustable shutter added to the noise that the camera made, this mechanism was one of the features dispensed with in the efforts made to design a quieter camera.

15

Studio and Indoor Lighting

TWO BBC PRODUCTIONS, both involving extensive filming in the studio, *Colditz* and *Fall of Eagles*, presented an interesting contrast in lighting techniques—in each case largely determined by the spirit of the production as a whole.

Fall of Eagles was a series dealing with the fall of the Habsburgs and the end of the Austro–Hungarian Empire. One of the episodes directed by Rudolf Cartier, was a glitteringly costumed and staged production reflecting all the brilliance and colour of Viennese high society in the early decades of this century. Among the people featured in the various episodes were the Tzar and Tzarina of Russia, Edward VII, Clemenceau, young Kaiser Wilhelm, and the diplomatic entourage of each country. To reflect the hard glitter of their surroundings and to add to the atmosphere, there was a tendency to light these scenes to a higher key than normal. The overall filler light was also raised to a slightly higher level. The highlights and shadows both had more detail in them than normal, and this helped to set the mood of the scenes.

With more glitter and a more expanded view you reduce the contrast. By generally raising the light level and therefore increasing the relative exposure you are not overexposing as such but the contrast between highlights and shadows is less—it is a flatter type of photography. In *Colditz* where one was aiming for a generally rather more sombre effect to correspond with the atmosphere of a castle prison, the contrast ratios were kept higher.

PROBLEMS ON "FALL OF EAGLES"

Some sequences of *Fall of Eagles* posed some unusual problems both for the lighting and the camerawork owing to the abnormal physical conditions on the set. It was typical of the sort of unexpected technical challenge which awaits the cameraman working as he does in television in an area of film production where he has little say in the way sets are built, sites are chosen and things are prepared generally.

The scene was supposed to be the Russian royal yacht. High level diplomatic negotiations were in progress between the Hohenzollerns and the Habsburgs, when they were trying to divide up Europe each to their own advantage. The set consisted of a deck and a superstructure. One had to bear in mind that Rudolf Cartier is a big thinker and plans action and camera movements accordingly. He made artists not only walk around the deck, but, up on to the superstructure and along it. So a crane was needed in order to cover all their movements, up, along and down again and following the actors around.

The main problem was that this was a very large set and it was built in a studio which was not suitable for taking a structure of such a size, but only a medium or small sized set. Not only was the set too large but it was built in the centre of the studio which meant that the gantries that ran through the centre of the studio, one in each direction (crisscross), were at too high an angle. The light falling on the artists was far too acute.

Consequently the lighting gantries were only about 2 ft above the heads of the actors who stood on the top superstructure. This meant that any lights which would normally be placed on the rails overhead to light the lower deck would cause the artists to be extremely overlit when they walked up on to the superstructure. This problem could not be entirely resolved but was circumvented by placing most of the lights on the gantries furthest away from the centre of the ship. These were the side gantries, which were not really the perfect position for lighting such shots, but at least they avoided burning out the actors on the superstructure. The side gantries were used for lighting both the superstructure and the lower deck. It would not matter if actors passed through the lighting for the lower deck as they were not very close to the lights. Only for some lower deck sequences could some (very little) top lighting be used because it was angled far too high due to the way the set had been constructed.

The lower deck area was key lit from one side and filled from the other. Even on the lower deck the actors were directly under the central gantries which meant that the light from here would have come down on the top of their heads and shoulders. For the superstructure, lamps were placed on the far side and end gantries but round a little more, again with the key maintained from one side (two brutes). Even so, the brutes had to be tipped downwards and were still giving light from a fairly steep angle on subjects on the bottom deck. To compensate for this, fairly substantial fill lights were placed along the far end wall, to lift the general lighting level to that of a bright sunny day.

The two key lights jointly covered the whole usable stage area and care was, of course, taken to ensure that they were shaded off with barn

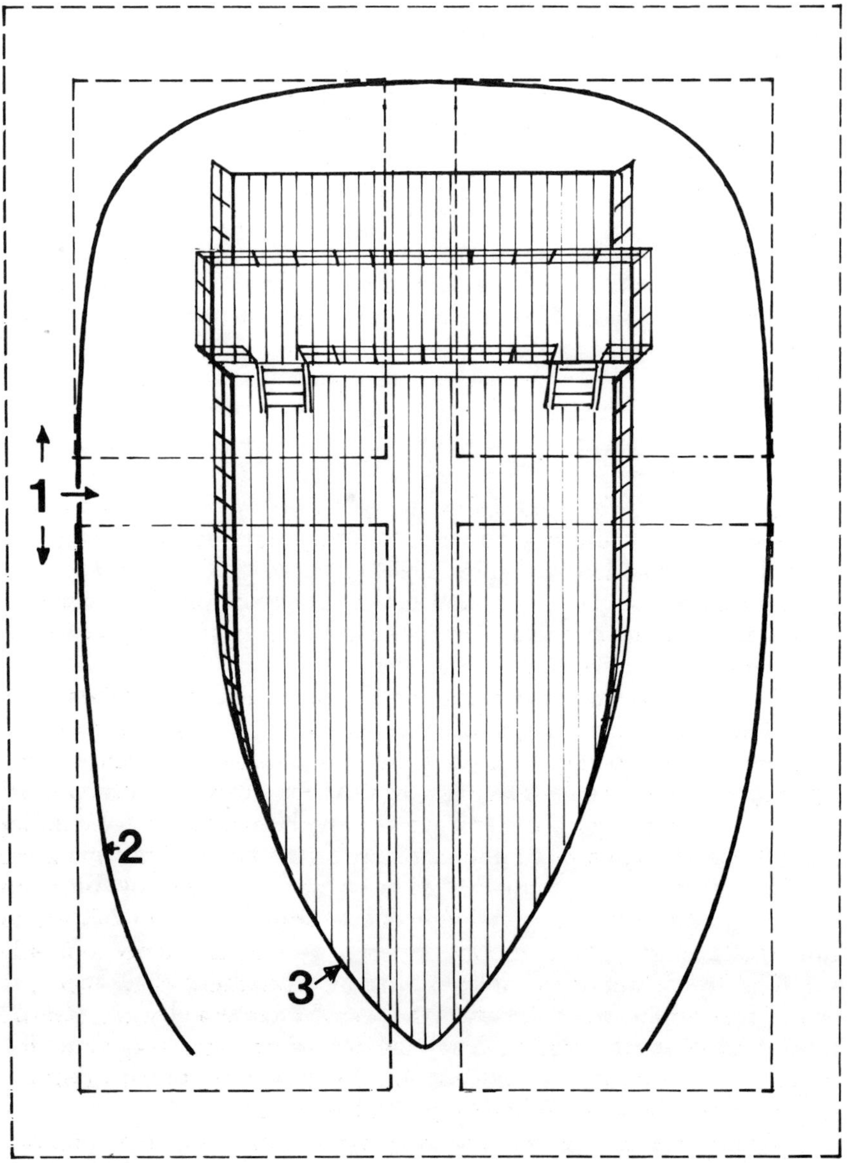

Fall of Eagles Deck scene built in a film studio at Ealing. The rear part had a high superstructure with companionways for access. 1, Studio lighting gantries. 2, Cyclorama background. 3, Rail around fore-deck of ship. 4, Superstructure.

doors to avoid any overlap of the two light beams and the risk of double shadows. The two lamps were placed very close together and the cut off points made to coincide, thus giving the effect over the set of a single lamp. A single brute would not have spread wide enough to cover the area because the lamps had to be so close to the set. You can match up the lit areas on the join between two arcs by observing the effect visually on the floor area. The intensity of the two lamps must also be adjusted to match one another. The light was more or less flat-on to the set but was "lifted" with a kicker—a strong side light to get modelling and some shade. In such a situation you would normally try to avoid shooting in exactly the same direction as the key light was coming from. As the camera comes round you obviously gain modelling. Night sequences on the same set presented fewer problems, as is usually the case.

"Colditz" Lighting

The interior for *Colditz* represented the courtyard of the German castle being used as a prison for allied officers during the Second World War. It was constructed within the large studio at Ealing, occupying most of the available work space. The production under discussion was the second television series on this subject. The first had been done by two different cameramen. So the second presented a *fait accompli* in terms of planning and facilities.

After the first series the whole set was broken down, taken away from Ealing studio and put into store. For the second series the original set was restored to the studio but this time a concrete replica of the original cobbled yard was laid down which provided exceptional realism even to the naked eye, since the irregular patterns of cobbles running in different directions, and features such as drains and manhole covers were moulded in full relief. It was almost indistinguishable from what we had seen a year previously when we went to Colditz Castle to film background material to start the series. As a consequence, not only was there the pictorial appeal for certain shots but there was no need, as there had been in the earlier series, to keep the camera view clear of the floor level. Moreover, the cobbles provided a first class background for any high angle shots and, indeed, absolute freedom of camera movement all round and up to first floor window level.

The entire courtyard provided scope for various close groupings around small areas, doorways, a de-lousing shed, etc. and a permanent basic lighting set-up was provided from gantries and cradles overhead. The lighting layout and plot (the way it was rigged) was repeated on the second series because it was the easiest and quickest thing to do. Consequently the lighting had to be done largely on that basis, although some minor additions were made. Five multi-light incandescent units arranged to cover the studio area with top lighting were rigged to provide a guaranteed minimum light level in shadow areas regardless of the particular lighting being used for any scene. This is, however, an individual, personal technique for use on some large sets. This extra top light gives a threshold exposure so that you do not have to meticulously light every corner of the set that is seen. The whole set has some light on it and even the darkest corners have some faint detail. It is also easier to light a set which already has some light. There is something about lighting a studio set from total blackness whereby the lights do not seem to have the same effect—or brightness. There is too much darkness around to see the set. The answer seems to be massed overhead lights giving even illumination all over. The lights are in sections to cover the various parts. In the case of *Colditz* there were five banks giving minimum illumination to the fioor and walls of the set. For day "exterior" work these lights imitated the sky light—a slight halo of light coming down on to people as opposed to the backlight or three-quarter back illumination. But for night work you would not use it and you want as much blackness as possible.

Apart from this modification the existing lighting gantries were rigged above the courtyard "walls" all round and also a gantry was placed across the open area of yard in each direction. This held a mixture of arcs and large incandescent units which would be suitably filtered. Without moving the lighting it was possible to select overhead lighting for the background and any areas of the courtyard. Four large (incandescent) skypans provided fill light from behind the camera position in each case. Although there was a basic lighting scheme for the scene in general, modifications were called for in specific areas; for example, in a close shot where emphasis was needed on a particular character, or background feature. A general direction for sunlight was established, varying according to the times of day. The direction of this key light is never so critical in large scale shots particularly those containing much activity, as in more "empty" ones because the general movement on the screen does not allow that type of critical judgement. It is possible, as a short cut to save time in rigging the lights, or for convenience, to ignore that aspect of continuity and rely on the effect being carried out even if the key lighting varies from shot to shot. It is much more important where a light lands than the exact angle it comes from.

For *Colditz* the lights, though in the same position, were used in a different way from the first series, because no two cameramen light the same shot in the same way. This was no disadvantage. The set-up was quite workable and could cover everything, up to 360 degrees. In fact, two panning shots did move through 360 degrees following people and also showing the great door, the daylight outside, and the exterior of the castle. *Colditz*, with its pre-rigged lights was not a typical case.

An "Exterior Interior"

Part of the action in *Fall of Eagles* took place on what was supposed to be the train used by Lenin to return to Russia from Switzerland, through Germany. It was night, and the "set" consisted of three authentic wooden carriages dating from the 1890s. The action was supposed to be 1917. Lenin, his wife and a friend were in the central coach. It was small, but full of people with children and the suitcases and other baggage of people travelling home. From a cameraman's viewpoint, the main problem was one of lighting—trying to get as moody an effect as possible, bearing in mind that any shot that was taken, apart from a close-up, was going to show quite a large portion of the carriage as background (which also had to be lit) so that all the lights would have to be hidden. The carriage was a small square box with seats in it, and had well-loaded luggage racks. When the racks did not contain luggage we put it there because it was only with the help of this luggage that we could hope to hide the lights we needed from camera view.

Behind the three carriages on the end of the train was a flat waggon onto which we had driven a 15 kW alternator in a Volkswagen which could supply power to the lights as the train moved along. We shot the whole time with the train moving because we also wanted the movement of the people although the blinds were drawn so you would not see any landscape going past and it was, in any case, dark outside. We had chosen actual night time for shooting because if it were light outside you would be bound to see it through, or at the corners of the blinds at some stage or other.

As people in the carriage were also moving around all the time—getting up, going to the end, coming through the doors, coming into the foreground—so they were inevitably going to walk in and out of the light sources. These lamps were very close to the people anyway as they moved about—often only 2–3 ft away.

Carriages were at that time lit by candles, and we had these glowing in small candle brackets at the sides, so the lighting had to resemble the character and mood created by these "practicals". Consequently, nothing should be very bright. There could also be an area or two with no light at all as long as it could be followed through with a highlight so that you could see what was going on. This could not really be done with the zoom lens, which had a maximum aperture of T3·3. So we had to use prime lenses on the camera with apertures around the region of T2. We could then use inky dinks, which are only 100 watts—a leftover from black and white days when you were working with 250–300 ASA materials and could afford to employ very low power lighting. Now, with colour, such lamps have limited effect but being small they could be hidden behind luggage and when people walked past them the difference in intensity between 2 ft and 3 ft was not very great. If more powerful light had been used the people would have been "burned out" much more easily. These lights were attached to the luggage racks with clamps, because there was no scope for using stands or polecats (long expanding poles with a spring on either end) both of which would have been visible and could not be explained away very easily in an 1890 carriage. Another difficulty was the hiding of cables that were supplying power to these lamps placed all around the carriage. They could in some cases be run down to and across the floor, or sometimes because of the inaccessibility of the lamps in relation to the entrance point of the cables, they had to be strung across the ceiling and held in position with tape. In that case we had to make sure to keep light off that area and preserve it as a black region in the picture.

In the confined space of the carriage, because of the close proximity of lights and people, we used spun glass diffuser or "Windolite"—a fine wire mesh with a cellulose covering—to reduce the intensity of certain lights. The complete lighting set-up can only be explained by reference to the diagram on page 166. There is a door A; at the other end a similar door, B. There was a seat C on either side facing door B, opposite another seat D; both Ds were facing door A, so the two people each sitting on C and D were facing each other. Behind C on the back wall was a half luggage rack and behind D there was another luggage rack which also went over into the next seat, E, which was facing B. So there was a double rack, E and D, and so on through the carriage, four sets of seats and a single seat at the end by door B. The camera was shooting through door A for the long shots because there was a soldier coming through door B. He fought his way down the crowded carriage so that he could talk to Lenin who was sitting (beside his wife) on the seat D facing door A where the camera was. The longest shot we could get was covered with the 10 mm lens which was the widest I could use. If we moved back any further we would include the door jamb G which would cut off the people sitting in seat D. The end of seat C was out of picture hidden behind the door jamb, which governed the widest shot. All the lights were placed on the luggage racks and hidden from the camera view by luggage which we put on the racks. There was a light up on the rack over C (right) that covered Lenin and his wife who were sitting at D (right). As a small kicker for them we had another kicker on the E D rack on the left-hand side. A kicker gives a soft modelling highlight because the light on C, the key light, was not very strong as we were working at T2 and at night. These were inky dinks. I took the condenser out of the key light in order to obtain the maximum spread, and the minimum intensity. Everyone else in the carriage was lit and cross lit from the racks but we did not want too much light.

All the lights were operative for the whole shooting, though occasionally for a close-up I would cut out one and put in another, from a different direction depending on the shooting angle. All the shooting was from A towards D or from the centre of the corridor coming across to C where the main artists were sitting. You light the whole thing and hide the cables, because if you were to bring in another lamp you would have to recable for that, which wastes time. The cables were run along the side, hidden in dark patches, or had an overcoat thrown over. Or we had one of the crowd artists lean over and block a lamp or cable from the camera view. This sort of thing can be a problem.

The alternator was at the B end. There was another carriage beyond, with a large glass door between so there was activity there with people passing by, etc. On the outside of our own carriage H, we had clamped two larger lights (750 watt pups) with blue filters to shine on to the outside of the next carriage to denote moonlight. On the carriage behind were two more pups shining on to the main carriage so that when people came through door B they would be lit with the blue light, as though they were coming in from the moonlight from direction J. When the door opened, a shaft of moonlight came in to the darkened carriage. The ordinary light in the carriage followed. Another carriage at end A was used for gear and excess people. We never shot through the glass door— which was always a background from which the Russian soldiers emerged. Whatever position we shot from, there was always plenty of depth behind. There was a slightly lower light level in the carriage beyond in order not to draw attention to it particularly. Only movement in the background would be visible.

The main feed for the cables could not come through door B because artists were coming through and the door had to be opened and closed. But a window was opened at K, we slipped the main feed through, and closed the window as much as possible, and then connected all lamps to the main box at K.

The candles were not killed by the lighting, because light was kept off the candle flames and their backgrounds. Practical lamps will register unless you use, say, a T 3·3 lens, where there is simply not enough exposure. Also you cannot alter the aperture much when you change the lenses. If you are using prime lenses of small aperture you will lose all effect of the practical lights. When you cut from material shot on one to that on another it will be noticeable. So, with low key practical lights, you have to light to a wide aperture and keep to it throughout the sequence in that set.

The practical lights (L) were candles on a bracket with glass round it between each pair of seats. The lighting followed this basis. Such a scene should have quite high contrast but if the lighting tended to be too high in contrast, a very diffused 250 w basher was brought in beside the camera.

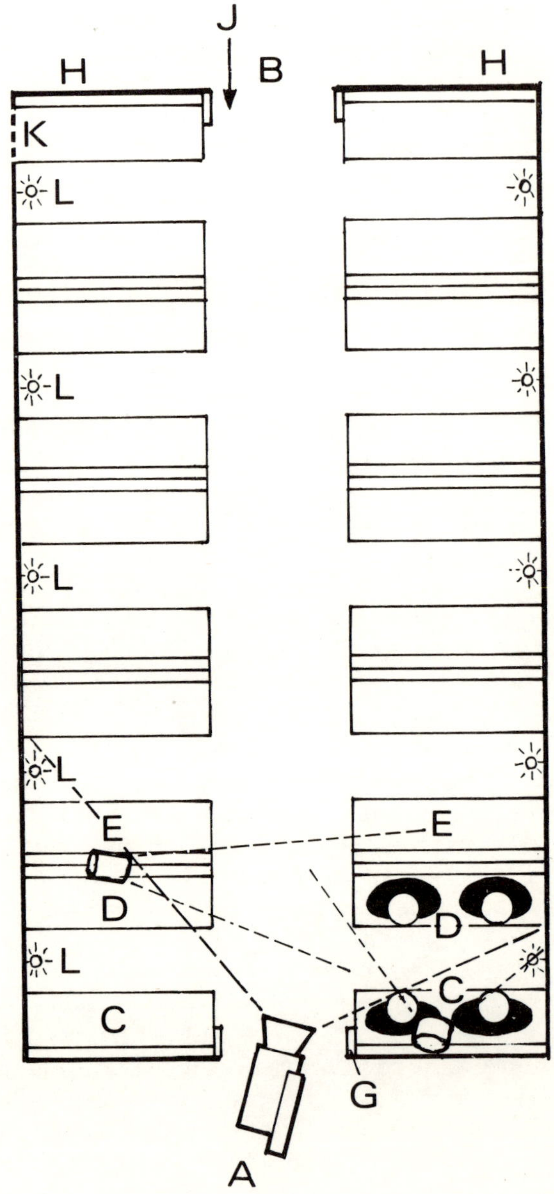

Fall of Eagles. The interior of a railway carriage (plan view) on the train in which Lenin was returning to Russia. Facing bench seats were arranged down each side. The curtains were drawn and the carriage was ostensibly lit by candles, one either side between each pair of facing seats. A, door, B, far door, C, D, E seats. L, (practical) candle lamps. G, door jamb. H, two 750 W lamps outside. J, direction of moonlight. K, window, inlet for power cables to distribution box. For a description of the sequence, see text.

For day shots the blinds were up and daylight came in, all lamps were removed and on long shots a little overall flood light from the camera position was provided to reduce the contrast between areas near the windows and the centre of the carriage, which was quite dark. Then, for close-ups a small inky dink provided a little modelling.

16

"Night" Effect Lighting

NIGHT EFFECTS in the studio are achieved not so much by employing a low level of light as by implying the feeling of night in the character of the lighting. For studio night effect scenes the same lighting principles apply as in similar night scenes shot outside—moonlight or one key. Such scenes actually match one another quite well when juxtaposed in the same film.

The lighting for "night" starts from black and is built up from that, often relying on highlights in the scene to put some detail into the large shadow areas. This is easier in the studio than outside. Whereas in a real night situation very few surfaces actually catch the light and reflect it very efficiently, indoors many features on the set tend to be naturally shiny. Often, in fact, because of this problem with night exterior street scenes, the surface of the road is sprayed with a fine water mist beforehand so that the resulting highlights give life to the dark areas.

Atmospheric lighting for night shots depends greatly on how many people appear in the scene and how they move about. One thing is permanent. At some point or other on the set it has to be evident that there is some moonlight. In other words the basic key light is a slightly blued arc, the idea of "cold" moonlight being an established cliché. This also means that if you are going to make a great play of this aspect, you must have only one key and one shadow. You want to see the moonlight effect and shadow demonstrated by actor movement, and so give the mood of a night exterior. If you are able to have the effect of practical lights (as, for example, we had with an overhead light that shone at night in the courtyard at Colditz Castle), or a light shining from a window, then that, in contrast with the blue moonlight, can be a warm incandescent light. You can use this as a contrasting effect to the moonlight so that you have now allowed yourself three different types of lighting—moonlight, deep shadow, and warm practical light for people to pass through, stand under or stand against. The action of each particular scene determines whether you may be permitted to bring all these into play, not all at the same time, but in steps, or in particular cases. When you know what the action will be you build up in your mind the kind of effects to be used and then transfer that to a physical creation of these different types of lighting through which people can pass, or move from one area to the other.

When you are in the areas of the set which consist mainly of moonlight then the moonlight is the strongest source—the key. If actors move from moonlight and shadow into the area lit by the practical light (e.g. the overhead courtyard light in *Colditz*, (see below), then that takes over in intensity and in effect, from the moonlight. The need for a single shadow does mean that there has to be enough power from one lamp. In some cases, as in *Colditz*, this can only be achived by using a wide aperture lens. On all night situations we like to be able to work at around T1·8–2·5. It is not only easier to light that way (one source—one shadow) but also if you are doing real night exteriors in streets or in any normal night location outside the studio, using a wide aperture lens, all practical lights like street lights, shop windows, buses, cars, etc. are picked up quite naturally as a background. This is excellent for lending a feeling of night atmosphere to the scene. If, under these conditions, you are working with a zoom lens whose maximum aperture is T3·5, you are at an immediate disadvantage, not only because you have less effect from your own lighting and consequently need more, but you have cancelled out much natural lighting, sometimes giving peculiar looking results.

In the *Colditz* studio set, we used a T1·8 lens at T2. Although we were working under controlled conditions we wanted the one-key-light effect, so the wide aperture was handy. In close-ups we could use as much light as we needed. But the main long shot sets the whole key of the effect. The main factors in controlling that are the power of the light and the position you can put it in (which can limit its power) in relation to the sensitivity of the film. With a single light source you may be working near the limits.

A wide aperture lens is often a 10 mm, where the depth of field is usually ample. You would not use this lens so much in close-ups because of distortion, but this depends on the circumstances. On *Colditz* we worked with a set of prime lenses with maximum apertures ranging from T1·8 to 2·8. Even for close-ups on "night" sets there was little lighting to do. The "night" scenes were shot with prime lenses, the "day" with the zoom. The prime lenses were used for night exteriors.

For night sequences on *Colditz*, in the courtyard at night, there were two basic practical lights—large industrial shaded lights on corner brackets, one over the entrance door and another over the entrance to the prisoners' cells under which the soldiers patrolled the perimeter of the gaol. Apart from these, there was only moonlight. Occasional lights in the windows could enhance the night effect but with lights out at 11 o'clock at night, any sequence taking place after that time had to be under the practical light or moonlight. There was a photoflood in each practical light, which gave illumination only under the lamp housing itself. We then had to reinforce the effect of that light on the ground by using an incandescent from the rail—2K lamps, flooded or half spotted, according to the effect required. It is axiomatic that a practical light, no matter what sort of light, always shines in the background surface to the picture whether a wall or the ground. For night, you try to arrange the light to be as near three quarter lighting as you can. If you have a long shot of a courtyard and there are two sentries patrolling, your key moonlight, as it were, is either absolute backlight or three quarter backlight from a brute, spreading right across the courtyard, and in the background is the warm (incandescent) practical lamp. The moonlight brute may have a half strength 85 filter on it which makes it slightly blue compared with a full 85. Hence you have the contrast of cold moonlight and warm practical lights from windows, doors, etc. You can keep the cold moonlight behind the subject in most shots but if you are doing a reverse shot, you can split the difference—keeping a large shadow area on the individual, cheating the light slightly when repositioning or switching on another one to represent moonlight. You try to avoid situations with reverse shots that will lead you into difficult or unrealistic lighting set-ups. When shooting night scenes, you cannot get a good night effect by having a frontal key. So you must think one shot ahead. You cannot do a second three quarter back lighting if you do a reverse shot, so a half side lighting has to do. It is not as good, but you have to compromise.

A scene in *Colditz* where moonlight, shadow and practical lights were all involved was one in which the security officer and the padre were seen walking across the courtyard discussing the fact that the chapel had been closed. The first shot in this sequence was a long shot of the entire courtyard. The two men came into the picture backlit by moonlight. They moved towards the camera, stood under the warm courtyard light and carried on their conversation, which was covered by close-ups. In the background were a couple of windows in deep shadow. These windows were softly lit from inside with a warm light representing room light, giving atmosphere and depth to the picture. When the men finished speaking, one moved out of picture into the darkness. The other walked through moonlight and then into darkness where he opened a door in the far distance and a stream of warm light came into the courtyard to show that he was going inside. The camera was left with only the moonlight falling on the courtyard cobbles.

Very little front fill light under the camera was used for these scenes despite the severe downward key illumination. The more simple the lighting the easier it is to handle—and the more effective it is. In the long shot the practical light itself was visible—necessary to account for it—but at other times you allow the light to be inferred by imagining such a source yourself, without actually showing it.

If the floor or ground in the "night" set is very plain and you are shooting an open area from a relatively high angle, you have to rely on the effect of one deep moving shadow which is either seen with the artist in the shot or moves across the field of view before the artist enters the shot. It is pleasant to see a shadow suddenly coming into shot, and then becoming the shot, so that all your interest is focused on it by the time the subject, who is making the shadow, comes in to the shot as well. I like the suspense of a night situation where this shadow emerges. It is, perhaps, a good idea to try for shadow effects in any shot that is angled downwards in night scenes even if the floor is not a good one. With the principle of lighting for night being to use three-quarter or full back lighting, the shadows always precede or run forward from the artist. You can play with these shadows.

With "night" sequences on the set for *Fall of Eagles* (page 158), the various lighting problems encountered for "day" scenes were considerably reduced. Night sequences usually give you considerably more licence when working in sets or circumstances which are far from ideal.

If you have to "cover up" where the set does not provide enough scope or where the situation does not permit ideal placing of lights, in "night" sequences you can often throw a shadow over the offending part or make a patch of light in another place to make up for some missing detail.

For the night sequences on *Fall of Eagles* we were using the same set but in this case the whole boat was ringed with lanterns. There was a three-quarter back arc light which gave the moonlight effect (with a half 85 to make it appear slightly blue). Then incandescent light was added to give a feeling of the light coming from the lanterns or a light that one never saw, such as a masthead light or a light put in by the authorities perhaps to light up the dance area on the deck where the people on board danced the polka. In such a scene, the lamps you put in to light various areas, can be adjusted as you wish to different degrees of blue to give a night effect, with a half or full blue filter in the incandescent light which would bring it to the same colour temperature as the arc lights with a half 85 (balanced up to moonlight). If you want not quite pure moonlight and not incandescent, you put in a half blue to make it a little colder. You can play with this in little patches here and there to enhance the night effect. Night lighting is really a patchwork of light whereas daylighting is *overall* light. There are more shadows in night than there are in day. There are more lit areas in day than there are at night. (The ratios of shadow and highlight account for the basic difference between day and night and why day-for-night shooting is not really the same as proper night shooting, i.e. shooting at night.)

In night lighting you deliberately induce shadows, by lighting selected areas and leaving others out. It is an artificial means of getting an impression of what it is like. The whole effect is an illusion in any case, as indeed is all photography. You look at the scene before planning the lighting and you picture in your mind what you would expect to see, or not to see, if it were real night. It is really a question of using your imagination. You may often find that the most characteristic effect of a situation comes from forces acting outside the field of view itself—contributions or influences from imagined causes that are appropriate to the scene you are about to shoot. The lighting can then be based on these, or they can, at minimum, supply a part of the character there.

You must, of course, think of all this in the context of the action that is to take place and where it will happen. According to what that action is, you may want to see it or not, or a part of it only. On this particular set we had a single four and a half minute continuous shot, tracking right the way round the rail of the boat with two people, who were talking all the time. All the props, ropes, lights and lanterns were constantly passing in front of the camera as it was shooting from outside the "boat". The two people moved from the well lit dance floor to the underneath of the superstructure which was quite dark, being night. But they were silhouetted against the lanterns and against the dancers in the lit area with a little moonlight coming through various gaps in the superstructure and onto the artists. They then came out into the moonlight which was tinged with the incandescent light of the lanterns. So there was blue light on one side and incandescent light on the other to give this effect. Then they walked into pure incandescent, because out of picture there might have been a mast lamp shining down on to the deck. There are many such possibilities to provide a reason for adding light without having to see the actual sources. In this case there was a mast but no mast light, although there could have been. This all helps to create the illusion. The two people then came round into almost full moonlight which became rear moonlight from another side of the ship as the camera moved round the set. To avoid the possibility of the now frontal moonlight looking too flat it was broken up with ropes and other dark features of the superstructure through which it shone. The superstructure also served a purpose in the composition in lighting so that the people were alternately obscured, half-seen and fully visible, but moving all the time so that at those points where you could not actually see them you were still with them, as it were. This movement, through varied lighting reinforced the sense of location, impression of moonlight and atmosphere. This is a very natural type of effect. The long, constantly moving coverage was a typical Rudi Cartier shot—where the subjects keep in motion the whole time through more than 180 degrees. The camera was outside the set beyond the deck rail, tracking round the whole time between the ship and the cyclorama and with the top of the deck rail in the foreground.

The lanterns on the *Fall of Eagles* deck scenes were practical lights, 60 watt domestic bulbs, behind yellow coloured lantern glasses. The effect that these were supposed to give was mimicked to a certain extent by the lighting. In certain places the lantern effect was supported or followed. The scope for this was seen in rehearsal before the shot was taken, and final adjustments were made to the lighting to take this into account. The lengthy take was a medium shot (tight two-shot) at an evenly maintained distance from the actors and no adjustments to the lighting were called for. The next cut was to a different area of the ship.

Although there is usually a high general light level where any filming takes place the actors are subconsciously aware of acting in a night sequence because the whole scene in a night shot is muted. So they become more stealthy or surreptitious in their behaviour as the atmosphere of the scene demands.

One thing which should annoy any cameraman is when, if he has lit a deep night sequence to appear like that, he finds that the whole light level has been brought right up when the material is transmitted. This sometimes happens if a director or producer sees the material on a monitor when rehearsing the VTR. If he brightens up the picture the whole overall effect is destroyed. Instead of being night it gives a sort of dusk effect with far too much detail visible. This you could say is a disadvantage to the cameraman supplying a properly exposed negative. Such a negative gives the producers the opportunity of revealing detail that should not be there.

There are occasions in viewing broadcasts when you think you have just seen a clumsy cut. It may look as if you, as cameraman, have done a couple of bad shots. But it may, in fact, be due to an intermediate shot being removed from the sequence. The lighting effects too, can be interfered with in much the same way, and with just as free a hand. On *Colditz* only one scene was tampered with in this manner and that, oddly enough, was a day for night sequence, and the only one in the series. A sequence covering the arrival by rail (shot on the Bluebell line) of the commandos was shot as deep night and had that effect in the rushes. When, however, the sequence came up on the television screen it looked like a badly exposed day shot. When, again, later in the same series, viewers saw a sequence showing an escaping prisoner at night, the same thing happened. This was all done in the VTRing, as instructed by the director.

17

Filtering with Daylight and Artificial Light

COLOUR MATERIALS are manufactured to be used with lighting of a specific colour quality in order to give results in which the colours are correctly balanced, i.e. as near as possible to the way they appear to the human eye. Film is usually supplied in one of two such forms: those designed for use under artificial (tungsten filament) lights and those for use in daylight. The quality of these light sources is defined by colour temperature which is measured in kelvins (K). The higher the colour temperature of a light source the higher its blue content. The lower the colour temperature the greater the red content. On this scale artificial light is taken to be light from sources which emit wavelengths averaging to about 3200K and daylight is rated at 5600K. These figures are sometimes expressed in mireds (short for micro reciprocal degrees) which are calculated by dividing the kelvin figure into one million. The mired rating has the advantage that the same degree of colour shift at any point on the scale is represented by the same mired figure, whereas a given change in the kelvin figure has a far greater effect at the low temperature end than at the high.

If a film designed for use in daylight is exposed in artificial (tungsten) illumination insufficient exposure is given to the blue sensitive layer, and the result is an image with an overall red bias or cast.

A film designed for use in artificial light, being exposed in daylight would appear excessively blue. It is possible to adjust the colour balance from one standard to the other by placing a suitable filter over the camera lens or the light source. It is normally more convenient to place it over the lens, but there are various occasions when the lights must be filtered in order to adjust their colour quality.

Although there are various approaches to the problems of filtering for colour balance certain methods recommend themselves on the grounds of practical convenience.

The colour of material shot outdoors is, of course, affected by the quality of light at different times of day. The colour temperature varies constantly through the day. At the BBC, however, we use neither a colour temperature meter nor filter on the camera for this type of correction but rely on the laboratory to keep the material in balance through the day. It would be a waste of time reading colour temperatures and filtering for every shot. Provided you do not shoot within about an hour of sun-up or sunset, the latitude of Eastmancolor negative film copes with the differences of daylight.

The rushes at the BBC are normally black and white, and colour prints, when required, are usually uncorrected. Occasionally, however, a corrected colour print is ordered up—if there is some doubt about the colour quality in a particular shot. Moreover, as you cannot print individual shots in colour, it must be the whole 400 ft roll or nothing—to avoid handling the negative in an effort to remove the particular shot needed.

With the advent of colour photography for television the range of filters used on the camera for normal shooting has become greatly reduced. Those mainly in use nowadays are neutral density filters and pola screens. UV reducing filters are used also, though only in certain conditions where an excess of ultra-violet radiation is present in the scene such as in the air, on mountains, etc. But the glass of any filter compensates to some extent for the presence of UV radiation. Other filters in use are the Wratten 85 and the 81 EF (= a half 85) which gives you a slight blue cast and is used when filming day for night.

Mixed Sources

The Wratten 85 filter is on the camera the whole time when shooting exteriors in daylight because the Eastman film used is colour balanced for 3200K and is an "interior" stock. It is also used when you film with mixed light sources. There are two alternative procedures for filming in a room lit by daylight through a window as well as artificial light from inside. The daylight is permitted to come through the window unobstructed and, with an 85 filter on the camera, all the incandescent lights are raised with blue filters to the daylight colour temperature.

Another way of doing it is to remove the 85 filter from the camera lens, use the incandescent lights unfiltered and place 85 gelatine sheeting over the windows so that the colour temperature of the daylight coming through the window is balanced correctly to the film stock and the lights. If you are using arc lights in conjunction with daylight indoors or outdoors you need no blue filter, because the arc has a higher colour temperature than daylight. However, because it is a little deficient in the green part of the spectrum a light green filter is placed on the arc to bring the colour temperature down to 5600K and achieve a perfect balance with daylight. The 85 filter remains on the camera, as it does wherever you are shooting with unfiltered daylight. Arcs are too cold to blend with daylight if the arc is using WF (white flame) carbons. With the LCT (low colour temperature) carbon in the arc you use a straw filter to balance the arc with daylight. Not many TV cameramen use these carbons as they are not as stable or high in intensity as a WF carbon, which is important for exposure.

The practical decision between these two methods is determined by the cameraman's preferences when working in a confined space, in conjunction with the fact that filtering windows is a tricky and arduous job. If the filter is not absolutely flat there is a great risk of picking up flare and reflections from the lights being used in the room. In most cases it is probably much easier to leave the windows as they are, put a filter on the camera and filter the lights.

There are often practical problems with fixing the filter to the window, avoiding vibration or wind disturbance, etc. A window is not necessarily an easy shape to cope with. The filter can be attached inside or outside without the edges being seen (usually with adhesive tape). A more recent material is a form of filter that lies flat on a window pane and can be readily peeled off again. But it is expensive and has to be cut to size and shape. In TV conditions there is no one with the time available to do this and time is the most expensive factor in film production. Moreover, in certain situations the windows themselves cause difficulties. Suppose you are several floors up in a building and the windows are inaccessible from the outside yet allow no disguise for taping material to the inside. There is little that can be done with window filtering in such a case.

Filtering on camera and lights is easily controlled, quick and easy to effect and should be recommended as the better method in television filming.

Colditz contained sequences involving the mixture of daylight with an existing interior lighting arrangement. The actual entrance doors to the built courtyard backed on to the entrance door to the studio. By raising the entrance door, a backing placed outside the studio wall, about 15 ft from the constructed courtyard, could be used as a genuine exterior of the view outside the castle gates so that vehicles, troops, etc. could be brought in through the gates during the shots. This produced the difficulty of balancing exterior light with interior-"exterior" light to give it the same colour balance. In this case the genuine depth outside the courtyard gates gave a realistic effect.

The lighting for such situations is tackled in a particular way. The genuine daylight outside determines the way in which you light the interior and the kind of lighting used indoors. You have a choice of the type of light source but you have to make sure that all the filters are correct in order to balance everything. You are using exactly the same lights in the studio area as in previous shots not mixed with genuine daylight, but different filters on them, because you have to put a Wratten 85 filter on the camera to balance the normal daylight to the film stock. With the 85 filter on the camera you must alter all the filters on other light sources. If, in previous shots in the studio, you did not have real daylight as a source, you would have been using an 85 filter on the arcs but no filter on the camera or on the incandescent lamps. Now, with an 85 on the camera to cope with the genuine daylight outside, a WF green filter must be placed over the arcs to bring their colour temperature into balance with the 85 filter on the camera. An arc with a green filter is correctly balanced to pure daylight, and so, as you have balanced the daylight to the film stock the arcs are correct also. Any incandescent lamps must have their colour temperature raised because they have a low colour temperature relative to that now prevailing. So to raise them to the generally raised colour temperature you put either a half or full blue filter over them. (This applies only when you are using an 85 filter on the camera. If you do not use an 85 filter on the camera you use your arcs with an 85 and do not filter the incandescents.)

You do not necessarily have to use the 85 filter on the camera only when you are using proper daylight. You may be using the 85 on the camera in a studio with daylight excluded if you need the filter for some other reason. In that case you must make sure that all sources are correctly balanced—you still have to use blues on incandescents and green on arcs.

The light loss is not considerable in either case. An 85 filter on the camera reduces the film speed by half a stop only. The trouble is with incandescent lamps, which lose 50 per cent of illumination with a blue filter. This means increasing the light power, i.e. using a 5K instead of 2K lamp. With arcs you lose less with a green filter than with the 85. The scenes can be matched by laboratories despite the involvement of different lighting.

PSEUDO-DAYLIGHT

In a studio set up with pseudo (incandescent or arc) daylight coming through the window, one approach is to use no filter on either the camera or the incandescent lights but to fit any arcs with 85 gelatines. The other way is to leave the 85 on the camera, blue the incandescents with the IL blue (incandescent light) gelatine and put a green gelatine on the arc. In this situation an arc would serve as a convincing sunlight through the window but to increase its blueness, a half 85 could be used on the arc. For such a case the arc provides the dominant intensity and a good clear and sharp shadow. For the effect of sun through the window it is not so much the power of the light that matters as the whiteness of it, i.e. the blueness relative to the other lighting. For this the half 85 is ideal.

A 10K incandescent lamp could be used instead of an arc, although it does not give such a hard sharp shadow. To whiten the light fractionally the lamp requires a quarter blue if all other incandescents are plain and there is no filter on the camera. If there is genuine daylight coming through the windows and there has to be a mixture of sources (and it is impossible to filter these windows with 85 sheet material) then you put an 85 on the camera and blue filter the incandescent lights, and put a green filter on any arc lights used. In a studio set-up where you are using an 85 on the camera and the "sunlight" is a 10K you can force a differentiation between this "sun" and the other incandescents by only half blueing the less powerful lights and using a full blue on the 10K, but there is a danger of the whole set-up looking rather warm. It is better to keep everything fully blued. If no arcs are involved you can remove all filters, except on the 10K which could have a quarter or half blue gelatine on it.

When evening light is seen through a window, the same rules apply because the intensity of the light, though evening, is still greater although the whole key will have dropped. If you are setting this up yourself, you can use incandescents unfiltered and the camera without a filter. The "daylight" outside must be colder. The reverse applies if you are shooting through a window. You keep unfiltered incandescent light in the room and filters on the outside lights. In real conditions where the camera is filtered the incandescent light inside the room would be very warm. If too warm, a half blue filter can be used to reduce that effect.

Day for Night Filtering

The filter used in day for night filming (see page 171) is rather like a half or quarter 85 filter; it undercorrects for the use of 3200K film in daylight, so giving a slight blue effect. If the 85 were removed altogether the picture would be much too blue. It is therefore replaced by a similar filter of lower density—commonly the 81EF, equivalent to a half of 85. It is possible in the studio situations, using arcs for daylight, to put a half or quarter 85 gelatin on the arc lights instead of a full 85 if you want the key light to be more, or less, blue. A half 85 could be used if you needed more actual intensity from the arcs where it did not really matter if the arc were slightly more blue—for example, where most of this light is falling on the background or, if it were falling on the artists where it was not frontal light.

Filters with Long Focus Lenses

When you are using a very long focus lens the depth of field is not very great even if the lens is stopped down quite a long way. If a filter is added there is a slight loss of definition. Rear-mounted gelatine filters do cause a focus shift which is noticeable when working around full aperture. You do not have thickness problems with thin plastic filters (which despite the material used have a fairly hard surface).

Filters for Special Effects

There is a glass diffusion filter, which, like gauzes, gives an overall diffusion in the picture. Or, the centre of the gauze can be clear to allow the diffusion to be varied by the setting of the lens aperture. Or you can smear petroleum jelly on a glass sheet held in front of the lens to give a clear picture surrounded by a diffused area. A "star" filter has crossed fine lines which turn every highlight into a star. There is also the faceted or prismatic optical attachment which gives multiple images of the same subject. The plane filters in use at the BBC are optical flats. Unless you are using a very long focus lens there is little focus shift. Gelatine filters are not very efficient nor economical to use. They attract dust and dirt and are very difficult to clean without scratching. You can use them to cut a neutral density to the shape of a subject you wish to partially reduce in density but such half filter methods are not possible with television work, where there is insufficient time to carry them out. Graduated ND filters are used, but confined to static shots. The normal sequence of neutral density filter is ·3, ·6 and ·9 (one, two and three stops equivalent, respectively).

Occasionally special effect filters are used for particular occasions. Such equipment can be hired, and this is the most economical way of doing it. Such hiring firms should check all equipment before sending it out as there is nothing worse than arriving on location to use a piece of equipment that does not work.

Fluorescent Tubes

A special problem arises in available light work when fluorescent tubes provide the chief source of illumination. It is particularly noticeable if you are shooting in a factory under these lights with perhaps some ambient light from windows, etc. The problem is that the camera shutter operates out of phase with the frequency of pulsating light emitted from the fluorescent tubes. This gives rise to a "beating" or strobing effect of varying exposure on the film. Some tubes are more prone to this effect than others but it is very noticeable if the tube itself is in the picture. If, however, you are also using your own lights, then according to how much light comes from them or from the fluorescent lights the beating effect begins to diminish. In medium and close-up shots you can completely overcome the problem of the beating fluorescent and still show the fluorescent light and its illumination in the background.

Fluorescent lighting is deficient in certain wavelengths, depending on the type of lamp. Daylight fluorescent tubes lack red content. This is made up for in the so-called "warm white" tubes which have a moderate red content. But, because the spectrum of a fluorescent tube is discontinuous, the film tends to react to it in a different manner from the human eye. Consequently the actual colour quality of the photographed scene may not emerge as expected. Kodak recommend that if you are shooting under daylight tubes the balance can be corrected with a 40 red filter, and with "warm white" you use no filter, as a basic recommendation. In the US, where more types of tube are in use, the range of corrections is more complex. Some increase in exposure would be called for with a filter, and making a test would be one way of ascertaining by a prior view with particular lamps. With negative film, however, colour corrections should be well within the capability of the laboratory when they make the print.

A green filter which compensates for predominantly fluorescent lighting does not affect flesh tones very much, so when it is used the resultant print is better balanced.

Discharge lamps such as in street lighting are no problem for general views where such lighting is characteristic of the scene and would be accepted as such. With close-up, however, you could control the light in the immediate vicinity by blacking out or niggering off the street lighting and introducing your own illumination locally.

18

Effects and Limitations

TELEVISION IS CATERING for an audience which, for years, has been accustomed to the quality, breadth and fine detail of special techniques applied in the feature film industry. Such effects are often so spectacular that they form the larger part of the film content—indeed it has become the practice of late to make such films purely as a vehicle for some new and ingeniously devised spectacular effect—and to give them advance publicity stressing just this. There is no doubt that such effects do make some considerable impact on the popular market, no matter how vacuous the actual film content, and have helped to retain for the cinema some of the audience appeal which has so diminished since the advent of television. It has been, as everyone knows, the policy of film production companies using conventional picture-theatre outlets to stress just those aspects in entertainment in which television is, or was, deficient at the various stages of its development—colour, wide screen, 3-D, stereophonic sound, spectacular effects and art-house films. This is quite apart from changes in presentation, originating from the essentially big-business character of the traditional feature production entrepreneurs. Eventually this led to a situation where only split-market production would answer the problem. Films were to be made for cinema presentation but with one eye firmly on their eventual use in television. Inevitably the large studios have become more preoccupied with pure television productions in recent years, resulting in a dearth of high quality films from traditional sources. But the spectacular, effects or "action" film carries on regardless.

Meanwhile, technology, in the shape of electronics, has caught up with ordinary film-making methods and in television at least, overhauled it to the extent that electronic images of the highest quality can be produced quite easily for the small screen, and special effects, essentially electronic in nature, can be achieved for any programme at the flick of a switch. Some of these effects may be similar to those which, by traditional filming methods, can only be achieved with elaborate set-ups that are both time consuming and costly. Others are effects which a feature film company might put together in the laboratory. In the feature film industry, now working to tighter schedules, far fewer effects are carried out in the camera. It may serve only to provide the necessary components from which the laboratory may build a convincing sequence by various forms of trickery—or the camera (and thus the cameraman) may even opt out of the obligation of producing effects at all, beyond some ordinary corrective measures called for in particular situations.

In filming for television sometimes the reverse situation obtains. A cameraman can be in a position something like those in the feature industry of pre-war days. He must do whatever he can in the camera. This is because he is not working in circumstances comparable with those in the feature industry where a laboratory can indulge in various experiments in effects for a particular production. Nor is the finance available for other than high-output routine processing. In the BBC the editor may well be cutting the first production in a series even before the camera crew has completed the shooting. The director may not even have had a chance to select the takes he would like to use. (Although this approach is undoubtedly affecting the quality of some material produced by the Corporation, it is, like so many short cuts, the result of the need for an enormous output to keep the network supplied with programmes.)

To the television cameraman, traditional camera techniques for effects (including some dating back to the early days of film) become peculiarly apposite to the case in point. This being so, it can be an advantage to be familiar (at least in theory) with even some quite antiquated or historical methods of doing things. They may be applied, perhaps in a modified form, to some situation in which he finds himself, and can often provide a simple solution to a tricky problem. Despite the improvement in all technical aspects of television image production, it is surprisng what a cameraman can get away with in terms of effects, provided he tackles the right ones in a suitable way. He cannot, naturally, expect to approach the type of effect obtained by electronic means, but a wide range of "realistic" or "natural" effects are at his disposal and can be produced by his essentially limited means. Most weather effects fall into this category.

WEATHER EFFECTS

For weather effects outdoors you are to a certain extent dependent on the weather you have at the time. But this is mainly if you are working at extremes—trying to film a bad weather sequence in bright sunlight or vice versa.

It is always much easier to gain a realistic effect if you are only filming in close-up. Sunlight can be cut off the subject with a large flag; the closer background area may be in shadow and "rain" could be induced from overhead. But whenever you are filming bad weather sequences in good weather, if you flag off the sun you are losing the key light. So you have to insert a replacement highlight in some way to preserve the dramatic effect. The most enhancing key light for a bad weather sequence would be a side- or three-quarter-back kicker—greatly improving the effect over that of a flat key light. It means that the main part of an actor's face is in shadow, and the expression is not too clear; that is quite a dramatic effect although something of a cliché. Such clichés are, however, now almost a code understood by the audience and indicating that certain conditions prevail.

Storm Sequences

A storm sequence, which may involve various effects, is often easier to carry out convincingly in the more controlled conditions of the film studio than on an outdoor location where you have to rely to a certain extent on the elements. Whatever you do in a studio you can adjust to the exact degree you want.

Outdoors, it is very difficult indeed to obtain the right type of lighting for a storm sequence (remembering always that TV budgets do not allow one to wait for suitable weather). For storms, one tends to think in terms of semi-darkness, and certainly a dark, heavy sky, which is unlikely to appear on cue! You are quite likely to get sunshine, in fact. Moreover, in TV filming you normally have to shoot on the day allotted and no other, when artists are available, the fire service can supply water for the rain and when you can obtain other ancillary equipment or personnel who can be called in for that day only.

Quite frequently, you have to represent a storm under other unfavourable conditions. Rain coming from fire engine hoses directed into the air cannot be controlled properly if the wind happens to be blowing in the wrong direction. The water must blow either from the side or from behind the camera. Otherwise, no matter what protective measures you take to keep the "rain" off the camera, it blows in front of the camera glass, filters, etc., and the picture is ruined. You may not even be able to see a picture at all through the camera. Sometimes you have to be prepared to move the shots around so that you can get the rain coming in the places where you need it.

You have another problem if there is *no* wind on an outdoor location. Unless you are going to have numbers of hurricane fans at your disposal, you cannot introduce an artificial wind effect. On the other hand, when you are working within the confined space of a studio a single fan is so strong that it must be carefully controlled in order not to have too exaggerated an effect. This is even more true of the studio rain machine whose overuse will show up easily on the film.

The studio rain machines consists of a series of pipes with holes in them. The pipes are spread over a deep area and crossways in a pattern. The artists are included in the rain area and get wet. But on long shots, you can have the effect of rain over a vast area, by making the rain fall in the foreground having first wetted the whole area behind, and the artists can pass *behind* the rain, thus staying dry. But it must be done only in long shot, and they must not come too close to the camera. In anything less than a long shot, water falling in front of the camera is not convincing.

In the normal arrangement, rain pipes cover the whole area of action. They are turned on for the shot and turned off again afterwards. The camera is kept outside if possible. Tarpaulins are used if the camera must be positioned in the "rain".

With average set-ups you must use backlighting if you wish the rain to show up. On exteriors, the light coming from the sky provides something of a backlight effect but you cannot backlight, as such, on exteriors. In the studio you just light the foreground artists, etc., release the rain and check from the camera position to see if you have enough spill back light on the rain. If not, then you purposely backlight it. The rain does not affect exposure.

On location, naturally, you have to accept the lighting which exists. In a storm sequence you do not wish to add light but to take it away. You can cut the overall light down with the aperture diaphragm. But you may wish to pick things out, or three-quarter backlight the artists, as in a studio storm sequence. Even in a studio situation you do not aim for a complete silhouette, but the foreground is quite dark and you pick everything out with a half- or three-quarter backlight. If you try to do this on exteriors, having reduced everything to a very low brightness level, you would need a huge number of arc lights to have any effect. You would also have to bear in mind that, on long shots, you could not get your arcs in the right position or near enough to give the effects you want.

You can never obtain much height for the lighting on exteriors in television productions owing to the cost of rigging and the way such preparations slow down the production process. In the studio, however, you can put a light at virtually any angle or height you like, no matter how long the shot, because the gantries permanently rigged above allow lamps to be mounted anywhere. And there is complete freedom of movement for the camera.

In a storm sequence you need illumination to provide the "lining" light or the light which is supposed to be coming from the sky. This could be described as the lighting effect by which you do not want to, but must, see the artists. In the studio there is always enough height available for rigging lights so that they are out of picture although at the right angle. If they are any lower, they come within view and, indeed, on location this lining light effect cannot be obtained because the lamps cannot be placed high enough when at a suitable distance. Location work is more complicated when it comes to providing such effects.

With long shot storm sequences outdoors you can only light in the foreground. But with heavy rain, which comes between the camera and the artists as well as falling on the artists, any foreground light overexposes the foreground rain yet does not reach the artists beyond because of the dense wall of water in front of the light. It is better, therefore, to omit the frontal light altogether and use the existing daylight. If there is sunshine you can hardly do anything to defeat the general brightness—and the storm is not likely to be very convincing. In close-ups you can flag off the sun and put in some backlight. A little backlight emphasizes the rain and should not look too artificial if it is not very strong. In normal outdoor conditions rain is backlit from the sky.

Snow Effects

For snow sequences foam is often sprayed down into the scene. Lighting with this effect does not make as much difference in the scene as it does with rain. There is no need to backlight large white blobs which show up clearly anyway. Frontal lighting merely reflects back into the camera.

For fog sequences you rely for a certain portion of the effect on a light fog filter mounted on the camera lens. The remainder comes from artificial fog blown in by a fog machine from the side of the scene. The total effect is a mixture of the two. If the blown-in fog becomes a little thin and wispy in certain areas, as often happens, the fog filter helps to fill the gaps and ensures an even effect. Filters are available in five fog strengths to use according to your needs, with a special one for close-up work. This is denser at the sides than the centre so that there is not too much diffusion on a face (assuming that it is designed for portraiture) although the background is at full density. The filter is not suitable for zooming because on the long shot position the centre of the picture is noticeably clearer. If you zoom in to a close-up using an even density fog screen you have to ensure that there is plenty of fog effect blowing in at that moment.

There is always the difficulty with these climatic effect scenes (fog-rain-snow) of maintaining an even effect throughout the sequence. It is largely a matter of memory. You have to memorize the effect throughout the sequence from a visual point of view. There must be no limitations in intercutting. Clearly you cannot intercut from a shot of one density to one of another. Yet it is difficult to remember the particular thickness of fog in any two scenes.

From a lighting point of view fog is shot more or less straight. With dry ice type fog you do not need any special lighting. Front, back and side lights all fall on the fog at the same time. However, with fog you do have to take into account that the picture is being lightened by the effect and, judging by eye, you have to make an adjustment to the exposure of, say, half a stop or so, depending on the circumstances.

Lighting effects are very much easier to carry out in the studio than on location. The flashes of lightning are relatively bright. On location they are hardly bright enough.

There is an established method of obtaining lightning effects in the studio. This is to use an arc light fitted on the front with a set of louvred shutters like a venetian blind. The arc is lit with these shutters closed. The shutters are pulled open and closed with varying degrees of gap, according to how long you wish the lightning flash to last. This method can be used on one, two or three arcs to increase the effect. An arc in a studio which is flashed on and off in this way lights up the whole of the shot—and gives a vivid impression of a lightning flash. To use an arc with shutters on location would be satisfactory on close-ups or two-shots because they are concerned only with a very limited area but for long shots you have to think of some other way of doing it. With the method outlined, the arc lights up only the foreground, whereas it is characteristic of lightning to illuminate the entire foreground and background area, albeit momentarily. This was done on a BBC series *Late Call* (see also page 43) by flashing the camera aperture wide open for a brief moment. The exact intensity of light does not matter—you simply flash it on. But it must be very strong.

One episode of *Late Call* involved a sequence where two people in a field were caught in a storm. The fire brigade pumped water from a local stream high into the air to provide the rain. Thunder and lightning were also called for. A tree under which the two people had just been sheltering was to be struck by lightning and explode.

One problem was the rain effect. There had to be enough to be visible, but not so much as to blot out detail in the picture. It had to look real—as if it were raining and not coming from a fireman's hose. The problem with realism was that it had to cover huge areas and the sequence was to be seen in long shot—both conditions which act against achieving a realistic result.

The final flash of lightning and blowing up of the tree had also to be done in long shot because we had to show the tree, the people in the distance having left the tree, the flash of lightning and the tree blowing up. This could not be done satisfactorily by intercutting special effects. Two brutes were made available for this scene—far more lighting than was being used in the daytime scenes for the rest of the production. These two brutes were fitted with shutters which, when quickly opened and closed would create another glow in the actual tree area to represent the lightning. (Naturally, for long shot areas, the sky, the fields, the distance, the foreground, etc., you cannot use lighting effectively for this effect. To cover that, you use the aperture control.) For the main shot everything else operated on the same cue—the flash of lightning and the tree blowing up (the rain and wind were there all the time, although the hurricane fan out in the field did not have much effect—except for blowing the occasional rainy gust). We arranged that, on cue, the assistant would flash the aperture stop open (it was a T1·8 lens stopped down to T6·3, deliberately chosen for its wide maximum aperture) to T1·8 so that the entire shot would momentarily be completely overexposed and almost immediately return it to T6·3. The particular lens had a quadrant scale and a lever with a little resistance connected to the stops mechanism. This procedure somewhat resembles the effect of lightning, where everything appears to go white.

The exploding tree effect was done with explosives packed in round a main branch which were set off momentarily after the flash. These explosives blew the branch off. Separate cues were given to operate the shutters on the lamps. The farmer who owned the tree was glad enough to have the branch blown off because he had been worried about the condition of the elm tree and the possibility that it was diseased. How the BBC found a location equipped with a tree whose owner wished to have a branch blown off is remarkable indeed!

Night Exteriors

Numerous night exterior scenes for television productions are filmed on location in actual night conditions. This gives a degree of realism lacking in the "day for night" method, however well executed, or in pseudo night exterior studio set-ups. Even the means to providing this night effect, however, requires some element of artificiality to make up for the difference between seeing at night and actually filming in the conditions.

Lighting

For all night exterior filming it is essential first to go on a recce, preferably with the director and an electrician. You must know exactly what you are going to do. The electrician needs to know what and how much cabling he is going to need and where he can place his generators. This avoids argument at a later stage. As the director describes the shots you should be assessing your maximum need in equipment or facilities. If you are involved in reasonably normal shooting all you really need to know from the director is, what and where are his long shots. Once you can light a long shot it is inevitable that you have enough equipment available to do everything else, because the long shot makes the maximum demand on equipment. To the demands of a long shot you add your other odd items according to your individual ideas.

For night effects you aim to use three-quarter backlighting. If you light from the front, you flatten the scene out and create an unpleasant semi-daytime effect. If you light your artists with lamps placed even as far forward as to give direct side lighting the shot begins to look extremely unpleasant. It is difficult to think of such an effect as being night.

Instead, you expect a figure outlined in three-quarter backlight—i.e., the whole outline. You can then bring a less strong key light a little further round so that you see a little more of the face and side. You can also add a weak fill light from the front to make sure that there is sufficient visual information in the shadow area (so that the laboratory and telecine processes can cope with it).

Apart from the key, the lighting can be balanced by eye. The only actual measurement necessary is for the key light. At night you can reckon in terms of foot candles (i.e. the light falling on the subject) as if in the studio, and in the daytime use the light reflected from the subject. Perhaps the ideal meter for night work is the Weston foot candle type, but this is no longer made. Instead it is possible to use the Invercone attachment. But an exposure meter is a very personal thing. One type seems to work well for one person and badly for another. Also you get used to your own meter.

The balancing of a lighting set-up is never measured. It must just look right, and to get this you simply look through the camera, grasp the front light and pull it back to make a correction in balance between the light sources. This kind of judgement becomes less reliable if you begin to tire after a very long period of night work. Then, you can safeguard your work by taking a very rough light reading of the filler light and compare it with the key. If it is no more than about one twentieth of the key light intensity then it is safe to assume that it will be satisfactory.

With night exterior shooting it is very easy to fall into the trap of overlighting and you need to keep a strong hand on yourself to avoid doing it, firstly by not bringing the key light round too close to the camera position and secondly by not putting in too much filler light. You can always err on the side of underlighting with filler. Excess filler light turns the effect into a day shot whereas with Eastmancolor the key light can be remarkably low—for night exteriors it may well be well below the manufacturer's recommendation. Normally, on day shots one works on the basis of 100 foot candles for an aperture setting of T2·8 while for night shots taking account of the fact that the key light is being taken further round towards the backlighting position, you allow yourself a stop underexposure, which would mean 50 foot candles for T2·8 and because it is night, you would reduce for good measure to 30 foot candles for T2·8. Even then, the rushes may show that you could clearly have worked at only 20 foot candles and yet achieved very acceptable results—owing to the working latitude of this material.

For night exteriors you have to set up your lighting before night falls, otherwise you waste a couple of hours of night shooting time. Also it is more difficult to move lights, cables and other equipment in the dark. But, when setting-up in daylight you have to imagine your lighting scheme as if it were in the dark. You then wait for dusk and as soon as you get a nil reading out of the sky, based on the shutter and film speed combination you are using you can light up and adjust lights and camera positions accordingly. With practice it is not at all difficult to work in this way. For the whole time, whether it be night or day, you have to imagine your set-ups because you usually have neither the artists nor the director with you. So you have to visualize what he and they are going to do. When it comes to the take you will probably not be far out.

The only special camera equipment that you might have on night exteriors is a set of wide aperture lenses, if you were unable to obtain the amount of light which is normally available. This might be due to the nature of the subject itself. Or it might be because you wanted to include some existing night features such as street lamps or lights in office buildings or lights reflected in a river and auxiliary lighting would eliminate or overbalance them.

Another case is where you need a wider aperture lens because you cannot for practical reasons augment the illimination. The area you are working in might not allow you to use a large generator, and instead you may have to use a much smaller alternator, for example, if you are on a river shooting from boat to boat and it is not possible to float a generator beside you.

In fact, you may have to make do with a small portable alternator of low capacity (carried on the boat you are shooting from) allowing only a few kW of light to be used, rather than hundreds of amps. The alternator is a small portable AC dynamo (petrol or diesel). The maximum output from an alternator is about 35–50 kW. You can use quartz lights and ordinary incandescents with this.

Practicals at Night

Practical lights in night scenes can be reinforced with photofloods by substituting them for the ordinary bulb in the same socket. But they can be an embarrassment because they are so bright. It is probably easier to work on either day or night sequences with the largest practicable aperture (i.e. taking depth of field and definition into account). This makes the scene easier and quicker to light because you need less light and therefore a smaller number of lights. The ordinary 75 or 100 w lamp provides ample light for the practical effect in the studio or on night-exteriors. In the studio a good working aperture is about T2·8 or 3·5. For night exteriors you can work with the lens wide open, always. The definition is good enough with prime lenses on 16 mm. But any focal length over 17·5 mm becomes more difficult to handle on account of the shallow depth of field. But 10 and 12 mm lenses are fine for this technique. With an Arriflex camera which has a T3·2, 10:1 zoom lens fitted, if used on night exteriors the lighting must be for T3·2 and the lens is normally used wide open throughout the sequence. The Zeiss zoom lenses suffer nothing in definition or quality compared with the current prime lens. The only benefit of such a prime lens compared with a zoom is the extra wide aperture available on it. However, the T3·2 maximum has always been a disadvantage with night exterior work. Zeiss are, in fact, developing a new range of prime lenses for the model BL cameras used by the BBC. So the zoom lens is likely, again, to trail behind prime lenses in quality.

Focus

In day photography the normal way to find the correct focus distance with fixed lenses is to read it with a tape measure from the film plane mark to the subject. This is not normally done with a zoom lens because you can magnify the image by zooming in, focusing, and then zooming out gain to the required framing. You can usually also focus by eye with zoom lenses on night sets, and with fixed lenses you measure with tape in the normal way. However, this needs some care because for such sequences the widest apertures are being used, which allows little depth of field. This is very important and only too often passed over nowadays that so many people rely on judging focus by eye only in all situations. Consequently, somewhat out of focus night sequences are by no means uncommon.

Night Sequences

A series of four-part 50-minute BBC productions based on Dorothy Sayers' *Lord Peter Wimsey* stories were typical of those requiring relatively large film content—in the region of 30 per cent—and including sizable filmed night sequences. Productions such as these are shot mainly in the studio because of the interior sets and multiplicity of artists required. Lengthy treatments with many artists involved usually indicates studio treatment. Only exterior material shot for an atmosphere which is a part of the story, are done on film. In one series of *Lord Peter Wimsey* there was a large exterior sequence of an exhumation in Highgate Cemetery, London. This famous cemetery contains the remains of many celebrities, including George Eliot, C. G. Rossetti, Karl Marx and William Friese-Greene. Filming was done on the location as it would be impossible to reproduce the extraordinary atmosphere of the actual Highgate Cemetery in a studio. In the story the exhumation was supposed to be an official affair—taking place just after the First World War. The effect was quite eerie—you could hardly help but make it like that. But we increased this atmosphere by keeping frontal light to a minimum, using plenty of backlight with kickers, to create many shadows and dark areas.

For a scene like the Highgate exhumation night sequence suitable equipment would consist of: two brutes on Molevators, three 10 K lights also on Molevators and, for good measure, two 5 Ks, four 2 Ks, two pups (1000 w), two North lights (flat filler lights consisting of indirect quartz lamps bouncing off a flat white surface in the lamp).

In this exhumation scene there was one sequence round the grave which was lit by four storm lanterns, one at each corner. In order to simulate that type of lighting slightly more pups than normal were used—with 750 w incandescent bulbs rather than 1000s in order not to overlight the sequence. In such a case light from the lanterns is not killed off because you make sure that very little, if any, light falls on the storm lanterns. You visualize what the effect of the storm lantern would be on the face of the person holding it or standing nearby and then adjust the key light accordingly, giving enough light but not so much as to distort the effect. We used proper storm lanterns with the wicks turned up a little. But the lanterns were seen either in long shot, so that you would see little more of them than the flicker of the light, or in such a way that you were looking up and seeing the lantern large in the foreground and, being so close, the amount of light coming from it was more emphatic. The exposure calculation was, of course, based on this.

We did a fairly extensive night sequence in another *Lord Peter Wimsey* series when we were working in the gardens of Cliveden, a country house in Berkshire. At the entrance to the main drive is a great marble fountain. The story involved a large fancy dress party at night with most of the guests either drunk or drugged. Several people were to splash around in the water and our hero had to climb up to the top of the central figure and then dive head first into the fountain. This was a simulated dive. He started to dive but then we cut to a double (a stunt man) to carry out the actual movement, diving from the top on to a pile of cardboard boxes place in the water to break his fall.

The garden scene was a vast sequence and we had only one night in which to do it. We were shooting from four opposing directions—flat on, from the left and from the right and from the back—360 degrees coverage. There was also a large crane shot where the camera was about 35 ft above the fountain shooting down on to it.

On the recce I had gone round the location with the director who showed the approximate areas we would be covering on this particular sequence. He was rather specific about this because (for various other reasons) we had so little time available. Also it was a lengthy sequence and would at one stage entail people falling into the water in the fountain, so this shot could not be repeated very often, and preferably not at all because of the difficulty of getting people dry. It was anyway a winter's night, which was a little unpleasant for the participants.

We had to take the various camera angles into account and light for each direction so that there would be the minimum movement of lamps and other heavy equipment throughout the night. It takes time to move a 225 amp arc on a Molevator over soft ground. We set up the lighting in daylight at 5.00 p.m. Each particular set-up had to be visualized working side by side with the director who stated which general angles would be used. At 7.00 p.m. it was dark enough to light up and quickly check how these set-ups would work out. Once it was dark and we had started shooting, as each shot presented itself, one could only make minimal alterations due to lack of time. As it happened, very few changes were necessary. Once the arcs were in position, each lamp had to be taken down from its Molevator and set up again standing on a cardboard base to save the grass from undue pressure in small areas. A crowd of 60 people plus technicians etc. represent a considerable expense for a television production to bear, so you have to work quickly in this type of situation.

We knew in advance what each set-up was going to be, and how much background was to be included, so all the lights had to be placed in such a way that none were in shot. There was a certain amont of latitude in shifting the camera position. There was also the governing factor of everyone standing around the fountain. The camera would be on one end of the crowd, as it were, and then in the middle. We needed to use only about half of the fountain and sometimes it was possible to hide lights behind the fountain itself. Some shots were done from a camera position in the water with the crowd around the edge of the fountain. We would be shooting at several angles which embraced about 200 degrees of the circle of the fountain. We wanted light for all these angles without having to move any of the units. So the lighting had to be suitable for all shots during the sequence, yet not intrude into any of them. The lights had to become in turn, back lights, side lights or even front lights (but not very much front light because it was a night sequence).

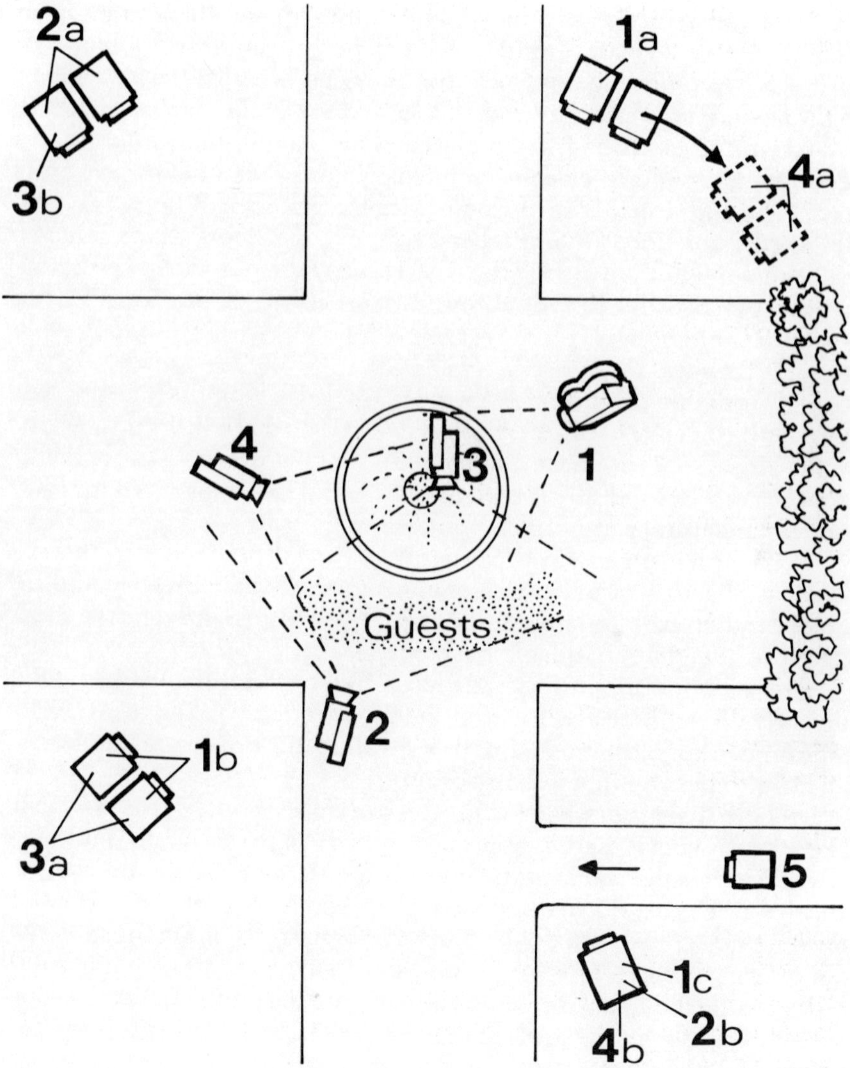

Lord Peter Wimsey. A garden sequence by moonlight. The setting was the garden of a country house. The centre of activity was a very large marble fountain at the junction of four wide gravel paths, one traversed by a hedge with a smaller path beyond it. This diagram shows the lighting for each camera position. The paired lamps are all brutes, diffused when serving as fillers. For a description of the sequence, see text. Camera position 1, on crane about 35 ft. high, looking down: 1a filler (one brute only), 1b, backlight key representing moonlight, 1c, brute filler for fountain area. Camera position 2 overlooking guests: 2a, key, 2b filler. Camera position 3 facing guests: As a backlight-key 3a, representing moonlight (although facing the camera it was high enough to be out of shot), 3b filler. Camera position 4: Brutes moved to 4a as key and single brute 4b backlighting guests. 5, 10K lighting along path to provide background detail.

For the main action a man had to climb up and then jump down into the water, a crowd was to be seen gathered round the fountain. In order to cover this huge area of about 200 degrees with different types of lighting and not to shift the lights, and because of the various angles to be taken, the lights had to be placed some way off (about 60 ft) and doubled up to give the required intensity and spread from each position. The additional cost of using twice the number of lights was undoubtedly absorbed by not having to move the lights which is more difficult at night than during the day. This expedient was, however, untypical practice. As this doubling up was liable to produce double shadows the lights were placed very close together. The resulting shadow was not visible as double.

If from one position there was an arc which would act as a three-quarter back light, because of a shot to be done three shots further on, from almost the opposite angle, were that light too close it could appear in the second shot. So plenty of ground had to be given for each camera angle and room to manipulate it.

From each angle only those lights not included in the picture were needed. If a light were just creeping into shot the camera would be moved rather than the lamp or the artist. Flare from lights tends to show up more at night than during the daytime.

It is a good idea always to keep a free head on the camera, particularly where there are artists in the shot, so that you can make small adjustments to follow them. But you obviously have to cut the shot when an artist draws you into a flare position.

The first big shot was from the top of a crane about 70 ft up in which Lord Peter Wimsey had to approach the side of the fountain, jump in, wade through the water and climb up the statue towards the camera which was looking down on to him. There was then a cut to the POV of the watching crowd, now looking up. The lighting for the crane shot was almost exactly correct for the ground shot. There was enough intensity. A double did the actual dive out of picture into the fountain. You did not see him actually hit the water. There was a splash and a shriek from the crowd. The camera was in the fountain with water in the foreground and Peter Wimsey (the real one) ducked under the water before the shot and sprang up out of it into view. The crowd reacted accordingly. He then waded to the side of the fountain and was pulled out by his friends, whereupon a small scuffle started and two more people fell back into the water. This was covered shooting up, down and sideways, nearly on both sides, all without moving any of the quadrant of double brute key lights, apart from a little front light brought in now and then to help pick out detail. The crowd covered about 100 degrees of the outer edge of the fountain and it was a full night sequence.

For the shots in the fountain the camera was about two feet from the water level. The tripod would not stand on the slippery curved base of the fountain so a rostrum top was sunk into the bottom of the fountain. The camera tripod was placed on that with the whole assembly held down by six 50 lb stage weights. Even so, the tripod tended to float so the crew had to hold on to it. The tripod points catch in the wood of a rostrum top. It is possible to put a screw and chain between the underneath of the tripod apex and the centre of the rostrum. But this would take time and we had only half an hour or so to do the shots with the camera standing in the water. The crew wore waist waders.

It is particularly important when working on night exteriors to work as quickly as you possibly can. No one really likes working on them as it goes on to three or four o'clock in the morning. After midnight things tend not to go right. It takes longer to move things, people slow down. The first day and night shooting period is always the longest one because you are doing an 18 hour stint even though the actual working time may be only 12 hours. In the BBC, for the second night you report back a minimum of 10 hours after you broke off from the previous night's work. On the following night you are doing 10–12 hour rota. We reckon that if you have a day location more than 40 miles distant from London you stay overnight down on the location. If a night location is more than 20 miles away, you stay down there for the following night or day. This rule takes into account the fact that many film locations are in rather inaccessible places, rather than ideally sited on trunk routes running into the capital. Indeed the sites chosen could be over rough terrain with no proper road at all.

MOONLIGHT

The most common standard effect in night lighting is moonlight. You expect moonlight to cover quite a large area, and you often have several long shots to do on night exterior locations. So your key moonlight, as it were, is usually an arc, placed quite high in order to simulate moonlight. You might have one or two brutes, according to the size of the shot. The rest of the light would be incandescent 2 Ks, 5 Ks or a 10 K.

Quartz (tungsten halogen) light is good for night work because its hard quality follows through with an arc when supplementary to it. You tend to obtain a more definite single shadow than you do with an incandescent lamp. If, for example, you were using an arc as a three-quarter back light on your artists and continuing the key light round in order to produce more detail on the side of the face and body you can do this very satisfactorily (placed much closer, of course) with a quartz. The quality of these two lights match in very well indeed. You filter the arc light, which is far too blue, even for night, so you use a half or full 85 filter and use the quartz as it is, unfiltered. The only disadvantage of the quartz light seems to be that the dichroic filters which you use for day exteriors cut the intensity quite severely and tend to lose their colour correction after a while. The loss of colour correction is gradual and not easily visible but suddenly becomes noticeable on the film. The life of these lamps is not great, and certain batches of lamps tend to blow easily, especially when the lamp is moved. Normally, they are quite sturdy. There are 750 w (red head) and 2 K versions (blonde).

Crews are not allowed to use Xenon arcs in the BBC (except for projection) owing to a safety regulation.

Photographing the moon itself is liable to produce a result that looks phoney—as it did in a production of *Moonstrike* where the moon, rising behind a long shot of a street looked like a backcloth with a light shining through a hole. This was shot some years ago in monochrome (working with faster stock—35 mm Tri X 250 ASA) which is faster than the current colour material. You had at that time a choice of four types of stock manufactured by Ilford and Kodak. You used the same stock—each cameraman had his own first love, as it were—and only for the odd shot here and there would you use a faster or a finer grain stock.

When working in black and white your prime concern was to have a stock that would give a pleasant fine grain result with the minimum amount of light. On night exteriors with Tri X and 4X material you could do long shots with a remarkable lack of light. But 4X was only introduced at the time the BBC turned over to filming in colour. The average for black and white was about 250 ASA. That for colour was 32 ASA. Adopting the new colour material was like stepping back a few years in terms of lighting power. It required great adjustment for some people to work with it happily. The BBC started colour work on 35 mm. But total colour production undermined the use of 35 mm on the grounds of cost. T2 lenses were available; some Arri BL's used T1·8. There were special fast lenses available on hire for specific shots, i.e. 1·4 or 0·98.

In the case of a shot including the moon, correct exposure for the moon would dictate the shot. Additional features such as foreground lighting would be added to balance.

Day for Night

If you are going to do a day for night sequence it is advisable to check first with the laboratory what particular standard they work to, as far as exposure is concerned. For most day-for-night sequences two stops underexposure is the maximum required. One and a half is also common.

You could do the day-for-night effect with only a pola filter and leave the customary slight blueing effect to be put in by the laboratory in printing. The best method though is to put everything you want in the negative—do your own blueing. Possibly, straight underexposure would work just as well for day-for-night without any blue effect (which is only a convention imported from the feature film industry). The amount of blue is controlled by the filter you use. If you take the 85 filter off the camera, you get a deep blue effect because the film is balanced for 3200 K lighting and you are using daylight. So you replace the 85 filter by an 81EF, roughly half the density of an 85, which allows some excess blue light to get through to the film. To soften the effect a little you can use a ·3 or ·6 neutral density filter. If you use a ·6 ND and the laboratory requires two stops underexposure for this effect the exposure compensation is already there, built in to the filter. So you can work with normal exposure readings disregarding the filter—which is the easiest and quickest way of doing this and does not require the meter to be reset.

Working at speed you do not wish in any case to deviate from your normal method of working.

The main objective to day-for-night technique is an aesthetic one—the effect simply cannot look natural because its whole basis is false. Daytime scenes mostly consist of a well lit area with small shadows cropping up here and there. At night you have huge areas of shadow with occasional small highlights (picked out to emphasize the general blackness, if light is added). How then can you turn huge areas of highlight into equally large areas of shadow? Blacking out everything initially with filters and lighting accordingly does not give the same effect.

In BBC television one very rarely shoots day-for-night. It used to be thought cheaper and easier. But in fact you need as much artifiicial light when you are shooting day for night as you do when you are shooting at night. In the days when we were working with monochrome there were other filters (such as a red filter to darken the sky yet raise foreground foliage tone) that you could use to bring the overall light level down. To cut out the sky, you needed heavy filtering, yet the foreground did not require such heavy filters to reduce it to a manageable night exposure. This meant that you did not need quite so much light. You could also reduce the area covered by the shots so that you did not have to light or pick out large areas. Instead of long and medium shots you tended to take close-ups and get more intimacy into the night shooting.

With colour, you have a slightly slower stock, which helps you reduce the brightness, but you have to increase the lighting for the foreground. You can do day-for-night exteriors in monochrome reasonably well if you can guarantee that you have at least three-quarter back lighting and a brilliant blue sky. In the western hemisphere a perfect blue sky appears on few days in a year. In Arizona and on the

West Coast of the USA there are places where you can depend on long periods of sunshine with clear blue skies. There you can get any long shots you need with day-for-night technique in colour. In the western hemisphere, with its characteristic white skies this is not possible. Such weather encourages the expedient of graduated filters. But these can only be used on static long shots although there are ways of losing the "hard" line of the graduated filter in the subject matter. You cannot put a person in the frame because the chances are that he will move into or out of the graduation. You cannot move the camera, as the graduation becomes visible as a separate entity. The graduated filter is tapered in effect on the edges. A gauze can be placed in the camera to gain a diffusion effect. The problem even with a straight line diffuser is that the result is not good because there are sure to be unevennesses in the horizon, such as a tree. As a result they are little used today. With colour film in such wide use you have the advantage whereby for example, if there is a white sky the result is not so objectionable because the other colours around, in effect, "soften" it. The colour stock does not seem to glare or flare so much in the sky because there is always a slight colour in it and the total effect is more satisfactory. In fact, in many respects, filming in colour is easier than filming in black and white. When you are shooting in colour the objects seen in the frame "separate" themselves quite naturally.

Flashback Sequences

One method of conveying the idea of flashback sequences is the use of fairly heavy gauzing, or vignetting using gauzes with the centre cut out. But with colour there is a greater difficulty because whatever is done must be visible also on the black and white screen, and the same feeling must be obtained from that. Flashback is usually only one or two shots and so is seen in contrast to the immediately surrounding shots. Where the whole sequence is a flashback the effect must, if anything, be more definite. Most TV owners probably do not have their sets too well adjusted. A degraded picture may be the general rule, so that a specially degraded picture to represent flashback is hardly noticeable. The final product may additionally be affected by electronic effects to be added afterwards. If it were merely a question of working up the effect on colour film, then the densely saturated filters used for black and white photography might give a suitable effect. The Wratten 29 gives far too red an image—rather macabre; the 23A gives an image which is not unpleasant—a medium red or dark orange. The effect in monochrome, however, is only a darker image which gives a picture that is not sufficiently different from the ordinary shots to make much impact. The Wratten 15—a dark yellow filter, gives a pleasant effect for this purpose.

If the film were dyed in sepia, which has been suggested, again the result would not be noticeable as distinct from the ordinary sequences in monochrome. You are left with the problem of creating a strong enough effect to sustain the impression through a long sequence.

STUDIO IMPROVISATION—STALINGRAD SEQUENCES

The BBC television series *Stalingrad* was adapted from a book by Theodore Plievier and the adaptation for the television production was done by Rudolf Cartier, who also directed. As with so many of his productions, this caught the public's imagination. The filmed contribution to it was purely and simply the vast scenes that could not be done in the live studio because of limited space available and could be done much better on film because of the very much larger canvas that one has in filming.

Basically, we had one large studio at Ealing (Studio 2) and it was lined with a white cyclorama reaching around four walls. The set, as such, which served for about five different locations throughout the filming, consisted of a slightly raised ground level. This was either an earth type of set and flooring seen against the white cyclorama for the ordinary spring and summer scenes or it was covered in sawdust and Vermiculite to represent snow. Added to this there was sandbagging and barbed wire. There was also a very large fan, or wind machine for the winter gale scenes. Bags of Vermiculite were poured into the fan, which blew it around. The whole thing was very simply and efficiently done (in black and white). In using the sawdust in conjunction with the snow there was a tendency for the sawdust to come out at a slightly different black and white density compared with Vermiculite or polystyrene. However, a few quick tests proved that using a G filter or a 15 filter with HP3 the sawdust came out much whiter than normal so that it matched the other material. The G filter did not affect the monochromatic colour rendition of anything else.

We had to use dry ice and smoke guns for some sequences not only to get the mist effects of the battlefields and the marshalling of the troops in the battle areas but also for the smoke effects that disguised some of the shortcomings of a medium stretched beyond its limits—i.e., shooting off the backing with the lighting gantries in shot. Smoke, mist and fog was squirted into the top of the scene to cover the overlap. The studio height then was about 20 ft. In modern studios the gantries have been brought down to a lower level and are movable. At that time the gantries at Ealing for economic and labour reasons were not movable. For this filming we literally used different parts of the same set for three weeks although each sequence was supposed to be an entirely different location in the film story.

We began with a burial party in an army cemetery. This sequence set the scene of demoralization caused by the enormous losses of troops, officers and other ranks. The same set was also used for the Stalingrad airfield, and we did a shot to represent the last aircraft taking off with high-ranking generals and VIPs on board—emphasizing the point that all the wounded were being left behind to be taken by the Russians. This shot was done in the studio without an aircraft of any description. The camera and 6 : 1 zoom lens were mounted on a large Transatlantic crane. We started with the crane positioned on the opposite side of the studio tight up against the cyclorama with the wounded and dying soldiers in the foreground fighting the guards as they try to board the aircraft. The camera tracked back at high speed and was simultaneously raised on the crane and the lens zoomed out to heighten the impression of movement and speed. Over this we laid the sound of the aircraft taking off so that the whole effect was implied—the camera was the aircraft. There were no more than a dozen wounded soldiers involved, on crutches, etc. and a couple of guards. Snow was blowing about, supposedly whipped up by the draught from the aircraft (this covered up some features in the studio that we would rather not have seen). With Rudi Cartier's work the idea was implication all the time and we got away with the most extraordinarily bold effects. This is much better in many ways for television filming than a direct, literal description by building elaborate reconstructions and using hundreds of people.

19

Composite Photography

Front Axial Projection

The front axial projection process is a method of combining real or live subjects in a studio with an artificial background prepared on a special projection "plate", still (transparency) or moving (film image).

The process uses a highly directional glass beaded reflector material, 3M Scotchlite screen. The effect of this material is such that when light strikes it most of the rays are returned in the direction from which they came. Thus, even with a relatively low-powered light source it is possible to achieve a very large and bright reflected image provided it is viewed along the axis of the projected beam. By the use of a semi-reflecting mirror, the camera and projector beams may be aligned and locked together on the same axis. Thus the camera lens picks up the image from the projector as it is returned by the Scotchlite screen along that axis. The camera and movie projector are automatically synchronized, frame for frame. The picture from the projector is sufficiently well illuminated to be brightly reflected by any surface covered with Scotchlite material, but is too weak to show up on actors or foreground objects—who are separately lit by studio luminaires. Shadows cast on the screen from the actors or foreground objects are not visible from the camera position. Pieces of screen material can be cut into shapes and placed in the foreground to reflect images of actual foreground features seen in the projected picture. The actors may thus pass *behind* them as if they were solid features. This adds to the illusion of depth in the picture as seen by the camera. The projected background must be shot in the correct scale and perspective to match the reconstructed foreground in the studio.

The moving background image requires an extremely accurate frame registration in the gate of both camera and projector. The camera material (whether 16 or 35 mm) must be printed on to negative perforation stock with an optical printer, unless the background is highly mobile, such as the passing exterior for a vehicle in motion. This gives a rock-steady picture with no movement in the gate.

The size of screen depends on the purpose for which it is to be used. The large background screen installed at the BBC Ealing Film Studio (Studio 2) measures 37 × 20 ft, for example. But a smaller, more mobile screen can be used for close-ups.

When lighting a subject in a front axial projection set-up you try to follow the lighting key and direction in the foreground in a way that will blend with that seen in the projected plate. This is the same in principle as with back projection or CSR backgrounds. If the key lighting in the plate is from a three-quarter frontal direction, you light the foreground also, with such a key. You balance up the brightness of the foreground and background plate by the easiest method. Taking a reading of the screen (this is easy with a camera which has a built-in through-the-lens exposure meter) you then light the foreground to the exposure indicated—i.e. with a reading of *f*3·5 off the screen, you give *f*3·5 for foreground key, plus or minus a little, according to eye or the particular scene involved.

The main drawback with lighting for front axial projection at the present time is that it does not allow any frontal filler lighting to be thrown on to the subject. Any light which comes from the front is reflected off the screen, and throws a shadow of the foreground subject across the background.

This shadow is visible because it is off the common axis of the camera and projector.

The system is also cumbersome and relatively immobile. Although it does allow a little panning you can not change the angle of the camera to the subject, neither can you track. Any movement of the camera towards or away from the subject would naturally alter the intensity of the projector light.

This intensity can, however, be adjusted to suit a dark or light plate.

If the system is properly used it can drastically reduce the often considerable costs of set construction for any scene, still or moving.

When shooting plates for front axial projection great care must be taken to match the plates to the known foreground, which might be a car or a train, for example. In the plate, the relative height and width of the scene, the lenses in use, etc., should all correspond to the dimensions of the studio set-up.

All these points must be noted so that they can be followed exactly in the subsequent studio reconstruction.

Front axial projection is often used to cover large areas of subject; a whole street may appear on the screen. So the precision of set-ups is very important to render correct perspectives.

Back Projection

This system is suitable for use as a background for a studio "vehicle" which is supposed to be either stationary or moving. The equipment for back projection takes up a large amount of studio space and the quality of the image obtained leaves much to be desired in terms of modern requirements. It is used far less these days than CSR, front projection or shooting *in situ* with real cars, boats etc. and real backgrounds.

Back projection has a limitation in the need for correct axial alignment of projector and camera even if they are not correctly aligned with the set itself. The projector is placed behind the screen (facing the camera) and throws a laterally reversed image on to it. The camera faces the screen from the other side, and films the image as a background to the action taking place in front. A problem arises if the projector is placed too close to the screen, when a hot spot could appear in the central screen area.

Although the same technique for shooting plates applies to CSR, front, or back projection, plates for the latter do not have to be so precisely registered. Consequently some plates used in back projection are not necessarily specially prepared for the production. Existing plates will often serve to cover a small area of view seen through a window without the need to send a team out to shoot fresh material each time.

Colour Separation Backgrounds (CSR)

Colour separation is an optical electronic process for superimposing a person or object on a background without needing to take them, or it, to the actual location. The real background must be shot separately, in much the same way as one designed for use in front or back projection. Just as certain rules apply to those, so there is an established technique in providing CSR plates.

Plates for colour separation should be very slightly out of focus so that you get a natural difference in sharpness between the foreground subject and the background to correspond with the partly subjective impression in real life.

Take, for example, colour separation plates prepared for a finished shot where two people are seen leaning on the wall of a river embankment, with say, a bridge, the river and its far bank as a background. To shoot the plate you line up two people leaning on the wall in the foreground, in the scale the director wants for the situation to be reproduced in the studio. In this case, the top of the wall is not included in the shot because the part of the wall to be seen is to be built in the studio. The camera is focused on the people. The people then move out of view and, leaving the focus as it is, the plate is shot like that. Two over-the-shoulder close-ups might also be required to cut in to this two-shot. The same technique applies: lining up the camera, focusing on the two people, removing them from the scene and shooting the background. The relevant information is relayed to the studio—the height of the camera and the lens in use on each of the three backgrounds.

The TM in the studio, armed with this information could line up his shot more satisfactorily than just by shooting a background, because it achieves the right perspectives and a realistic degree of defocus for the background.

To be quite sure that the background for colour separation shots is not absolutely sharp, you can focus slightly forward so that you are using only the furthest end of the depth of field. If the background is say, thirty feet away, this indicates that foreground artists are ten or twelve feet distant. With the slightly defocused background the visual perspective becomes a little more correct in the studio situation.

CYCLORAMA

One of the problems with erecting interior "exterior" sets in the studio is that of providing a background that gives a feeling of space beyond the various "solid" features of the studio scene. The cyclorama provides an economical solution. It consists of an enormous sheet of white canvas or other cloth stretched on a frame extending from the lighting gantry to the floor, a height of some twenty to thirty feet, depending on the particular studio. The frame, and its cloth hanging is semicircular and can extend horizontally almost from one wall of the studio to the other. A cyclorama can, in fact, be of any size, according to how much background area is required. It is possible to arrange one as only a small section behind a "window" or between two "buildings" on the set, or at the other extreme, a complete circle around the camera position. The reason for erecting a large cyclorama in a curve is to conserve studio space and allow the maximum working area. You can then work inside the curve. The smooth continuous background may be blended in to the floor area with the addition of a small section, or cove, at the foot—provided the floor area is of a similar tone.

The cyclorama is a very cheap, quick and efficient way of putting up a background because although it can, of course be white, it may also be blue for a blue sky or black to represent the night sky. There is also a cloud machine which projects cloud forms onto the cyclorama to give a little more detail in the background. The cloud machine has a glass slide on which cloud formations have been sprayed. A cyclorama has a perfect base on which to project coloured lights, as for light entertainment programmes, where the lights are constantly changed or swung around.

Stretching the cyclorama to remove all the blemishes and creases is quite a tricky job. You are very lucky if you get one entirely free from these faults. If the fault is very bad and you cannot correct it physically you can try and shift your camera angle so that the worst part is excluded, or you can move the artists so that they either cover it or are far enough away from it for the fault to be out focus. With a standard lens (say 20 mm in 16 mm format or 40 mm in 35 mm format) the camera can be placed some 25–30 ft distant from the cyclorama without shooting over the top, which leaves plenty of space for action.

In front of the cyclorama there is a gap before the ground row and in that space is placed some of the lighting for the cyc. But the most efficient way of lighting the cyclorama is from the gantry at the top because the lights are then far enough away to give an even overall illumination. If you light it from underneath behind the ground row the lamps are so close to its surface that hot spots appear before the light starts to fall off further up the cyc. It is easier to build up or reduce the level of light intensity if the lights are far enough away to give an even spread. The very long horizontal shape of the cyc enables you to cover a vast area in panning or any camera movement. This movement is restricted only by the shape of the set. It does not matter that the background is seen at an oblique angle in some shots because it is "flat" i.e. evenly lit, with a tone. If actual details are essential then a photographic cyc can be used. But these are tremendously expensive, and are rarely used for television filming. The plain cyc is basic to studio work because of its flexibility, relative cheapness and quick erection. The cyc is always the first studio feature to be erected (if needed) because it needs time to stretch, and the studio staff can make adjustments to obviate the creases while they are erecting other parts of the set. You can hang a white wide-mesh gauze three or four inches in front of the cyclorama which helps to eliminate the blemishes. The snag with using this gauze is that it tends to move if someone walks past quickly or opens a door in the set, and this movement is invariably visible in the shot. So it might be said that the method creates more problems than it solves. The gauze hangs from the same semicircular bar from which the cyc is suspended.

The basic method of lighting with a cyclorama is to set up the lamps to give perfectly even, shadowless background illumination, when looked at visually. You then check by a reflected light reading with a meter that the background light level is not too great in proportion to the strength of the key light you intend to adopt for the foreground and artists. The key is determined by the type of daylight you intend to represent. If you are shooting an interior-exterior, and the cyc gives you a vast

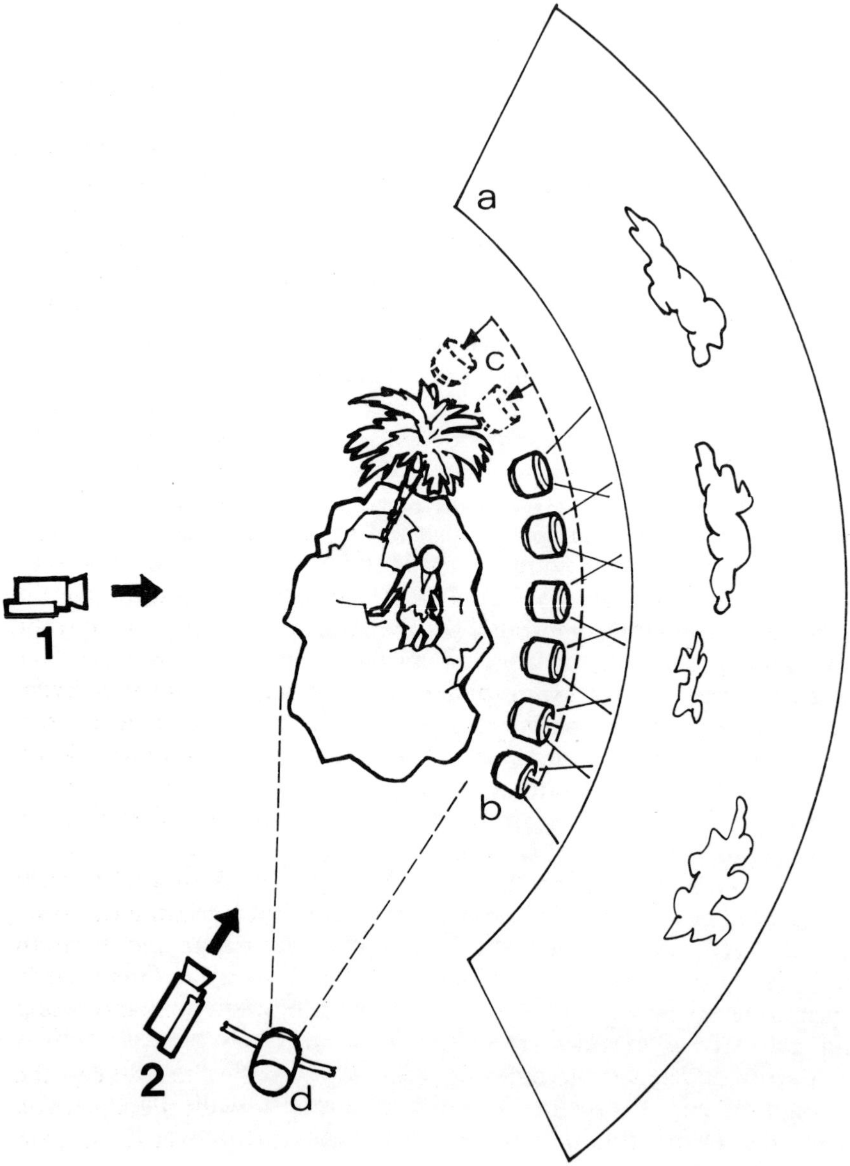

Typical cyclorama background with solid foreground features and deep curve of cyclorama behind (a). From camera position 1 gantry rail lamps, and ground row lighting (b) illuminate the background. Light (d) is the foreground key. From camera position 2, the lamps at (b) become visible, so are moved round to position (c) out of sight, and lighting far end of cyclorama.

field, as it were, the one thing that gives the game away is the lack of depth in focus. If you are shooting a real exterior your working aperture is automatically down to T8 or T11. This gives so much depth of field that practically everything within the picture is sharp.

A cyclorama background, provided it is not directly compared with a real exterior background, is quite convincing in itself. So you could never match a direct cut from an exterior to a cyc shot. You might get away with a cut via a third scene if the colour balance of each scene was correct and consistent throughout. Even then it is very difficult. Normally you would do *all* your exteriors in the studio or on a real exterior location.

If you wanted an evening sky effect on a cyclorama you could use coloured lighting but a better way in most cases would be to paint the cyc with the sky, including cloud scriations, etc. and then have a slightly warmer light than usual on the artists in the foreground. The colour temperature of the lights on the cyclorama can be altered as well, to balance the whole thing up.

Much of the use of coloured lights (as indeed all effects) involves an element of trial and error, not only for the cameraman, but also for the designer. He, the designer, might draw something on the cyc and the cameraman would then work with it. If it does not work out, the designer tries a little more, and then the cameraman, and so on. Eventually, between them, they find a compromise. The trial is of course a visual one; there is neither time nor finance to actually film test pieces. So it is a process of adjustment and manipulation. The error, if there is one, appears the next morning when you see the results projected on the screen.

The cyclorama should be seen out of focus at all times. This also helps to eliminate the blemishes. But if you particularly wanted a strong cloud effect on the cyc then you would make sure it appeared sharp. In most cases, however, you would let that go faintly soft. You often have to reduce the amount of light compared with the normal cyc background light level, in order not to kill the cloud effect.

There is another aspect to this case. If you reduce the light on the cyc to get the cloud to register, you need to work with a wider aperture, which means that you have less depth of field available—yet you want to include the clouds reasonably sharp, together with the foreground subjects. Alternatively, you can increase the intensity of the projected cloud image on the background and so step up the general light level. The background image is quite bright because it is projected by a small arc lamp (60–125 amp) through a concentrating lens system and on to an efficient reflector (the cyc). You can have moving clouds on a drawn or a static slide background. The projector is usually sited on the floor to one side (if the set allows) and throwing the image straight on to the cyc.

If the cloud formation is distorted by being projected obliquely relative to the camera position it does not matter as the change in shape does not show. It is possible to project another cloud formation in from the other side. The cloud background is not restrictive if you have static subjects in the foreground. It is more difficult to handle if you have action. Bearing in mind that cloud backgrounds are projected on to the cyclorama as a foreground projection at 45 degrees (because the cyc is not transparent) to the camera on either side, if there is action up and down towards, but mainly away from the camera there is a danger of the artist running into the cloud projector beam. You try to site the projector so that nothing crosses in front of it, as it is at floor level. For the most part you are not covering the whole backing and do not have to light it all with cloud.

If you light the backing from the top brightness tends to fall off towards the foot. This unevenness can be corrected, as previously remarked, by ground row lights.

It is possible that, if the set comes up to a certain level, say 3 ft and the lower part of the cyc is therefore obscured from camera view the hot spots will be, in effect, masked. The ground rows are then at sufficient effective distance for their light to be relatively even and diffuse. Top light can come down to meet them at this point.

When working in black and white you can have a realistic effect with a white cyc background and an earth or snow foreground. But in colour, you cannot have a white cyc all the time. There must be a picture on the cyc of a distant scene or some such thing. In colour you cannot keep showing the same piece of earth. You must put something else in to it or you must change your location. There is a greater tendency for similar locations to look different from one another in black and white than they do in colour. In colour, the lack of a prop could give away the fact that you have not really changed your location—that it is only another part of the same set.

20

Car and Chase Sequences

CAR SEQUENCES are very common in television programmes. For example, in all police serials much of the action takes place in, or with, cars. The classic car sequence involves shots inside the vehicle and external views of it travelling along the road. There are also "subjective viewpoint" shots from one vehicle to another, especially in chase sequences. External views are mostly shot either from the roadside or from a camera car moving along with the car being featured. Occasionally there is a shot from a building, looking down or even from the air.

Sequences may be shot in actual vehicles on the road, or in the studio using back projection plates and many consist of a mixture of both. But to obtain the plates it is still necessary to shoot on the road from a camera car moving along it. Back projection is used in preference to front projection because normally the background occupies only a small part of the picture, limited in area by the windows of the car. As it is relatively small, and in a real sense outside the car, with the action going on in front, some limitations associated with back projection do not apply. Moreover, the camera is not often called upon to change angle during the shot inside a vehicle so the problem of constantly aligning the camera along a projection axis is also bypassed.

Car sequences require a number of fairly standard techniques in lighting, setting up and camera treatment, in order to be completely convincing on the television screen. The fact of working in an actual car is not in itself enough to guarantee success in this respect. Some measures are corrective, creating a slightly unrealistic set of circumstances in front of the camera in order to gain an effect that appears natural in the end product.

CAMERA STABILIZATION

The first problem with shooting in or from a moving vehicle is the question of how to avoid the degree of camera movement that makes the filmed image difficult to watch. The hand held camera approach is very satisfactory for car sequences. If the camera is held firmly and the body braced against the side of the moving car, the body, and thus the camera, compensates for the unnecessary movement in travelling. In this way it is much easier to avoid over-jerky shots and make natural compensations by anticipating movements yourself. Because you are, in fact, trying to compensate for yourself against the movement of the vehicle, this gives sufficient correction to suggest the movement, yet does not look unreal.

Sometimes the camera is clamped to the body of the car. But this is done in a moving set-up which does not allow the presence of a cameraman, either because there is insufficient space for him to work within or because the particular angle chosen makes it impossible for the camera to be manned anyway. But in this situation the cameraman has no control whatever of the scene being filmed. So the results obtained in this way involve a calculated risk. The shot can be lined up and any extra light needed supplied by a battery lamp also attached to the car. The sound recordist, who may be sitting in the boot of the car, has to switch on the camera and lights and give the artist the go ahead. This is purely and simply a set-up situation and neither the cameraman nor the director knows what is actually being shot. So it is better if possible to avoid this approach. The usual case where this technique is applied is in shots covering the driver and a passenger sitting beside him or sitting in the back seat leaning forward. If the driver must be seen driving from his own side of the car, there is no other way of doing it. The only alternative for shooting the driver in profile is for the cameraman to put himself in the passenger's seat and cover him from there. If a hand-held camera is held correctly and the body is firmly in contact with the car, shots taken in this way can be freely intercut with those taken by a camera firmly mounted on the car without any difference in the amount of camera movement becoming apparent.

When bracing yourself you can get a good position by tucking your arms into your sides and pushing your back hard in to the seat, rather like a tripod. There is enough movement in the car to give the sensation of being inside although the camera is stabilized to some extent. But most of the sensation of movement is conveyed by the background flashing by.

Choice of Lens

When shooting the driver and the passenger from either the driver's or the pasenger's side, it is best to use the wide angle lens (10 mm) because you need the maximum depth of field to get both people sharp. They will probably be talking and such a dialogue sequence should normally cover both in this way. However, the disadvantage is that the perspectives are slightly false. The driver, in the foreground, will look proportionally large compared with the passenger who appears much smaller than he should, and further away (as, in fact, the car appears wider than it really is). This looks rather strange. There was an instance of this in a sequence from *The Brothers*, a serial about a transport firm where, because of the generous proportions of a lorry driver's cab, the passenger looked minute and absurdly distant! The result looked very funny. The wide angle lens, however, allows a good picture of the driver and passenger to be obtained without much being "cut off" by the picture frame. Also, with a 10 mm lens the effect of vibration is reduced, though if you want a close-up of the passenger from the driver's side using the camera clamp on the car door, quite a high degree of magnification is possible without vibration becoming evident. When planning a car interior sequence it would be sensible to order up a side clamp, and, for a frontal two-shot, a bonnet clamp to allow you to shoot through the windscreen.

LIGHTING

The starting point when filming all car interior sequences in daylight is to reduce the difference in light levels between the car interior and the background to a ratio that will look realistic on film, which tends to exaggerate such differences. The car interior is, in effect, too dark compared with the scene visible through the windows beyond the passengers. That is because it is lit entirely from the windows around and not from above. Exposure must be based on the background visible through the windows and the light level in the car interior brought up to somewhat nearer that level. But the background must still be the brightest portion of the picture.

To provide lighting for a car interior you might want one or two small hand battery lights on suckers that could be mounted either on the bonnet, or the back or side windows, according to the area to be covered. If the car is on the move nothing but battery lights can be used because of the problem of running power cables to any other type of light.

As stated, the main purpose of the battery lights is to give an exposure on the artists that is compatible with the exposure in the background. There is only one place you can light from, through the windscreen. This is a quite natural effect because it is where the main light in a car comes from. You also add a kicker light from the back window, behind the artists. Lighting would thus be a matter of balancing these lights with the background. But that is a relatively simple matter because the lights can only be placed in certain positions and these are in any case the only places you would want light to come from. The kicker on the back of the head is there only to outline the back of the head which would otherwise tend to blend somewhat with the car interior background. A suitable light for the windscreen in a static situation in daylight would be a mini brute. Generally, you have less light available with a moving situation. But with battery lights, by spotting or adding another lamp you can achieve more or less the same intensity of illumination on the subject. If, in that situation, you use more than one lamp from the same direction, you are not likely to be able to see that there is more than one shadow, partly because of the amount of movement in the scene and also because of the angle of view—you are shooting at right angles to the direction of the light.

Shooting for Back Projection

Many car sequences call for material to be shot in car interiors in the studio, the view through the windows being provided by back projection. The shortcomings of back projection are hardly in evidence if the projected image is confined to such a small image as a car window. The scene is inevitably fairly mobile and the camera is not required to change angle or move in closer, during the shot. In fact, such shots are usually from fairly standard taking positions and do not result in any complications that way. The rear projected image is made to fit the window and the whole sequence can be shot in the normal way with the "plate" synchronized with the camera shutter.

The principal disadvantage in back projection plates, as opposed to filming the real thing, is the decrease in quality of the image outside the window. This is due to several factors—the granular effect of the back projection screen, lack of contrast, grain present in the negative added to that in the print, and a lack of focus in the screen image. The screen image tends to appear woolly in many such scenes. In filming the studio set with back projection the brightness of the screen image determines the overall light level of the scene. If the set is overlit the realism in the relative brightness of interior and (projected) exterior is upset. As the image available from a projector is, in relative terms, dim, you are limited as to how far you can stop down the camera lens and thus the depth of field is restricted. Focus is naturally concentrated on the characters in the foreground and often depth does not extend sufficiently behind them to render the screen at the windows completely sharp. In a real exterior scene, on the other hand, the brightness of the scene is determined by the exterior lighting. The interior is brought up to strength with the help of lights. This level of brightness allows small apertures with great depth of focus and thus the backgrounds are virtually certain to appear quite sharp. Even with the brightest projection light the studio set-up would disallow such small apertures. Car interiors always involve focusing at relatively short range where the available depth of field is inevitably small.

Back projection ceases to be of real value when it becomes too time-consuming an operation. This applies mainly at the studio end when the "plate" is combined with the set. Every change in camera angle must be matched by a change in projector angle and this also means a general re-alignment of equipment which is cumbersome and unwieldy. All this takes time.

In fact, all moving car, train, boat or aeroplane sequences, even static drama shots with action in the background, are much better done for real and it is usually quicker this way. It is also true that the electronic system of Colour Separation Overlay (CSO) gives a much more realistic result.

Shots taken looking forward, or backward, in line with the road would be shot at the actual vehicle speed to be represented on the screen, so you may take this as the standard.

In a given situation then the backward looking plate is taken while the car is moving at a real speed of 40 m.p.h. A forward looking plate is the same. The background shot for the driver would be taken with the car moving at roughly the same rate, 40 m.p.h., but it is possible that you may encounter a case where a recurring feature such as a row of trees placed at regular intervals causes a disturbing flashing effect in the background. To avoid a strobing effect from these you might reduce the car speed by a nominal amount, say, 5 m.p.h.

There still remains the need to shoot the plates to provide for the back projection, however. Certain rules apply to this and must be quite rigidly adhered to if the scene is to appear at all effective. A plate must be provided as a background for each of the camera angles to be shot in the studio car interior. These represent the backgrounds that would normally be seen in each case if it were actually in the travelling car.

If you had two people in the car, driver and passenger, you would probably need back projection plates to insert behind each individually, and also one for going behind the two people together (i.e. two singles and a two-shot). In this case the two people may be shot from head on as if through the windscreen. You would take your two shot plate directly out of the back of a car. You then need two side plates for the individual shots. These are for side, or profile shots of each. If you were going along a normal road, the background that you put behind your driver would be further away than the background placed behind the passenger. Naturally, the closer you are to a background the greater is the sense of speed (if they are supposed to be shots from a vehicle travelling at the same speed in each case). The back projection plates, however they are shot, must show this difference in relative speed for the two backgrounds.

For the passenger background shot, where the actual background is the outside of the road and therefore closer to the car, the speed should be reduced by at least one third, that is to say 28–30 m.p.h., in order to give the *impression* of 40 m.p.h. In practice, the actual speed selected largely depends on the particular background. If it were a pavement with shops and people you would not reduce the speed much as there is sufficient depth in the background to correspond more closely with the view from the other side of the car. If, however, it were a bank or hedgerow very close by, you would reduce the speed very much more–the closer the subject the slower the vehicle should be moving while you shoot in order to give a continuous feeling of travelling at 40 m.p.h.

You would shoot these plates separately unless you had an expensive three-camera simultaneous filming set-up on the back of a camera car. But this way you would probably not, at normal camera speeds, be getting a satisfactory result.

The factors which apply in shooting a real car set-up whether with three-quarter, front or back or side shots (e.g. the background distance) also apply in shooting plates. You get the right set-up by imagining how the conditions will be in a real situation with passengers. Sometimes, to check the set-up you can place someone in the position that the actor is going to occupy in the studio shot to see that the angle is correct. This is very useful for determining correct camera height (lens height). Small factors such as these do not matter much individually but they all combine to give a realistic effect once they are added together. The continuity girl is given the correct lens focal length, and lens height used to shoot any particular plate. She needs this information back in the studio to help in setting up a matching studio situation to preserve the correct perspective.

A BBC adventure film entitled *Terracotta Horse* involved many car sequences. It is typical of the type of production that requires extensive shooting actually in the car, and so illustrates many points that apply here. Basically it consisted of four groups of people travelling in different motor cars. There was a family of four travelling in a Land Rover, a "goodie" and "baddie" in an E-type Jaguar and there was a "baddie" in a Citroen DS. Another man travelled in a 2CV. This Citroen 2CV we used as our only tracking vehicle. It makes a superb hand pushed tracking device with the camera in the back because it has a very soft, oil-loaded piston suspension. You can drive this car over ridiculously uneven ground with the camera in the back and obtain reasonably steady pictures. When you cannot use the engine because of the noise being picked up in sound sequences, it can be pushed by a number of people when put out of gear. This gives very smooth tracks, and is very economical.

On several occasions one had to get inside one of these four cars in order to do sound or silent sequences as the production progressed.

If you are shooting without sound there is one person fewer to be concerned with. In a car sequence this can mean that you do not have to force someone into a small space, as there may really only be sufficient room for the cameraman and the artists. The microphone also has to be considered, although the miniature mikes in use today can be easily hidden somewhere in the car behind the gear lever, under the seat or even in front of the person concerned, so that one of the artists covers the mike. In the BBC we use self-blimped cameras such as the Arriflex BL or the Eclair.

All the sequences shot inside the car for *Terracotta Horse* were, in fact, hand held. There is no room for a tripod in a small car. There was one occasion, however, when we used a tripod. This was for the four-shots taken from the back of the Land Rover—with two people in the front seat and two on the middle seat. We used a baby tripod, and there was room for the sound recordist and, in some instances, the director. But it is left to the cameraman to instruct the artist and check their acting and dialogue, decide when to shoot and where to cut for most car sequences where the director cannot be present. The director can, however, check the sound at least, by hearing it replayed afterwards. One or more directional microphones may be hidden away within the structure of the vehicle to pick up conversation, which is balanced properly with the background noise of the car's engine. Occasionally the car noise is too great, calling for a re-positioning of the microphones.

In an E-type Jaguar such as that used in *Terracotta Horse*, you can only obtain a two-shot by sitting behind the driver and passenger unless you have a proper front support. But as too many front views become monotonous in this case we filmed from behind and the characters were seen in profile when they talked. But they had to be "cheated" in, i.e., moved closer together than normal to close the gap. This is something that can be set up before actually shooting. In the shot it does not matter if one person disappears for a moment as long as they do reappear. This you watch through the viewfinder all the time. The widest lens we had was a 10 mm, which just included both people when the camera was positioned just in front of the boot, and we were sitting in the boot. This gave a good view of the landscape and road ahead coming towards us.

The main difficulty in the Land Rover four-shot was to position all four people naturally yet see all four—they had to be cheated for this too. The cheating was adjusted according to whether we were shooting from slightly to one side or dead centre. In the *Terracotta Horse* we had two children on the back seat who were looking towards the camera because they were looking out of the back of the car watching the cars that followed. One had to be very careful to bear in mind that they would be looking camera left or camera right according to the previous shot. If the previous shot was the "baddies" car, travelling right to left, then one had to make sure that the people, when they looked round were looking out camera right (see diagram).

Consider the situation: One car is immediately behind. From the side of the road you have shot both cars going along, travelling right to left. When you move the camera inside the *front* car everyone must be looking camera right to look at the following car, so if the camera were in the back of the front car shooting on the occupants looking back at the following car, the camera must be placed on the left hand side of the car (Y) in order to allow everyone to look camera right. If the camera were on the other side (X) everyone would be looking out camera left, which is wrong. To summarize: the vehicles are approaching the camera on the side of the road filming them going right to left on the screen. When the camera is placed on Y the people watching the car behind the characters must look camera right. So if the camera were on X they would automatically look camera left which would be wrong because you have crossed the centre line. The figures (actors) 3 and 4 (see diagram) must look *right* in that shot, and 1 and 2 also. You frame them on the left of the screen so that they look right automatically. If you want to cross the line you could do a direct reverse shot though in this particular situation it would not really be necessary. In the Land Rover example in the diagram, from the *Terracotta Horse*, the camera was either slightly off centre (in the back) so that they could look camera right in this instance, or was in No. 4's seat shooting No. 3, and again this would be all right because he would still be looking right and again in No. 2's seat shooting the driver who would be looking forward, with an occasional glance over his shoulder which was still right, with the background still going past in the right direction.

With the pursuing car, the camera was in the centre (Z) behind the two occupants. This method means that for the whole sequence you will be shooting from inside the cars but there is no reason to cross the line, except if, for example, you were behind 1 shooting on 2 or behind 3 shooting 4 with 4 calling to 3, 1 or 2. Then, if they looked round, you would not use the shot as they looked round to the back of the car. You would use the shot up until the time when they started to look and then cut back to Y with them looking the right way. They just start to turn to give you a cut on the move. It does not matter that this fraction of a move is in the wrong direction as you overlap this on the proper shot. So it is hardly a move at all in fact—they merely look as if they are going to. For both these shots you overshoot (i.e. you get them to complete the moves) but always with the proviso that the end of the shot cannot be used. The editor knows what to do.

The *Terracotta Horse* was a superbly organized production. 1248 set-

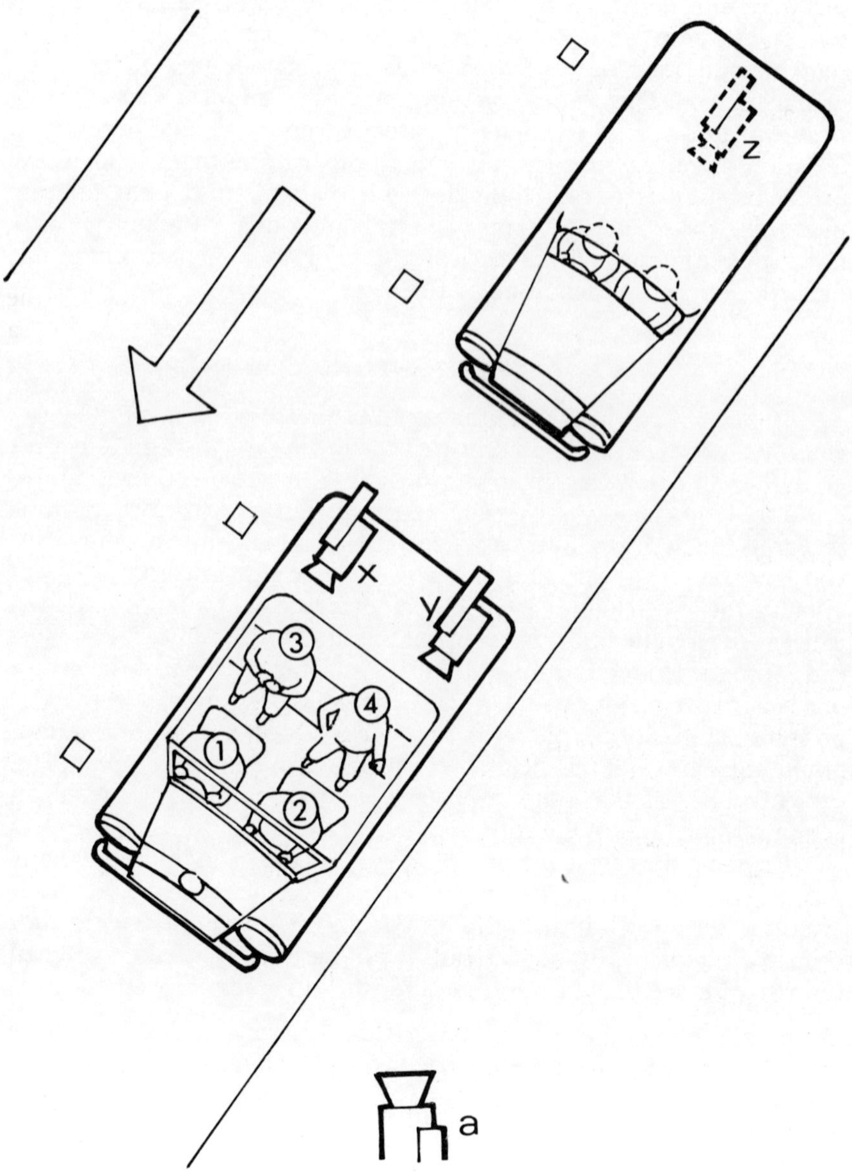

Car chase sequence in *Terracotta Horse*; typical camera treatment for such occasions. In this case the traffic was moving on the left hand side of the road with the cars being right hand driven, so that in the car in front for instance (1) is the driver and (2) the front seat passenger; (a) is the roadside camera position for a static long shot, (x) and (y) are camera positions on the leading car and z the position on the pursuing car. These shots are described in detail in the text.

ups were shot, with only one retake because the camera assistant forgot to set the stop and it was hopelessly overexposed. Even so, he remembered 1247 times! We shot just over 31,000 feet of film, and printed 23,000. This was for six 25-minute programmes. So the cutting ratio was just over 4:1 which was rather exceptional. The production was almost entirely sync-sound, with all the features that usually cause problems—artists having difficulty with dialogue and remembering their lines, the sound problems of aircraft and other extraneous noises, not to mention mike and boom shadows! For about 50 per cent of this film, the shots were each done in one take.

Direction of Movement and Centre Line

In any filmed chase situation you must make up your mind before you start, exactly in what direction the actors are to go. Everyone must go in that direction, say, from left to right. You must keep them in this position. If you change the direction of one or other of the protagonists they must meet or run away from each other, unless, for story reasons, you have had a specific shot showing the change of direction. If you visualize the screen figures going out left of screen, you will not go wrong with the centre line however complex the situation—and car sequences can cause cameramen to forget. The easiest way to think of the centre line factor is to imagine yourself tracking from a dolly, tracking crabwise on some stationary people. They are facing out camera left at a certain point, they are looking head on, beyond that they are looking out camera right—at that point you have crossed the line. The head-on position is the limit of the cut.

Crossing the centre line is the easiest mistake to fall into and many people who are well aware of the problem nevertheless make this error when the set-up is a little complicated. This is where the master shot principle stands you in good stead. If no master shot is taken you can still visualize one in your mind's eye for the purposes of orientation.

Value of Master Shot Principle

Although many people are against using a master shot, it is a very good safeguard and is worth taking even if you do not intend to use it in the film or sequence. It is also very useful for the editor for cutaways in emergencies. Some cameramen make a habit of visualizing in every case the situation that should have been the master shot. Unless you can punch into your mind at the very beginning the right positioning for all the people and objects in that area, then sooner or later you are almost certain to make mistakes about people looking left and right of screen. When you are working fairly actively within an area and are called upon to provide numerous small shots, as with sequences filmed in and around vehicles, you frequently have to correct movements and directions by reference to the mental image of the master shot and you may have to pick the director up on this point. He is expecting you to orientate the action correctly in the screen area. You are organizing the director from an editor's viewpoint as well.

Many directors leave the choice of camera position to the cameraman. He takes it for granted that you give him the right angles. (In a bad, unrepeatable situation it would be possible to flop the negative but this really is the last throw! You get slight loss of focus, increase in grain, etc.) Curiously, many directors, both young and old, cannot get this direction rule right. Some freely admit it. It is perhaps easier for a cameraman to realize this than for a director because he is looking through the camera most of the time.

21

Interviews

IT IS A MATTER of some irony that the interview, a purely "sound" situation, should have become such a strong element in television, which is essentially a visual medium. There is no doubt that people often feel that they have gained something by seeing a well-known public figure in the flesh, as it were, on television. Possibly each man consciously or otherwise forms his opinion of the speaker more by what he sees than what he hears. He might judge that an exceptionally overweight politician will make a lazy leader. Another unfortunate whose eyes happen to be closely set may be instantly branded as untrustworthy. Beyond this, and, indeed, one might say beyond the first few minutes, the entertainment value of talking heads, at least in visual terms, would seem to be limited. Such a programme must lean heavily on the interest in personalities but much more often in what is actually said.

The cameraman has little scope for holding attention on what is frankly a tedious interview; likewise he can add little to an interesting one. He is there to record in the best possible way and with the most appropriate lighting and framing the "performance" of the interviewer and his victim. He hopes to catch the best reactions and in many cases he will catch every reaction because he may have to run a couple of thousand feet of film with the camera continuously trained on one person being interviewed. Occasionally, apart from shots of the interviewer asking questions which will probably (on film) be shot at a different time, there may be one other camera angle such as an effect shot to be used once or twice in the interview.

PURPOSE OF THE INTERVIEW

A discussion set-up, as such, is a departure from the normal interview situation because this could involve an exchange of views between two people of equal rank. Here there would probably be a strong desire on the part of the programme director to avoid playing down either person or appearing to give one an advantage over the other by technical means.

At least a surface of impartiality must be preserved by a national broadcasting institution (and preferably by all broadcasting organizations) and if anyone appearing on the medium is to be damned, it would ideally be out of his own mouth. Naturally, the director has the legitimate power to steer a speaker towards his known views on a subject however odious, and get him to reiterate them before a camera. It is not good interviewing, though it may be skilful technique, to get the person to speak the director's opinion, only in his own words! The objective is not to have the interviewer dominate the subject, nor should this be reflected in the camera treatment. The real aim is to draw from the person opinions (or from politicians, statements) that will interest the viewer. This may indeed involve challenging the person though that challenge may be successfully beaten off and even rebound on the interviewer. Again, it would not be the purpose of the programme to dwell on the interviewer's embarrassment—he is simply a part of the medium like the director, the camera and the television set in the living room.

Cameraman's Role

As far as discussion programmes are concerned the cameraman must be perfectly clear what his function is to be. He is not supposed to get too involved in what is said. Some people claim that it is even a disadvantage if he is interested. His job is to concentrate on the filming—and that can be difficult enough if (using 400, 800 or 1200 ft rolls) he is holding one shot for ten, twenty or thirty minutes without a break! Of course, a cameraman has little say in what goes on.

The interview or discussion is planned by the director. It often takes place at very short notice. The cameraman must organize his equipment, and crew, prepare the location, light, rehearse (if necessary) and film what takes place. The planning of the shooting, angle and approach, may or may not be his concern depending on the individual director he is working with. In the early days of television much more responsibility for these matters devolved on the cameraman. Today his role is narrower and others have assumed responsibility for much of what he used to do.

Why on Film?

The most basic reason for filming an interview rather than using television cameras is that the subject is not available for interviewing in the studio. In some cases it may simply be more convenient to film them in their own surroundings, the limited dimensions of which may preclude the use of elaborate outside broadcast equipment. The situation may be inconvenient for such equipment and the relative lightness and mobility of 16 mm film cameras makes the job more straightforward even with several cameras and their crews shooting simultaneously. Interviews also often demand working at some speed and this, too, is easier with film.

Problems with Filming Interviews

From a cameraman's point of view interviews are the most tedious and technically unsatisfactory area of film production. They are unappealing visually and offer no scope for variety of treatment, which in any case is probably not wanted by the producers of the programme. In terms of raw stock consumption interviews are expensive and wasteful.

From the practical standpoint they are something of a penance. You sit behind the camera with your eye to the viewfinder for up to half an hour at a time (if you are using 1200 ft magazines) and are hard put to keep awake listening to the drone of words. Even if they be pearls of wisdom, you are but swine! In making such interviews one has seen the camera begin to tilt down and the headroom gradually diminish as the poor cameraman begins to doze off—it has happened to us all. It is difficult to judge what is the worse situation, the 1200 ft magazine approach, or the innumerable 400 ft rolls that churn through the camera as the director tries to get his victim to say what he wants him to say.

Another problem with filmed interviews indoors is the frequent lack of working space. More often than not you have to shoot in a small living room which allows little opportunity for placing either the camera or the lights where you would wish. This is on many occasions with no foreknowledge of the circumstances in which you will be operating that day, and therefore no opportunity to "recce" beforehand.

In filming for television you must try and be prepared for the unexpected. You can go in to the studio in the morning and suddenly find that you are going to meet the Queen—anything is possible at a moment's notice. This, incidentally, brings in a subsidiary point which does not concern people engaged in making feature films—the question of the crew's personal appearance. This is additional to the factors of behaviour and tact. Film industry people tend to dress very informally. But in television you may find yourself filming in special circumstances and for this reason cameramen sometimes wear a suit. You endeavour to dissolve into the background and not to be obtrusive in any way. Dressing appropriately helps to achieve this.

System of Working

Because of the likelihood of shooting in difficult conditions at short notice, evolving a system of working that is both quick and efficient affords the best protection. It should be possible to move into a location, set up and light the shots (using the assistant as a "sitter-in") and be ready in less than thirty minutes for the subjects to appear and the interview to start.

It is best to use a small number of lights of relatively low intensity because of the small size of the room (in most cases) and also to minimize the strangeness of the situation from the interviewee's point of view. One does not wish to blind a person with large or brilliant lighting nor worry him or her not to do this or that, not to lean that way or look this. On no account should you try to restrict them in any way. In these circumstances you must accept anything and everything that is there.

A suitable set of lights for this type of work would be, for example, a maximum of four quartz-iodine "Redhead" (tungsten halogen) units of 750 watts each. We used to employ "pups" for this type of job. Those were 500 or 750 watt projector type lamps, but these have been superseded by halogen lighting. One of the four lights is used as the key, one for filler and two as backlights or "back kickers". No extra light is needed for the background because in a small room the distance between subject and background is very small and so the general spill light from the key and filler is sufficient for that purpose. As with drama lighting, a personal preference is to keep the background brightness down to about a half to three-quarters of the key lighting value according to the type of production.

The interesting filmed discussion, *Inside No. 10*, between Mr Heath, at that time British Prime Minister, and the Bishop of Oxford on the subjects of politics and religion was a typical example of the type of production which requires the kind of treatment just discussed. It consisted of two half-hour programmes. We shot for about one and a half hours and used three cameras. One was trained on Mr Heath and one on the Bishop. Both had zoom lenses fitted. The third was a static camera giving a semi-profile of Mr Heath. The three cameras ran simultaneously and it was up to the two operators on the zoom cameras to judge whether and when to take close shots—according to the content. This set up involved lighting for three cameras at the same time in a small room. The basic problem was to keep the lights out of the other camera lenses, but still to obtain a full exposure and good modelling, although the people were looking in different directions. The lights were ordinary full quartz units.

We always work to a set timetable for this type of job. The plan was to arrive at 10 Downing Street at 10.30 a.m., get all the equipment in, do

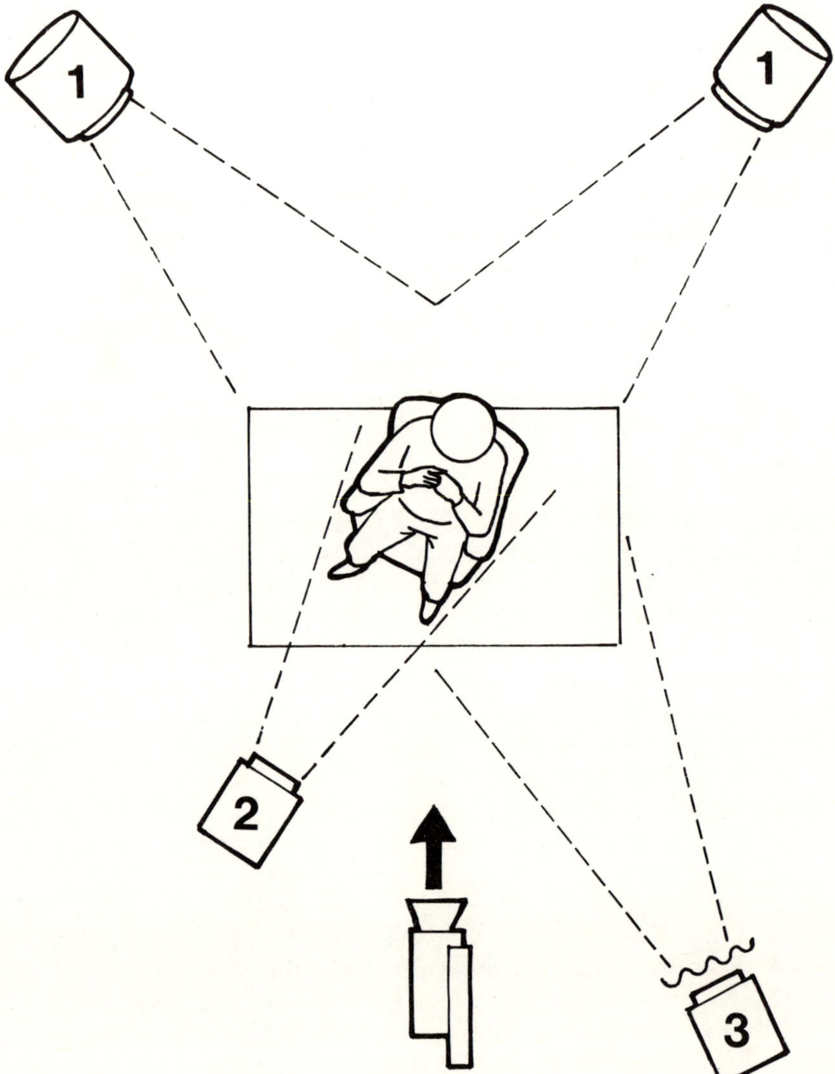

A standard simple lighting set up for a single individual being interviewed, using four identical 750 W lamps. This set up can be put together very quickly and will provide adequate lighting in most such situations. 1, backlights, rim-lighting the person from either side. 2, key light (very high). 3, soft filler, for shadows (lamp diffused).

as much lining up as possible until 11.45 a.m. when we had to vacate the building. We could not return until 2.00 p.m. and the interview was to be at 3.00 p.m. So we had only one hour to finalize all three camera positions and the lighting and check that everything was under control before the Prime Minister walked in at 3.00 p.m. We lined up on people in the chairs and did as much lighting as we could, then, after lunch, finalized the lighting. Although the two people were to face one another you could still get your individual key in positions that would be out of range of the other camera. They were lit as three different shots—two full face and one profile. The camera covering Mr Heath was behind and on the left of the Bishop, the camera covering the Bishop was behind Mr Heath and on his right. This is the correct arrangement because when each person looks at the other he is looking in the right direction. The third camera was in a low position—a director's quirk unkindly stressing the heavy jowls of Mr Heath. The key for Mr Heath, because the camera was on his right, was placed opposite the camera behind Mr Heath, (see diagram) but out of shot because it was high and far enough over for the stand to be out of the other camera's shot. For this type of set-up you must never set too wide a lens angle on the camera otherwise you include the lights. You make the long shot just wide enough to avoid getting the other man's key light in your picture. This is often not as wide as you would like, losing you the advantages of a wide setting. The key light goes as high as possible. However, if the subject is wearing spectacles you risk getting peculiar shadows from their frames. In this instance the key lighting for both people was set high up. The low camera had to take a chance on the lighting. As in any "effect" shot in an interview or discussion set-up, it had to accept the existing key as we could not insert another. Such a shot, as in this case, obtains more or less profile lighting. The backlight is then inserted where possible for each individual.

The key lights were 2 K quartz, the backlight and kicker, wherever it could be added, was from a 750 quartz unit. That for the Bishop was placed beside Mr Heath's camera. The backlight for Mr Heath was next to the camera trained on the Bishop, but further back and spotted to the required intensity. Four fillers were bounced off the ceiling and wall because there was no angle at which a proper filler could be placed without it appearing in the view of one or other of the cameras. They gave an overall illumination. So, although they were in the wrong position these three lights raised the general light level. The only other addition was a little extra light on the background of each person. For the Bishop's background there was a spotlight shooting across almost on the same line as the light being directed up to the ceiling.

With this type of set-up it is largely a question of fitting lights in wherever possible, and if the lighting is not quite right that is un-

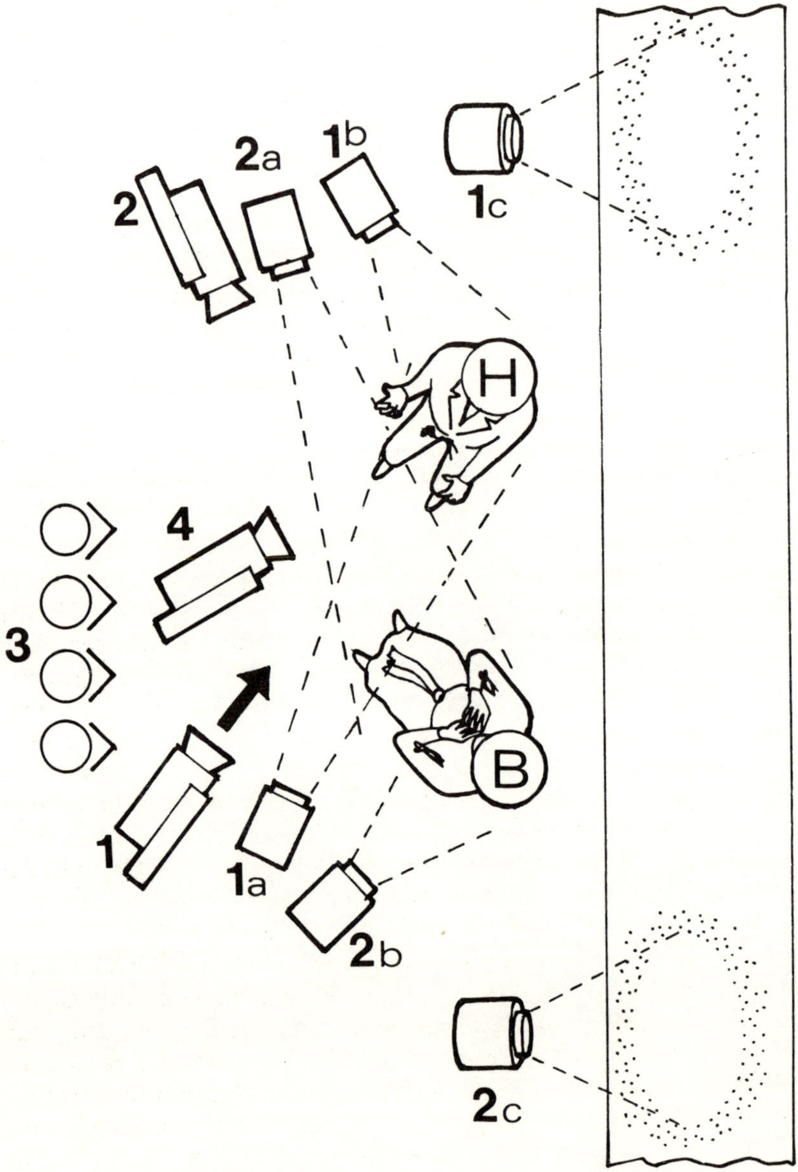

Lighting set up for discussion or interview, such as *Inside No. 10*, between Edward Heath and the Bishop of Oxford. Camera position 1 favouring Heath (H): 1a, key light. 1b, rim light. 1c, background light for H (750 W QI). Camera position 2, favouring Bishop (B): 2a, key light. 2b, rim light. 2c background light for B. (750z QI). 3, general soft fill light from 4 × 750 QI lights bounced off ceilings and walls. 4, Camera position for cutaway shots.

avoidable, and is not really too critical. Fortunately, not too much light was needed for background because the room was quite light. Although Downing Street is a quite spaciously proportioned house, it is so full of furniture that there is little room to manoeuvre so we had to move some of the furniture aside to allow some working space.

SHOOTING WITH THE AUTO CUE

The teleprompter or auto cue is a piece of equipment which fits on the front of the camera, through which you film a person who reads a script visible in the machine itself. It is used where the person has to talk so extensively about a subject that it would be impossible for him to memorize what he needs to say. Yet at the same time he can look straight into the camera lens as if addressing the television viewer directly.

The auto cue consists of a metal framework inside which there is a semi-silvered mirror placed at 45 degrees to the lens. Below this there is another semi-silvered mirror which reflects a movable scroll of paper placed below the camera (and connected with a master machine behind or at the side of the camera) on which is typed everything that the commentator has to say. When the reader looks into the camera he sees in front of the lens through the semi-silvered mirror all the words that are moving on the scroll below, something like a pianola roll. The lens does not pick up the reflection of these words. There are one or two slight disadvantages with this equipment from the cameraman's point of view. Because it is quite a large piece of apparatus to go in front of the camera it slightly off-balances the pan and tilt movement, although in these circumstances you usually do not need to operate very much as the speaker is a captive subject, sitting or standing and looking at the camera. The camera must be tripod-mounted because of the weight of the unit. An extra half stop in exposure should be allowed to compensate for any losses due to the mirror surfaces.

To cut in for close shots the auto cue can be wound back for the commentator to repeat a certain section of the text. The roll is driven electrically, and the man or woman operating the slave machine can adjust the speed so that it is correct for the commentator's natural, or required delivery speed. For the commentator the great advantage of the auto cue is that it allows him or her to concentrate on the delivery, the meaning and expression, rather than fight to remember the words. The speed would be determined during rehearsals, although adjustments can be made in the same way during the actual shot if the commentator reads too quickly or too slowly. The letters in the machine are capitals a good half-inch high and the screen measures about a foot across. The commentator normally reads the centre line.

When working with the auto cue you must avoid having the camera too far away and with a long focus lens setting otherwise the commentator is unable to see the lettering. If, on the other hand, you come too close to him or use too high a magnification, you can see his eyes moving across the line. You try to work at a medium distance, which disguises the mechanics of the system, as it were. You must also try to ensure that the subject does not become too rigid in his looks and position, as if he were supported by a headrest as in the early days of photographic portraiture. As much natural movement as possible is desirable to make the set-up appear realistic.

For an auto cue sequence you might start with the teleprompter directed at the artist and then move the camera off to another subject. You should use a geared head on the tripod for this rather than a friction head which will not give good movements with such a weight. You can only site the camera and teleprompter back a certain amount on the support to try and reduce the nose-heavy effect, but even with lead weights clamped on the pan bar you must have the positive movement of a geared head, with its two speeds. You can release either direction of movement on this head—i.e., have the tilt geared and the pan free—with no friction except a pressure nut at the side. But it is inclined to give rough movements.

22

Filming Works of Art

THE FILMING of works of art presents a number of challenges to the cameraman due both to the nature of the works themselves and the locations in which they might be found. The very nature of static art objects would seem alien to that area in which film and television has its chief strength—the recording of a moving image. But art objects are not "absolutely dead things". Provided the objects have the necessary interest, in themselves, and the cameraman can find it, there is much that he can do to put them across with some of the spirit in which they were created. He has the advantage over a museum guide in that he can positively direct the attention of the onlooker to particular features, and then compare them with the whole almost in the manner of the trained art critic, a point enlarged upon below. He can draw out what is to be seen with favourable lighting, more favourable indeed than that by which the public is normally expected to view the object. In some cases he provides a view of unparalleled quality, providing an opportunity to view a work under ideal conditions when in fact it might normally be virtually invisible. With his lights he can show in all its brilliant colour a great painting hanging on the dark walls of a baronial hall; through the cameraman's telephoto lens are revealed carved details in a ceiling boss high up among the ribs of some gothic vault in central Europe.

If the rewards of filming great works of art are considerable, they are not easily achieved. For most arts films and certainly for arts features, the art works will be filmed *in situ*. On the grounds of expense, carriage and insurance, moving objects to studios would be ruled out, besides the administrative effort required to find a way through the mass of regulations that rightly safeguard the majority of such works. Again, many, if not most owners or guardians of such works may refuse to expose them to the risks of transport from one place to another for the benefit of a film or broadcasting organization. The work of art may, indeed, be untransportable; it might even be the building itself.

The location in which a work of art must be filmed can give the cameraman many headaches. Such a location may contain all the factors which militate against obtaining filmed sequences of reasonable quality. Yet arts feature films are the one area above all others, where the quality of the image is of paramount importance. It can be compared with architectural photography in providing absolutely no justification whatever for lack of the most critically sharp focus, attractive and appropriate composition, good lighting and excellent colour rendition. The colour rendering is of such importance that it may be necessary to call in expert opinions from the art world to advise in the printing of filmed sequences of paintings—as in the case of the BBC television series *Civilisation*.

The cameraman does, of course, have certain factors working in his favour with such films: the fact that the subjects *are* stationary, that the scenes do not involve live artists or frequent rehearsal and that the film is unlikely to be freely intercut with electronically generated material which can show up differences in quality. *Civilisation* was, in fact, filmed on 35 mm in colour which ensured the maximum quality in the image—all other things being equal.

Interest and the Static Image

One would imagine that, as in the case of the material to be represented in *Civilisation*, relatively static subjects would be more difficult to make interesting. However, as we have noted, a static subject can stand by virtue of its own interest and the mere fact that one subject moves and another does not, will not create any particular difficulties. If some subject is static and it calls for movement then you can put in your own with the camera. You might move it along or around the subject. But there is a risk attached to this approach. The movement must not be arbitrary—there must be a *reason* for it. Much photography of static subjects, especially with benchwork (where photographs of works of art are filmed under studio conditions) is so purposely made to move that it becomes monotonous. From time to time you see a bench subject such as a painting treated in such a way that you know you are not going to be allowed to see it stationary—the camera will move about, pan up, pan down, zoom in, zoom out—all for no particular reason other than that the director, or whoever is responsible, has been told that nothing must be static.

This approach is entirely wrong. There are many occasions when you want things to be static, especially where paintings and sculpture are concerned. (Sculpture is a slightly different case because the cameraman can use his lighting to model it and his camera angle and range to interpret it.)

Filming Paintings

When filming a painting you normally start with a general view to place it in its context. If the painting is on a wall or mantelpiece, then there is always something else on the mantelpiece to frame up with the picture or there is some furniture around the side. In this way you show the picture in its real setting. Then you move in to a closer shot—within the frame of the painting. This would be from a square-on position. But unless the angle covered by the camera goes well beyond it, there is nothing worse than to show a little of the picture frame in your within-the-picture shots. That frame is never level or square and always looks terrible on the screen. This is almost a cardinal sin. So arrange the camera angle to be just within the frame.

If the painting is to be seen as a whole and also requires some details to be shown you should always let the viewer see the whole subject and even those details for a reasonable period of time and with a stationary camera. In a gallery it is quite natural to view a painting initially as a whole. It may be some time before you put on the "zoom lens" in your mind's eye and move in to examine a particular section of that painting. You look at that area from a stationary viewpoint—and then another, again from a static point of view.

With your two eyes and brain you do not act as the camera does in some filmed sequences that you can see on television, with the camera roving around with hardly a pause. The technique is dreadfully predictable; you know the camera is going to zoom out because it zoomed in, or across to the right because it has moved the other way.

A good principle with this type of subject is to try and keep the treatment as static as possible—cutting to the next shot rather than zooming or panning. Now and then a little movement will break up this stationary treatment. But, basically, with this type of subject you wish to see things rather than be distracted by camera movement. One might zoom if one thought that there was a distinct connection between a medium shot and a close shot in the same picture.

For example, a picture of a woman who had her arm outstretched and her hand resting on a baby would suggest a fuller treatment, which would certainly be justified. Perhaps one would like to see first of all the full shot of the woman and the baby, but the fact that the hand was resting on the baby's head is rather pleasant, particularly if the hand is well painted. So you might zoom in and pan down the arm to a close-up of the hand and head. There was a definite lead, as it were, inherent in the material from the medium shot (the whole picture) to the point you were moving into. But a zoom shot must be almost imperceptible—so smooth and soft that it does not distract the eye, does not jar, nor says to you that there is a zoom and a pan, as such. The camera should seem to float.

The content of a picture might, of course, influence the way in which you cover it. For example, a busy battle scene might well be interpreted with many cuts following one another, rather than zooming and panning. The mood and spirit of any picture should govern the way you shoot, and cut the sequence.

The way the editor is to cut is implicit in the way you have shot it. If you shoot in this fashion the editor is compelled to follow it. If not, then he can shift for himself. If he were determined to defeat a cameraman's objectives he could duplicate the footage, as it is a stationary subject!

Large Paintings and Murals

Camera treatment with paintings of average size is relatively straightforward. With larger painted surfaces, including murals and tapestries, certain difficulties arise from the size of the subject itself and the kind of treatment the director is likely to envisage with a larger scale subject.

On a number of murals on *Civilisation* we had to track along to cover the subject. But tracking along a mural is a much easier movement than panning across it, because with tracking the perspective remains the same throughout the movement. So as a general rule if you have to cover the whole of a large painting, track rather than pan. With tracking, you establish the set-up and then just glide along.

Panning Flat Surfaces

If you are panning, you place the camera in the centre of the mural (or with any type of panning shots on a flat surface). But the camera is further from the subject at the beginning or end of the shot. There is also a problem with "stagger". If you are panning at the same speed for that part of the mural which is nearest to you, as you were for the furthest part, as the camera approaches the nearer part you tend to get "stagger", a juddering of the image. This is because it is so close to you, and, although you are moving at the same speed you are covering a much greater area at that rate. Whenever you pan round to something which is close to you the linear speed increases and you are covering a relatively greater area. Therefore, as the camera pans to a subject which is nearer to you, you have to try and slow down the pan gradually as you approach it, the nearer it is to you. You cannot check whether you will get stagger by any visual means. You simply bear it in mind, and you are conscious of the approximate panning speed that produces stagger. If the camera has a variable-opening shutter, you can reduce the stagger effect by increasing the shutter angle slightly. If you are panning over a flat surface you have to pull focus as you pan. You tape measure the distances, perhaps the beginning, end and two measurements in the centre. The depth of field would cover the slight differences. But when you are panning you always establish the camera in the central position *of the pan*, so that although there is a little distortion at the beginning and end there is none in the main central area.

All pans, like tilts or zoom shots are governed by the feeling that you or the director have for that particular shot.

Perspective Distortion

When panning across murals, you should always try to diminish distortion whenever possible and find a central position. But this also depends how long the pan is to be and how much of the picture you want to take in. If it is a static shot and you want to include quite a wide area you try to get as near to a central position (flat on to the subject). When panning you try to use a lens which itself is non-distorting although with modern lenses there is remarkably little distortion. In 35 mm work the 2 in. (50 mm) lens is the normal eyesight lens giving the minimum perspective distortion. On 16 mm film the equivalent is the 25 mm, but you would use anything between the 17·5 and the 25 mm. If you had to use a *wider* angle there would be distortion. But, with flat surfaced subjects, if you use a lens of narrower angle the perspective distortion is not very noticeable. (This also applies to long shot exteriors, panning across the horizon.) You can use a wide angle lens from a fixed central position when shooting a painting but try to avoid tilt.

You have no need to worry about keystoning (where the sides of the subject lean inwards) on the establishing shot which shows a painting or tapestry in its surroundings. But once the camera moves in closer to the subject tilt distortion should be avoided. For many establishing shots of pictures you find that you have to use the 10 mm wide angle lens, which does have a certain degree of inherent distortion. But being back somewhat and a little to one side of the picture this does not matter. Once you close in on the subject with the 50 mm lens on 16 mm there is no barrel or perspective distortion.

The main things to avoid with this type of subject are very oblique shots, which give quite unacceptable results and, even more important, shots in which the camera tilts up or down. If the camera can be level then the small distortion that occurs at the sides is not too apparent. But if you are shooting from below, keystoning is obvious. On *Civilisation* some of the pictures were so high that we had to shoot from a rostrum. In Pisa, there was a marble pulpit to be filmed which was about 10 ft up. For this, we used an 8 ft rostrum so that we could then zoom in on the subject quite comfortably. With pictures that were tilting as they hung on the wall, we always tried to find the central axis. This made it easier when operating from floor level. If the paintings were flat-on to the wall we might have to raise the camera another 6 or 8 ft.

Avoiding distortion is often a matter of compromise—you save major distortion in one direction knowing that you will get it in another. But the skill in this is knowing how to compromise in the right direction.

LIGHTING AND REFLECTIONS

One is hardly called upon to "light" a painting; it is more a question of providing even illumination, because everything else has been put there by the artist. It is therefore quite straightforward to light a painting in ideal conditions—it is only a matter of using flat surface copying technique. You should use a flat and flooded light. You may have to build up the lighting but you do not need hard light for modelling, etc. For example, a 6-light mini brute covers a wide area and gives a strong spread of light. If you are shooting a flat surface from a central position, you might light with a soft-light on one side balanced by another soft-light on the other. With subjects of smaller area only one soft-light on one side of the camera is necessary. With a flat surface where the light you are using is not placed too far round to one side there is always a danger of reflection problems.

If you are filming a small painting and the camera is quite close, you would not necessarily move the lighting unit in close. The closer it is, and therefore the brighter the light, then the more you stop the camera lens down. Consequently you bring up the surface of the painting more, because of the greater sharpness and depth of field. One advantage of photographing flat surfaces where there is no movement within the frame and you yourself do not make any movement (and if you have any problems with insufficient exposure) is that you can always run the camera at a lower filming speed. This also avoids the need for strong illumination on the picture itself, thus protecting the painting from fading and the effect of heat. The light can be positioned much further away than it would otherwise be. In some cases where you would usually need more light for a normal filming speed you can make do with much less—which might be all that you can command in the situation.

REFLECTIONS

Reflections are a constant hazard when filming paintings and other flat surfaced subjects. The only solution is to move a light around until there is no reflection from the picture or wall surface. As all the light must then come from that direction, you build up the lighting at that point to the level required. In certain cases where the reflection in the painting surface originates from a large window opposite, this must be blanked out. With reflections you must always check the picture through the lens, especially during pans and tracking shots.

The worst problem with reflections is with those artists who painted with a heavily laden brush and in such a way that there is a chunky surface. This, no matter where you place your lights, will reflect back into the camera as the light catches the various surfaces.

The most problematical paintings for filming that we came across on *Civilisation* were those by Franz Hals. The tones he used in the clothing and background were so deep in relation to the faces and lace of collars, etc., that it was virtually impossible to draw any detail out of them although it was indeed, there. The surfaces of the paintings were shiny, and if we placed the lights in such a way that there were no reflections, there was not enough illumination to light the surfaces that we really wanted to show. We sometimes had to put more light on the darker portions of some paintings than elsewhere, by shading off the light with barn doors or other devices from the lighter areas, such as the face or hands. This was almost like "dodging" a print under an enlarger in still photography. Usually you have to do this with the very large group paintings such as those by Hals and Gericault which are full of detail and light and shade.

Another hazard in filming paintings is sometimes encountered in the rather severe measures exercised to preserve them. A number of the paintings featured in *Civilisation* were in the Louvre. When we were filming in the Louvre, there were officials running about with thermometers making sure that the temperature of light did not rise to more than about 5 degrees above normal. This was rather ridiculous because as soon as one set a light one had to kill it. The temperature they had in mind was about the level emitted from a 60 watt bulb!

While shooting in Windsor Castle and Hampton Court Palace in a programme that preceded *Civilisation* called *The Royal Palaces*, we gained considerable experience in filming works of art. It is certainly not an insuperable problem to remove reflections from a painting which is seen in a static shot. But when the camera must track through three rooms whose walls are laden with paintings, panning left and right as it tracks, then the problems are much more acute. A painting may be seen as clear in one part of a shot and not clear in another part of the same shot because, as the camera tracks, the painting picks up reflections from another angle. A number of such highly mobile shots occurred in both productions.

Whereas it can be problematical to remove reflections from some paintings for stationary shots, *any* camera movement increases this problem. It can take hours to light such a shot because you can only use a trial-and-error method repeatedly. It is also a matter of very precise timing. If you decide to pan off a particular picture at a given moment you must first be clear to pan on to the other picture without picking up reflections in that. This procedure would have to be repeated for each rehearsal and for the final take.

A tracking shot through a hall of mirrors is no easy task, and besides that in *The Royal Palaces* we did several such shots in *Civilisation*. There was one particularly challenging one in Nymphenburg Palace just outside Munich. We had seen it on the recce and thought about it, and had one or two pieces of equipment made specially for the job. It took some time to light because it meant that not only did both the camera and the lights have to be hidden from all the mirrors but you had to light literally 360 degrees of subject because if you looked into a mirror you could see all around. It really meant that all the lighting equipment had to be at floor level. Fortunately, the mirrors in this very large interior, although they ran all round the room (the ceiling was gold and silver plaster) did not quite come down to the floor but were about two feet clear of floor level and reached to within about a foot of the ceilings. The lighting equipment on the floor was shining in many different directions to get the right modelling and exposures all around. The camera had to be at the right height for proper perspective. At a particular stage the camera panned up to the ceiling but did not come down to the mirrors and walls until the reflections of the lights in the far part of the floor were not in picture. The whole scene was somewhat contrived because of the complexity of the lighting problem. The camera movements had to be governed by the restrictions imposed by the equipment; at certain points the camera was directed towards the walls or ceilings, partly to avoid including in shot the lighting equipment on the floor. There were also strong light reflections from the floor surface in certain areas and the danger of including a reflection of the camera itself with the crew, in the picture.

The shot started in a rather splendid yellow and gold room with a silver ceiling and the camera began by panning down from that ceiling to two closed doors. The doors operated themselves from inside and beyond were seen the great mirrors and about one third of the room. As the camera tracked forward more room was seen and reflections of the room in the mirrors at which it was looking. At a certain point when there was an increasing risk of including something unwanted in shot the camera panned up to the ceiling of that room, still moving forward. It did not pan down again until all the lighting in the area around the original door was out of picture. This lighting was on the floor to the left and right of the camera just out of sight until immediately after the camera panned up to the ceiling. You cannot, of course, light a mirror; you are lighting the walls between the mirrors, and the ceiling. The whole of this scene was covered in one continuous shot.

SCULPTURE

Sculpture, a three-dimensional subject, is photographed in much the same way as a human being. There are the same shapes and forms, you must create the same modelling effect. A well known cliché with sculpture is to place it on a turntable and film it revolving. Or you can track round it or pan up and down and you are not subject to the restrictions of filming with flat surfaces.

With sculpture you have thickness and depth of field to consider, so you have to watch these carefully. But it would also depend what you are trying to show. You should watch for distortion in the image of a sculpture of which a part projects towards the camera. You would use intermediate focal lengths—17–25 or 32 and certainly not use settings on the wide angle end of the zoom, and likewise avoid long settings, especially if there is a part such as an arm extending towards the camera. You should move the camera further away but not so far as to flatten the shape with the magnification required. With a long focus setting you need less background area. If you move in closer or use a wide angle lens a larger background area is covered, which may cause unwanted extraneous features to be included in the picture area. You may in some cases be compelled to use the long focus lens to avoid immovable background objects (by covering a smaller area), or to assist in throwing background features well out of focus. You may focus forward a little to use only the rear part of the depth of field to cover the object, and thus have the background even further out of focus.

LIGHTING

The kind of lighting used on sculpture or objéts d'art depends also to some extent on the kind of film they are being shot for—whether the prime objective of a sequence is informative value, where you would light it fully with less deep shadow than if you were just seeking dramatic effect. With lighting for informative value there is far more scope than with flat-surfaced subjects. You have to make allowances for the colour of the subject. If it is white you should make sure that the background is of sufficiently different colour or density so that the sculpture is to stand out well against it. You can do a little with backlighting, of course, and modifying the effect of the existing background with the strength and direction of light you put on it. With white subjects, after arranging the key light correctly for modelling, you can take a reflected light reading to find the differences between this white object and the general aperture level i.e., a key light set for T4 (foot candle reading) may give T5·6 or T6·3 readings off the subject itself. You can then with very white subjects, follow the T6·3 reflected reading. With a medium or off-white subject the T5·6 reflected reading would be followed. There is a chance of losing detail in lighter coloured sculptures. The lighter the subject, therefore, the less light you use.

A bronze is the exact opposite. If you light to T4 you might expose for T3·5. You have to make sure also that the front light does not kill the modelling that the key light gives, even though it is a dark subject. So, here again, you have to keep the key light rather bold. Where you gain, however, with bronzes is in the beautiful highlights and reflections that they give. You can produce too many, but not if the number of lights used is kept to a minimum.

With silver, you expect many highlights, so it is not a good idea to use a pola screen over the lens or anti-reflection sprays on the subject to remove them. You can hold the spray in reserve for removing really bad and distracting flare that is coming straight in to the camera lens and cannot be avoided.

Glassware such as cut glass etc., should also show its highlights. You start by lighting the glassware from the preferred angle and see how it works. You can then move any lights which cause distracting flashes.

On occasions in BBC work we have introduced artificial backgrounds to the objects—green baize, blue card, etc., brought along specifically for the shot. Occasionally you might put a hard or soft shadow on such a background or leave it as it is or keep light off the background altogether.

There is no particular problem with lighting an object which is to be revolved. You are obtaining all possible permutations from one light and the shadow constantly changes. You light the object from a particular angle, say the frontal view, then, when the object is revolved everything else falls into place, say, with the back of the head there will be less shadow. Shadows will then begin to re-emerge as it comes round again to face the camera. In effect, your key light is moving. It would perhaps be interesting to set a key light to revolve around an object rather than the other way round. It would have to be high to avoid a camera shadow.

Because of the problem of gaining sufficient exposure in certain circumstances, *Civilisation* called for a considerable amount of slow motion photography. We took only a limited quantity of lighting with us in order to gain mobility, and, except for about four occasions we made do with that. Great areas whch we could not light had to be filmed with one of the three specially geared motors we had made to turn at 12, 8 and 4 frames per second respectively. It was only necessary to plug the motors in to the camera to obtain the appropriate filming rate. In Chartres Cathedral we used the 4 frame movement.

The normal motor was designed to run at 25 frames. We had a variable speed motor which would run from 32 fps to 16 fps but was unreliable at low speeds. Any shot which had camera movement in it would be accurately timed and, using a Moy head, a geared tripod head with hand-operated wheels (as opposed to friction) head. It was reasonably easy to gear and time any shot. Sometimes we had Kenneth Clark included in the shot. We has a shot in Chartres Cathedral where the camera panned down from the vaulting and across to Kenneth Clark who would turn towards the camera to speak. This was shot at 4 fps. For such shots the entire camera movement would be timed, and Kenneth Clark would turn at a very slow speed to compensate for the fact that the camera was turning at either 8 fps or 4 fps. Then we would immediately cut to a closer shot for dialogue, filmed at 25 fps where, being from nearby and covering only a small area it could be lit with ease. This technique allowed us to make great long shots with the minimum amount of light—with no more than half a dozen 750 w quartz multibeam lights. We lit the altar and choir and surrounds of Chartres Cathedral turning at 8 fps, with only 15 kW of lighting and using the 18 mm T1·8 lens (a 35 mm) wide open. (25 frames is 1/60 sec.; 12 = 1/30; 6 frames 1/15; 4 frames about 1/8 sec.) With these slow filming speeds we would first set up the shot and operate the camera normally and time it with a stop watch so that a pan and tilt say, would take 10 sec. from A to B. We would then rehearse the shot to take 60 sec. to carry out (because the shot is to be taken at 4 fps) i.e. 6 times the normal time, with a stop watch again. Laboratory reports indicated a normal negative for density.

The lighting techniques used in *Civilisation* were governed by the fact that we had a 15 kW alternator and we hoped that we could rely on finding a local supply of 5–10 kW. So we carried equipment that could cope with that. In some places we went to they did not have more than about 5 amps and the wiring was terrible. We wouldn't dare put anything on, or a church which had been there since the fourth century might go up in flames! So we would use the alternator wherever we could.

23

Poetry Reading

THERE ARE MANY occasions in filming television material when, despite the fact that the subject may be one of intense human interest and several people are taking part, there is virtually no drama in the physical sense. Movement may be prescribed by circumstances inherent in the situation—indeed it may be alien to the mood of the production to introduce any. Some of the more cerebral television studio features often content themselves with physical movements of the persons within the limitations of a studio chair, where in close-up movements of the head and features are of prime importance and a gesture of the hand is the most emphatic action that can be expected. Often, such a telling point will be missed because the camera at that moment is framing the speaker in big close-up. The cameraman is perhaps more concerned that his subject does not suddenly shift in the chair and pass right out of shot. Much of this depends on the particular mannerisms of an individual who is being filmed.

A prior experience of that person, such as a politician who makes frequent television appearances, may be passed on by the director to the cameraman and the artist may become known as a rather animated speaker.

As a cameraman one is certainly looking for interest in the picture, not merely in movement but in shapes, line, expression on the face and any other characteristics that single out an individual. Certainly you cannot force movement in to a static situation. Constant camera movement or zooms are artificial and probably uncalled for in the majority of talking head situations.

Changes in angle introduce variety and the scope for action and reaction between two persons, but in most cases there are two angles, one on each subject, with perhaps another on the more dominant personality.

This depends on the situation and the type of subject and programme.

C. Day Lewis Series

Occasionally there is a programme which seems to call for the bare minimum of camera activity. The interest is centred purely on the subject and the camera must not be felt to intrude. Such a case was the series of programmes covering a choice of poems made by the British Poet Laureate, Cecil Day Lewis, during the closing months of his life. The filming was done early in 1972 and was directed by Norman Swallow, head of BBC Television Features.

The presentation of a programme consisting solely of poetry readings was considered by many to be a risky undertaking. Previously, poetry had featured only as a constituent of arts programmes, and the shortcomings of the visual medium applied to an essentially non-visual art form presented something of a challenge.

C. Day Lewis himself was enthusiastic about the idea of poetry readings on television, and he, Jill Balcon and Norman Swallow had had a number of discussions about how it could be done. By the time definite plans for the series had been laid, Lewis had undergone a major operation and did not himself know that he was dying of cancer. It was decided that because his weak condition would not allow him to make the necessary journeys to the BBC studios, the whole programme should be filmed at his home in Greenwich. Lewis himself was told that the BBC thought the programme would have a more intimate atmosphere if it were made in the poet's own home.

In this series of six half-hour poetry readings Lewis and his actress wife, Jill Balcon, were to read a selection of poems representative of the whole spectrum of (mainly) English poetry from the sixteenth century to the present day, and including a couple of Lewis's own. For two of these programmes, one guest reader was invited—the actors Marius Goring (for the programme on satire) and Sir John Gielgud (for that on death). These were broadcast under the collective title *A Lasting Joy* and were subsequently published, together with various comments the poet made on them, in a book of the same title. The poems were grouped under programme headings or themes representing the primary events or phases and forces in human life and experience—Childhood, Human Heroism, Satire and Hatred, Love and Friendship, Times and Seasons, Death and Immortality.

The BBC was making this programme partly as an historical document; it was, in fact, completed about a month before Lewis died, and the last programme was broadcast the day after he died as an obituary—before the whole series was shown in its proper sequence. That programme consisted of poems about death—surely one of the most poignant television programmes ever made. Anyone who watched it could not fail to be moved. Lewis, who had been ill for many years, must surely have known that he was dying. By the end of the filming we all felt very close to one another. And by way of celebration on completion of the programmes he brought out half a dozen bottles of champagne. We were sitting there drinking and trying to be merry when we all knew that it would probably be the last time we should see him.

The team from the BBC which handled this series was confined to four members who, prior to the event, were sworn to secrecy in the knowledge of Lewis's certain death in a few months. There was one sound man, the cameraman and his assistant and one electrician in the unit, plus the director and sometimes his secretary. The unit was required to work quietly and efficiently, not to upset Lewis. It turned out to be a most exhilarating fortnight.

The working schedule for the programme consisted of one two-day session, then a break for a fortnight, followed by completion in another three days. So there were about five days of actual shooting in all.

The approach was to be absolutely straightforward with no zoom shots or special effects, and using ordinary "lounge" style lighting. (We took lights with us and a generator, because there were power cuts at the time the filming was done.) It was to be a quiet, unsensational treatment focusing all attention on the man himself. This approach paid off, as there was a measure of dignity in the programmes that matched the occasion.

Camera Treatment

At the beginning we had set up a long shot of the room which showed the seated readers in their various positions. This shot served as the main title backing for each programme. Whenever we came to a particular person reading a poem they would be located as seen in the long shot, and we shifted the camera accordingly. Because of this working method the readers always retained their correct relative positions as far as their direction of looks was concerned, if they happened to be looking at each other.

The initial long shot showed Lewis in the centre of the picture and on frame right either Marius Goring or John Gielgud, whichever was present, and on frame left, Jill Balcon. When Lewis "handed over" to the next speaker he would look left of screen for Jill and right of screen for Marius. When the camera came round to Jill she looked right of screen to Cecil, but close right of screen to Marius. So we maintained continuity throughout.

On this programme there was little direction, as such. The camera was moved around according to who was talking, not necessarily full face. It was basically a one poem, one shot treatment, with no cutting in between at all. There were also some reaction shots, necessary to add variety. And some changes of camera angle. But even these were all single shots.

The fact that it was all to be filmed in a small room and there was no cutting in to poems limited you to some extent. We picked the best sized shot but allowed no gimmicks in the filming. The biggest close-ups were head and shoulders—not "television" close-ups. Occasionally we re-shot because of faults in reading or unsatisfactory delivery.

With this type of programme, as with interviews, it is advisable to keep the camera well back and use a longer focus lens than normal to get the framing you want, bringing the subjects to you rather than taking yourself to them. If the subject is not used to a camera he should not be asked to fight it. Flattening of perspective, a familiar characteristic of long focus shots, is only very marginal with the appropriate focal lengths, 35 mm or 50 mm on a 16 mm camera.

The decision to use long, medium or close shots was determined very largely by the content of the poems, whether it was intimate, quiet or reflective. The approach we used was to get a line-up of camera and artist, have the rehearsal of the poem, and from then onwards make slight alterations or determine the closeness of shot used. Some more flamboyant poems we shot in wider view, though, on the other hand, the expression in the face and eyes would help the effect of some of these readings.

For the rehearsal, each poem was read right through. The director worked out with us which would be the best type of shot for the poems—the mood, delivery, and the particular reader were determining factors. In the case of Jill Balcon, who is a very attractive woman indeed with a lovely face, we tended to want to be photographically as close as possible for the full effect of the delivery. Her face, and particularly the expression in her eyes, we thought, were extremely fine.

Cecil Day Lewis, who was under great stress although he did not let one know it, had a very strikingly lined face of some grandeur. But, because of the circumstances, one felt that one did not want to intrude too much on him. So we kept to an ordinary close-up in preference to big close-ups of him.

With Marius Goring and John Gielgud the expressions were good. But Gielgud is a tall man so it was necessary to come back with the framing quite a way to get him in, although he was seated.

With this type of situation you have to bear in mind the style of delivery. In *A Lasting Joy* the poems were all read, not acted, nor delivered from memory. In any such case each shot would also have to be adjusted according to how the book or paper were held. If it were a book, you would want to see a little of the book, but because of movements made by the individual you would not want the book to be coming in and out of picture in a disturbing way, or not quite being in picture and the person looking out of frame, which is rather ugly. In such a case you would either take the shot closer so that the book was definitely well out of frame and the viewer would realize that the subject was reading though he would not see what was being read. Or the framing would be back sufficiently to show what the person was reading from and this would be a part of the composition. Any normal movement of the reader would then be less significant in terms of the picture composition. With readers, you do sometimes have to ask the artist not to bring the book or paper up so high that he covers his mouth or face. Hand gestures that are relevant or "photogenic", reinforcing points in the reading should be included, perhaps shown clearly in medium shot or, at least, in a wider shot than you would normally choose.

All the readers were sitting, so a stand microphone was positioned just out of screen, slightly below and to one side. On the long shot where there was little dialogue, an effects mike was used over the top out of frame. The sound on this series was excellent, despite the presence of main road traffic outside the house. In this case the sound was, if anything, more important than the picture. A very competent sound man was assigned to this job.

For the programme of poems about death, Sir John Gielgud was present. Throughout these programmes we had frequently been filming the readers using big close-ups of their faces. Bearing this in mind and also the circumstances under which we were filming this particular programme, it follows that the camera would allow little to go by unnoticed. It is one of the extraordinary powers of television that it affords a directness of access to a person via a big close-up of their face so that the least affectation or pretence is seen to be so and the most genuinely felt emotions, provided the camera does not inhibit the subject, are observed with a keenness that is hard to equal in real life. Under these conditions the camera does not allow a person to put the normal barrier of distance between himself and those he addresses. During this last programme, Sir John Gielgud was reading Shakespeare's famous sonnet beginning "Shall I compare thee to a summer's day . . ." in which, speaking as a poet, he tells his lover that although time takes its toll of their physical person, they may live on after death through the everlasting power of poetry. Perhaps it was the immediate relevance of these lines to the present circumstances, or the awesome feeling of frailty that everyone was conscious of on this occasion, but as I watched through the camera at the big close-up of Gielgud's face, I saw that he had started to cry. It is a strange feeling when looking through a camera and observing such a thing in close-up that one is intruding into someone's thoughts. You feel as if you want to shut your eyes. Equally, in happier circumstances it is one of the benefits of being a cameraman that when you get in close you really *do* see people—nothing phoney will convince at that distance. With this type of work you are watching the person almost like a viewer because once you have set up your composition you are free to concentrate on what is being said, and how the person reacts.

The intimate contact with people that the film cameraman experiences, is a particularly rewarding aspect of filming for television. However, only with a close working relationship between the cameraman and his director can the television film be made to live, rather than be merely a record of an image.

Appendix

FILMING DIARY

7th March

Contacted Rodney Bennett by phone on a preliminary discussion about *Madame Bovary*. Discussed methods of shooting night rain sequences of man on horseback—fire engine versus stirrup pump and relative costs—also early morning shots using diffusion filters until recce on the 24th indicating shooting "on the blink".

14th March

Production conference with Ian Engleman for *Boston Symphony Orchestra* in *Great Orchestras* series.—Taking 2 BL's with mini locks to 10 to 1 zooms plus 16 mm T 1·4 lenses—flying to Boston on Monday 14th April after finishing *Bovary* on the 11th—concert shooting 17th and 24th plus break up of hall upon concert on the 30th. Documentary build-up, interviews, and "pretty pretties" on remaining days—seems to be a good stiff schedule—electrician to carry one-man kit of lights for interviews plus battery light—five lights for concert hall are there.

After Boston conference, saw John Read about *Monet* which recce's on my return from Boston, starting shooting in France during the first week in June until July.

24th March

Recce on *Madame Bovary*—started at Ely Cathedral—could be a lighting problem, decided to use the available lighting plus a minimum of my own, plus wide aperture lenses—all to save cost and keep mobility as schedule only allows $\frac{3}{4}$ day for interiors—exteriors of Ely quite simple with artists and hansom cab—all supposed to be Rouen in 1850—decided on angles and backgrounds plus an Elemac dolly and tracks—On to Lavenham to discuss fairly tricky night sequences—decided to keep lights down to alternator strength and again threw away zoom and used fixed wide aperture lenses. On to Sudbury area—scrapped two locations due to inaccessibility for alternator and night lighting—found another two much better.

25th March

Continued recce—no further problems except for the occasional one re alternator and hard standing. Returned to London.

26th March

Packing up and organizing equipment for shipping to Boston next week when I shall be in Suffolk for *Bovary*—this is my own camera to go and am to have a hire one for *Bovary*.

1st April

Travelled to Sudbury in morning—unpacked and organized equipment for shooting in afternoon. Shot the silent sequences—no sound, no problems!—Weather not good.

2nd April

Shot church choir-boy sequence mainly in rain—problems in matching shot for shot in variable density light—end of day brilliant sunshine and two shots to go—so left over until after another location.

3rd April

Everything chucked at us today, except thunder—matching problems even more acute as not only the variation of light, but snow and hail has to be cleared from shot—sound far from co-operative with distant noises vis-à-vis the sun or lack of it—a very frustrating and worrying day—all rushes O.K. to date.

4th April

Ely Cathedral sequences—shot with wide aperture lenses and minimum light—blocked out non-stained glass window because of bad lighting balance—shooting out of sequence creates problems as changeable daylight filters through the windows. Exteriors in good light for a change.

7th April

Near disaster day—wedding sequence at Polstead Church (Maria Martin and the Red Barn!) in howling freezing gale followed by a cloudburst—matching problems again.—Afternoon location on farm and yard—good light to start—then violent thunder storm—the cloudburst again—now fighting time as well as weather—Elemac breaks down—last shots as daylight begins to fade—change location for one night shot of a man wearing a black cloak riding a white horse in a narrow lane at night. The classical shot!

8th April

Lavenham—street dressed with cobbles and peat to cover white line in road etc.—Rouen 1850—Day, evening and night shooting—No problems except weather, finished night shooting as blizzard started.

9th April

Day and night exteriors at same location—had decided again on recce that for financial reasons and speed mobility I would shoot all night exteriors with minimum light plus prime lenses of T1·4 and T1·8—Consequently using this low level of lighting and underexposing 1 to ½ stops as usual I could use quartz plus alternator—first time this trip we had luck with weather—dry and cold—completed four difficult sequences with 23 set-ups in 5½ shooting hours.

10th April

Final shooting in afternoon—child and butterfly sequence—subjective flashback.

14th April

Fly to Boston, Massachusetts.

Shot List

"MADAME BOVARY"

PART TWO

T/K Page	*Shot*	*Slate*	*Action*	*Sound*
3 (p. 82)	19		H/A 2S EMMA/RODOLPHE	
3 (p. 82)	20		L/A 2S EMMA/RODOLPHE He helps her down	
3 (p. 82)	21		LOOSE 2S EMMA/ RODOLPHE They come fwd. EMMA looks at dovecot. Turns back to RODOLPHE	
3 (p. 82)	22		2S EMMA/RODOLPHE (fav. EMMA) (dovecot b/g)	
3 (p. 82)	23		TIGHT 2S EMMA/RODOLPHE (fav. RODOLPHE) He kisses her.	
3 (p. 82)	24		TIGHT 2S EMMA/RODOLPHE (fav. EMMA) PAN EMMA L.	*EMMA:* No, no. It cannot be . . . *RODOLPHE:* I love you, Emma . . . love you . . . . *EMMA:* You frighten me! Let's go back. Where are the horses?
3 (p. 83)	25		LOOSE 2S EMMA/RODOLPHE	

	They come fwd. RODOLPHE X's L. 2S RODOLPHE/EMMA	*RODOLPHE:* I need you Emma; your eyes; your voice, your thoughts. I can't live without you.
3 26 (p. 83)	TIGHT 2S RODOLPHE/EMMA	*EMMA:* It's wrong. It's madness . . . to listen to you. . . .
MIX TO		
3 27 (p. 83)	LS HORSES	
	PAN R. TILT DOWN 2S RODOLPHE/EMMA	*EMMA:* We must go back.
	ZOOM IN EMMA	
		RODOLPHE: Not back . . . But on.
	RODOLPHE OUT L.	
3 28 (p. 83)	2S RODOLPHE/EMMA	*EMMA:* What's that for?
	EMMA sits up. HOLD 2S	*RODOLPHE:* To cut one of the reins. Then I shall mend it, and that will explain why we have been so long. After all, it's the first time.
	He kisses her. Goes out L.	
		EMMA: The first time. Yes.
	EMMA lies back.	

Shooting Schedule

WEDNESDAY, 1st MAY	FILMING DAY

Location:	The Highlands, Bufflers Holt, Buckingham. (*As Monday, 29th April*) Vehicles to enter Railway Cutting through Radclive.
Unit Call:	0930 on Location.
Artists Call:	0900 ready to leave Hotel. Young Sylvia .... DANIELLE CARSON Myra .... SARAH SUTTON Farmer .... EDWARD BROOKS Boy in Cart .... PETER VAUGHAN-CLARKE Mrs. Longmore .... ELIZABETH CHAMBERS
Costume/MU:	0900 ready to leave Hotel, having dressed and made-up Artists.
Transport:	0900—*Minibus* to take Artists, Makeup, Costume to Location On Wrap—Minibus will take Artists back to TC Main Reception, then return to Buckingham. TBA—*Car* to call for Miss Dandy Nichols, bring her to White Hart Hotel, Buckingham, then return to London. P.A. will meet the train at Bletchley Station, to pick up ALISON DOWLING + Matron.
Props:	0915 on location. Horse + Cart: David Goodey *Tel:* Reading (0734) 883334.
HAP:	1100 Hot rolls and coffee/Lunch/Tea on location as Monday.
Vis. Fx:	Set up TREE for next day.
Itinerary:	0930 Ep. I, TK7 1100 Coffee 1130 Ep. I, TK7 cont.

1300	LUNCH
1400	Ep. I, TK7 cont.
1400	WRAP

Artists staying overnight: DANDY NICHOLS, ALISON DOWLING.

Unit Base: White Hart Hotel, Buckingham.

Filming Schedule

"CIVILISATION"
Film schedule—March/April/May/June 1968
to cover locations In France/Italy/Germany/Norway/Scotland/Ireland
for programmes 1 (5657/0192) 2 (5657/0193) 3 (5657/0194) and 4 (5657/0195)

		Prog./Producer
Saturday 2nd March	crew cross to France M. Gill flies to Angers via Paris	
Sunday 3rd March	crew travelling	
Monday 4th March	film Angers (silent) Sir Kenneth flies out via Paris	(3) M. Gill
Tuesday 5th March	film Angers (sync.)	(3) M. Gill
Wednesdah 6th March	travel to Poitier	
Thursday 7th March	film Poitier	(1) M. Gill
Friday 8th March	crew travel to Pisa Sir Kenneth and Michael return London via Paris	
Saturday 9th March	crew travelling	
Sunday 10th March	crew travelling	
Monday 11th March	M. Gill flies to Pisa	
Tuesday 12th March	crew arrive in Pisa	
Wednesday 13th March	film Pisa (silent) Pisano pulpit Sir Kenneth flies out	(3) M. Gill
Thursday 14th March	film Pisa (sync.) Baptistry	(3) M. Gill
Friday 15th March	travel to Pistoia and film Cathedral pulpit (sync.) pm travel to Florence	(3) M. Gill
Saturday 16th March	film Florence	(4) A. Turner

Sunday 17th March	Florence	(4) A. Turner
Monday 18th March	Florence	(4) A. Turner
Tuesday 19th March	Florence	(4) A. Turner
Wednesday 20th March	Florence	(4) A. Turner
Thursday 21st March	Florence pm travel to Siena (?)	(4) A. Turner
Friday 22nd March	film Siena pm travel to Assisi	(3) M. Gill
Saturday 23rd March	film Assisi–Giotto frescoes	(3) M. Gill
Sunday 24th March	Assisi	(3) M. Gill
Monday 25th March	Assisi	(3) M. Gill
Tuesday 26th March	travel Urbino	
Wednesday 27th March	film Urbino—Ducal Palace	(4) A. Turner
Thursday 28th March	Urbino	(4) A. Turner
Friday 29th March	Urbino	(4) A. Turner
Saturday 30th March	travel Ravenna	
Sunday 31st March	film Ravenna—tomb of Theodoric and church of San Vitale	(1) M. Gill
Monday 1st April	film Ravenna	(1) M. Gill
Tuesday 2nd April	travel Padua	
Wednesday 3rd April	film Padua—Giotto frescoes	(3) M. Gill
Thursday 4th April	Padua	(3) M. Gill
Friday 5th April	travel Mantua	
Saturday 6th April	film Mantua—Mantegna frescoes	(4) A. Turner
Sunday 7th April	crew travel to Nice or Marseilles Sir Kenneth and Michael return London via Milan	
Monday 8th April	crew travelling	
Tuesday 9th April to Monday 15th April	*crew on leave over Easter*	
Tuesday 16th April	crew return to France	
Wednesday 17th April	crew travel to Senanque	
Thursday 18th April	film Senanque	(2) P. Montagnon
Friday 19th April	Senanque	(2) P. Montagnon
Saturday 20th April	Senanque	(2) P. Montagnon
Sunday 21st April	crew travel M. Gill flies to Nimes	
Monday 22nd April	film Orange/Arles Sir Kenneth flies to Nimes	(1) M. Gill
Tuesday 23rd April	Nimes	(1) M. Gill
Wednesday 24th April	Nimes	(1) M. Gill

Thursday 25th April	travel Moissac M. Gill returns London	
Friday 26th April	film Moissac	(2) P. Montagnon
Saturday 27th April	Moissac	(2) P. Montagnon
Sunday 28th April	travel Cluny	
Monday 29th April	travel Cluny	
Tuesday 30th April	film Cluny	(2) P. Montagnon
Wednesday 1st May	exteriors Tournus travel Autun	(2) P. Montagnon
Thursday 2nd May	film Autun	(2) P. Montagnon
Friday 3rd May	travel Vezelay Sir Kenneth travels to Holland via Lyons and Paris (for Henry Moore presentation)	
Saturday 4th May	exteriors Vezelay	(2) P. Montagnon
Sunday 5th May	break—or exteriors Sir Kenneth returns from Holland	
Monday 6th May	film Vezelay interiors	(2) P. Montagnon
Tuesday 7th May	travel Chartres	
Wednesday 8th May	film Chartres	(2) P. Montagnon
Thursday 9th May	Chartres M. Gill flies to Chartres via Paris	(2) P. Montagnon
Friday 10th May	Chartres	(2) P. Montagnon
Saturday 11th May	Chartres exteriors	(3) M. Gill
Sunday 12th May	travel to Paris	
Monday 13th May	Cluny exteriors	(1 & 3) M. Gill
Tuesday 14th May	Cluny exteriors	(1 & 3) M. Gill
Wednesday 15th May	St. Denis	(2) P. Montagnon
Thursday 16th May	St. Denis	(2) P. Montagnon
Friday 17th May	Cluny exteriors	(1) M. Gill
Saturday 18th May	Cluny exteriors Sir Kenneth flies to Cologne for Aachen	(1) M. Gill
Sunday 19th May	travel to Aachen M. Gill flies via Cologne	
Monday 20th May	film Aachen—Treasury (sync.)	(1) M. Gill
Tuesday 21st May	film Aachen (sync.)	(1) M. Gill
Wednesday 22nd May	travel Cologne and film?	(1) M. Gill
Thursday 23rd May	film Cologne	(1) M. Gill
Friday 24th May	travel Oslo M. Gill and Sir Kenneth return London	
Saturday 25th May	crew travel to Oslo via Denmark and Sweden	

Sunday 26th May	crew travel to Oslo via Denmark and Sweden	
Monday 27th May	crew travel to Oslo via Denmark and Sweden	
Tuesday 28th May	crew travel to Oslo via Denmark and Sweden Sir Kenneth and Michael fly to Oslo	
Wednesday 29th May	film Oslo	(1) M. Gill
Thursday 30th May	film Oslo	(1) M. Gill
Friday 31st May	film Oslo Sir Kenneth returns London	(1) M. Gill
Saturday 1st June	crew take 4.00 pm ferry to Newcastle M. Gill flies to London	
Sunday 2nd June	crew on ferry	
Monday 3rd June (Whit Monday)	crew arrive in Newcastle at 7.00 am travel across to Oban and Mull	
Tuesday 4th June	crew travelling Sir Kenneth and Michael fly to Glasgow and travel by car to Mull	
Wednesday 5th June	cross to Iona	
Thursday 6th June	film Iona (sync.)	(1) M. Gill
Friday 7th June	film Iona (silent)	(1) M. Gill
Saturday 8th June	crew travel to Ireland Sir Kenneth and Michael travel by car to Glasgow then fly to Dublin	
Sunday 9th June	crew travelling Sir Kenneth and Michael travel by car from Dublin to Tralee	
Monday 10th June	film Dingle Peninsula	(1) M. Gill
Tuesday 11th June	film Dingle Peninsula	(1) M. Gill
Wednesday 12th June	film on island of Skellig Michael (silent) Sir Kenneth returns London via Shannon airport	(1) M. Gill
Thursday 13th June	film Skellig Michael	(1) M. Gill
Friday 14th June	film Skellig Michael	(1) M. Gill
Saturday 15th June	crew return London M. Gill flies to London from Shannon	
Sunday 16th June	crew travelling	

Still to be filmed:	London churches 1 day silent shooting	(8) M. Gill
	St. Paul's, London 1 day silent shooting	(8) M. Gill
	Saltwood Castle 1 day sync. shooting	(3) M. Gill
	Ely Cathedral 1 day sync. shooting	(6) P. Montagnon
Film crew:	cameraman: Tubby Englander operator: Ken Macmillan assistant: Colin Deehan grips: Bill Paget sound: Basil Harris assistant: Malcolm Webberley lights: Jack Probert Joe Cooksey	

Glossary

Note The usage of some terms in this glossary can vary between different countries and even between one studio or production company and another in the same country. US equivalents are given for terms used in the UK or within the BBC but these terms need not be mutually exclusive.

ALTERNATOR (US: GENERATOR). Portable, petrol (gasoline) or diesel powered dynamo generating alternating current.

ANSWER PRINT. (See SHOW PRINT).

ART DIRECTOR. (See DESIGNER).

ARTIST, ARTISTE (US: PLAYER). Actor, actress, presenter, etc.

AUTO CUE. (See TELEPROMPTER).

BACKLIGHT. Light striking the subject from behind, or a side-back position increasing the apparent separation between subject and background.

BACK PROJECTION (US: REAR SCREEN PROJECTION). Method of projecting static or filmed picture as the background of a scene. Normally used nowadays only for scene where the projected area is relatively small—eg, scene through a car window or through the windows of a house viewed from the inside.

BATTERY LIGHT. Small portable lighting unit deriving power from a battery pack, and operating independently of a main power supply, alternator, generator etc.

BRUTE. 225 amp focusing spot arc lamp; the most powerful lighting unit used in television filming.

CAMERA REPORT. Form provided by cameraman accompanying exposed stock to the laboratories, and ordering the processing. Contains all necessary information.

CENTRE LINE (US: THE LINE). An imaginary line drawn across a scene which, provided it is not crossed by the camera in adjacent shots, ensures consistent orientation of subjects or direction of movement.

CHAT SHOW. (See TALKS PROGRAMME).

CLAMP. Camera or lamp mounting with suction grips to attach to flat surfaces such as windows or doors of a car or other vehicle.

COLOUR TEMPERATURE. Method of determining the relative colour quality of a light source. Based on a standard of the temperature in degrees celsius measured from absolute zero by which a theoretical black body must be raised in order to radiate light of a certain quality. It is measured in Kelvins. The higher the temperature, the bluer the light; the lower, the pinker.

COMMENTARY OUT-OF-VISION. (See COMMENTARY OVER).

COMMENTARY OVER (US: VOICE OVER, VO, OFF-CAMERA). Scene in which the voice of the commentator is heard but he or she is not seen.

CONTINUITY GIRL (US: SCRIPT GIRL). Person, usually female, who makes careful observations and notes of action, props, clothing and other details of scenes so that continuity is maintained through the adjacent shots of a sequence. The production secretary is the director's personal assistant with wide organizational duties in the production of a BBC programme.

CSO Colour separation overlay. (See CSR COLOUR SEPARATION).

CSR COLOUR SEPARATION (US[FILM]: BLUE MATTEING[VTR]: CHROMA-KEY). Optical (in film) or electronic (television) process for superimposing a subject on a background shot separately on a CSR 'plate', avoiding the need to take the subject to the actual location where the plate was shot.

CU, CLOSE-UP. Shot in which the subject appears as if viewed from close range.

CUTAWAY. Shot which is not of the main action or subject in a scene, but can be inserted between main shots to avoid jump cuts or to introduce a lapse of time or subject of indirect interest.

CYCLORAMA, CYC. Large plain sheet of canvas or other material stretched on a frame and used as a background for studio 'exteriors' with suitable lighting or projection on its surface.

DAILIES. (See RUSHES).

DAY FOR NIGHT. Method of underexposure which, when done in suitable daylight conditions, gives an effect that more or less approximates to night time.

DESIGNER. Person responsible for designing and overseeing construction and installation of sets.

F-STOP, F NUMBER. Relative aperture of a lens at its various diaphragm openings. F-stops are determined by dividing the focal length of a lens by the effective diameter of the diaphragm.

FILLER LIGHT (US: FILL LIGHT). Light filling, or softening the shadow areas created by key lighting and regulating contrast so that it is suitable to be photographed.

5K. Five kilowatt incandescent lamp.

FOM. (Film Operations Manager). Person providing technical liaison between BBC film and production departments.

FOOT CANDLE. Unit of illumination for measuring light falling on a surface in readings taken of the light source from the subject position. In theory, the light intensity of a 'standard candle' at one foot. (Equal to one lumen per square foot).

FRONT (AXIAL) PROJECTION. Process for combining live studio action with a projected moving or stationary, background and suitably treated features in the set. The camera and projector lenses are aligned on a common axis.

GANTRY (US: LIGHT GRID). Semi-permanent variable-height structure to take lamps etc.

GEARED HEAD. Camera mounting, which, by means of geared controls allows smooth, precise camera movements.

GEL. (See GELATINE).

GELATIN (E), JELLY. Translucent filter fitted over the front of a lamp to change the quality or colour of the light emitted. Wire mesh and gelatine scrims diffuse and reduce the light.

GRIP. Member of crew whose duty is to carry equipment about, and sometimes push a dolly or move a crane during a shot when required.

INTERIOR/EXTERIOR. Set representing exterior scene, constructed and used in the studio.

JELLY. (See GELATINE).

JIB (US: BOOM). Arm of a camera crane.

KEY (MODELLING) LIGHT. Main light which establishes the lighting level of the scene and models the subject.

KICKER. Lamp simulating the visible known key source in the scene, but not providing the actual key modelling light.

LIGHTING BRIDGE. (See GANTRY).

LOCATION SEARCH. (See RECCE).

LS LONG SHOT. Shot in which the principal subject appears distant from the camera. The whole of a human figure is shown.

MASTER SHOT. Shot covering the complete sequence.

MATTEBOX. A combined lens shade and filter, matte or screen holder mounted in front of the camera lens.

MCU, MEDIUM CLOSE-UP. Shot in which only the subject's head and shoulders appear.

MOLEVATOR. A power operated high stand for brute. Extending from 6–14 ft. approximately.

MONITOR TV VIEWFINDER. (Electronic). An electronic viewfinder attachment that provides a view through the finder on a film camera. The image is shown on a separate monitor screen.

ND, NEUTRAL DENSITY FILTER. Screen material which absorbs all wavelengths of light equally. It reduces overall light intensity without disturbing the relative balance of colours.

NEG/POS SYSTEM. Method of photography by which the camera stock is processed to form a negative image, and a positive print is made from this on a separate strip of film.

NG TAKE. Unsuccessful take. Literally a 'No Good' take.

NORTH LIGHT. Lamp using indirect QI lamps, giving a diffused fill illumination.

OB, OUTSIDE BROADCAST (US: REMOTE). Outside Broadcast. An OB television unit uses television cameras either relaying images to the studio or broadcasting station or recording on to videotape there or on location.

OPERATOR (US: CAMERA OPERATOR, ASSISTANT CAMERAMAN). The technician who operates the camera. The cameraman's assistant, or the cameraman himself if he does his own operating.

PAN. Pivoted camera movement in a horizontal plane.

PAN GLASS. A glass filter once used to determine the tonal values in monchrome of the scene about to be filmed. Still useful for watching sun and cloud movement or looking directly at light sources to find the centre of a light path.

POV, POINT OF VIEW. Shot taken as if from the point of view of the artist concerned.

PRACTICAL LAMP. Lamp appearing in the actual scene being photographed. It may, or may not have some effect on the actual lighting in the scene.

PRIME LENS. Any lens of fixed (non-variable) focal length.

PRODUCTION ASSISTANT (US: ASSISTANT DIRECTOR, AD). Organises the production with schedule planning, calling of actors, arranging make-up and wardrobe, transport and equipment. Co-ordinates film and television parts of composite productions.

PRODUCTION SECRETARY. (See CONTINUITY GIRL).

PUP. 500, 650, 750 or 1000 w incandescent spotlight.

QUARTZ. 650, 750, or 1000 W (redhead) 2 K (blonde) tungsten halogen lamp.

QUARTZ IODINE, QI. (QI) (See QUARTZ).

RECCE (US: SCOUT, SURVEY). The search for, inspection and assessing of locations for filming purposes.

RECONNOITRE. (See RECCE).

REVERSAL. Film material in which a positive image is obtained directly without printing on to another strip.

RIM LIGHTING. Light creating a narrow highlight around the edge of a subject.

RUN UP (CAMERA) (US: SPEED). Period between starting the camera and reaching full speed.

RUSHES (US: DAILIES). First ungraded prints made by a laboratory from material shot in the previous day's work and processed over-night.

They are delivered at a viewing theatre where they are seen by the producer, director and technicians.

SHOW PRINT (US: RELEASE PRINT). The final print from a negative correctly graded for density from scene to scene.

SPANISH WINDLASS (US: TIE-DOWN, CHAIN). Rope connection between underneath of tripod mounting plate and stage screw in the floor which, when tightened by a lever inserted between the strands ensures that the tripod remains rigid.

STABILIZER. System for providing a stable image when a camera is held or mounted on a moving or vibrating support.

STAGE SCREW. Screw which can be driven into wooden floor to provide an anchor point for cable etc.

STOCK (FILM) RAW. Unexposed film material.

SUNSHADE. (See MATTEBOX).

TALKS PROGRAMME (US: TALK SHOW). Programme in which the main content is conversational.

TELECINE. Machine for running film for transmission or for transfer to VTR.

TELEPROMPTER (US: PROMPTER). Machine fitted to the front of a camera which provides a continuously moving script for the commentator or artist to read while appearing to look directly at the viewer.

10 K. Ten kilowatt incandescent lamp.

TIGHT TWO; LOOSE THREE. Shot closely framing two people; shot of three people surrounded by space.

TM, TECHNICAL MANAGER. Chief technician in the electronic studio (TV), responsible for planning lighting and putting it into operation, plus administrative responsibility for crews.

TRACK (SHOT). Shot in which the camera and its mounting move horizontally, usually on a wheeled vehicle which may run on tracks. Perspective in the scene alters as the camera approaches or moves away from the subject.

T-STOPS. System of lens aperture calibration which takes acount of the total light transmitting effect of lens, which can vary from one to another. For that purpose, more accurate than F-stops.

TRANSMISSION PRINT. (See SHOW PRINT).

TUNGSTEN HALOGEN LAMP. (See QUARTZ IODINE).

TWO-SHOT. Shot including two people where they form the main subject.

VTR, ELECTRONIC VIDEOTAPE. Method of recording image and sound on magnetic tape either direct from a television camera and microphone, or from film via a telecine machine.

VOICE OVER, VO. (See COMMENTARY OVER).

ZOOM SHOT. Shot in which the magnification of the image is altered without changing the perspective. Effected by a gradual rearrangement of optical components in a lens, in response to the operation of a zoom bar or handle.

Index

Heinrich Caro and the Creation of Modern Chemical Industry

Chemists and Chemistry

VOLUME 19

A series of books devoted to the examination of the history and development of chemistry from its early emergence as a separate discipline to the present day. The series will describe the personalities, processes, theoretical and technical advances which have shaped our current understanding of chemical science

The titles published in this series are listed at the end of this volume.

Heinrich Caro and the Creation of Modern Chemical Industry

by

Carsten Reinhardt
University of Regensburg, Germany

and

Anthony S. Travis
Sidney M. Edelstein Center, Hebrew University, Jerusalem, Israel

KLUWER ACADEMIC PUBLISHERS
DORDRECHT / BOSTON / LONDON

A C.I.P. Catalogue record for this book is available from the Library of Congress.

ISBN 0-7923-6602-6

Published by Kluwer Academic Publishers,
P.O. Box 17, 3300 AA Dordrecht, The Netherlands.

Sold and distributed in North, Central and South America
by Kluwer Academic Publishers,
101 Philip Drive, Norwell, MA 02061, U.S.A.

In all other countries, sold and distributed
by Kluwer Academic Publishers,
P.O. Box 322, 3300 AH Dordrecht, The Netherlands.

Printed on acid-free paper

Printed in the Netherlands.

... there is a set of ... philosophers–those who challenge the possibility of any knowledge, or at least an exhaustive knowledge, of the world.... The most telling refutation of this as of all other philosophical crochets is practice, namely, experiment and industry. If we are able to prove the correctness of our understanding of a natural process by making it ourselves, producing it from its preconditions and making it serve our own purposes into the bargain, then it's all over with the Kantian ungraspable "thing-in-itself." The chemical substances produced in the bodies of plants and animals remained "such things-in-themselves" until organic chemistry began to produce them one after another; whereupon the "thing-in-itself" became a thing-for-us, as, for instance, alizarin, the colouring matter of madder, which we no longer trouble to grow in the madder roots in the field, but produce much more cheaply and simply from coal tar.

FRIEDRICH ENGELS

Ludwig Feuerbach and the End of Classical German Philosophy, from new trans., 1976, of *Ludwig Feuerbach und der Ausgang der klassischen deutschen Philosophie* (Stuttgart, 1888).

The German colour establishments are at once the most perfectly developed and scientifically managed organisations in the world and pay dividends up to 35 per cent.... At first the German chemists came to England for capital to work out their ideas, and many were engaged in the Manchester district.... Brilliant chemists left England to achieve great success in the German research laboratories.... The industry is a great asset to Germany

SIDNEY M. HIGGINS

Dyeing in Germany and America, With a Chapter on Colour Production (Manchester, 1907), 80-82.

Heinrich Caro (1834-1910). (Deutsches Museum.)

CONTENTS

Introduction

A "wonderful genius for discovery, and a marvellous enthusiasm for chemistry" were the qualities that the British chemist Arthur Green ascribed to the German chemist Heinrich Caro whose life and times are the subject of this book.[1] Heinrich Caro is best known today as the inventor of new chemical processes that, in the two decades commencing 1869, enabled the Badische Anilin- & Soda-Fabrik (BASF) firm of Ludwigshafen, Germany, to ascend to first place among European, and indeed international, manufacturers of organic chemicals. To his contemporaries he was known variously as an experienced calico (cotton) printer, a creative research chemist, a highly knowledgeable patent specialist and expert witness, a consultant on technical matters, and, in England (where he worked for seven years), the type of individual who might have prevented the decline of the British dye and organic chemical industry. This latter view was prevalent from around 1900 among many leading British academic chemists. It persisted and was especially strong just after the outbreak of World War I, when, it was claimed, a letter to the London *Times* suggested that the only way to revive the British synthetic dye industry–then of considerable strategic importance–was to: "Find a man like Dr. Caro and give him a free hand."[2]

Heinrich Caro was the antithesis, in style and roots, of what was once a common stereotype, that of the Prussian technologist. Thus he lacked thoroughness, order, and self discipline. This was in complete contrast to the better-known chemical inventor Fritz Haber, who displayed all the characteristics of a typical Prussian. It was Haber's synthetic ammonia process, in the hands of BASF, and developed along the organisational and institutional lines of industrial research and academic-industrial collaboration pioneered by Caro, that sustained the German war effort.[3] Both men, incidentally, were of Jewish ancestry, and baptized.

Caro, a complex man at times difficult to work with, was nevertheless always respected. Throughout his industrial career, he was in every sense a man of enterprise, successfully introducing new processes and products, and benefiting from royalties on his patents, profit-sharing schemes, and the acquisition of substantial shareholdings and seniority at BASF. His enormous energies were fired as much by love of music and poetry as by his none-too-narrow perception of chemical science and its application to industrial problem solving. He was also profoundly influenced by his intimate experience of the movements for social and political reform that swept across Europe in 1848, and the aftermaths, particularly the industrialisation of Germany. Such variety and historical richness cannot fail to attract our attention, particularly since much of the life of Caro, upon whom honours and decorations were bestowed "by Princes and by Universities and Scientific Societies," has remained, until our present studies, essentially an untold story.[4]

Fortunately, and thanks to Caro's sense of history, we can explore his life's work. Caro left us the means to share his hopes and purposes, his successes, and his setbacks, particularly during his formative, and certainly most interesting, years. The source is the Caro Nachlass held at the Deutsches Museum, Munich, which is one of the largest archival holdings in chemistry at that museum. Caro's writings, notebooks, reminiscences, and correspondence preserve a rare perception of the second half of the 19th century as seen from the viewpoint of a chemical inventor whose career was spent almost exclusively in industrial service. In addition, Caro's strong, flowing hand, steady and regular, recorded otherwise rare background material on natural dyes and calico printing during the 1850s, when he entered into industry. He carefully preserved the letters received during the 1860s from business contacts, and these provide a unique insight into the beginning of the changeover from natural to synthetic dyes. And for the 1870-90 period, the great age of synthetic dyes, the Nachlass is supplemented by archival material held at BASF, Ludwigshafen. It was during this latter period that the opportunities thrown up by the new technology, particularly discontinuities with the past brought on by academic chemistry, and the experiences and reputations of the start-up companies founded in Germany during the mid-1860s, fostered the emergence of the modern dye and organic chemical industry.

It is entirely appropriate, then, that this present biography embraces much more than its ostensible subject. It intertwines Caro's upbringing, education, apprenticeship, and inventive streak with the evolution of science-based technology, at first in England and then in Germany. In contrast to the much-studied German influence on British chemistry of August Wilhelm Hofmann at London's Royal College of Chemistry, the English influence on the early development of German organic chemical technology, particularly the transfer of information and skills through Caro, is less well known. This is why Caro's Manchester period is a principal focus of our study, particularly how his approach to invention and problem solving developed in a social milieu made up of: chemical manufacturers and entrepreneurs; British, German, French, and Swiss academic and industrial chemists; calico printers and dyers; and agents for textile chemicals and patents.

Our detailed study of this period provides the background to Caro's better-known achievements at BASF that are delineated in later chapters, where the focus changes to the nature of organisation of coal-tar organic chemical manufacture, and the impact of legislation on chemical technology. What emerges is a clearer appreciation of the early development of modern science and technology, and of how they drove one other. Understanding is aided by the fact that chemical concepts and theories of the second half of the 19th century can be expressed in terms that are familiar to the modern chemist, though we should not forget that at the time they represented the very frontiers of knowledge. They were also the outcomes of an extraordinary industry-driven intellectual ferment in which every important development in the European organic chemical industry until 1914 was prefigured.

The manufacture of synthetic dyestuffs from coal-tar aromatic hydrocarbons, mainly benzene, naphthalene, and anthracene, grew rapidly after 1860. The origins of the industry lay in the serendipitous discovery in 1856 by William Henry Perkin, one of Hofmann's students, of the first coal-tar dye, later known as mauve. By the end of 1858, Perkin had opened a factory near London to manufacture the dye, which was an almost immediate success. Competitors and imitators soon discovered a second coal-tar dye, a brilliant red known as fuchsine or magenta, and dyes that were derivatives of the red. At first the coal-tar dyes struggled to compete with colorants from natural products, but soon ways were found of fixing them to cotton, the basis of the fastest growing sector of the textile industry. Often, success was brought about by the skilful adaptation of existing dye-using technology, and the ability to overcome the scepticism of dyers and calico printers steeped in secrecy and tradition.

It was as an apprentice to a calico printer in Mülheim, in the Ruhr Valley, that Caro acquired the sort of knowledge that would later enable him to identify potential novel artificial dyes in ways that were beyond the capabilities of those without a background in practical textile coloration. In Manchester during 1860, Caro discovered a new route to mauve, and a novel and important black colorant that was extracted from the residue of his mauve process. He also investigated all the new coal-tar dye processes. Caro's understanding of the special needs of dye users and agents for dyes, and his after-sales service, enabled him to promote and sell the novel products of his employer, and bring about extensive usage of artificial dyes.

This was to be the prelude to a giant stride into a new age of daring innovations. In 1869, academic and industrial chemists, foremost among them Perkin and Caro, managed to replicate by a commercially viable process a complex natural product, the widely used red dyestuff known as alizarin. Artificial alizarin heralded the downfall of the natural dye industry, and the start of the age of science-based invention, what is often known as the second industrial revolution. As the pace of invention, innovation, and competition accelerated, many of the new artificial dyes were themselves threatened with obsolescence. Product turnover times became shorter and shorter, and the range of products expanded incessantly. To keep up with these developments, firms had to implement strategies for long-term survival. This called for new modes of organisation, including collaboration with academic chemists, and the establishment of industrial research laboratories where new products were invented and the products of competing companies were carefully screened and analyzed.

These activities had a tremendous impact on protection of intellectual property rights for chemical discoveries, and led to calls for reform of patent systems, particularly in Germany. Through his personal involvement in all these activities, Heinrich Caro, both before and during his time at BASF, personified the emergence and development of the synthetic dye and organic chemicals industry. Apart from his inventive genius, Caro was undoubtedly the leading international expert in chemical patents related to dyes. He became deeply involved in litigation, negotiation, and licensing arrangements, especially in Germany and England, and through this work provided the foundations upon which conventions and cartels, some international in scope, could be concluded. It is no exaggeration to state that the inauguration of these activities shaped a completely new industrial and scientific environment, one that influenced political and economic history until the middle of the 20th century.

That history and drama also pervaded Caro's life comes through clearly from the accounts of his childhood and youth. His love of poetic language endured throughout his life, as evinced by his own history of the dye industry, delivered to the German Chemical Society in 1891, and of which Arthur Green noted:

> [I]n many respects, he was a poet. He did not necessarily write in verses, but anyone who has read the Lecture delivered before the Berlin Chemical Society on the Development of the Dyestuff Industry would realise that it was an absolute epic and one of the most beautiful pieces of writing imaginable.[5]

Caro's career had great technical breadth, which is not easily understood by audiences who eschew detailed chemistry. Nevertheless, we emphasise at the outset that the reason Caro matters is his chemistry, and wherever possible we discuss not only what Caro did, but how he did it. Accordingly, apart from chapters 1, 2, 10, 11, and 12, this study presupposes some knowledge of chemistry. Moreover, we make no apology for the abundance of trade names and structural formulae, which is what industrial organic chemistry was, and is, about, and without which the story would not be complete. However, we have made every effort to spare the reader the need to struggle through the more technical material in chapters 3 through 9 in order to appreciate how Caro became such an internationally recognised inventor. And, to add emphasis from afar, the lectures, publications, and letters appearing in prominent British periodicals such as the *Times* of London and *Nature* show us why the British chemical industry really did need men like Heinrich Caro. Thus it is through Caro's career, which spanned and involved every transformation taking place in the emergence of the synthetic dye industry, that we have the clearest understanding of what was happening in both Germany and Britain between 1860 and 1890, and even in some ways until 1914 and beyond.

To compass so many overlapping aspects of Caro's life, and an abundance of both technical and business detail, sometimes moving back and forth in time, we have been somewhat circumspect with respect to the structure and content of this book. Most chapters are driven by distinct themes, and though this dictates some repetition, it does enable us to demonstrate the different impacts that certain developments had within different historical contexts.

We have used Caro's correspondence, publications, and unpublished writings as the basis for our research, and, wherever possible, verified his reminiscences by referring to other sources. While a few gaps in the record remain, and for the early period many of the letters Caro received are not matched with his responses, it is fortunate that a fairly complete picture of Caro's life in industry can be drawn. We set out to cover all the essential questions about Caro's career, and sometimes even of those who worked closely with him in cases where the information can be found only in the Caro-related archives. They also contribute to the story of the dye and allied industries, particularly where the material informs us on the typical ways in which business was done and partnerships planned through networks of correspondents. Thus in chapters 3 and 4, it is the specificity of detail in the letters and dispatches from the 1860s–not always models of 19th-century restraint, rectitude, and correctness–that makes the story compelling, and come alive. Brought together and interpreted for the first time, the transcriptions and translations from the Caro Nachlass comprise the only original extensive surviving documentation on any aspect of the early English synthetic dye industry.[6] Previous histories of the industry in England before 1870 have relied on reminiscences of participants, invariably somewhat partisan and self-congratulatory in nature; patent records and associated litigation, which are no less distorted; and the occasional scientific publication, which does not reveal information of commercial interest.

Chapter 1 deals with Heinrich Caro's social and cultural background, drawing upon his own accounts of childhood and adolescence in the sometimes less-than-peaceful capital of Prussia. This is the initial period setting, with Caro's assimilated Jewish family struggling to make ends meet but placing great emphasis on his education. Caro recalls the events that shaped his later outlook and how he decided to make chemistry his career. Of particular interest is his description of the activities of a liberal-radical association of schoolboys in Berlin during the period leading up to the March 1848 revolution. Caro's retrospective account of the subsequent turmoil, extracts of which appear in the appendix to chapter 1, also adds considerably to the better-known histories of the events. Chapter 2 describes, briefly, Caro's vocational and academic chemical education in Berlin (1852-55) and, in detail, the hard years spent as an apprentice calico printer in Germany (1855-59).

Each of the next three chapters explores a major theme in Caro's English years in Manchester (1859-66), where he was engaged by a firm that specialised in the manufacture of chemicals for the textile industry. His work as an inventor included overcoming the problems of applying novel dyes, maintaining close contacts with academic chemists in Manchester and London, bringing together a team of talented Germans, and the circumvention of patents of rival firms. Caro's essential qualities, the most important of which was his skill in invention, were nurtured in this environment. He often started with simple ideas based on intuition and analogy and, once he had obtained a precious product, resorted to explanation in the language of the chemist. This was a true blend of craft, industrial experience, and scientific knowledge.

The outcome was that by the time Caro left England, he had contributed to the new way in which dye-making practice and chemical theory developed in concert and were mutually reinforcing. In some respects, there was at first little break with the past, since the new synthetic dyes relied on prior science and technology in the processing and application of natural products. This period did, however, precede a paradigmatic change in the subdiscipline of organic chemistry brought on by the increasing academic interest in coal-tar dyes, and the need to express their chemical constitutions. After 1865, with the availability of Kekulé's novel benzene theory, previously elusive structural formulae could be drawn for the coal-tar aromatic compounds and their derivatives. It was by serving so successfully as a servant of coal-tar dye chemistry that the benzene ring became an essential component of academic organic chemistry.

These chapters, through the transcriptions, are also important for the light they throw on wider aspects of life in the chemical industry of Manchester during the first half of the 1860s. In particular, the sharing of knowledge through various informal channels, including at an inn frequented by calico printers, chemists and agents, and German clubs, is emphasised. This complements the records available in the notebooks and papers of Henry Roscoe, professor of chemistry at Owens College, which cover the period after Heinrich Caro left England.

Chapters 6, 7, and 8 describe Caro's career at BASF, Ludwigshafen, during the period 1868-90 from the standpoints of invention, academic-industrial collaborations, and the industrial research laboratory, respectively. These are the institutionalised features of the modern chemical industry whose origins we owe to Caro. The three chapters also describe how in Germany science and technology promoted economic development. Chapter 6 shows how BASF, capitalising on Caro's inventiveness under the watchful eye of senior partner Friedrich Engelhorn, rapidly moved into the realm of science-based invention. In May 1869, the academic chemists Carl Graebe and Carl Liebermann sold the rights in their synthetic alizarin patents to BASF, and Caro was assigned the job of finding a commercially viable route to this important colorant, which he achieved within weeks. Whereas previously dyers and textile printers had prepared their own dyes, often with the assistance of colourists, the success of artificial alizarin around 1870 meant that dye manufacture became the domain of the specialists, the coal-tar dye factories, and particularly BASF. Nevertheless, prior training as a colourist was still essential, even in the dye-making factory. Again, this enabled Caro to recognise the potential of several compounds that others would have missed.

Chapter 7 covers Caro's initiation of academic-industrial collaborations, particularly with Adolf Baeyer at the University of Strasbourg, and from 1875 at Munich. Baeyer's total authority over a leading academic research school, typical of the German institute system, enabled him to bend the direction of its research towards the needs of BASF. Lengthy research and development campaigns became the order of the day. Caro inaugurated the two-decade-long industrial search for synthetic indigo, a project in which he collaborated closely with Baeyer. Moreover, Baeyer was for a time delegated full responsibility for indigo research at BASF, and remained the decision-maker during this endeavour. Though Caro's own product, based on Baeyer's academic research, was shortlived, it owed its very existence to two factors: backing from BASF and Caro's analytical skills and imagination.

Chapter 8 shows how Caro was also instrumental in the founding of the modern industrial research laboratory. This was of enormous significance

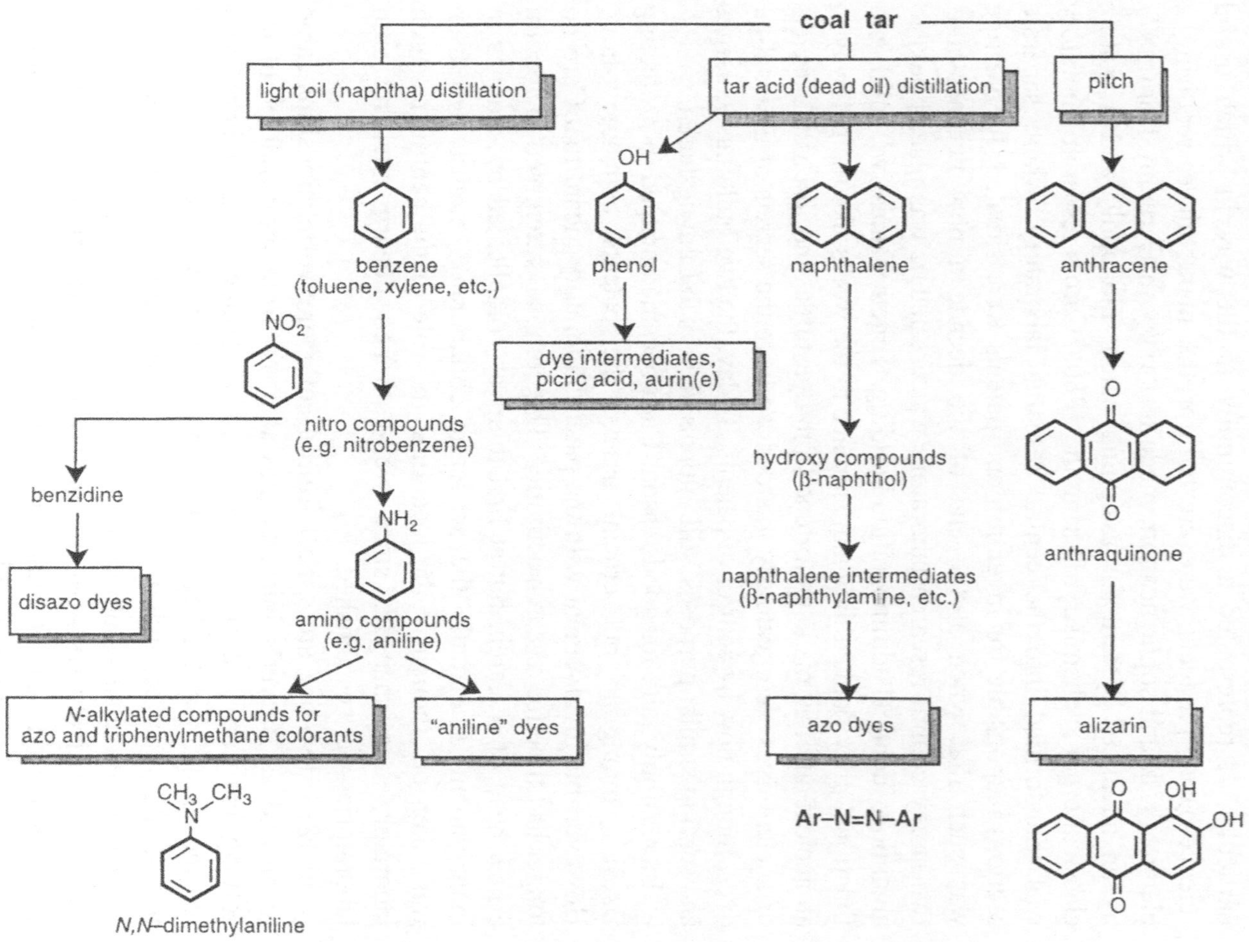
coal tar
light oil (naphtha) distillation
tar acid (dead oil) distillation
pitch
OH
benzene
(toluene, xylene, etc.)
phenol
naphthalene
anthracene
NO2
dye intermediates,
picric acid, aurin(e)
O
nitro compounds
(e.g. nitrobenzene)
hydroxy compounds
(β-naphthol)
benzidine
NH2
O
anthraquinone
naphthalene intermediates
(β-naphthylamine, etc.)
disazo dyes
amino compounds
(e.g. aniline)
N-alkylated compounds for
azo and triphenylmethane colorants
"aniline" dyes
azo dyes
alizarin
CH3 CH3
N
O OH
OH
Ar–N=N–Ar
O
N,N–dimethylaniline

for the future of industry in general, and of the chemical industry in particular. It represented a discontinuity in the way in which useful science-based products were created for the marketplace, requiring a blend of risk and sophistication, made less risky in Germany from 1877 by an advanced system for assigning patent monopoly and a mature classical organic chemistry. During the 1880s, Caro's research laboratory was transformed into the central research laboratory, where separate sections responsible for invention and patents were situated. Its prestige was such that when at the end of the decade a new purpose-built two-storey central research laboratory was erected, it was placed next to an almost-identical administration building. Together–massive, solid, and functional–they flanked the main entrance to the works like the gateway to an ancient city that made its fortune from dyestuffs. And just as the secrets of ancient dyes were jealously guarded, so were the secrets of the coal-tar dyes, though now by control of patents. Today, the two buildings, enlarged and serving similar purposes, still impress visitors to Ludwigshafen.

Increasingly, and for good reason, Caro became engaged in protecting BASF's intangible but crucial assets, the patents and know-how. However, his involvement with the patent laboratory meant that Caro no longer had time for research activities. The company attempted to appoint a new head of research, but at first this was complicated by changes in management. Eventually the academic collaborator August Bernthsen was taken on, though in the meantime the role of the central research laboratory had changed, since well-equipped departmental research laboratories were established.

In 1883, two of Caro's most fruitful collaborative relationships came to an end as Baeyer's interests moved away from industrial problem-solving and Caro lost his favoured status as protégé of Engelhorn, who left the company at the beginning of the following year. Caro was in his forty-ninth year. Seemingly shorn of inventiveness, he remained at the Ludwigshafen factory until the end of the decade, dealing during 1888-89 almost exclusively with patents and associated litigation. Nevertheless, even that period was not without its exciting moments nor lasting impact, particularly in England, where BASF opposed Ivan Levinstein, the leading Manchester dye-maker. Caro and Levinstein came to respect each other as their firms stood on opposite sides of the courtroom while engaged in patent litigation, and after BASF and Levinstein settled their differences over Caro's naphthol yellow, they became close friends. This episode, and its sequels, the subject of chapter 9, emphasise the importance of Caro's work on patents and as expert witness, and how he vigorously advocated provisions and new interpretations for the meaning of chemical invention. It also demonstrates how chemical theory and practice, and legal understandings of their meanings and applications, were essential components of power struggles for control of markets.

Chapter 10 shows that despite all the aspirations towards modernity, life in the factory was not always smooth, nor was Caro the exemplary, thorough, and orderly German inventor, at least from the perspective of his colleague, and later adversary, Carl Glaser. This provides an opportunity to weigh up Caro's shortcomings against his achievements. Chapter 11 describes how for two decades from 1890, when Caro left Ludwigshafen but joined the BASF supervisory board, he became an active observer of the dye industry as its first historian, a source of advice, and a celebrity.

Finally, chapter 12 makes clear why there is a need to revise and correct the versions of Caro's life, and those of other German pioneers in the dye industry, that were presented between 1900 and the 1920s by British chemists and industrialists who rewrote the history of the industry to suit their times and needs. This happened in the years following Caro's death, particularly the early stages of World War I, when there was an abrupt stoppage in the supply of German-made dyes, and the government created a state-sponsored dye-making company known as British Dyes Ltd, run by "well-meaning elderly gentlemen" rather than scientifically qualified men.[7]

New historical accounts appeared in the 1920s, following the transformation of British Dyes into British Dyestuffs Corporation Ltd, and its negotiations with the German dye cartels. Against this background, distinguishing reality from representation, we discuss why and how Caro became an icon among British chemists, certainly as much as among their German counterparts. In doing so we deconstruct part of the legend, though without detracting in any way from the incomparable achievements of the romantic, complex, and extraordinary German inventor who was responsible for the growth of the most innovative of the 19th-century's chemical industries.

Acknowledgements
We wish to thank Christoph Meinel and Elisabeth Vaupel, who supported and encouraged this study. Henk van den Belt, Ute Deichmann, Andy Hammond, Ernst Homburg, and Otto Krätz provided much valuable information and useful discussion. Peter Morris deserves special mention for his critical and extensive comments as the manuscript went through its final drafts. Thanks are due also to Chava Agmon, the Caro family genealogist. All of them have prevented a number of errors from creeping in. Any that remain are our own.

Research for this study was supported in part with research grants and assistance made available to Travis from the Deutsches Museum, Munich; the Stifterverband für die Deutsche Wissenschaft im Rahmen des Programms Chemie und Geisteswissenschaften; and the Lemelson Center for the Study of Invention and Innovation at the National Museum of American History, Washington, D.C. Part of this book was written while Reinhardt was 1998-99 Edelstein International Fellow in the History of Chemistry and the Chemical Sciences.

We are grateful to librarians and archivists in many places: at the Deutsches Museum, Munich; BASF Archives, Ludwigshafen; Bayer Archives, Leverkusen; the Sidney M. Edelstein Library, Jewish National and University Library, Jerusalem; ICI/Zeneca Specialties (now Avecia) Archives, Blackley, Manchester; Royal Society of Chemistry Library and Information Centre, London; Science Reference and Information Services of the British Library, London; Science Museum/Imperial College Library, London; Imperial College Archives, London; Newham Museum Service, Plaistow, London; Manchester Central Library; the Museum of Science and Industry in Manchester; and the John Rylands University Library of Manchester. Particularly valuable assistance was provided by Lothar Meinzer, Ruth Fromm, and Annette Wolpert (BASF), Wilhelm Füßl and Christiane Hennet (Deutsches Museum), Hans-Hermann Pogarell (Bayer), Hava Nowerstern (Edelstein Library), Nicola Best (Royal Society of Chemistry), Jo Ward (Newham), and the late Kenneth Magee (ICI/Zeneca, Blackley).

This book began as the expansion and revision of a series of articles published by Travis. Reinhardt is largely responsible for chapters 6, 7 and 8, and Travis for chapters 2, 3, 4, 5, 9, 10 and 12. The others are the result of close collaboration. We thank the Society for the History of

Technology, publisher of *Technology and Culture* (Travis, Anthony S., vol. 39 [1998], pp. 105-115. © Society for the History of Technology), the Society for the History of Alchemy and Chemistry, publisher of *Ambix*, Macmillan Press Ltd., Watson Publishing International/Science History Publications, and Kluwer Academic Publishers for permission to reproduce portions of texts from our own publications.[8]

Permission to reproduce documents and photographs is acknowledged from the Deutsches Museum, BASF Archives, the former Zeneca Archives/Library and Information Services, and Chris Makepeace of Disley, Cheshire. The map of Berlin in chapter 1 is reproduced by kind permission of Walter de Gruyter & Co.

Finally, we thank Joan E. Mentzer for editorial assistance, Angelika Mak for preparing the indexes, and David Darom and staff at The Hebrew University of Jerusalem for preparing figures.

Chapter notes and sources

Heinrich Caro's eldest daughter Amalie was responsible for gathering together her father's papers, the Caro Nachlass, which she deposited at the Deutsches Museum, Munich. She also transcribed certain documents, and probably recorded in typewritten form Caro's reminiscences of his boyhood and youth, all of which were included in the Caro Nachlass.[9]

Archival material in the Caro Nachlass at the Deutsches Museum is identified by DM NL93, followed by a box number. The material, including correspondence, is not fully catalogued. A 1921 directory of correspondence provides a list of names and dates, and includes items not addressed to Caro. In addition, there is a card index. Catalogued correspondence is indicated by DM HS (Handschriften) followed by a reference number, as DM HS 1977/72/1.

We have relied extensively on Elisabeth Vaupel's biographical study of Carl Graebe, and Evelyn Wiedenmann's dissertation on Baeyer's indigo synthesis, based on the Graebe and the Baeyer-Caro correspondence, respectively, at the Deutsches Museum. Particularly useful were the transcriptions in the second volume of their dissertations. Most of Caro's outgoing correspondence from 1883 to 1890 is preserved in a book of copies, totalling 284 letters written between May 1883 and July 1890, and also held at the Deutsches Museum (DM HS 8096). We have used a transcription of this volume made by BASF employee Friedrich Geißler and held at BASF Archives, under reference W1 Caro.

Items from the copy book are indicated as Geißler transcript, followed by a page number.

Documentary evidence, especially where it is scarce, is supplemented by published and unpublished memoirs and reminiscences, particularly of August Bernthsen, Carl Glaser, and Ernest Ehrhardt, because of their close connections with Caro at BASF. Bernthsen and Ehrhardt are important sources, particularly in connection with technical information provided to them by Caro that is not available elsewhere. However, they both suffer from time compression and inaccuracies, especially regarding dates.

Meldola correspondence held by the Newham Museum Service, Plaistow, London, is identified by Newham.

Documents at the former Zeneca Archives, Blackley, Manchester, are identified by Zeneca Archives. These have now been transferred to the Museum of Science and Industry in Manchester.

Unless otherwise noted, translations from the German are our own. In quoting both English and translated German correspondence we have corrected spellings of names and places. To avoid repetition of cumbersome company titles, the firms once known as Badische Anilin- & Soda-Fabrik (the "Badische"), Farbenfabriken vorm. Friedr. Bayer & Co., Meister, Lucius & Co. (Meister, Lucius, & Brüning), and Aktien-Gesellschaft für Anilin-Fabrikation (the "Berlin Aniline"), are generally referred to by their present-day names: BASF, Bayer, Hoechst, and AGFA, respectively.

1
Chemistry and Revolution

It was Heinrich Caro's fate that he passed from childhood to adolescence during a turbulent period of European history, one smouldering with social unrest. It was his good fortune that he grew to manhood during a period of European enlightenment, in which industrialising nations were poised to engage in the most challenging enterprise of modern times, that for which scientific ideas became the basis of industrial power. It is our good fortune that he has left extensive records of those early years, even if often in the form of reminiscences that were shaped by later events. They are important because the social background and the political and economic climate in which he grew up were significant to his later choice of career, and moulded his outlook, which, as we shall see, certainly irritated his less-admiring colleagues.

Caro's reminiscences reveal a happy childhood and tremendous natural talent, stimulated by a caring family and close friendships, as well as by acute awareness and curiosity, and freedom to roam and explore in nature. His parents very much loved music and the opera, and instilled in the young Heinrich a passion for the deeply romantic that soon found expression in poetry and an interest in novels about lone adventurers. Medieval knights provided role models for childhood games, and patriotic sentiments were enhanced by the mood of Prussia at mid-century, particularly openness to certain minorities in its midst. The Caro family was of Jewish origins, though now entirely secular, and felt strongly bonded to others of similar background and tradition. This much we know from Caro's personal reminiscences, which provide an account of his life prior to entry, in September 1852, into Berlin's Gewerbeinstitut, the leading trade school of Prussia.

This chapter draws mainly on two documents in the Caro Nachlass. The first is a curriculum vitae that Caro handed to his head teacher on 5 September 1852. It was written in a poetic style, with overly long sentences, in parts immature, and obviously intended to impress a committee of examiners, though it was actually censored by the head teacher. The second document, from which extensive extracts appear in the appendix, is Caro's eyewitness account of the dramatic events of 1848, recorded in 1908, towards the end of his life. His description of Berlin during one week of March 1848 is not altogether different from scenes in Victor Hugo's *Les Misérables.* Both documents were transcribed by typewriter, presumably by Amalie Caro. In our translation we have tried to both imitate his style and, where possible, use, more or less, Caro's own words.

Caro's early years

Heinrich Caro was born on 13 February 1834 in the town of Posen (Poznán of modern Poland), the commercial and intellectual centre of the Polish-speaking areas of Prussia. Posen lay some 200 kilometres east of Berlin, the capital of Prussia, and the German language was imposed on the population. The name Heinrich Caro reflected the merging of Jewish ancestry with German culture. On the father's side, illustrious predecessors included rabbinical leaders who once inhabited Adrianople, the Turkish city that, incidentally, gave its name to the important red cotton dye obtained from the madder plant. According to the Caro family tradition, a predecessor was Rabbi Abraham ben Avigdor Caro, who died in Prague in the 16th century.

The Caros had participated in the great migrations of Jewish traders and artisans across Europe. At some stage they reached Portugal, then moved to Glogau in Silesia, and on to Posen, where Heinrich's grandfather opened a grain business, with his son, Simon, as partner. The home and business was situated in the Dähne'sche Adlerapotheke [pharmacy], in the Marketplace. Forebears of Heinrich's mother, Amalie Schnitzler, came from Holland, where her grandfather dealt in jewelry in Amsterdam and later moved to Breslau, in Silesia. From this family came a number of scholars and a banker, and there were close connections with well-known writers, poets, and musicians.[1]

According to Amalie Caro, Heinrich's father, Simon, had a "distinguished appearance and fine nature, did not speak much, and belonged to those people who despite all their industry and character, depending on the conditions surrounding them, sadly are not fortunate in self advancement." Caro's mother was "exceptionally gifted and spiritually uplifting." Of the six children born into the Caro family, only two sons, Heinrich and Julius, survived. Julius was two years older, and a genius in practical matters and entered into business: "We find him involved in remarkable measure in new developments in Berlin ... By misfortune, he lost his possessions and died at the age of forty of a serious illness."

Caro's birthplace in Posen, the "Dähne'sche Adlerapotheke," in the Marketplace. Sketch by Heinrich Caro. (Deutsches Museum, DM NL 93/10/1.)

At right, from top, in descending order:
attic for storage of plant specimens;
apartment of Caro's parents;
apartment of the pharmacist;
pharmacy.

Middle:
cross indicates apartment of grandfather.
At left:
office of grandfather, above premises marked J. J. Heine.

What we know of Heinrich's childhood, youth, and early aspirations is derived mainly from his 1852 curriculum vitae, which also described how he had come to decide upon chemistry as a career.

> My earliest recollections are of an entirely enjoyable childhood. My parents, who had lost some of their children, gave all their love to my older brother and myself. I

> was surrounded by my grandparents who did everything to give happiness and pleasure to their grandson.... My mother especially occupied herself with my education. She taught me how to read and write, and it is to her unstinting patience that I am grateful for my memorising the twelve times table. My natural intelligence and interest in learning made it easier for mother. By contrast, I possessed a vivacity and uniqueness which made it hard for her and which I did not give up, even when I was sent to school at the age of five.

After school, when not playing with other children, he read translations of books such as *Robinson Crusoe*, "the drama popular among all children," or, with a young friend, admired the "strangely shaped instruments" in the pharmacy and watched with fascination as the Provisor (educated pharmacist who worked for the proprietor) made up preparations in the laboratory.

> It always gave us real and inner pleasure to look at the chemical experiments performed by the Provisor. Now [September 1852] I am in the process of devoting myself to the science of chemistry out of the love of it. However, should it not be self-evident from the first young impression that this would influence eventually my choice of profession?[2]

At his junior school, Heinrich Caro made good progress and was often praised by his teacher. But soon he had to part from all these familiar things–relatives, teachers, and friends–because his father decided to leave Posen for Berlin at the beginning of 1842. The reason was no doubt the wish of Caro's father to escape the restrictions imposed on Jews in Posen, and to provide Heinrich and his brother with better educational opportunities, which was in keeping with the aspirations of secular parents still rooted in Jewish tradition. This deserves some words of explanation.

The lot of Jews in Germany had improved considerably following the French Revolution of 1789, and the spread of Napoleon Bonaparte's empire. In those parts of Germany on the left bank of the Rhine that were under French control, and in most of the French satellite states in the west of Germany, Jews were assigned citizens' rights. In 1812, a Prussian edict gave the Jews, until then under special control of the state, full rights as citizens, with the exception of access to public office.[3] These rights included free movement, unhindered choice of profession and of marriage, and opportunities to purchase land. However, during the period of restoration, 1815-48, when Prussia controlled a larger and more diverse area than "traditional" Prussia across the Elbe, these initiatives were not extended (some were reduced). Moreover, the Prussian reforms were not expanded to the "new" territories acquired through the Congress of Vienna, especially Posen, where almost 40 per cent of Prussian Jews lived. This is probably why Caro's father, in common with many others, sought a new life in Berlin, particularly now that official enquiries were about to commence in connection with a law on the condition of the Jews (Gesetz über die Verhältnisse der Juden).

Heinrich, his brother, and their mother spent a few winter months in Breslau, at the home of the grandmother on the mother's side. They then joined the father in Berlin.

> I was still much too young to feel the hurt which every separation brings with it, and was too much a child not to find a new source of pleasure from leaving familiar surroundings.... It was during my eighth year that I left Posen for Berlin. The expectations of seeing Berlin with my own eyes were so strong that I wished that the slowly-moving post coach was fitted with wings. I had heard of Berlin so much and had so often seen images of it projected as a panorama by the camera obscura.... Finally, after 36 hours, I saw the towers of Berlin, the smoking chimneys, the mass of houses.... My youthful curiosity was very tense, and was increased at every moment by new sights. The mass of human beings! The shouting and calling, the masses of carriages![4]

In Berlin, the family took up residence in an upper-middle-class neighbourhood, and maintained a moderate lifestyle on the father's income, most of which came from investments in lands on the Baltic Sea.[5] Heinrich Caro joined the first class of the Köllnische Realgymnasium, and soon made friends with his classmates. He also gave the teachers good reason to bring him to order, and was often reprimanded because of his noisy behaviour. Caro had particularly fond memories of his senior teacher, who taught him French and arithmetic.

But this peaceful and stable milieu was soon interrupted: "Suddenly there was a double tragedy in our family ... and for the first time I learned the meaning of pain. My dear aunt, the sister of my mother, died." This tragedy made his mother depressive and permanently sombre, and she was hospitalised in a private institution. Then Heinrich and his brother contracted a long and debilitating children's illness. They

> lost consciousness and had the wildest feverish visions. Eventually, after a long time, the force of the illness waned, but when we called for mother she was not there. On top of this, my poor father was now in a hunched and unfortunate condition because of pressures of his business life.[6]

This had a considerable impact on Caro's education:

> For a quarter of a year I had been absent from school because of the illness, and even though still very young I had reached my ninth year. What I had gone through had touched my soul too deeply for the experience to leave me quickly.

Nevertheless, Caro managed to advance from one class at school to the next, though he soon forgot his good intentions and preferred playing with friends to completing homework. He was fascinated by books about medieval knights and everything to do with the middle ages, which became subjects of his dreams and fantasies.[7] One Christmas, Heinrich received a knight's uniform as a present, which enabled him to play out his favourite roles. His brother received a similar outfit, and was the first victim of these romantic inclinations. They battled with other children in the streets:

> Soon my beautiful outfit was spoilt by the feats of my adversaries and the lance was broken. I returned home sad and crying. Following the novels about knights, which had stimulated in me the preference for the Middle Ages, I began to read works of other authors that I could get hold of.[8]

The favourite author of Heinrich and Simon Caro was Friedrich Schiller, whose works had a prominent place in the father's library. Heinrich became so enthusiastic "about these beautiful ballads and romances that I read them so often that I knew them off by heart, and could recite them with pathos to my father." Love of Schiller and other classical authors led Heinrich to join with some of his classmates once a week to act out scenes from ballads and novels. However, his school work suffered until his mother's return following three years of absence.[9] After this, music, adventure, and drama pervaded Caro's childhood.

Caro tells us that his mother instilled in him a serious interest in music.[10] In her earlier years in Breslau she had known the young Felix Mendelssohn-Bartholdy. Now, in Berlin, the opera composer Giacomo Meyerbeer, a close friend of Heinrich's father, was a frequent visitor at the Caro home.[11] Though the Caro family became increasingly integrated into mainstream Prussian life, the circle of friends was still mainly Jewish. Heinrich Caro also learned German folk tunes and listened to bands of infantry regiments.

At the age of twelve, Heinrich was influenced by more than music. He also included drawing, nature studies, and collecting minerals and insects among his broadening range of interests. "Soon afterwards I gave up these interests and returned to reading, the source of fantasy and new ideas." Particularly prominent were translations from the English of books such as James Fenimore Cooper's *Last of the Mohicans* and Walter Scott's novels.

> These helped with my German composition which I liked best of all of my written school work. My youthful mind was now receptive to new and majestic impressions brought to me by a mountain trip to the Harz and the Riesengebirge, in the company of my father and family.... Earlier we had been satisfied with just strolling along lonely paths in the Tiergarten and singing joyful songs.

In 1846 there was a new trip that affected Caro very much, "because it was the first time that I saw the sea." He now entered an age in the life of every boy that is "marked by forceful changes." So far he had been youthful and unselfconscious, preferring play and happy events over more serious aspirations. This was starting to give way to an "undefined dreaming and longing." Caro's mind received every impression much more than previously. He could now be enthusiastic for

> ideas, friendship, and the Fatherland.... Soon the friends that I had were no longer sufficient for me. I viewed them as only superficial and hollow people who could neither participate nor understand my views. How much, therefore, did I yearn for a new friend who could become a participant in all my thoughts, feelings and sentiments. And such a person soon turned up in a classmate who was endowed with a truly poetic mind. Eduard Tempeltey was the name of my friend and he was attracted to nature, much venerated Schiller, as I did, and could, like me, enthuse in ideal dreams.... However, on one point we were different. He had by nature been endowed with poetical gifts. But not I. Despite this failing in me, I was inspired by his example, to the extent that I thought I could courageously mount Pegasus who would take me through the air to Parnass.

Despite the fact that he filled a book with poetry, Caro knew that he was not a poet. A new occupation had already struck him, the study of chemistry, the beginnings of which were inspired by a series of "beautiful demonstration experiments" at school.

> From the very first moment of chemistry lessons I felt a remarkable attraction to this science ... There were in my class some other pupils who liked experiments. We soon joined together and with our small savings bought retorts, heating lamps and other apparatus and began to repeat quite seriously the experiments seen in the chemistry lessons, though not every experiment succeeded.[12]

This activity gave Caro much pleasure, and kept his attention even after he left the Untertertia (fourth year) class at school.

Caro's artistic talents were fostered, probably around 1846, at an informal drama circle made up of a group of seven friends who were interested in history. They called themselves the Seven Wise Men, "impoverished but rich in hopes and ideas for the future," and included Richard Peters, later co-founder with Caro and others of the Verein Deutscher Ingenieure, and son of the owner of the house where they met; Meyer Levy, later a well-known Berlin jurist whose life was cut short by murder; a certain Gregor, later a civil engineer; Alvensleben, musician and composer; Julius Weingarten, professor of mathematics; and Chodowiecki, grandson of a copper engraver. Three young ladies ("The Three Graces") acted as hosts. One was Anna Peters, who, because of her industry, was nicknamed *rosenfingerige Eos*. "Remembering this happy time of adolescence," Heinrich Caro would in 1874 name the phthalein dye eosin in her honor.[13] The next phase of Heinrich's life introduced him to the world of politics. Much of Europe at that time was dominated by the "congress system" of the Austrian Chancellor, Prince Metternich. Though it had brought about considerable stability, the system was also repressive. There were few compromises, and none between the emerging liberal and nationalistic movements and Metternich. This epoch, characterized by censorship and the absence of a free press, and persecution of opponents, later became known as the "Vormärz" ("Before March [1848]"). Among the earliest responses was Ludolf Wienbag's *Ästhetische Feldzüge*, or Aesthetic Campaigns, of 1834, which led to the formation of the "Young Germany" political and literary movement that opposed the way in which Germany was ruled and lobbied for removal of press censorship. By the mid-1840s, liberal aspirations had captured the imagination of many young men in Prussia, particularly among students and the rapidly emerging working class, who from the spring of 1847 began to suffer from severe famines.

Numerous associations of citizens and workers were established, as well as groups of boys, all generally interested in local political and economic issues. Particularly important were the reading "circles" or groups, the most notable, and largest, of which was the Berliner Zeitungshalle, founded in September 1846 by the publisher Gustav Julius. In his premises was a library of 500 journals and newspapers that could be consulted for a low subscription. Julius published the journal *Berliner Zeitungshalle*, the voice of radical democratic thought, with a readership that included middle-class business people. (Today a plaque at the site of Julius's former premises commemorates his role in the political events described here). Other places where the news was avidly read, even if heavily censored, included the Konditoreien (pastry and confectionary shops) and the meetings of youths, including the group that Caro joined, where there was a strong element of entertainment:

> This was a time of special relationships, that had too much influence on my mental development to be omitted here. As early as 1847 associations of boys had been formed almost simultaneously in Berlin. This was initiated by the parliamentary influence of the Unified Landtag, whose views were of interest to everyone at that time. Boys at the age of 14-16 from different schools and educational institutions and of diverse character met in organised gatherings, to improve their mental education with joint work.... This was achieved by our trials of free speech in the gatherings where we discussed statutes, acceptance of new members, and other things.... I joined one such group, called the Germania, during my time in the Obertertia [class in the Realgymnasium for boys of around thirteen years of age], and because I proved myself to be a studious member I did not miss one evening's entertainment (that's what we called those social gatherings) without giving a performance on the piano, singing or reading poetry. The anticipation of applause and the wish to excel over others was naturally the most important feature.... There was never a meeting at which I did not ascend the stage as an impassioned orator.... The meeting place of the Germania was a large room, with tables and benches on which were seated some 30-40 boys (this was the number of members at the peak of the association).[14]

The organisation of, and the debates at, the Germania were run on parliamentary lines. Three boys, comprising the committee in charge, including the president and secretary, sat at the head table. The boys also produced their own newspaper. This experience, Caro recalled, certainly determined his response to the events of 1848.

> Having forgotten my predilection for science ... I wished to climb the stage and shout to the masses "Citizens!" ... I decided that I would like to become a lawyer ... In my fantasies, I saw myself in the stages of becoming a minister.[15]

Though the Germania and similar groups encouraged the spread of liberal ideas among its members, this did not represent any official warming to democratic values in Berlin. Throughout the German states the old governing classes still held sway and industrialisation remained hampered by the disparate interests of the various principalities, even though they were linked by the Prussian-dominated customs union, the Zollverein. There was no single unified economic area, and citizens were denied participation in government. When the economy began to slow down in 1847, and famines became widespread, the middle classes and skilled artisans felt increasingly threatened. This was especially true for workers in the textile industry, in which mechanised factories were already displacing craft-based processes. In Prussia, King Friedrich Wilhelm IV (who had come to power in 1840) and his government made no effort to adapt to the changing situation. The citizens began to clamour for new political structures and economic policies.

This was the background to one of the most enduring experiences in Caro's life, the revolution of March 1848. It was an event of such magnitude that it would shape not only his destiny but also the destinies of all Germans, including Karl Marx and Otto von Bismarck, as protagonists of the two diametrically opposed political directions in post-revolutionary Germany. During one turbulent week, disorder entered young Heinrich Caro's life as the city of Berlin was gripped by the revolution, in which long-standing grievances finally exploded into protest. Caro later remarked that "in one way or another these impressions were a moulding influence on my later thinking and feeling."[16]

Caro's family belonged to the liberal-minded bourgeoisie, and (at least by 1848) lived in a conspicuously affluent part of the city in a building known as the Prince's House (Fürstenhaus). This was a complex occupied by residents, offices, and the Werder'sche Gymnasium. On one side, Caro tells us, was the office of the Intelle[i]genz-Blatt, an agency that handled newspaper advertisements. On the other side was the "hated" Royal Prussian Censorship Bureau, while at the mezzanine level was the house of the "all-mighty" mayor of Berlin, Heinrich Wilhelm Krausnick.[17] Next door was the assembly hall of the Gymnasium. And a little to the west was the office of Gustav Julius's *Berliner Zeitungshalle*. The combination of liberal-radical newspaper office, repressive state institution, and home of the unloved mayor of Berlin ensured that the neighbourhood was a centre of attention in March 1848 and caused Heinrich Caro to witness the disturbances firsthand.

Though the outbreak of the revolution was inspired by earlier events in Paris during February, the revolutionary movement was not imported into Germany, but was the outcome of many internal tensions and problems. At the beginning of March 1848 a series of uprisings erupted in the German states, though mostly in the capitals, and together they formed a united German revolution, since most of the aims and actions were similar. The uprising began in western Germany, especially in the Grand Duchy of Baden, and resulted in the Märzforderungen (March demands)–for arming the people, freedom of the press, the end of the ban on political parties, the democratisation of the jurisdiction, and a national parliament. This brought about the installation of liberal "March governments" in most German states. The revolution took a particularly strong hold in the two bastions of restoration, Vienna and Berlin. In the capital of Prussia unrest grew from 7 March on, when people gathered near the "Unter den Zelten," a popular drinking and dining establishment in the Tiergarten, and made the same March demands as elsewhere. One week later, on the evening of 13 March, troops and demonstrators clashed, and street fighting broke out. This was the beginning of the week that led to Bloody Saturday, 18 March 1848.

For the young Heinrich it was a highly charged adventure, one that heightened his creative senses as a dreamer and poet, as well as love of epic drama, as captured in his description of the turmoil.[18] Caro's father, normally a retiring man, was, in accordance with both his aspirations as an emancipated and assimilated Jew and his bourgeois social standing, elated by the uprising that momentarily brought hope of political liberty and unification of the German states. As Heinrich explained, there was, in all the states, large and small, a popular sentiment for liberty, and the middle classes were anxious for unification.[19] His graphic account of the events, in which his family found itself embroiled, with fighting close at hand and barricades erected in nearby streets, will be found in the appendix to this chapter.

Promises of reform that followed the uprising remained unfulfilled, and hopes for the emergence of a liberal democracy, the sort that Caro and his young friends and family had yearned for, were dashed. Prussian society became increasingly engaged in economic affairs, particularly manufacturing, and at the same time somewhat apolitical. Simon Caro's business affairs may well have improved, perhaps through some involvement with the textile industry (which, as we shall see, later assisted Heinrich's entry into the calico printing industry).

Now there were different influences on Caro's life, which was dominated by trips with the family to the Harz mountains and to factories and mines, in every way nurturing his natural curiosity. Together these increased his interest in nature and science. His parents understood that this was much more than a passing phase, and gave every assistance and encouragement, including the supply of books, collections, and apparatus. Heinrich remained close to friends, with whom he gave family theatrical presentations and in which he had the main roles. The heady mixture of stage, lights, and applause allowed him to pass many happy hours. In the evenings the group of friends sang parts from operas and oratorios. Caro, however, recorded that in many ways all these pleasures had a negative outlook, creating in him a superficial attitude. "My mother attempted to bring me to more serious matters." When an opportunity to work in the laboratory of the Realgymnasium arose, Caro "gave up these fanciful thoughts."[20] This move towards a more permanent interest in chemistry must have taken place around 1850.

> [U]nder Dr. Hagen I occupied myself with chemistry in a practical way. It interested me so much that I took up this activity in my free time, and in my home. At the earliest opportunity I purchased the necessary items for undertaking experiments.... In the beginning, I worked together with friends brought by me to this activity, repeating the experiments done at school, but then I went further and began to work more independently, following the instructions in chemistry books.

Caro did not drop this work, unlike his other interests such as reading, drawing, and singing. The preference for chemistry became greater and greater. "On free days I occupied myself with experiments. My parents did not like this so much ... because of the many smells in our home ... but mother understood my seriousness and she encouraged me in these endeavours." Meanwhile, in the summer of 1850 he entered the senior (Prima) section (eighth- and ninth-year classes) of the Realgymnasium. Just over two years later, early in September 1852, Heinrich Caro completed his secondary education. During the final weeks he prepared the lengthy curriculum vitae on which much of this account is based for submission to an examination by the state inspectorate. Copies were distributed to family members and one transcript survived, revealing, as we have seen, both Caro's mischievous behaviour in the classroom and the origins of his great interest in chemistry. Caro was aware that he was about to embark on a new and important phase of life. The need to produce the curriculum vitae, with an account of his earlier years, and his hopes for the future, provided the stimulus for considerable reflection.

> I was much too self confident, believing that I could succeed in everything with great ease ... My fellow students ... had become more serious, learned more and left me

> behind. I discovered when I entered the Prima ... that there were gaps in my knowledge of certain subjects. However, it was thanks to the class teacher, Professor J. Seltmann, who warned me of where I had gone wrong, and encouraged me to catch up, that I became more studious.... I still associated with my friends, and we shared the most beautiful sonnets from the German classics and Shakespeare.... This reading circle did a great deal to increase my literary understanding and taste.

Heinrich Caro reaffirmed his growing attraction towards an interest in chemistry:

> Meanwhile through the great kindness of Dr. Hagen, who recognised my love of chemistry, I was admitted to his chemistry laboratory at the Realgymnasium, and that enabled me to acquire practical knowledge of chemistry under strict supervision.... Through these circumstances I now had the opportunity to penetrate deeper into this wonderful science. This finally determined the choice of my profession, a subject which for years had attracted my mind.... I decided therefore to devote myself to natural sciences, and in particular chemistry. This science which is in itself attractive has at the present time a powerful influence on all the branches of the trades and promises to become even more so. And it was that which made me decide to take up the study of practical chemistry and thus choose a profession in which thoroughness and efficiency will bring one recognition. To make of myself a thorough and efficient person is my sincere hope and striving.... So now I have arrived at the point where I have to leave the situation which not only the past years but also many other things have made dear and worthy for me. I am now going from the Gymnasium into a free and more independent life. Thanks go to my parents and teachers who have brought me to this destination.... If therefore I am striving for the good and noble that, God knows, is my heartiest wish, so my teachers have played the greatest part in it and it will be by my most serious endeavours to show them my gratitude through my life itself.[21]

This prose did not impress the head teacher. In an addendum to the later transcription of this document, Caro described the response:

> The original of this curriculum vitae was submitted to the director of the Köllnische Realgymnasium at Michaelmas 1852, on the occasion of my school-leaving examination. The director, August, called me to his office just one day before the oral examination—it was a Sunday. I found my otherwise always amiable and well-meaning teacher in a state of great excitement, red in the face, walking heavily up and down, and mumbling words that I could not comprehend. I was only able to understand: Dickens Boz and Boz Dickens [For heavens sake, my God!]. Helpless, I just watched this volcano explode. Finally, the explanation [for this behaviour] was given. My curriculum, which I had worked on with so much industry, and that I had written in the expectation of unanimous praise, my mother had copied with motherly pride as an eternal memorial and the whole family had admired, this nice opus had been reviewed by the director and declared by him as totally unacceptable.

The reason the head teacher could not accept the curriculum vitae, Caro tells us, was because it contained information that would not have been well received by the external examiners from the ministry of education present at the oral examination. The head teacher

> asked me urgently and quickly to prepare a new curriculum vitae, without literary taste, short and sober, as was usual, and to give it to him the same day. One can imagine how deeply my pride as an author was hurt. Tears more than flowed out of my eyes. My desperation quieted the choleric but well-meaning man. He turned more and more towards encouraging and asking me [to rewrite it].

It was then that Caro found out that it was the discussion of the Germania group that was the stumbling block. In the year 1852, Germany had returned to the "reactionary political situation," and the mention of the now strongly discredited groups of pupils would have caused some difficulties for the head teacher, who had earlier been suspected of democratic leanings. Caro went home, took a piece of paper, and rewrote his curriculum vitae.

The head teacher, incidentally, was Ernst Ferdinand August (1795-1870), a mathematician who was in charge of the Köllnische Realgymnasium from 1827 to 1870. In April 1848 he had helped to form units of armed schoolboys from the Primaner class of the Real-gymnasium. These units were attached to others made up of citizens, the "Bürgerwehr," who had taken over the responsibilities of the military in Berlin.[22] August, no doubt, had earlier played a role in encouraging his students, including Heinrich Caro, to participate in groups such as the Germania.[23] The very different situation prevailing in 1852, in which liberal and democratic ideals were supplanted by a general enthusiasm for industrialisation, would endure throughout the decade in which Caro was to complete his education and apprenticeship.

Appendix

Abridged and annotated account of Heinrich Caro, "Beschreibung meiner Erinnerungen der 48er Märztage, miterlebt als Tertianer, aufgezeichnet 1908."

This account of the March 1848 revolution in Berlin was probably dictated by Heinrich Caro to his eldest daughter, Amalie. Since it was prepared sixty years after the event, it was inevitably influenced by later published histories and reminiscences, as well as by the reaction of the Caro family. Heinrich's assimilated Jewish family, and many similar families, had particularly strong interests in the successful outcome of the revolution. During the second half of the 1840s, Jews who retained their faith, or were registered in their communities, comprised 2 per cent of the population of Berlin, while a much larger but unknown number were completely secular and often baptized as Christians. Together they played prominent roles in social and economic life, including in the textile industry, in banking, and as traders. They had also been accepted into local political life, a trend that was enhanced with the rise of revolutionary movements. In 1847 the assembly of representatives of the city (the Stadtverordnetenversammlung) called for complete emancipation of the Jews.[1] They were also to play prominent roles in the events of the following year.[2]

Caro commenced his account of the revolutionary turmoil that overcame Berlin during March 1848 by noting that at the beginning of that month, "Berlin was still quiet and did not participate in such [revolutionary] events." Most citizens, in Caro's opinion,

> did not know until that time the meaning of terms like constitution, liberty of the press, etc. Having grown up in the protective regimen of the ruler of the country, without contact with the outside world, without interest in politics, one was more or less content with prevailing conditions and sympathised with the slogan "Quietness is the first duty of the citizen [Ruhe ist die erste Bürgerpflicht]."

It was on 13 March that the quiet of Berlin was rudely disturbed. Caro had an indelible recollection of his first encounter with the events that were to follow:

> On that Monday evening I was with my schoolfriend Siegmund Friedlaender, the son of a very respected banker and goldsmith, in his parents' home, at Schlossplatze 13, in order to take a private lesson in French conversation given by Monsieur Henri, an honest German, but in spite of that a much sought after teacher of French. Suddenly

> there was a great noise and rumbling of horses. We ran to a window and with numbed astonishment saw a troop of dragoons rush across the square in the direction of [Unter] den Linden.[3]

The French lesson was abruptly cancelled, though the cause of the disturbance was unknown. Then on the Wednesday, the guards took umbrage and fired a few shots. Accounts of the event became exaggerated, and it was even described as an attack by "Animalised Soldateska."

The first clash between citizens and troops took place in the evening at the Stechbahn, close to Schlossplatz. There was one fatality, and many people were wounded.[4] The mayor was blamed as the source of the grievances, since he had done much to restrict the liberties of the citizenry. The people of Berlin had clamoured for a "constitutional system based on the English model, for freedom of the press, removal of censorship, and above all the liberty of smoking in the Berlin streets." They demanded the mayor's dismissal. He was not noted for his popularity.

> [F]earing for his personal security, the mayor gave orders to the school caretaker to barricade from the inside the two portals of the entrance to the complex where we lived. This prevented me from going out in the evening. However, I liked it very much to live inside a "surrounded" fortress. I saw myself in the role of Körner's "Zriny."[5]

The following day was marked by an uneasy quiet that gave way towards the evening because "the people of Berlin could not stand together without joking, and they laughed at the guards."

The mayor had actually made an abortive attempt to bring calm to the situation, and even led a deputation to the king. Subsequently, troops again clashed with citizens at the Schlossplatz, though as far as Heinrich Caro was concerned the week passed slowly away.[6] At this point in his account, Caro remembered that it was from the semaphore [perhaps the Chappe telegraph] on the observatory of the university in Dorotheenstrasse "engaged in its fantastic riddling play" that the citizens of Berlin had earlier learned about the February revolution in Paris. He also witnessed the semaphore movements bringing this information, though without understanding them. Next day Heinrich was informed of what had happened in Paris. This certainly had a considerable impact, though it is not clear whether the response that he described took place immediately afterwards (following the news about Paris that arrived on 27-28 February), or after 13 March.

> [F]rom then, with burning studiousness, I observed the several stages of the progressing revolutionary movement. This was expressed more vividly by my closest friend from the Obertertia, Eduard Tempeltey, the born poet, later author of "Klytemnästra" [actually *Klytämnestra*, published in 1857, and dedicated to the English King George V] and other tragedies and dramas, and cabinet secretary of Duke Ernst of Koburg-Gotha [Saxe-Coburg and Gotha].... My friend wanted to influence the ruling class with calls for liberty, such as "Death to the tyrants" or "Rise German men." Tempeltey was armed with a pistol without a flintlock under his belt ... and I followed in his footsteps, apart from the pistol, because there was only one. And I helped him not only with composing the rally calls and posters, but distributed them secretly.... Then we took off with pride and satisfaction.[7]

On 15 March, news of the victorious revolution in Vienna, the power centre of Metternich, reached Berlin. Three days later, on the morning of Saturday 18 March, the minister of the interior agreed that there should be a law permitting freedom of the press. It was also agreed that a meeting of the Unified Landtag should be convened for April to prepare a constitution, and to bring about unification of the German states. The citizens of Berlin gathered in the streets and meeting places, expecting announcements of reforms.

> From the early morning of that wonderful spring day a joyous feeling could be felt, especially in the square before the castle, where a great mass of people had assembled. They were extremely excited and discussed the news that had come into the city. The king had promised to a deputation of citizens that he was shortly to order a constitution. Everyone was glad of the return to calm, especially after the excitement of the last days. One year earlier, the king, when opening the first Prussian parliament [Unified Landtag], had declared that he did not want a piece of paper to stand between him and his people. Now this paper was to become reality though it was understandable to just a few politically educated people because of its hieroglyphical language. My father too had heard this rumour and went off to obtain confirmation. When he returned joy beamed from his face. Yes it was true. The entire Berlin citizenry and particularly the business sector would assemble in the middle of the day before the castle in order to show its gratitude to the king. As noon approached, my father took my brother Julius to hear this ovation. My mother, one of her friends, and I remained at home. My father and brother did not return for lunch. At about 2 p.m. we peered out of the open window to look for them. The street was bathed in warm and peaceful sunshine and was empty of people. Then, suddenly, we saw several people rushing from the Werder'scher Markt and around the corner of Jägerstrasse.... In the next moment we noticed with breathless astonishment how the frenzied crowd surrounded a guard in the street and attempted to take his weapons. He defended himself, though they had already tore the sabre from him. He held his gun horizontally in order to protect himself, but in the struggle the weapon was turned against him. A shot was heard ... Meanwhile, with great difficulty the unfortunate guard raised himself from the ground and stumbled along

> from house to house trying to find refuge. But all the entrances were closed and this mortally wounded man had to drag himself to the school where the caretaker Stange took him in and laid him down on straw. Immediately, I was driven by compassion and curiosity, and ran down the staircase to the wounded man in the schoolyard. I have never forgotten the sight! This was the first victim of the revolution that I saw and the first dying person that I had seen in my life. With his own gun he had been shot in the side. Where he fell, which is today the Reichsbank [Imperial Bank], King Friedrich Wilhelm IV later had a memorial tablet installed. After a long period of uncertainty, my father and brother returned, both unharmed, but in a miserable and agitated state. I never saw, either before or after, my otherwise quiet, dignified and restrained father so excited and furious. He burst into our kitchen, looked for an axe and wanted to return to the street without any explanation. It appeared as if the whole city ... was preparing for vengeance against a treacherous act. "Betrayal" was the terrible word which we heard from our father after we had quieted him down considerably and dissuaded him from his warlike intentions. And then we learned what had happened. As a great mass of people presented the king with a joyful ovation, two shots were suddenly fired from the castle. At this apparently prearranged signal, the dragoons surrounding the square attacked the defenceless crowd. Everybody shouted "Betrayal" and attempted to save himself from the soldiers who appeared from all sides. My father fled with my brother to the Konditorei "Josty" under the Ste[c]hbahn and then escaped through a window in the direction of the Werderschen Mühlen. This was the impact of a historic misunderstanding on a serious, quiet and rational man and one can understand that this never completely explained incident of 18 March could entangle such a deep moral fury.

The fatal events of Bloody Saturday were far from an unfortunate misunderstanding. More than 10,000 people had assembled in the square before the king's castle. At first, the citizens responded warmly to the king's announcement of concessions. But as the crowd swelled, it began to demand the withdrawal of the military. It was now confronting the very basis of the Prussian military state and the authority of the king. According to Caro, it was the king who gave the order to clear the square, apparently on advice from his brother, Prince Wilhelm. Two shots were fired, probably haphazardly, and panic broke out. It was more likely, however, that the response was directly from the military, which had acted in a similar way during the previous days.[8]

> All reason was silent; only the blind feeling of vengeance gained the upper hand in the souls of citizens. This feeling, until then quite alien to the good citizens of Berlin, now expressed itself in many ways. With great interest I saw events that I had only heard and read about, but never seen with my own eyes. First there was the erection of a barricade. How often had I in my most vivid fantasies imagined such an event

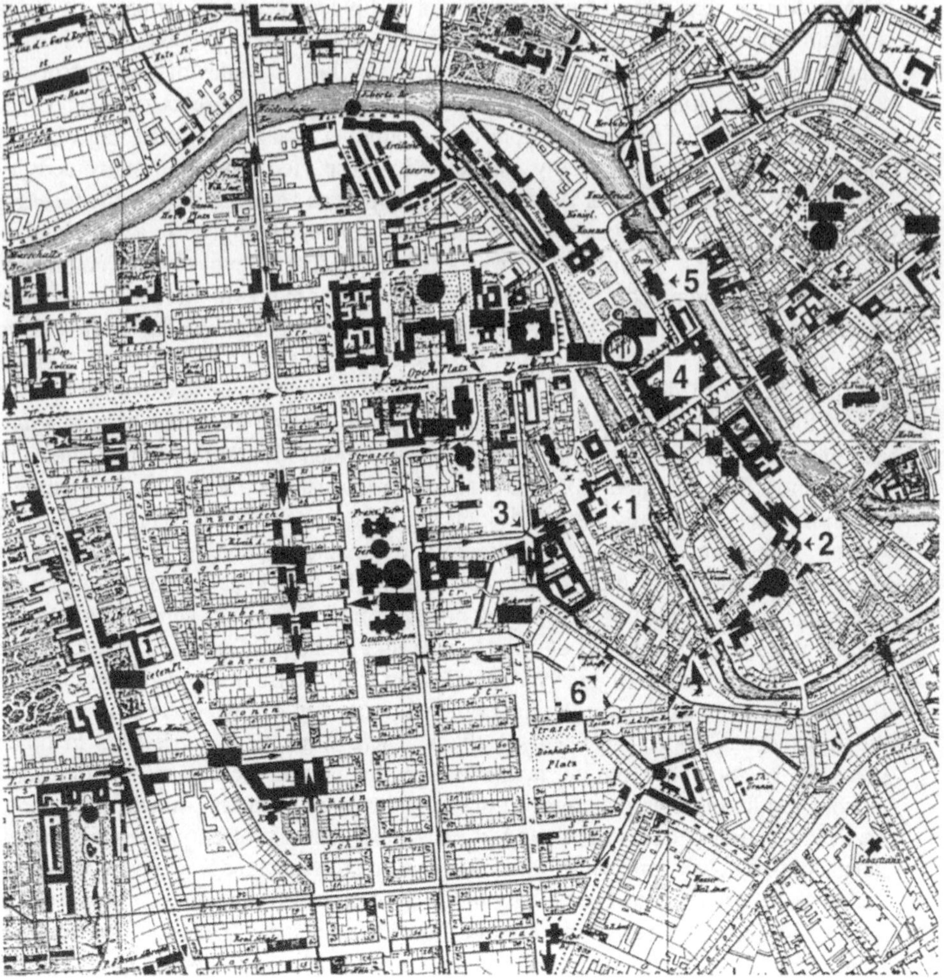

Map of section of Berlin, 18 and 19 March 1848. (Reproduced by kind permission of Walter de Gruyter & Co.)

Key
1. The Caro family home
2. Heinrich Caro's school
3. Offices of Gustav Julius's *Berliner Zeitungshalle*
4. King Friedrich Wilhelm's castle
5. Cathedral
6. Gewerbeschule

Lines across streets are locations of barricades (double lines represent more substantial barricades). Solid black rectangles show positions of infantry and wished to see it myself. And now such a barricade was being built before my eyes in the Jägerstrasse at the corner of the Oberwallstrasse. At first, the citizens stopped a slow moving horse-carriage, then they detached the horse and sent it away with the driver. The carriage was overturned and placed across the street.... A solid and carefully made barricade was made from sacks filled with sand, barrels and, mostly, cobble stones from the street. Then I saw how the tiles of the roof of the Zeitungshalle of Julius at the Oberwallstrasse were stored for use as missiles. From the newspaper office on the first floor of the building a large blood red flag was put out. This office had, incidentally, already been suspected of revolutionary activity and [Gustav Julius's Berliner Zeitungshalle group] was considered to be the meeting place of agitators. The newspaper, edited by Julius, belonged to a progressive political movement. In any case, it was self evident that a revolutionary committee existed that had prepared for these March days, even if the revolution, as it was later described in the reactionary press, had not been arranged exclusively by "Poles, Jews and Frenchmen." ... After all these events there was quiet until around 5 p.m., when darkness began to descend. Both sides prepared for the inevitable battle. People armed themselves, built barricades, took tiles off roofs, and made defences at street entrances. The army became increasingly concentrated around the castle. Then the first cannon shot was fired. Soldiers attacked various streets, though, as I remember, the shots were like tightly slammed doors far away. I confess that I had expected a greater impression from a cannonade and in the beginning was somewhat disappointed. But soon things changed. The impact was like that of thunder and lightning, and an unending continuous noise, sometimes strong, sometimes less so, intermingled with the chimes of church bells and sounds that instilled indescribable fright and horror.... The night sky was reddened in an unusual way as if from a great fire. And that is what it was. We heard the next day that the extensive workshops of the Royal Iron Works had been set alight. There were many more fires in other places in the suburbs. From our house we saw the glow in the sky and the flames, a terrible and unforgettable picture! In our neighbourhood shooting was heard. Heavy barricade fighting had started and it was said that Tyrolean sharpshooters of outstanding bravery and capable of firing with great accuracy achieved wonders. People were prepared to believe anything. By contrast to elsewhere, the barricade which had been built before my eyes in Jägerstrasse and the barricade later built in front of our house using stone from the entrance came to inglorious ends. Both had been left undefended and were removed during the night by a patrol of guards. There was one victim among our neighbours, after soldiers fired at the newspaper office from where tiles had been thrown at them. The servant girl of a family that we knew well was fatally wounded. At our home, the officers warned us to move away from the windows otherwise they would shoot. To this we reacted quickly, and avoided direct participation in the battles taking place. My parents hid their most valuable items in the ovens of the classroom of the Gymnasium at the suggestion of the trustworthy school caretaker. Nevertheless, we did not sleep a wink. In vain I placed my head under a blanket in an attempt to silence the sound of the terrible shooting. No sleep came to my tired eyes and my excited mind conjured up the most terrible visions of the fighting. Then it gradually became quieter. Night passed, and with the

> morning dawn sleep eventually overcame us. I was still so young. I awoke in the light of sunshine, and the ghostly nighttime spook had passed. Everything was quiet, just like a Sunday. There was no shooting or ringing of bells. I asked myself: Had it all been a bad dream? I almost believed that it was so. But one look at my worried parents and then a glimpse down to the street at the remains of the barricade convinced me that a night of terror had passed over our Berlin. My curiosity got the better of me, and unable to restrain myself I went down to the street to find out what had happened there.[9]

At this point, Caro, perhaps to emphasise that he was there, and certainly to add to the sense of drama, and intensity, changed to the present tense:

> Fortunately, the door of the building is already open. I climb over the debris in front of the house and as carefully as a red indian on the warpath, just like the last of the Mohicans, make my way past houses ... then to the Mint, on to the bridge over the River Spree, and on and on in the direction of the castle. My caution is unnecessary, for no enemy endangers my life. Everything is still and lifeless. In this way I arrive at the Stechbahn (today the red castle). And there suddenly I am confronted with a sight that fills me with horror and makes me shudder. The whole castle square is a war camp full of soldiers of all kinds.... But much different from those of the spring parades.... Everything is serious and there is no hint of play. The various troops are out of formation, standing around and lying down in a disorderly fashion. Guns are placed together. The soldiers, obviously tired from the night's fighting, are resting. It is the moment of respite after the battle that so often I had read about! And while my eyes wonder around with the most intense fascination a terrible sight momentarily strikes me. There, in the middle and at the sides of the square, lay strange brown, motionless and soundless rows of frightening shapes. I hardly dare to look there again. These, I assume, are the fallen warriors. Driven by compulsion, I glance once more, only to realise that they were not human corpses, just the backpacks that the soldiers had taken into battle. Much relieved, I continue with my discoveries, furtively moving under the Stechbahn to the corner of Brüderstrasse, and then proceeding without being stopped by any soldier until I arrive at the entrance of Breitestrasse which now lays in the deepest quiet, but which a few hours before had been the scene of the most bitter night fighting. The cobble stones tell me that. The street is sown with the white pasteboard cartridges of innumerable bullets and with the charred roof tiles that had been thrown down from the roofs and out of windows. In other places the paving is also torn up, with signs of their removal everywhere, and of the fighting at the barricades. Other curious people have dared to venture out and with muted voices they told each other terrible tales: Here, the artillery had fired with Kartätschen [grapeshot, a cluster of small iron balls] on innocent citizens; there, the citizens, their supply of bullets exhausted, in desperation poured boiling oil on the soldiers. Citizens had also fought back with hacked-up lead and spiral steel projectiles. Rumours were rampant: stories of terrible wounds that never heal; of hundreds of dead soldiers removed quickly, loaded onto Spree barges, and brought during the night to Spandau, under the guise of bread.

The deeply reviled Prince Wilhelm, later Wilhelm I, seventh king of Prussia and first German emperor, was blamed for much of the bloodshed, though Bismarck later successfully projected him as a much loved emperor, an affection evoked for political purposes to symbolise a unified Germany. (In 1858, Wilhelm took over the administration from his then-insane brother, Friedrich Wilhelm IV.) This accounts for Caro's sarcasm as he explained the role of Wilhelm in bringing about the bloodiest events.

> The culprit of all this was the hated Prince of Prussia, the "Kartätschenprinz" (our later much-loved Emperor Wilhelm). He had given—one knows that precisely—at noon in front of the castle the pistol signal for the attack on the joyous assembled Berlin citizens. But now he had secretly made off. Early one morning, the king, a very good person but wrongly informed by the prince, had given the order to cease shooting and sent away his bloodthirsty brother, who had dared to tell the king: "You take your prayer book and leave me the sword." He was thrown out of the castle.... The king could not stand the shooting. A truce was arranged, and there was peace.

In the street battles, more than 227 citizens and between sixty and seventy soldiers lost their lives. The commander of the Prussian troops, General Karl Ludwig von Prittwitz, doubted both the commitment and fighting ability of his men in the deadly street confrontations. He advised the king to withdraw the troops from the city and to besiege it from outside, a common and usually successful tactic of the 19th-century military. But the king, probably shocked by the events, and despite his own opposition to the popular movement, submitted to the revolutionary demands.[10] He brought an end to the fighting because he realised that this was the only way to save the crown and prevent the spread of revolution to the countryside and other provinces, particularly the Rhine province.[11]

On Sunday 19 March, and after the street fighting had subsided, the Berliners first gathered their dead and marched to the castle, unhindered by the military. There the king paid homage to the victims, an action that on both sides was interpreted as humiliation of the monarchy (though subsequently it was put to good political purpose when Friedrich Wilhelm was promoted as a popular king of the people). Three clergymen also paid honour to the dead of Bloody Saturday–one Protestant, one Catholic, and, notably, one Jewish.

Among the places that Caro visited was his school, damaged by intense fighting, which caused it to close that summer. But now there were "more important things to do ... to hang a big black-red-gold ... flag through windows and prepare to wear the tricolor badges on our hats and caps and in our button holes, because the city was drunk with victory. Everyone was in the streets, the houses were decorated with flags in festive colours that were, until then, either unknown or known only in the memory of the old student associations [Burschenschaften, who first used black, red, and gold] … the tricolor had to be visibly shown everywhere to demonstrate our liberal and German-national feeling."[12] In those days it would have been dangerous to wear the black and white colours of the Prussian state.

> It was the first time in memory that Berlin was without soldiers. Following the King's orders the victorious guard troops had left, obedient but sad, without singing and music. The city was exposed to the mobs and therefore it was necessary to create immediately a civic guard. There was a general arming of the people as protection against enemies, both from within and without.... Citizens were encouraged by calls from the streets to join this newly organised civil defence organisation.... The doors of the armoury (Zeughaus) were opened and the weapons kept there distributed in the various parts of the city. My father also received military equipment, a brand new gun with bayonnet, and a sabre and an ammunition bag.... At night everyone wanted to rest. But things did not turn out as planned. Already during the day, our building was the subject of interest and curiosity. As during the previous days people halted there and looked up to the windows of the mayor's home. It was not at first known that the frightened man did not come home after leaving on Saturday morning and had stayed somewhere in safe hiding. When he dared come out of hiding on Monday morning he was recognised in the street, and was beaten up and forced to resign.[13]

Prince Wilhelm fled to England, where he sought refuge for two months, prior to returning to Germany. A liberal cabinet was appointed, the so-called March Ministry, and a Prussian National Assembly was elected.[14] However, during the following months interest focused mainly on events in Frankfurt, where the German National Assembly gathered at the Paulskirche. There, plans were drawn up for a pan-German central executive power, led by a Reichsverweser.

It is difficult to imagine the apprehension and excitement of a 14-year-old boy confronted with these changes, his school destroyed and his older school friends parading with armed units. Even more changes were to follow. During the final months of 1848 the first phase of a counter-revolution in the German states was implemented, most notably in Vienna after bloody fighting and in Berlin with a *coup d'état*, but it did not lead to civil war. In November, Prussian troops regained control of Berlin, and the king imposed his own constitution. In April 1849, Friedrich Wilhelm IV refused the imperial crown offered to him by the Paulskirche parliament, though he remained the king of Prussia. In the following month, Prussia was placed under emergency law. This second phase of the counter-revolution was aimed against left-wing members of the Paulskirche parliament and–in Prussia–against the lower chamber. Most of the liberal and conservative members left the German National Assembly and thus were dashed the hopes of a liberal and national revolution. The remaining members of the Paulskirche parliament attempted, in vain, to rescue the constitution. The remnant of the parliament moved to Stuttgart and was finally dissolved in June. The geographical centres of this second, May Revolution, were Saxony, the Palatinate, and Baden. The Prussian military suppressed the revolutionary movement, though not until July 1849 in Baden, where order was restored through trials of high treason, summary executions, and prison sentences. The harshness of the Prussian military created enormous ill-feeling among the German democratic movement, with which young Heinrich Caro and his father had so strongly identified. It would long outlast these events.

2

Calico Printing in Mülheim

Caro's chemical education

In October 1852, Heinrich Caro gained entry to Berlin's Königliches Gewerbeinstitut, the leading trade school of Prussia. Two years earlier the school had introduced a chemistry course, one that catered for young men intending to pursue careers in local industries. The emphasis was on chemical technology, analysis, and laboratory work.[1] Caro also enrolled in a chemistry course at the University of Berlin. By this time, however, Caro's parents were in poor financial shape. Heinrich was too proud to request assistance from wealthier family members, but was fortunate to receive a scholarship from the Seydlitz foundation. This came about in part because of Heinrich's mathematical capabilities, demonstrated during one of the first lectures he attended at the Gewerbeinstitut. The lecturer, college director Nikolaus Druckenmüller, was so impressed with his student's performance that he immediately arranged for the stipend, and continued to encourage Heinrich Caro throughout his time at the college.[2]

Driven by a combination of natural ability and the sure knowledge that in the future he would have to support himself, Caro spared no efforts with his studies. From October 1853 he was allowed to undertake experiments on a regular basis in the chemical laboratory of the institute. His teachers were Karl Friedrich Rammelsberg (chemistry and mineralogy) and Gustav Magnus (chemical technology).[3] Both were of Jewish origins, as were several students and assistants at the Gewerbeinstitut during the 1850s and 1860s. The latter included August Leonhardt, who was to join Caro in Manchester; Ivan Levinstein, later the leading dye manufacturer in Manchester; and Carl Liebermann, co-discoverer of the alizarin synthesis. Denied free access to leading university positions, these men, through their involvements with the application of chemistry, were setting agendas that would dominate many areas of academic and industrial chemistry for the remainder of the 19th century.

Caro's mastery of chemistry enabled him to supplement his meagre allowance by private teaching at the Gewerbeinstitut.[4] The first laboratory assignment under Rammelsberg was the preparation of sodium nitroprusside, a member of a class of salts discovered at the end of the 1840s. Through the sodium nitroprusside experiments he became interested in the preparation of sulphuric acid, and in 1854 wrote up what he called his first "childlike" draft patent that described an improved concentration process for the acid.[5] That Caro undertook such an exercise in registering inventiveness beyond the confines of his laboratory notebook is ample proof of the emphasis on practical application in chemistry courses at mid-century.

Toward the end of 1854, Druckenmüller and Magnus began to guide Caro in the choice of a career. At first, the sulphuric acid industry seemed most promising. They were also aware that the German textile industry, then in its first phase of large-scale expansion, needed chemically trained colourists. Caro's teachers suggested that he take an interest in calico printing and dyeing, especially since the Prussian government was considering the establishment of a teaching post in these subjects, either at the Gewerbeinstitut or, more probably, in the western province of Prussia, the Rhineland.[6] Druckenmüller and Magnus must have singled out Caro as an ideal candidate, advising him to undergo training as a calico printer. To this end, on 13 February 1855, Heinrich Caro's twenty-first birthday, Druckenmüller signed a letter of recommendation stating that Caro's work

> in every scientific subject which is taught here is of an exceptionally high standard. The laboratory assignments in which he has already occupied himself with independent investigations have benefited from the fact that he had undertaken chemical analysis before entering the Gewerbeinstitut.[7]

In seeking to embark on an apprenticeship in calico printing, Caro set out on his first steps toward membership of an elite band of highly paid professionals, the textile colourists, specialists in preparing and fixing dyes and in creating designs and patterns, particularly on cotton fabrics. This was also one of the most prestigious occupations for chemists, with salaries far in excess of average academic positions. It also made apprenticeship positions difficult to attain.[8]

To appreciate the applications of chemistry to calico printing and coloristic endeavours, it is necessary to review the background to some of the industrial products and processes that were now to become relevant to Caro's career. The main emphasis is on the madder dye and its commercial forms (including, for sake of completeness, developments until 1862), the processes for indirect printing on textile fabrics, and methods for detecting adulteration of dyes.

Madder

The most widely used dyestuff employed in calico printing was that obtained from the root of the madder plant. Large-scale cultivation and processing of madder was an important activity in France and Holland, particularly during the 18th century. The dye was released by mechanically breaking open the root. It was widely available as a fine powder, graded according to fineness and other criteria. Madder was well suited to hand block printing, Turkey red dyeing (a complex process introduced to Europe from Asia) and, later, selective dyeing of areas of cloth to afford printed effects.

Madder came to the fore in the 17th century as the main dye used in the production of European calico, or cotton, prints. However, these prints were a threat to well-established woollen and silk industries, which is why between 1686 and 1712 heavy duties, and prohibitions on import and manufacture of printed cotton goods, were introduced in France, England, and Prussia. Cotton dyeing and printing was taken up elsewhere in Europe, notably in Mulhouse (independent of France until 1798), Russia, Bohemia, Switzerland, and various German states. The laws against printed calico were eventually relaxed in Prussia (1752), France (1759), and England (1774). This was especially important in England where mechanised production of cotton goods commenced in Lancashire during 1779, in which year six million pounds of raw cotton were imported. By 1790, cotton imports stood at forty-six million pounds, and after 1800 cotton cloth was printed in ever-increasing amounts with roller machines. During the 1850s, twenty million pieces of calico cloth were printed in Britain alone.

Printing with madder was achieved indirectly. One process involved covering areas of bleached fabric with resist waxes or pastes prior to dyeing. After dyeing, the wax was removed, leaving white areas that could be hand coloured by pen, brush, or block. Such methods had been used extensively in the Far East and were also adopted in Europe at the commencement of calico printing. This resist (or reserve) style was used widely with madder and Turkey red until the 1850s. Another process involved printing one or more fixing agents, or mordants, onto the fabric, which was then dyed. This gave the dyed-style prints, in which the madder dye afforded shades of black, red, purple, or brown, according to the mordants. Britain was the major importing nation for madder dye used in calico printing and Turkey red dyeing. The dye was present to the extent of no more than one or two per cent in the root, and the products were always expensive.

In 1826, Parisian manufacturing chemists Pierre Robiquet and Jean Jacques Colin had isolated the principal colorant in madder by treating madder powder with sulphuric acid, followed by sublimation, which afforded a crystalline solid. This they called alizarin(e). A second substance was obtained, which was named purpurin(e). The elemental compositions of alizarin and purpurin were reported, along with the chemical properties. The most significant aspect of this work was the fact that the amount of available dye could be increased by the action of sulphuric acid. The research was applied to large-scale working, as patented by Robiquet, Colin, and A. Lagier, of Avignon. The product, known as garancine (and for some time as Lagier's bloom of madder), was introduced in 1830, and had three times the dyeing strength, or tinctorial power, of the powder. Garancine was made by successively washing the powder with water, treating with acid, boiling, washing, drying, and, finally, grinding with a small amount of chalk or sodium carbonate to neutralise any acid retained in the woody fibre. One hundred kilograms of madder gave about a third of its weight of garancine.

Thus although the colouring principles, mainly the alizarin, were not separated in the commercial product, they were now available in a more easily useable form. The cleaner dyed fabric required less after-treatment, especially less soaping. Garancine became especially popular in Lancashire, where in 1847 Simon Pincoffs set up a factory for its production near Middleton, close to Manchester. His main client was the large calico printing works of Salis Schwabe & Co., at Rhodes, also near Middleton. Schwabe was one of the largest printworks in the world and exhibited calico prints prepared with madder and garancine in London at the Great Exhibition of 1851. Lancashire, where most of the world's "fast and cheap" cotton prints were produced, became a massive consumer of garancine for good commercial reasons:

> its most valuable property is that while giving the same essential colours as madder, it permits the addition or admixture with it of a number of other dyestuffs of a much cheaper price, and this enables the manufacturer to produce prints of a good appearance and of fair stability of colour, at a lower cost than with the use of madder or garancine alone.... there are establishments in which nothing else is employed in the production of madder colours. Even in Turkey red it is beginning to be much used.[9]

Ongoing applications of chemistry to the study of natural dyes led to the introduction of an even more useful madder product not long after the Great Exhibition.

Pincoffine

The Schunck family of Manchester were partners in the calico print works of Schunck, Souchay & Co. of Belfield, Manchester. Twenty-two-year-old (Henry) Edward Schunck entered the business as works manager in 1842, after gaining his doctorate in the Giessen laboratory of Justus Liebig. Schunck's chemical training enabled him to undertake research into natural dyes in a private laboratory. From around 1845 his main interest was in the constituents of the madder root, using samples that were readily available in the Manchester factory. Schunck subjected alizarin to oxidation and obtained a product that he named alizaric acid. He also isolated from the root a substance that he named rubian, and the effective ferment (enzyme), which he called erythrozym. The latter released the free dye. The importance of this work to the manufacture and use of madder products was immediately appreciated.

Schunck's investigations had shown that alizarin was freed from its glucoside, the combination of dye with sugar, by fermentation, that sulphuric acid brought about the same cleavage, and that the acid did not harm the colouring matter. Consequently, a new chemistry-based approach to the manufacture of madder derivatives became available. The outcome was a dye noted for excellent purples obtained in dyeing and printing, and which brought about further economies in the use of mordants. This was pincoffine (a name used mainly on mainland Europe) or commercial alizarine (as it was known in Britain), based on Schunck's experiments and manufactured by Simon Pincoffs. It appeared in 1852, and was made by subjecting the neutralised product from the sulphuric acid process to high-pressure steam in a closed vessel. By 1861 more than three million pieces of calico had been dyed with pincoffine in East Lancashire and Scotland.[10] The principal consumer was Schwabe & Co.

The extracts of madder

One reason why madder could not originally be printed directly was the great amount of extraneous matter present with the dye. The cleaning processes necessary for removal of this matter from dyed cloth were so harsh that they would have damaged other dyes printed with the madder. This is why mordants were applied first to bleached cloth. Roller printing with mordants, followed by dyeing with madder, required six steps, the last two of which, soaping and cleaning, were repeated twice, with thorough washings in between. A new method of printing that required just four steps was introduced around 1840. This involved direct application of the madder dye mixed with thickened mordant. After printing, the cloth was treated with high-pressure steam for one or two hours to fix the dye. The results were the steam, or topical, colours.

Garancine and pincoffine, despite their superiorities over madder powder, were not altogether satisfactory steam colours. Purer forms of madder were investigated, particularly during the 1850s. In 1860, Emile Kopp, at Sauverne, north of Strasbourg, undertook a series of experiments on Alsatian madder that had been grown for six months and from which he obtained alizarin and purpurin, using sulphurous acid. The extracts were found to possess forty times the dyeing power of good madder. The merits of Kopp's sulphurous acid process did not escape the attention of the chemists G. A. Schaaff and G. E. Lauth of Strasbourg. They were aware that the acid did not harm the colorants and this allowed maximum recovery of garancine from the residual material. Schaaff and Lauth made substantial modifications to the sulphurous acid process and by 1862 were able to separate almost pure alizarin and purpurin. Moreover, they transformed Kopp's experiments into an economic process through recovery of residual madder and fermentation of used liquor. The tinctorial power was claimed to be ninety times that of good madder.

The Schaaff and Lauth process attracted great interest from several chemists at the 1862 London International Exhibition. August Wilhelm Hofmann praised the researches on madder that since the 1820s had led to understanding of the fermentation process, and to the production of garancine and the madder extracts, and expressed the hope that the new process would bring about the industrial preparation of almost-pure madder dyes, enabling more cost-effective direct printing. Hofmann also summarised the uncertainty concerning the constitution and synthesis of madder:

> Madder has probably given rise to more researches and experiments, and to a greater number of really valuable memoirs, than any other colouring matter; and yet our knowledge of madder, as compared with that which we possess concerning other colouring principles, is still extremely confused and uncertain. It is scarcely going too far to say that the successive labours of chemists on this subject have tended rather to complicate than to simplify it.[11]

Chemistry and new printing processes

Colourists were also engaged in processing fabrics, and were responsible for the introduction of chlorine bleaching of cotton at the end of the 18th century. While cotton used in Turkey red dyeing needed the minimum of bleaching, cotton cloth that was to be printed with madder mordants required up to nine treatments in the bleaching process to remove the unwanted substances that caused madder to stain unmordanted areas.

A far-reaching innovation in the production of prints had taken place after 1810, when bleaching agents based on chlorine were used to achieve patterned effects on predyed cloth. This was known as the discharge style. However, the fumes of chlorine made the working conditions extremely unpleasant. The technique was improved by using a solution of bleaching powder, and according to the author Edward Baines, "[t]his is one of the most beautiful facts in the chemistry of calico printing."[12] The discharge processes added a completely new dimension to the decoration of textiles and permitted imitation and rapid production of the popular Indian cottons, which is why they came into widespread use in both Mulhouse and Lancashire. They were also applied to indigo-dyed cloth for production of so-called Africa prints, or Manchester batiks.

The spectacular success of cotton prints became the stimulus for studies on new processes for discharging colour, especially milder alternatives to the chlorine-based processes. In 1852, the French colourist Emile Kopp experimented with arsenic acid as a discharge agent, and filed patents for the use of arsenic and phosphoric acids in discharge printing. Kopp also devised a process for the economical production of arsenic acid, which was taken up by the manufacturer Charles Kestner of Thann. The availability of arsenic acid in the textile industry greatly facilitated the manufacture of the important aniline red dye in the 1860s.[13]

Label of calico printer S. Schwabe & Co. of Middleton, near Manchester. (Edelstein Collection.)

Adulteration

The high value and extensive use of both madder powder and garancine encouraged adulteration, a phenomenon so widespread that leading chemists were called in to devise simple and rapid methods for detection of valueless additives, which included both mineral and vegetable substances. A method for detecting the presence of minerals–such as powdered brick, ochre, yellow sand, and clay–was established by Jean Pierre Louis Girardin and Joseph Houton de Labillardière of Rouen in 1838. They found that on calcining unadulterated madder in closed platinum crucibles, about five to nine per cent of ash remained (the actual figure varied according to the source of the root).

Vegetable contaminants, which included oak and mahogany sawdust (and various other ground dyewoods), fustic, ground-up almond shells,

306 *DYEING AND CALICO PRINTING.*

has also resulted in the detection of the existence of a combination of the mordant and lime with the colouring matter, viz., if madder had been used containing calcareous matters naturally, or if chalk had been added in the dye-beck.

All these observations refer to madder only. As regards fleur de garance and garancin, irregularities in the mode of heating, the material used in the construction of the dye-beck, and many other conditions, have no prejudicial action upon the process of dyeing. Generally speaking fleur de garance can be used instead of madder in all cases where clearing is required, but madder is preferable for the kind known as triple pink (rose-red) ; fleur de garance,

FIG. 22.

again, is suitable for purples and blacks ; for red and black a mixture of fleur and madder is used, which yields a deeper black than fleur by itself.

On the large scale madder dyeing is performed in well-constructed, water-tight, wooden tanks, heated by steam, and provided with properly contrived rollers moved by means of straps so as to impart to the goods stretched on these rollers a suitable motion, and thereby to cause a regular renovation of the points of contact between the bath and the cloth. Fig. 22 will give the reader some idea of this contrivance, which is also in use for the dunging, branning, and soaping processes. As regards the practical

Madder dyeing. (William Crookes, *A Practical Handbook of Dyeing and Calico-Printing* [London: Longmans, Green & Co., 1874], 306.)

BLOCK-PRINTING.

The child to the right hand of the printer is the "tearer," whose business is to keep the colour equally spread out over the surface of the colour-box.

See page 472.

PAINTING IN RESERVES BY HAND.

(Top) Young girls engaged in applying dyes with a hand block to machine-printed cloth. Caro's detailed descriptions of bleaching, dyeing, printing, and finishing processes included notes on the young people, girls and boys, and adults engaged in these activities.

(Below) Applying the resist paste to the roller of a cylinder printing machine. (William Crookes, *A Practical Handbook of Dyeing and Calico-Printing* [London: Longmans, Green & Co., 1874], opposite 292.)

bran, and fir bark were much more difficult to detect.[14] Following Girardin's studies, colourists were advised to employ dyeing trials with mordanted sample strips that were then compared with a standard. Calcination and dyeing tests were carried out in many works by the early 1850s. This provided an important role for the chemists and colourists who also operated in-house production of garancine.[15]

Heinrich Caro at C. & F. Troost

According to August Bernthsen, who relied on an account given to him by Caro, the aspiring trainee calico printer confronted considerable difficulty finding employment, at least until his father made the acquaintance of either Albert or Max Troost, partners in the C. & F. Troost weaving and calico printing factory at Luisenthal, Mülheim, in the Ruhr Valley.[16] Through this connection Heinrich Caro entered the Troost factory, probably in April or May 1855. His first assignments were mainly manual and analytical work, helping out wherever needed in the works though making at least some use of his scientific knowledge. However, he was not permitted entry to the calico printing section, almost certainly because specific processes employed there were jealously

Label of C. & F. Troost factory, ca. 1856. (Deutsches Museum.)

guarded trade secrets understood only by the works colourist, Achille Steinbach, of Mulhouse. While Bernthsen's account is here at its least reliable, since he based it on what he remembered of verbal information supplied by Caro, there does exist the transcription of a three-year contract for Caro's apprenticeship signed by the Troost brothers on 1 September 1855, and applied retroactively to 1 May. As an apprentice, Caro was assigned to Steinbach, who no doubt enabled Caro to brush up on the French that he had studied both at school and with "Monsieur Henri."

Caro's contract with his first employer included thirteen clauses that, among other things, required him to submit to rigid self-discipline and long hours. It is worth describing here not only because it must have been typical of similar contracts entered into by apprentice colourists at mid-century, but because no other source of such detailed contractual information is known to have survived. Caro was expected to undertake the tasks of a chemist, and "conscientiously to do everything within his power to bring about improvements."[17] In order to complete his assignments,

> Mr. Caro has to keep a diary into which he must enter daily everything that takes place and that he has learned and experienced relating to the manufacture in the printing factory, and to include the results of experimental investigations. This belongs to C. & F. Troost.[18]

Gaining familiarity through this type of record keeping and preparing detailed scale drawings was typical of apprenticeship activities in several trades.

The working hours were fixed at 7 a.m. to midday, and 2 to 7 p.m., but were to be extended as required. Heinrich Caro had to commit himself for a period of three years at an annual salary of 350 Thaler for the first year, 400 for the second year, and 450 for the third year.[19] Caro was obliged to reach an agreement with Steinbach, whereby the latter would provide him with instruction in the craft of calico printing for the sum of 800 Thaler, payable by Caro; and Steinbach's fee would be provided in the form of an interest-free loan to Caro from the Troosts, repayable on 1 May 1858.

During the apprenticeship, and in addition to the daily diary, Caro was required to "keep a book of recipes that will contain all information relevant to the factory of C. & F. Troost. This book belongs to C. & F. Troost. And, in addition, Mr. Caro must make use of the instruction, and of all the results, for the benefit of the factory."[20] This was perhaps an arrangement whereby, among other things, the Troosts gained access to Steinbach's processes for their future use after he left the firm. If Caro succeeded to acceptance as a colourist at the Troost factory, then his salary would be increased to 600 Thaler yearly, and the proprietors would forgive 200 Thalers from their loan.[21] Following termination of the contract, Caro was forbidden from taking up employment in any German calico printing factory that was in competition with C. & F. Troost for a period of three years. Should he do so, his salary would retroactively be reduced to 25 Thaler per annum, and he would be obliged to return anything in excess of that sum and to pay the Troosts a massive financial penalty of 5,000 Thaler.[22]

Heinrich Caro accepted these conditions, knowing full well that in the event of success with his training as a colourist he would be well qualified as a teacher of calico printing, or assured a secure and well-paid position in the burgeoning German textile industry. His income was meagre, because he was saving to pay off the Troosts, which meant that his lifestyle would be restricted for a time. All he could afford for living quarters was an unheated attic in a peasant's cottage close to the factory.

Caro's sketch of the cottage he lived in at Mülheim am Ruhr, 1855-59. His place of abode was the unheated attic. (BASF Archives, from an original in the Caro Nachlass, Deutsches Museum.)

Despite the hardships, the activities of the factory provided plenty of opportunities for learning about the range of chemicals employed in calico printing, and even of meeting suppliers of dyes and other textile chemicals. Among the latter were Thomas Roberts and John Dale of Manchester, and their German employee, the chemist Rudolph Koepp, who together visited Mülheim in the summer of 1855. Roberts and Dale were partners in Roberts, Dale & Co., specialist in dyewoods and oxalic acid, an important chemical used in calico printing, wool dyeing and printing, and silk dyeing with wood colours.[23] They had brought their sons to Germany for further education.[24] On the same trip, John Dale also visited the Mannheim chemical works of Carl Clemm-Lennig, uncle of August and Carl Clemm, later to become co-founders of the Badische Anilin- & Soda-Fabrik (BASF).

The Troost brothers were impressed with the efforts of their apprentice long before the Gewerbeinstitut issued his exemplary graduation certificate in October 1855: "In analytical chemistry he has acquired sufficient ability. This is aided by his theoretical knowledge that enables him to solve all assignments in experimental chemistry with certainty, acumen, and rapidity." The director and teachers released Caro

> with the certain expectations that he will easily find his bearings in all aspects of industrial chemical practice, and is capable of solving all the problems put before a thoroughly educated technical chemist.[25]

They had accurately evaluated Caro's potential and determination; he worked so hard in the Troost factory that for "three years it was said that he was unaware that Mülheim had a church steeple."[26] Calico printing consumed his entire being. His perseverance and rapid progress, drawing on his chemical education and a philosophy of self-help, were to become the hallmarks of a man who would change the course of the history of dye technology.

Heinrich Caro's first contribution toward new innovations at the factory was probably made when he overcame a problem associated with madder dyeing carried out during winter months. The slow drying in the cold caused the red colour to turn brown. According to Bernthsen, this was at a time when Caro did not yet have access to the printing section and, as a result, had to rely on a young female worker to spirit away unseen samples of newly dyed cloth. Caro undertook experiments on the dyed cloth, and devised a steam box that accelerated the drying process without loss of colour. The foreman was greatly impressed, as were the owners.[27] Caro certainly proved then that he had the dexterity and ingenuity that were essential qualities for a successful colourist. Bernthsen stated that it was on the basis of this innovation that Caro received his apprenticeship.[28] However, the steam box was more likely devised during the winter of 1855-56, well after Caro had received his contract. Nevertheless, apart from any doubtful connection to Caro's contract, this story certainly emphasises the extent to which colourists and calico printers protected their trade secrets.

In 1856, William Perkin in London discovered the first aniline dye. That same year Heinrich Caro co-founded–through his membership in the Hütte, an association set up in 1846 for those interested in manufacturing at the Gewerbeinstitut, and his contact with Richard Peters–the Verein Deutscher Ingenieure, which attracted members from a wide range of industrial activities. Both Perkin and Caro at this time relied on the existence of support networks for development of their industrial careers. Perkin, working alone in London, found this through a dyer in Perth who understood the limitations of existing natural and semi-synthetic purples and mauves, particularly their great expense and lack of fastness. Caro relied on the calico printing factory and the members of the Verein for practical and intellectual support.

While Caro's notebooks were, strictly, the property of the Troost concern, he did retain, or perhaps copied, a few of the various diaries and journals that he was required to keep. Those that survive cover the period 1856 to 1859, and the diversity of their contents provides considerable information about his duties, as well as about the activities of what must have been a not untypical, and certainly enterprising, calico printing factory. The main dyestuff employed was that obtained from the madder root. The application of the madder colour, especially in printing, presented considerable technical challenges to colourists. As already noted, it was rarely printed directly, and then only in steam or topical printing, when the dye mixed with mordant (the nature of which determined the final colour) and thickening agent was printed onto the fabric and then fixed by the action of steam.

Various methods had been devised for creating designs and patterned effects indirectly on cloth. For example, single-colour patterns were obtained from madder by first printing or painting the mordant as a thickened paste onto the areas to be coloured and then dyeing the fabric. Important mordants were salts of aluminium, for red, and salts of iron, for maroon to reddish brown. Chocolate brown, black, purple, and pink could also be produced. When several mordants were applied to the cloth, with different strengths in different areas, a number of colours and shades were obtained in a single dyeing operation. Other processes for affording patterned effects involved the use of resist and discharge pastes.

The founders of the Verein Deutscher Ingenieure on their trip to attend the inaugural meeting at Alexisbad/Harz, 12 May 1856. Caro remembered that he was in a carriage on this occasion. (BASF Archives.)

Though roller printing had enabled the rapid production of continuous lengths of fabric, the quality could not equal that obtained with hand block printing, which was better suited to both mordant and discharge pastes. Hand block printing had been mechanised through the use of the perrotine machine, invented by Jérôme Perrot in 1835, and both perrotines and roller machines were employed at the Troost works.[29] An unusually strong commitment to the perrotine demonstrated that the Troosts' customers required high-quality prints.[30] Further, the preparation of the pastes used in printing required considerable chemical expertise, as Caro found out when he laboriously undertook small-scale trials on samples of cotton.[31]

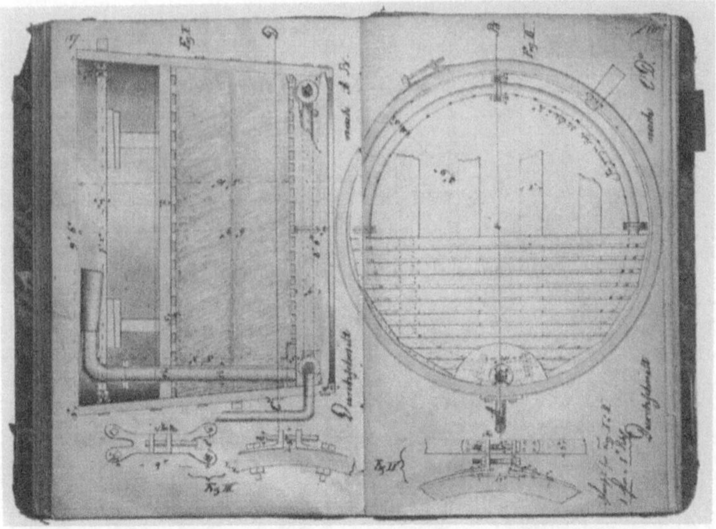

Drawing of bleaching apparatus in notebook of Heinrich Caro. ("Fabrik der L[o]uisenthaler Aktien-Gesellschaft für Spinnerei, Weberei & Druckerei, Nr. II, 1858-59," item no. 37925, Deutsches Museum.)

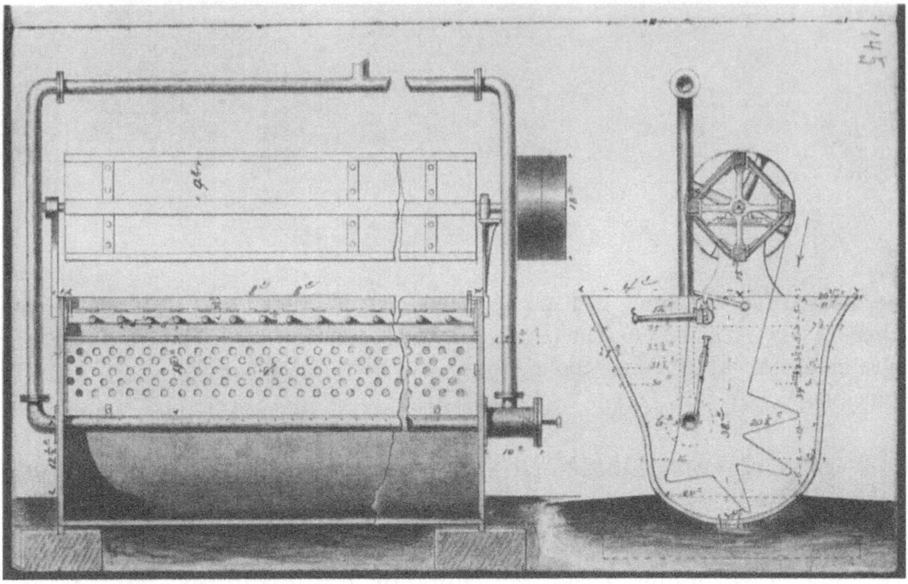

Washing apparatus in notebook of Heinrich Caro. ("Fabrik der L[o]uisenthaler Aktien-Gesellschaft für Spinnerei, Weberei & Druckerei, Nr. II, 1858-59," item no. 37925, Deutsches Museum.)

Mechanised block printing with the perrotine machine. According to Heinrich Caro's notebooks, by 1859 the Louisenthaler works had installed nine machines of this type, the most modern of which were supplied by the manufacturer Hummel of Berlin. (Edelstein Collection.)

Dyeing of cloth mordanted for madder colours relied on thorough pretreatment to ensure that the colour would not take on the unmordanted area. This was achieved by a complex process of chemical bleaching. The Troost factory operated the then-common multi-step bleaching process that, after singeing of cloth to remove loose fibres, involved, successively, treatment with lime, dilute sulphuric acid, resin soap, soda ash, chloride of lime (bleaching powder), and dilute acid.[32] The cloth was then washed and dried. After mordanting and dyeing, the colours were rendered bright and brilliant by soaping and clearing.[33]

While familiarising himself with these operations, Caro also kept abreast of the technical literature, noting in his diaries the latest progress in the production of madder-derived products, especially garancine, and other dyes.[34] The Troost factory employed garancine by the mid-1850s, because it was better suited to dyeing and had found limited use in the direct application to cotton cloth through steam printing.[35]

Garancine in the Ruhr Valley

The most complete surviving record of what must have been typical procedures used for producing garancine from madder during the mid-1850s are to be found in a notebook written up by Caro toward the end of his time at Mülheim. The descriptions cover processes that were well established by 1850. Caro's notes show that madder was the dye most extensively used in calico printing, and that some 481,080 Prussian pounds were consumed at the Troost factory in 1856 alone.[36] These notes also demonstrate that many calico printers and Turkey red dyers found it worthwhile to undertake the in-house processing of madder to garancine.

Caro observed that "Sulaica" madder from Smyrna was found to give the best results in dyeing (Sulaica is a girl's name in Turkey).[37] Troost purchased madder from the Dutch merchants Ferdinand Gallonkamp (Amsterdam), Maris & Schippers (Willemstad), and W. Bunge (Rotterdam). Madder was expensive, and the price varied from 33 to 57.30 florins per kilogram.[38] The expense and the low concentration of dye in any of the forms in which it was received by users encouraged widespread adulteration. This made testing essential, again requiring not a little expertise in the methods of chemical analysis.

Caro's description of tests for madder shows that methods for exposing adulteration had changed little since the late 1830s. The most reliable quantitative test for inorganic contaminants involved incineration in a closed platinum crucible. The test for added organic substances was by dyeing of small strips of mordanted cloth in dyebaths of known concentration, followed by comparison with a standard.[39]

According to Caro, the manufacture of garancine was commenced at the Troost factory in 1851 by a colourist named Raiser, but it was only through the introduction of improvements that the process became economical.[40]

The description of garancine production in the factory, with the aid of beautifully executed ink and hand-coloured drawings, is among the most highly detailed of the many textile and dye-processing stages that Caro recorded. The first step was crushing of the madder with wooden hammers, followed by mixing with dilute sulphuric acid, then boiling the mixture in a wooden vat that was fitted with a steam pipe, deacidification with lime, filtration, washing, and pressing. The garancine was then ready for use.[41]

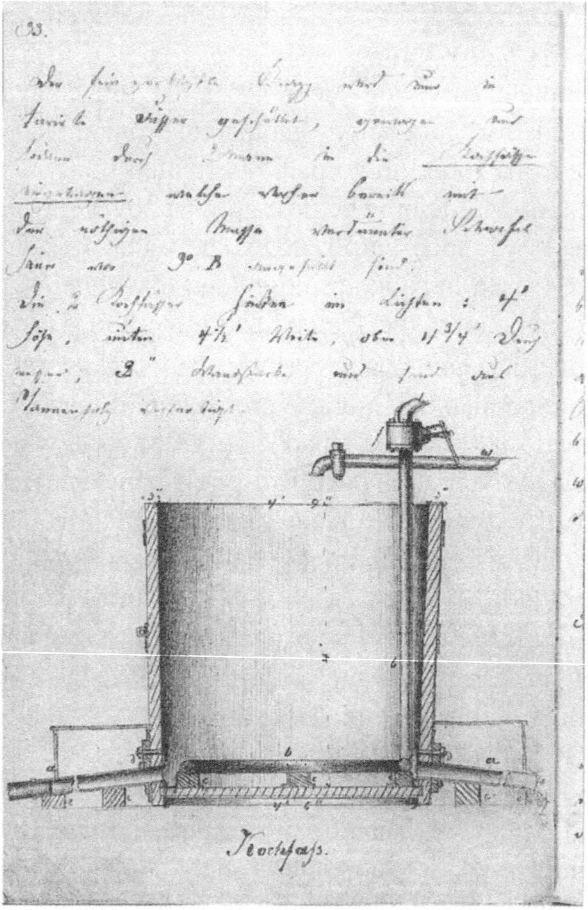

Caro's drawing of cedarwood vat used in the preparation of garancine by treatment of crushed madder root with sulphuric acid. The madder root was ground, sometimes by two men working with wooden hammers. Prior to treatment, the madder was tested for adulteration by incineration in a platinum crucible. Caro described how he also undertook comparative dyeing trials starting with strips of cloth onto which mordants for red, violet, and yellow were pre-printed, and then repeated this operation with other mordants. ("Fabrik der L[o]uisenthaler Aktien-Gesellschaft für Spinnerei, Weberei & Druckerei, Nr. II, 1858-59," item no. 37925, Deutsches Museum.)

In calico printing with garancine, less soaping and clearing were required than if ordinary madder powder was used. Also, a light treatment with chlorine, called "chloren," or chloring, was sufficient to recover the whiteness of undyed areas of fabric.

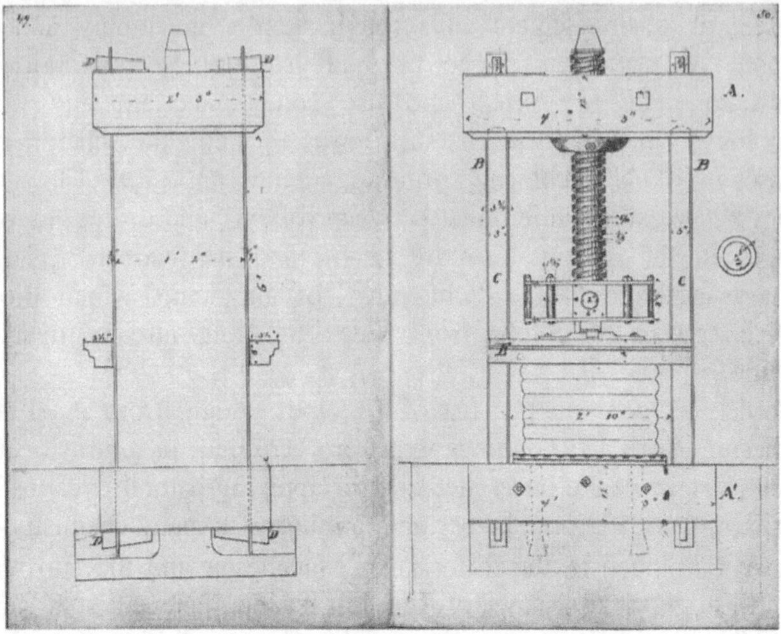

Caro's drawing of a press for drying and collecting garancine. ("Fabrik der L[o]uisenthaler Aktien-Gesellschaft für Spinnerei, Weberei & Druckerei, Nr. II, 1858-59," item no. 37925, Deutsches Museum.)

Other processes studied by Caro included indigo printing, which was also an indirect process, and the preparation of the purple colorant known as murexide. The latter was the first semisynthetic dye, made from uric acid (derived from Peruvian guano) and demanding considerable chemical expertise. Although murexide faded under acidic conditions, it was a popular dye throughout Europe during 1856-59, made by both specialist chemical manufacturers and dye users.[42]

A visit to Manchester

By early 1857 the Troost concern had been absorbed into the Louisenthaler Aktien-Gesellschaft für Spinnerei, Weberei & Druckerei.

(In the company name, the village of Luisenthal was changed to Louisenthal, no doubt to provide a more French-sounding title, associated with high fashion.) Caro's conditions of employment remained unchanged. He had made rapid headway with his apprenticeship, and in March 1857 was given instructions from Max Troost for a journey to Manchester, accompanied by an employee named Kellermann.[43] Their purpose was to investigate advances in textile machinery and make purchases of new items. The original handwritten instructions are difficult to read, are brief, and use some uncertain and obscure terminology, but it is clear that Caro was to study the machinery and processes involved in chloring, printing, calendering (glazing the surface of cloth by pressing while moist between rollers), and drying, as well as advances in the various uses of steam, and its recovery. The final instruction referred to the "whitening" of garancine, which probably meant discharge of colour from areas of cloth already dyed with garancine.

A notebook containing a list of "Recipes bought from A. [Frap] in Manchester, April 1857" shows that Caro acquired, in return for a cash payment, details of the latest methods for applying natural dyes in dyeing and printing.[44] In addition, he became familiar with many chemistry-based processes employed in the factories of Manchester and the surrounding district through the assistance of Rudolph Koepp, the chemist at Roberts, Dale & Co. Among the new processes that Caro would have heard about in Manchester was that of treating garancine with steam under high pressure to produce a colorant that gave excellent purples, the pincoffine or commercial alizarine of Simon Pincoffs. Murexide was also available in Manchester at this time, made by Robert Rumney, and also in some calico printing factories in Lancashire.[45]

The Manchester visit certainly introduced Caro to the large-scale industrial application of organic chemistry, especially manipulation of natural products, and their applications in textile processing, dyeing and calico printing. He was also able to develop useful personal contacts among dye and chemical manufacturers and colourists. The experience, and familiarity with the most advanced printing and other textile machinery, must have been of great value when he returned to the Mülheim factory.

Multicolour roller printing machine. (Frederick Crace-Calvert, *Dyeing and Calico Printing: Including an Account of the Most Recent Improvements in the Manufacture and Use of Aniline Colours*, eds. John Stenhouse and Charles Edward Green [Manchester: Palmer & Howe, 1876], 76.)

During 1857-58, Caro had to undertake ten months of military service in the Royal Prussian Reserve-Guard Infantry Regiment, Berlin. His spare hours were spent as a guest in the household of the Berlin calico printer Jacques Meyer, father of Richard and Victor Meyer (later a leading chemist).[46] Meyer's works, trading as Breslauer, Meyer & Co., employed the colourist August Leonhardt, who, like Caro, hailed from the Province of Posen and had studied chemistry at the Gewerbeinstitut.[47] These connections would become particularly useful for Caro in the years to come.

The enforced absence from the Louisenthaler works required Caro to extend his contract until the autumn of 1859. His notebooks indicate the rate of expansion of the works until that time: from the single boilerhouse of 1849, to the second of 1854, and the third of 1858.[48] Calico printing facilities had been increased, bringing the number of perrotine machines to nine, and roller machines to five, including two from Mather & Platt of Manchester.

By this time plans for the Prussian government's proposed teaching post in calico printing, the reason why Caro had joined the Troosts in 1855, had been abandoned. Caro, it appears, expected to succeed Steinbach on the latter's departure from Luisenthal. However, according to Bernthsen, Steinbach decided to stay on because of marriage to a local woman and that was the cause for Caro's leaving the calico printing factory as soon as he had fulfilled the conditions of his contract. Though Caro had built up considerable contacts with dye-makers and calico printers in Germany, his sights were directed toward events taking place in England, because of the restrictions imposed on employment in Germany by his contract with the Troosts. William Perkin's novel mauve dye, made from coal-tar-derived aniline, was being manufactured on a large scale, as was aniline red (fuchsine in France, magenta in England), discovered early in 1859 and, like mauve, made by oxidising commercial aniline. Also available was the yellow coal-tar colorant picric acid, made from phenol.

These were exciting times for dye-makers, even though the new artificial products were often considered to be nothing more than fads that would disappear as soon as tastes in fashion changed. The main problem was that they were difficult to apply to cotton, which placed restrictions on their application to calico printing. Their brilliance, however, made them very striking, and encouraged research into new processes of manufacture and of fixation onto cotton. The major English centre for the manufacture and use of dyes was Manchester, whose vitality had impressed Caro in 1857, and it was to this humming industrial city that he travelled in the autumn of 1859.

3
The Manchester Years, 1859-1866

Introduction

In this and the next two chapters we follow Heinrich Caro's first foray into synthetic dyes and their various applications at Roberts, Dale & Co., the firm he worked with for seven years in Manchester. Certain of Caro's activities arose from the need to investigate novel reactions as a response to the patent monopolies of the main English rival, Simpson, Maule & Nicholson of London. The enterprise in Manchester was aided by a number of German chemists and colourists, many of whom would later make substantial contributions to the German dye industry. Though not all the new products and processes were successful, they did enhance Caro's familiarity with both academic and industrial coal-tar chemistry. Moreover, his assistance to English and Scottish dye-users during the 1860s as they experimented with coal-tar products brought about a further merging of calico printing technology with the practice of chemistry. Caro's perseverance, his own experiments in dyeing and printing, and his travels to factories and agents in Britain and on continental Europe contributed to the widespread acceptance by dyers and printers of aniline dyes. On this he also built his own reputation. It was while working in England that he acquired the skills for inventing, manufacturing and marketing synthetic dyes that he would later exploit to such great advantage in Germany. At the same time, Caro came to learn about the ways in which legal monopolies on new chemical inventions were acquired through patents and, often, complex litigation.

Fortunately, it is this creative English period for which we have access to the most detailed archival sources, held mainly with the Caro Nachlass. These sources include trade literature, recipes, laboratory and accounts notebooks for the period 1862-63, trade and scientific correspondence for 1860-67, and transcriptions of retrospective accounts written by Caro and other Germans who spent time in Manchester. Thus the recipe books for dyes indicate clearly that Caro's functions included those of technical assistance in the application of natural and synthetic dyes to the clients of Roberts, Dale & Co. In this, they show continuity with his training as a colourist, and confirm the critical role of colourists in the establishment of synthetic dyes, thus demonstrating that for all its unprecedented aspects the synthetic dye industry was firmly embedded in prior technology.[1] These sources also tells us far more about the trials and tribulations of Roberts, Dale & Co. than can be revealed about other pioneering English firms, such as, in London, Perkin & Sons and Simpson, Maule & Nicholson, in Huddersfield, Thomas Holliday, and in Manchester, Ivan Levinstein.[2] Caro also adds considerably to the story of William Perkin's mauve, since, through his inventiveness, Roberts, Dale & Co. became the only other manufacturer of this colorant in Britain.[3]

It is particularly significant that the date of Caro's joining Roberts, Dale & Co. coincided with the establishment of the aniline dyestuffs industry. William Perkin's mauve, or aniline purple, was a favourite colour in the fashion world during 1859. In May of that year it had been joined by François Emmanuel Verguin's fuchsine, or aniline red, first made by Renard frères of Lyon. Perkin refused to license the manufacture of his potassium dichromate oxidation process for mauve to other British manufacturers, which is why several chemists, dyers, and chemical companies were soon looking for alternative methods to gain purple and red dyes.

These included David Price, who undertook research for Simpson, Maule & Nicholson, and came up with a method that gave a red, but in too low a yield to make it commercially viable. For a time, Simpson, Maule & Nicholson had to be satisfied with manufacture of the intermediates nitrobenzene and aniline, and developed a healthy export market for the latter. During the winter of 1859-60, Edward Chambers Nicholson, a partner in Simpson, Maule & Nicholson, and Henry Medlock, a consultant to a Coventry dyeing partnership, independently came up with a greatly improved method for the aniline red, using arsenic acid. Both filed patent applications in January 1860, but since Medlock was first, Nicholson allowed his application to lapse. Later in the year Nicholson's firm acquired Medlock's patent. By 1863, Simpson, Maule & Nicholson monopolised the British market in aniline dyes through its control of the most important aniline red patent, and rights to patents for derivatives of aniline red, particularly aniline blue and (from late in 1863) the Hofmann's violets.[4] This posed the greatest challenge to Heinrich Caro.

William Henry Perkin (1838-1907), ca. 1860. (Edelstein Collection.)

Edward Chambers Nicholson (1827-90), partner in Simpson, Maule & Nicholson. (Zeneca Archives.)

Carl Alexander Martius (1838-1920), in 1862, when he was an assistant of A. W. Hofmann in London. (Caro Nachlass, Deutsches Museum.)

Carl Schorlemmer (1834-92). (Edelstein Collection.)

Roberts, Dale & Co.

Heinrich Caro arrived in Manchester during September or October 1859, bearing letters of introduction to (Henry) Edward Schunck from his former teacher Gustav Magnus and from Theodor Goldschmidt, who manufactured murexide and other dyes in Berlin. In November, Caro received a letter from Jacques Meyer, who asked him to contact Schunck's firm as well as the calico printing factory of Salis Schwabe & Co. to enquire about their products. This letter served as another useful reference.[5] Caro also possessed a family link with the textile industry in Manchester through the cotton goods merchant, Louis Behrens.

Caro was now seeking a post that would enable him to build upon his training as a colourist in a calico printing factory. He was especially attracted to the new chemical manufacturing processes used to produce both novel variants of natural dyes and coal-tar, or aniline, dyes. In October 1859 he was offered employment as private assistant to John Dale, a partner in the firm of Roberts, Dale & Co. He was originally assigned to routine analysis, but he was soon taking on the duties of a colourist engaged in all aspects of dye preparation and application for the benefit of the firm's clients in, mainly, Lancashire and Scotland.

The partnership of Roberts, Dale & Co. had been founded in 1852. John Dale had previously managed a calico printing factory, and his yellow colorant picric acid (trinitrophenol), a derivative of coal-tar phenol, had been displayed at the Great Exhibition of 1851. At the same time, and independently, Thomas Roberts placed on show the mineral pigment ultramarine. In the mid-1850s they turned to the production of oxalic acid, and, around 1860, solid caustic soda. The weekly output of oxalic acid around that time was no less than nine tons, from a process that required forty tons of coal for each ton of acid, and that was noted for the "neatness and simplicity with which the several operations are performed.... Roberts, Dale & Co. are the first manufacturers who have succeeded in carrying out the process [of Joseph Louis Gay-Lussac] in practice on a large scale."[6]

Among the employees at the end of the 1850s was Rudolph Koepp, who, not long before Caro arrived in England, returned to Germany, where he set up an oxalic acid factory with Richard Kirshaw, former manager of Roberts, Dale & Co.[7] Koepp's departure may well have created a vacancy that Caro was available to fill. The salary was one pound per week, which was not unreasonable, since during the 1860s another competent German chemist, Georg Lunge, earned a similar sum in the alkali industry of Lancashire.[8] Caro must have been glad to join the ranks of analytical chemists, which, according to his later good friend Raphael Meldola, was the "pinnacle of success."[9] This was because analytical work was the principal task of trained chemists in industry at that time. The title "analytical chemist" also served to discriminate between the scientific chemist and the pharmacist. No doubt, Caro called himself an "analyst" because it signified a colourist with a high level of training in chemistry.

Roberts, Dale & Co.'s laboratory was situated in the factory at Cornbrook, Hulme, close to the centre of Manchester. There Caro investigated dyeing using "French madder," an alizarin preparation (almost certainly Pincoffs's commercial alizarine), garancine, dyewoods, and other natural products.[10] Around 1860 these were important items of commerce. Apart from garancine and other madder products, some 150 tons of madder were consumed each week in East Lancashire alone. As for dyewoods, in which Roberts, Dale & Co. specialised, dyers required 300 to 400 tons each week, and printers some sixty tons.[11]

Heinrich Caro quickly picked up English, and got to know the printers and dyers in Manchester and district, as well as Henry Roscoe, professor of chemistry, and his assistants, at Owens College in Quay Street. Caro's place of residence was City Road, Hulme, not far from the factory. The frequent appearance of foreign visitors at Roberts, Dale & Co. made his mother tongue, and an excellent knowledge of French, a considerable asset. Several Germans came to visit the factory as guests of John Dale, including, in 1860, the chemical manufacturer Carl Clemm-Lennig, of Mannheim, and in September 1861, Friedrich August Kekulé, on the occasion of the annual meeting of the British Association for the Advancement of Science. In 1862, Gustav Kirchhoff and Robert Bunsen from Heidelberg, accompanied by Roscoe (former student of and collaborator with Bunsen in photochemical studies), made an inspection of the newly opened Roberts, Dale & Co. factory in Warrington, called Mersey Bank Works.[12] Five years later, and following his return to Germany, Caro would join Robert Bunsen in Heidelberg.

Caro's mauve process, its application, and aniline black

Caro claimed to have undertaken independent chemical investigations soon after he joined Dale (as he had done at the Troost factory). In 1860, he discovered a new process that would establish his reputation as an inventor of synthetic colorants. Caro acquired some nitrobenzene, then sold as essence of mirbane for giving pleasant odours to soaps and perfumes, and reduced it to aniline. By subjecting the aniline to a variety of oxidising reagents he discovered that certain copper salts–those used in dyeing processes–gave the mauve colorant. The process, patented jointly with John Dale in May 1860, was scaled up using a mixture of copper sulphate and sodium chloride.[13] The product was probably made on a small scale at Cornbrook during 1861, and sold by Roberts, Dale & Co. to dye users.[14]

So impressed were Roberts and Dale that, according to a surviving draft deed, in 1862 they entered into a profit-sharing partnership with Caro for working the patent.[15] Large-scale manufacture probably began early in 1862, by which time Caro had become more closely associated with Roberts, Dale & Co. than with Dale alone. Caro's mauve process did not infringe the original 1856 patent of William Perkin, since English patent law permitted the filing of different processes for the same product. Perkin's firm, Perkin & Sons, was now confronted with its only competitor for mauve in Britain, excluding the efforts of French firms to sell their products in England through agents and in infringement of Perkin's patent.[16]

A prerequisite to the manufacture of mauve was a regular and economical supply of aniline. One firm was renowned for its large-scale production–Simpson, Maule & Nicholson. Though enquiries were made, it is not known whether aniline was purchased from this source.[17]

Caro's mauve process was considered so promising that Roberts, Dale & Co. decided to manufacture its own intermediates on a considerable scale. Toward the end of 1861, the firm purchased two nitrobenzene stills, or reactors (in which coal-tar benzene was nitrated), and one aniline still (in which the nitrobenzene was reduced), from R. B. Pillmer of Blackfriars, London. Pillmer's sketch of the nitrobenzene reactors strongly resembles illustrations of equipment normally credited to the pioneering efforts of Edward Chambers Nicholson, who around 1859 replaced large glass nitration flasks, or "boltheads," with cast-iron stills. Indeed, Pillmer may have been Nicholson's supplier of plant for use in these processes. This sketch, in a letter giving detailed instructions for use of the apparatus, is the earliest surviving transaction for the supply of closed vertical reactors fitted with steam-powered stirrers. In November 1861, the three reactors were sent from London by the Great Northern Railway to Warrington for installation in the Mersey Bank Works.[18] Commercial aniline, which was then a mixture of amino compounds, was also acquired, notably from Read Holliday in Huddersfield, and Wilson & Fletcher, dye-makers in the East End of London, though probably more for comparative purposes and technical examination than for use in manufacture. Caro's notebooks show that both firms' products were subjected to his scrutiny by distillation and analysis.[19] Wilson & Fletcher later purchased mauve from Roberts, Dale & Co. for resale in London.

Mordants for mauve and aniline dyes. The most important challenge, however, was that of fixing the new aniline dyes to fabrics, cotton in particular, and of winning dyers and printers over to the novel products. The introduction of Caro's mauve process required that the technical problem of dye attachment to cotton be solved. The same problem had been confronted by William Perkin while working with English and Scottish dyers and printers during 1858-59, and also by John Lightfoot Junior at the Broad Oak Print Works, Accrington, during 1859-60, but neither had come up with an entirely satisfactory solution. During 1860, calico printers had managed to print aniline colours mixed with albumen-based mordants directly onto cloth (instead of dyeing mordanted cloth). The method of application was similar to that used since 1850 for pigments such as ultramarine, which encouraged the application of aniline dyes and pigments together as an extension of what was known as the pigment style.

How the matter was tackled at Roberts, Dale & Co., and the magnitude of the problem, are revealed in correspondence between Caro and Breslauer, Meyer & Co., of Berlin. Breslauer, Meyer & Co., no doubt through Caro's intervention, had entered into a contract with Roberts, Dale & Co., whereby they were to jointly develop mordants for mauve. The terms stipulated that within a specified time neither party was to obtain outside assistance. This ensured that useful results remained well-kept secrets. At first, Jacques Meyer must have been well pleased with his collaborative venture, based on Roberts, Dale & Co.'s close working relationships with Lancashire's leading calico printers.

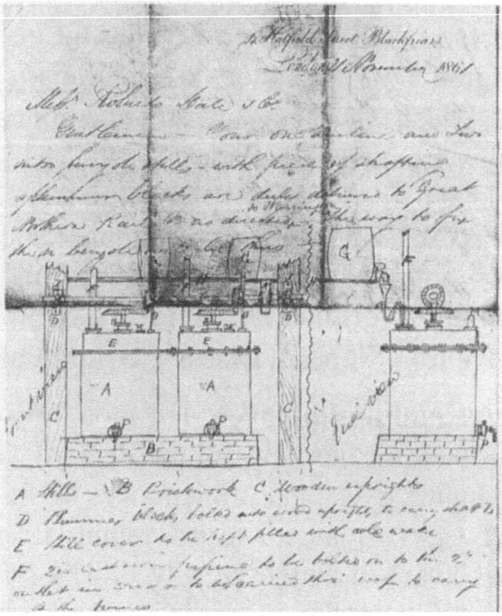

Nitration equipment (still) shown in letter from R. B. Pillmer & Co. to Roberts, Dale & Co., 21 November 1861. This was used to convert benzene into nitrobenzene. Similar equipment was used in the reduction of nitrobenzene to aniline. (Deutsches Museum, DM NL93.)

Roberts, Dale & Co. label, with samples of aniline black printing. (Deutsches Museum, DM NL93.)

Thus on 20 March 1861, John Gallemore Dale, one of John Dale's sons, jointly with Nathaniel Lloyd, manager of the Foxhillbank Works (Littlewood, Wilson & Co.), filed a patent for a process that specified tannin as the fixing agent instead of the more expensive animal mordants.[20] It was rapidly introduced for use with mauve at Schwabe & Co.[21]

Caro tried albumen, and his process was demonstrated in the summer of 1861 before Meyer and his consultant Dr. Franz Leopold Sonnenschein, a chemist at the University of Berlin. These first trials appear to have been satisfactory. However, Meyer was not happy with other results, related to the use of tungsten salts. On 16 June he advised Roberts, Dale & Co. that, while the Manchester experiments were unsuccessful, those conducted in Berlin showed considerable promise. Meyer explained that his firm's latest set of experiments were aimed at reducing or eliminating the amount of expensive "W[olfram] saure Ammoniak" (ammonium tungstate) used in a fixing process that employed albumen. According to Meyer, lead impurities in the tungsten compound contributed to fastness.[22] On 7 August, Meyer wrote to Caro complaining that he had been waiting eight weeks for a promised report of experiments carried out in Manchester.[23] Fourteen days later he wrote again: "it is unclear to me why your present experiments with albumen do not give results as good as those done in your laboratory in our presence, or in comparison with the tannin procedure of the young Dale." Meyer, however, remained optimistic, expecting Caro to solve the problem with the introduction of "cheap tungstate of soda," encouraged by the fact that he and Sonnenschein had been offered a tungsten compound in London at half the price asked in Manchester.[24] Caro failed to come up with a suitable process, and Dale and Lloyd's tannin process for aniline dyes, that worked without tungsten compounds, satisfied the needs of cotton printers and dyers.

Aniline black. The yield of Caro's mauve process, like Perkin's, was low, perhaps no more than five per cent. A considerable amount of dark oily residue remained. From this residue Caro in 1862 obtained the first commercial aniline black, a product that brought considerable profits to Roberts, Dale & Co., since, unlike the other coal-tar colorants, it adhered readily to cotton. The black was particularly popular on mainland Europe, where the Manchester-invented product was marketed by the aniline dye manufacturer J. J. Müller-Pack of Basel, whose firm around 1863 had

Caro's calico printing sample, prepared using mauve paste and aniline black, at Edmund Potter & Co., Dinting Vale, 1862. (Deutsches Museum, DM NL93/9.)

Caro's calico printing sample, prepared with blue mauve and the mineral pigment vert guignet, at Edmund Potter & Co., 1863. (Deutsches Museum, DM NL93/9.)

close links with Roberts, Dale & Co.[25] In 1862, Caro's black and his mauve paste were printed at the works of Edmund Potter & Co. of Dinting Vale, close to Manchester. One year later, Potter employed blue mauve, made with "aldehyde acrolein," and the inorganic colorant vert guignet.

Caro's fast black was superior to logwood and madder blacks, and its applicability was due to the presence of residual copper salts used in the oxidation process that afforded mauve. In January 1863, John Lightfoot Junior patented an aniline black printing process, based on investigations he had first undertaken in 1859. This involved direct printing of aniline onto cotton fabrics. However, the process had a corrosive effect on the steel engraved rollers of the printing machines and, as a consequence, interest in Lightfoot's process in Britain was restricted.[26] Lightfoot sought out new applications for his black process, especially in the less-mechanised calico printing industry on mainland Europe, where hand blocks, which possessed none of the disadvantages of the steel rollers, were still in extensive use. Lightfoot sold rights in his patent to J. J. Müller-Pack, who found a good market in Switzerland and Germany. Roberts, Dale & Co. considered this to be a serious threat to Caro's black, though Caro later stated that he had been offered a sum of money by Lightfoot to suppress the Roberts, Dale & Co. process.[27] Dale and a man named Wilson, probably of Wilson & Fletcher, London, had substantial interests in the black business, covered by tight agreements with Müller-Pack. In March 1863, Dale and Wilson hurried to Basel with the intention of overcoming any differences with their Swiss partner. Dale reported to Roberts:

> Found when I and Wilson had got here Muller[-Pack] had written and telegraphed to London that he was coming to London and that he wished to meet me and Wilson there to settle as to Bl[ac]k ... and that a joint conference may be the only way to settle the matter ... but be quite certain that the Bl[ac]k agreements shall be [written in] Bl[ac]k.... I have tonight to meet them all together and put the matter right.[28]

Roberts, Dale & Co. continued to work with Müller-Pack, and with his plant manager, Albert Schlumberger. Caro visited Müller-Pack early in 1863, and noted the latter's process for the manufacture of aldehyde green from aniline red. At the end of 1864, however, Müller-Pack was forced into bankruptcy as a result of contamination of groundwater and soil in the vicinity of one of his two factories by waste arsenic compounds used in the aniline red process.[29] Early in the following year, Müller-Pack moved to Paris, taking Schlumberger with him, and soon recommenced

Year and product	Invented by (date of discovery shown if different from year of first production)	Synonyms	Recipe
1858 Tyrian purple	Perkin (1856)	aniline purple, mauve (1859)	commerical aniline/ potassium dichromate
1859 fuchsine/aniline red	Verguin	roseine, rosaniline	commerical aniline/ stannic chloride
1860 magenta/aniline red	Nicholson Medlock		commerical aniline/ arsenic acid
1861 aniline blue	Girard and de Laire		aniline red + aniline
1861 mauve	Caro (1860)		commercial aniline/ copper salts
1862 aniline black	Caro		residue of Caro's mauve process
1862 aniline green	Usèbe	aldehyde green	aniline red + aldehyde
1862 rosolic acid	Caro (Müller; Kolbe and Schmitt; Persoz 1859)	aurin(e) yellow coralline	phenol + oxalic acid + sulphuric acid
1862 cyan brown	Caro		picric acid + potassium cyanide
1863 aniline black	Lightfoot (1859)		direct application of aniline to cotton during printing
1863 phosphine	Nicholson	chrysaniline	by-product of magenta manufactre (Nicholson's process)
1863 Hofmann's violets	Hofmann		aniline red + alkyl halides
1863/64 induline	Martius and Caro		azobenzene + aniline
1863/64 aniline yellow	Martius and Caro		nitrous acid on aniline
1863/64 phenylene brown	Martius and Caro	Bismarck brown (c.1870), Manchester brown, Vesuvin (BASF)	nitrous acid on *m*-diaminobenzene
1864 Martius yellow	Martius and Caro	Manchester yellow, jaune d'or (France), chrysonaphthalic acid, dinitronaphthylalcohol, binitronaphthalinic acid, dinitrohydroxynaphthalene, naphthalene yellow	naphthylamine → diazotise → naphthol → dinitronaphthol

Leading coal tar dyes and Caro's colorants, 1856-1864

The list of synonyms is not comprehensive, except in the cases of Caro's products.

his connection with the synthetic dye industry. In September 1865, Schlumberger advised Caro of a new aniline violet paste available from Charles Kestner of Thann.[30] A further expression of the mutual interests in novel colorants and their modes of application was a joint paper by Schlumberger and Thomas Roberts presented in 1866 to the Comité de Chimie of the Société Industrielle de Mulhouse.

Research into the possibility of using the black of Roberts, Dale & Co. as a dye for wool, which was much more difficult than its application to cotton, was entrusted to Carl Schorlemmer, assistant in the chemical laboratory at Owens College.[31] The role of copper, which was retained in the black, intrigued both Caro and Schorlemmer.[32] Direct aniline black printing found more widespread application in Britain following Charles Lauth's introduction of an insoluble copper compound in 1864.[33] Rights to this process were also purchased by Müller-Pack. It became an important source of business for manufacturers of aniline salts.

The German network

It was against this background, and the increasing demand for novel colorants, that Caro and Roberts, Dale & Co. set out to capture some of the synthetic dye market. This they achieved with varying degrees of success between 1860 and 1866 by exploiting colorant-producing reactions of aniline, toluidine (the amino derivative of the coal-tar hydrocarbon toluene), naphthylamine, and phenol. The novel processes were in part responses to the outcomes of patent litigation over aniline red (called magenta, roseine, and rosaniline–strictly the name of the free base–in Britain, and fuchsine in France) and aniline blue, and to the industrial consequences of Hofmann's academic research.

The invention of novel dyestuffs and processes for applying existing and new colorants was assisted by the entry of several Germans, at Caro's instigation, into the two factories and laboratories of Roberts, Dale & Co. Probably the first to join after Caro was August Leonhardt, the former colourist at Meyer's Berlin factory, who in 1860 offered Caro a new process for the application of logwood dyes. How it was handled by Caro demonstrates a new found awareness of his own worth, and a recognition of the importance of Dale's network of customers and agents. Caro brought Dale in as his equal partner, and in April a contract was drawn up in which the English patentees, Dale and Caro, would share 60 per cent of the income, and Caro would retain the remaining 40 per cent on behalf of Leonhardt.[34] In December 1860, Leonhardt filed a patent in London for preparing refined indigo using finely divided metals, and the process was considered the most important innovation in the preparation of indigo since the Great Exhibition of 1851. These activities brought Leonhardt to Manchester, probably late in 1860, and, except for an extended trip to Germany, he remained with Roberts, Dale & Co. until 1867.

By 1864, Roberts, Dale & Co. had accumulated a remarkable selection of German chemists and colourists, including Hofmann's former assistant Carl Alexander Martius. The main effort was presided over by the John Bull-like figure of Dale senior, who, on arriving at the Cornbrook laboratory, would ask: "Well Dr. Martius, well Caro, have you not got anything fresh to show me?"[35] At first, fresh discoveries were patented jointly with Dale, but later the Germans began to patent their new inventions alone. Patent records show that over the next three or four years they pursued investigations on new ways of manipulating natural dyes, on the modifications of mauve and magenta, on the creation of new synthetic colours, and on devising processes for more efficient production of intermediates. At the Mersey Bank Works, Ludwig Schad engaged in most of these activities between 1864 and 1866. Other German workers were A. H. A. Pflughaupt, Gustav Bischoff, and, later, Carl Vogt. Among the external consultants was Carl Schorlemmer, who in 1862 proved the equivalence of the four bonds in the molecule of methane (marsh gas).

At least one French chemist was employed at Roberts, Dale & Co., Alfred Paraf from Alsace, who early in 1864 left for the United States, where he became involved in the introduction of aniline black and embroiled in litigation with J. J. Müller-Pack.[36]

Aniline red

After mauve, aniline red was the colour most associated with the early years of the synthetic dye industry. In an attempt to circumvent Medlock's patent, Caro investigated routes to aniline red, commencing in 1860 when he used lead nitrate as an oxidising agent during work that led to the mauve reaction. Though Caro obtained a red colorant, and it was manufactured for a short while around 1861-62, he and Dale came to the conclusion that this could not compete with the arsenic acid process, which, in common with other British dyemakers, Roberts, Dale & Co., began to exploit.[37] However, this met with strong and unrelenting opposition from Simpson, Maule & Nicholson, the owners of Medlock's patent. In June 1861, Wilson & Fletcher became the first firm to be confronted with court action, and two years later judgement went against it. Nicholson's main expert witness in court was August Wilhelm Hofmann, head of the Royal College of Chemistry in London. The consequence of the court decision was that from June 1863 no British firm, apart from Nicholson's, was permitted to engage in manufacture of the red using arsenic acid. Roberts, Dale & Co. probably worked its version of the arsenic acid process until the threat of court action brought an end to this activity.[38]

Caro's colleagues also investigated other processes that gave aniline red. In August 1864, Pflughaupt filed a patent for a process using atmospheric oxygen at elevated temperature on neutral salts of aniline. However, the specification was not completed, and for a time Roberts, Dale & Co. retreated from the manufacture of aniline red, at least until 1865, when the monopoly on the arsenic acid process was broken following a determined and successful battle by Thomas Holliday of Huddersfield to make this process public property.

Manufacture of the red with arsenic acid underwent extensive improvement at Roberts, Dale & Co. in the hands of August Leonhardt, who developed a process for recovery and reuse of the arsenic acid. This overcame the sort of environmental problems that had led to Müller-Pack's downfall in Basel. Leonhardt's process was so successful that he continued to promote its introduction after returning to Germany, first with Meister, Lucius & Co. (later Hoechst),[39] then in partnership with Leo Gans, making aniline dyes for Cassella and, finally, for his own company established at the end of the 1870s. Leonhardt claimed advantages over Coupier's competing nitrobenzene oxidation process for aniline red, invented in 1867, and which found great favour after 1870. In particular, Leonhardt noted that the acidic conditions under which Coupier's process was conducted caused rapid destruction of the expensive wrought-iron reactors, which was not the case when the less-corrosive arsenic acid was used.

In an 1876 account, written in English for the Philadelphia Centennial Exhibition, Leonhardt stated that he had had "fifteen years of personal experience in different establishments in Germany and England. With the excellent state of health in our manufactory, we are of the opinion, that not the least danger is to be apprehended under professional guidance."[40] This indicates that Leonhardt was working on arsenic acid oxidation at Roberts, Dale & Co. from 1861.

Aniline blue

Early in 1861, the range of aniline colours was extended with the discovery by Charles Girard and Georges de Laire, two French chemists working in the English aniline factory of Théophile Jules Pelouze, that the presence of excess aniline in the reaction mixture for the red led to a blue colorant. They patented the process in France and Britain, and the patents were acquired by the Renards, who licensed the manufacture of aniline blue to its cross-Channel ally, Simpson, Maule & Nicholson. The latter's aniline blue appeared in Britain from July 1862, and the popularity of the dye encouraged considerable interest at Roberts, Dale & Co. Aniline blue and aniline red were also manufactured in Germany, without fear of patent litigation, since no satisfactory comprehensive system for assigning privileges for inventions existed in the various principalities.

By the middle of 1862, Caro had become Roberts, Dale & Co.'s principal contact with British and foreign firms, and was frequently sent on sales trips to Scotland and London. In October 1862, Caro was in Germany to seek out new products and business opportunities at a time when cotton shortages in Lancashire caused by the American Civil War had reduced consumption of Roberts, Dale & Co.'s products. The trip included a visit to the Clemm factory in Mannheim, where Caro received a communication from Dale: "I am glad to hear you have taken the opportunity of staying to get what information you could more especially about aniline blue." Roberts, Dale & Co. received a consignment of aniline blue from Clemm, with the clear intention of adding it to the product range, "but will leave the admixture till you return when we will arrange to meet those who require a Blue shade."[41] Dale had also encouraged Caro to pay a visit to Hofmann on the return journey to Manchester: "In coming thru London it would be a pity to lose seeing Hofmann so by all means do so."[42]

Not long after his return from Germany, Caro was offered an aniline blue process by Dr. August Eisenlohr of Heidelberg, no doubt as a result of his investigations and enquiries when in nearby Mannheim. Eisenlohr, who had studied chemistry at the University of Heidelberg and obtained his

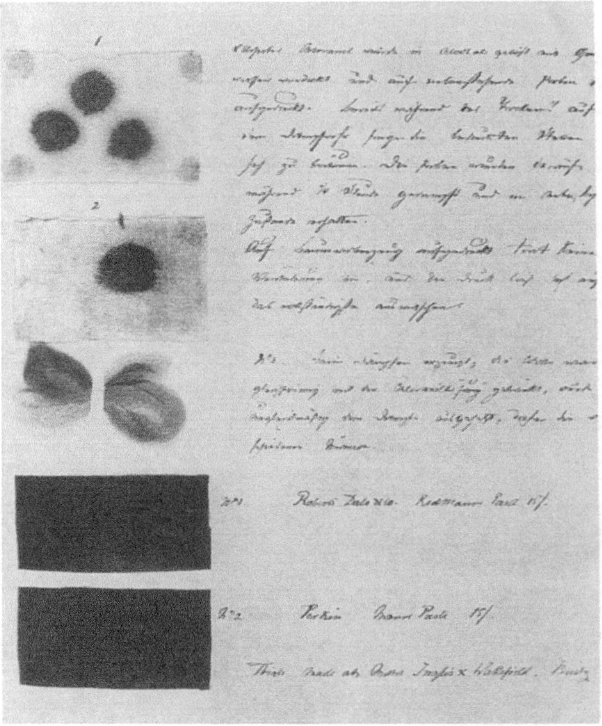

Page from notebook of Heinrich Caro, showing results of comparative trials made at the Scottish firm of Inglis & Wakefield with red mauve of Roberts, Dale & Co., and mauve paste of Perkin & Sons, 1863. (Caro Nachlass, notebook for 1862/63, item no. 37933. Deutsches Museum.)

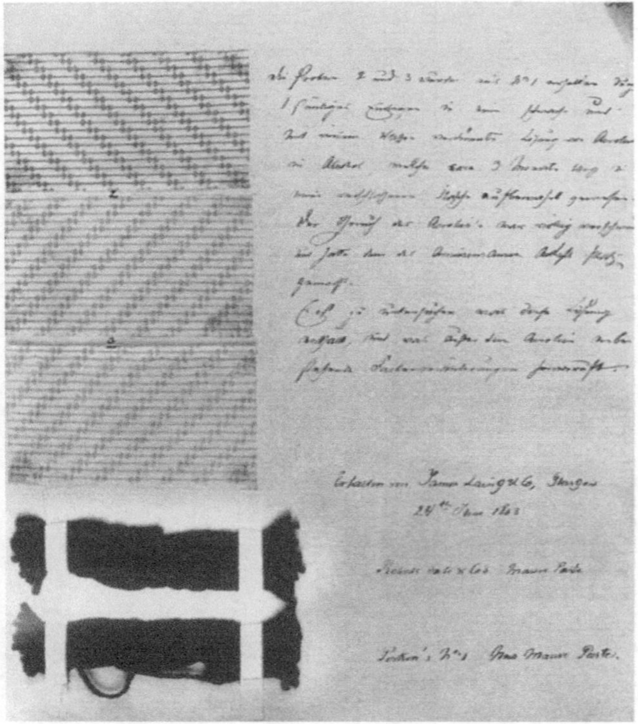

Page from notebook of Heinrich Caro, showing trial dyeings for James Laing & Co., Glasgow, comparing Roberts, Dale & Co.'s mauve paste with Perkin & Sons' new mauve paste, 24 June 1863. (Caro Nachlass, notebook for 1862/63, item no. 37933. Deutsches Museum.)

doctorate at the University of Göttingen, manufactured aniline dyes, and late in 1862 began investigating the possibility of sales in England, as well as of licensing his process to an English manufacturer.[43] For the latter purpose he was represented by the chemist James Alfred Wanklyn. Until the end of 1862, Wanklyn was an assistant of Lyon Playfair at Edinburgh University, and early in 1863 he joined the London Institution. It was probably during the break between these posts that Wanklyn visited Heidelberg, then an active centre for dye manufacture, to discuss with Eisenlohr the latter's blue process. The main difference between Eisenlohr's aniline blue process and that of Girard and de Laire was the presence of an organic acid, specifically benzoic acid, in the aniline blue reaction mixture.[44] This certainly improved the reaction, and promised to be a valuable invention provided that it could be shown to be substantially different to the Girard and de Laire process.

MANUFACTURE OF ANILINE BLUE.

Manufacture of aniline blue from aniline and aniline red. (William Crookes, *A Practical Handbook of Dyeing and Calico-Printing* [London: Longmans, Green & Co., 1874], opposite 176.)

At the end of 1862, Roberts, Dale & Co. experimented with the process of Eisenlohr, who on 22 December submitted to Caro an account for aniline blue totalling £5 and 9 shillings. Roberts, Dale & Co. was experiencing problems in obtaining a soluble aniline blue, similar to the sulphonated product that Nicholson had recently introduced, and Eisenlohr suggested that this might be due to the dye-powder mills or to the fact that Caro did not employ sufficient alcohol. Eisenlohr described differences in shades, both red and green, obtained by his process, and stated that for wool the red shade was good enough, "because wool absorbs more blue than red and that only for silk is a green-shade product important." He also described a dyeing method for silk, and mentioned that he had visited the lower Rhine and the manufacturer Carl Neuhaus in Krefeld.[45]

On 29 January 1863, Eisenlohr acknowledged receipt of a letter from Caro dated 23 January, and a sample of Nicholson's aniline blue. Eisenlohr was then engaged in trials to produce a green shade of the blue, but required more time. He thanked Caro for offering to sell his products, and mentioned that he had turned down an offer from Yorkshire because he believed that the wool-dyeing factories there would buy through Dale. Eisenlohr also claimed that he was able to produce a better soluble blue than Nicholson's. Finally, Eisenlohr notified Caro that Wanklyn would soon write to Dale about a contract for Eisenlohr's blue.[46]

On 2 February 1863, Wanklyn wrote to John Dale:

> I have had a good deal of talk with Eisenlohr and send the results. He thinks that sufficient time has now elapsed for you to get to know pretty accurately what the sale of the blue colours is likely to be, and that the agreement between your firm and him should contain a stipulation as to the amount to be taken weekly.[47]

Seventeen days later, Wanklyn advised Caro:

> We sent off ten days ago 3½ lbs of an exceedingly fine greenish-blue; have you received it, and can you let us know how it is liked by the silk dyers? We have no hesitation in saying that the sample will prove superior to what Nicholson commonly sends out and are desirous to have it fairly tried as soon as possible.
>
> How does the violet shade suit?[48]

Carl Schorlemmer was put to work on investigating the blue processes by comparing the products from using inorganic and organic salts of the red. On 24 March 1863, he wired Caro, then in London: "Most decided difference between acetate and inorganic salts, particulars by post."[49]

Roberts, Dale & Co., decided that Eisenlohr's process was a distinct improvement over the process employed by Nicholson and that this provided an opportunity to negotiate with the southern rival:

> Give Nicholsons to understand that we are determined to work it unless we can come to some arrangement with them about it–we believe it to be no infringement of

> Renards patent–We think if Eisenlohr goes himself, he will not get above half what we could get from Nicholsons–should it come to this course being thought to be the best.[50]

There was, however, a threat to these negotiations in the form of a patent filed by A. W. Gilbee in London during 1862. On discovering this, Roberts, no doubt in a state of near panic, communicated from Basel in March 1863:

> Wanklyn's [and Eisenlohr's] blue is superseded by a patent taken out in London by Gilbee and published in Newtons Journal of the 1st of March–Muller[-Pack] is much annoyed at this patent–he says it is his process taken out by some one that has given it from their works, and that he has been making it at least 12 months.... I may say however that both Wanklyn and Muller[-Pack] are cut out and my opinion is that Simpsons have bought the patent of Gilbee.

Roberts, in an attempt to secure a rival route to the blue, recommended that the deal with Eisenlohr should be tied up as soon as possible: "tell Caro not to lose time with Eisenlohr or Wanklyn."[51] A draft contract between Roberts, Dale & Co. and Eisenlohr, dated 20 March 1863, included clauses to protect both sides: "Should in the meanwhile Roberts, Dale & Co. discover any process for making the Blue Colour herein named either cheaper or better it is agreed that Dr. A. Eisenlohr shall be made a joint partner." Word equations made clear the major difference between the process licensed to Simpson and that of Eisenlohr:

> Magenta + Aniline = Girard [the process worked by Simpson, Maule & Nicholson]
>
> Magenta + Aniline + Benzoic Acid = Eisenlohr.[52]

At the end of March 1863, Eisenlohr failed in his efforts to conclude a contract with Roberts, Dale & Co. for supply of his aniline blue, after Caro had undertaken experiments with the products of Simpson, Maule & Nicholson and, from their outcome, offered less-favourable conditions to Eisenlohr. Eisenlohr then travelled to London where he visited Hofmann, who advised him to approach Nicholson.

Though Eisenlohr was cordially received by Nicholson, he failed to sell either his process or the product to Simpson, Maule & Nicholson. On 26 April, Eisenlohr advised Caro:

> Dear Friend,
>
> Today I received your letter of 18 April from Glasgow. I thank you very much for it, because I see that, despite the fact that we were unable to come to a business

decision in London, you still wish to continue our friendship. Be assured that that is also my wish.

Since then I have been busy with preparations for a patent [for aniline blue]. I have found out that some of the acids mentioned have to be deleted. I am convinced that it is only in the presence of organic acids that rosaniline salts afford the blue. You are aware that when the acetate of rosaniline [magenta] gives aniline blue, the cause of formation of the blue is not the magenta, but the presence of acetic acid. The same effect should be found with other organic acids. In any case, the process is different from the one of Girard and de Laire, since they do not name organic acids. With the base [of aniline red, rosaniline] and aniline they do not get blue; the important thing is the addition of the organic acid. I wish very much that you look into this more carefully, and without prejudice, and that you either agree with my opinion, or consult with [George Carey?] Foster and Schorlemmer or others.

According to Eisenlohr, the London chemist Hugo Müller "did not believe your [Caro's] written opinion, which I allowed myself to show him." He continued:

I will describe to you with all honesty, and completely, my visit to Nicholson, where I was sent on the advice of Prof. Hofmann. I met him [Nicholson] at his factory.... The welcome was very warm.... I discussed with him the incompleteness of Girard's patent, and he agreed with that. He said he would like another good patent that did not oblige him to pay a royalty of £6,000 per year [to the Renards]. He would like to halve that sum.... I explained to him the general differences between my process and that of Girard. In my case aniline salts give a blue after one operation; in the other case in two operations, and that, furthermore, the process of Girard did not yield blue. He [Nicholson] knew quite well that it was only possible to produce a blue by reacting together rosaniline, aniline, and acetic acid [though this was not stated in the Girard and de Laire patent]. He claimed that he made the acetate of rosaniline right from the start, that is, from the time of the filing of the patent, and he showed me relevant records that confirm this, and give the quantities of acetic acid consumed [though Nicholson's supply might also have been employed in the reduction of nitrobenzene to aniline]. It is very important to obtain a sample of Nicholson's blue, perhaps from a laboratory collection, to establish this claim. He said that as soon as he read the announcement of my patent he asked his agent Price to arrange a meeting with me. That did not happen because Wanklyn thought that we would be bound by contract to Dale. Nicholson himself proposed to leave any decision to the chemists.

Nicholson, probably aware that Eisenlohr's blue process was indeed a potential threat, wanted a report comparing the two processes prior to arriving at a financial arrangement with Eisenlohr. Though Nicholson was prepared to make an advance to Eisenlohr, this was prevented by his partner, Simpson. Nevertheless, Eisenlohr displayed considerable optimism:

> Despite the fact that there are reasonable chances that I may come to an arrangement with Nicholson soon, I am still willing to revitalise the former connection with you if you offer me acceptable and reliable conditions [concerning aniline blue]. This is especially the case if you offer me the commission on sales in England and Scotland that I lost because of your refusal. And I want to have these sales because the price is higher in England than here. Though I do not want to make any proposals to you about that, I would suggest that you combine forces with [the chemical manufacturer] Gg[George] Miller in Glasgow for exploiting my patent.

Eisenlohr then asked a favour of Caro concerning an offer of a post for Carl Schorlemmer: "Because my assistant chemist, Mr Schönfeld, will leave me soon for further education, I would like to ask you to inquire if Schorlemmer would be willing to work with me." Schönfeld was probably the first chemist taken on by Friedrich Bayer & Co. for a short time in 1864 ("Dr. Schönfeld"). (Schorlemmer remained at Owens College, where he would eventually become the first professor of organic chemistry in England).

Eisenlohr then returned to aniline blue, and particularly the supply of aniline red salt, which he was considering producing:

> Of all products I know, that of Nicholson is the best. The Mannheim [Clemm] product is arseniate of rosaniline and contains 30 per cent arsenic acid. Nicholson's product is free of arsenic acid and I want to know about his process. I also worked with the sample that Wanklyn bought from Nicholson in London. The Clemms work with lime [calcium hydroxide], and the arseniate of rosaniline seems not to be decomposed by the lime. They dissolve [the mixture] in sulphuric acid, to dissolve also the lime, and concentrate. Somewhat better is the method with hydrochloric acid [to afford hydrochlorate of rosaniline] but I do not know any details about it.[53]

A few weeks later, on 13 May 1863, A. W. Hofmann established that aniline blue was rosaniline (magenta) in which three hydrogen atoms had each been replaced by a phenyl (C_6H_5) group, that is triphenylated rosaniline. This work was stimulated by the threat posed to Simpson, Maule & Nicholson by Eisenlohr's process. It was the first major scientific discovery related to the coal-tar dyes, and was announced to scientific audiences almost simultaneously in London and Paris.

In September 1863, an embittered Eisenlohr wrote to Caro concerning alleged rumours that the latter had spread concerning Eisenlohr, and that had led to considerable financial loss. One was the claim that Caro prevented Eisenlohr from concluding a contract with Dale. Another was that after Eisenlohr had come to an arrangement with "Müller" (Müller-Pack of Basel), according to which Müller-Pack acquired rights for Eisenlohr's blue in England, Caro then allowed a contract to be drawn up between Dale and Müller-Pack for a soluble sulphonic acid salt of the blue. The outcome was substantial losses, according to Eisenlohr, both for himself and for Müller-Pack. However, and despite all these uncomfortable facts, Eisenlohr acknowledged that Caro spoke in his favour to Dale. Eisenlohr also mentioned that he had a good chance of obtaining a seal for his patent, following what he claimed was a forthcoming publication by Hofmann on the role of organic acids in the aniline blue process. Whatever the outcome, Eisenlohr was anxious that his friendship with Caro should not be affected.[54]

Hofmann's publication of the equation and constitutional formula for aniline blue had some bearing on the commercial standing of Eisenlohr's process after it was adopted in London by the dye manufacturer and merchant Hugo Levinstein, who also employed Wanklyn as a consultant. At the end of 1863, Levinstein was confronted with a claim of patent infringement from Simpson, Maule & Nicholson. The subsequent court action led to a judgement against Levinstein early in 1865. The court concluded that benzoic acid was not essential to formation of the blue, and that the Girard and de Laire patent was valid. Once Eisenlohr's process had been discredited, Roberts, Dale & Co. had no reason to renew their contact with him. Ironically, Eisenlohr's process became the method of choice among manufacturers, though the role of benzoic acid in facilitating the reaction remained unknown.

Aniline violet

In May 1863, and immediately upon understanding how aniline blue was formed, A. W. Hofmann alkylated aniline red and obtained a violet colorant, later known as Hofmann's violets because the shade could be varied by adjusting the extent of alkylation. Hofmann's patented process of May 1863 was licensed to Simpson, Maule & Nicholson, the Renards, and a German firm. Early in the following year Hofmann's colour did not yet seem to be a serious contender to mauve, which was by then commercially available in crystalline form. In February, Dale reported to Caro, then in Glasgow:

> The Hofmann's Violet I always was afraid would to some extent come in competition with our mauve–I am glad to learn its [lack of] permanency will be its death blow for certain.[55]

There was further comfort from other trials that demonstrated the poor fastness, relative to mauve, of Hofmann's colour. From the Springfield Works came the report to Caro:

> The trials which I made when you were here, with Hofmann's violet, compared with your mauve crystals. I have confirmed in subsequent experiments–Hofmann's although a brighter colour, is so fugitive, that even one day's exposure produces a sensible difference in shade.[56]

However, it was the brilliance of Hofmann's violet, and the price advantage, that caused it to displace mauve.

In 1864, Hofmann showed that aniline red, blue, and violet belonged to a family of compounds, and that the production of blue and violet relied on replacement of hydrogen atoms in the amino-groups of aniline red. However, very little else was known about the chemical makeup of the aniline dyes.[57] The problem was that there was no way of expressing the constitutions of aromatic compounds, which included all the aniline (and phenol) dyes. The aromatic moiety was just a blob in which there was an unusual, and unknown, concentration of carbon atoms.

Since production of aniline blue and violet were, like aniline red, controlled by Simpson, Maule & Nicholson, the ambitions of other English manufacturers of coal-tar products, including Roberts, Dale & Co., were frustrated. In response, Caro was encouraged to investigate alternative processes and different reactions of aniline and other amino compounds.[58] Caro also investigated the coal-tar product phenol (carbolic acid), then recently available in Manchester as a pure product, following the work of Frederick Crace Calvert.[59]

During 1862, Caro had shown great interest in the reactions of phenol that afforded colorants, and had invested much time in the study and preparation of the most important member, the red known as rosolic acid. It was made from phenol, oxalic acid, and sulphuric acid (as a result of Roberts, Dale & Co.'s preeminent position as a manufacturer of oxalic acid). In addition there was the yellow-brown paste known as aurin(e), a mixture of uncertain composition, but considered to consist of rosolic acid and a compound christened aurine.[60] Charles Lowe & Co., based at the Phoenix Works, Newton Heath, Manchester, was, like Roberts, Dale & Co., engaged in the manufacture of dyes derived from phenol, in addition to Dale's picric acid. This had led to exchanges between the companies, and Lowe probably became a supplier of phenol to Roberts, Dale & Co.

C. A. Martius

Among the German chemists that Caro had attracted to Roberts, Dale & Co., none contributed as much to novel coal-tar dye discoveries as did Hofmann's former assistant Carl Alexander Martius, who in 1867 was to found jointly with Paul Mendelssohn-Bartholdy at Rummelsburg, near Berlin, the Gesellschaft für Anilinfabrikation, a predecessor of the AGFA corporation.

It is not only Martius's inventions in England, nor his subsequent fame as German industrial entrepreneur, that make him important in this story. His surviving correspondence with Caro from the months prior to his joining Roberts, Dale & Co. around August 1863 reveals clearly the nature of information and materials, some from Caro's competitors, that were transferred from Hofmann's London laboratory to Manchester, and how Martius was also undertaking experiments in the same laboratory, without the knowledge of his colleagues, for the benefit of Roberts, Dale & Co. There is also an important historical dimension attached to this correspondence. It is the only contemporary account, apart from the records of Hofmann's assistant, Herbert McLeod, and Hofmann's own publications, of how and when Hofmann made the discoveries that were to elevate him to the role of academic father of the coal-tar dye industry.[61] Finally, Martius's correspondence demonstrates how aspiring entrepreneurs planned their enterprises in the tough and uncompromising world of the 19th-century European chemical industry.

The first indication of when Martius began to assist Roberts, Dale & Co. can be found in one of Caro's laboratory notebooks. This shows that by March 1863, Martius was supplying Caro with samples of aniline, toluidine, and aniline blue.[62] It was at about this time that the possibility of Martius's joining Roberts, Dale & Co. came up. Thus in April, Martius advised Caro that he needed a commitment before the 20th of the month regarding an offer of a post at the Warrington laboratory. Martius explained that the urgency had to do with his need to inform Hofmann by the end of April whether or not he wished to remain in London for a further twelve months. Martius asked Caro for help and advice on how to get a commitment from Dale. Though Martius was of the opinion that the salary offered to him was inadequate, he would not be too demanding provided that he received an assurance that he would work in a well-equipped laboratory. Caro was asked to make this quite explicit to

Dale. If a compromise was reached, then Martius would travel to Manchester for two days to discuss the matters in hand.

The next part of the letter was about materials and experiments, and the limitations imposed on Martius's activities in London. Martius promised to send during the next few days a package of chloroacetic acid with which Caro could undertake some unspecified trials (that were to be repeated also with chlorobenzene). Martius made it clear that "I cannot do it here. My hands are tied as long as I am Hofmann's slave." In his attempts to prepare congeners of aniline blue, Martius treated aniline red with both naphthylamine and toluidine, but the products were less satisfactory than those obtained from the reaction of aniline with aniline red to afford the stable aniline blue. The reaction between naphthylamine and the benzoic acid salt of rosaniline, which was studied at around the same time in France,[63] was aimed at inserting the naphthyl group into aniline red. It

> has not been successful until now. I obtained a violet dyestuff, but its properties are not so good. In general I find nothing in favour of naphthyl and tolyl dyestuffs because they are not stable like phenyl. With our violet dyestuff we go ahead. [Caro later added: "This is Hofmann's violet," though this violet, the alkylated derivative, was discovered by Hofmann only some weeks later, in May 1863.] The production process seems to create no difficulties. Now I am working on a wonderful blue stuff of azobenzene [or benzidine; perhaps induline]. This dye has a good future. It is a pity that I am observed by my colleagues and cannot work on such things without hindrance. I also undertook some rough trials with "oxalatin" [oxalic acid salt] coming out of the Warrington factory and I think the impure mixture contains other acids.

Martius asked Caro to request of John Dale "several pounds of this crude oxalate, the product of the second, since I would like to go on with it." Other information proferred by Martius included the offer of a professorship for Hofmann at the University of Bonn: "Hofmann has not finally made up his mind about Bonn."

One chemical reaction of interest was the action of nitrous acid on aromatic amines, studied at the Royal College of Chemistry since 1858 by Peter Griess, and closely followed by Martius, as well as by William Perkin, who also expressed to Martius his opinion on Caro's mauve. Martius informed Caro:

> At the last meeting of the Chemical Society, Perkin and [Arthur] Church lectured on a new base they obtained by the action of nitrous acid on naphthylamine. At this lecture I talked to Perkin about your process of manufacturing mauve. Perkin says

that the yield of your mauve is too low to be a threat to his own process. But he admits that the mauve paste is very good.

In matters of business, Martius considered, incorrectly, that "Perkin is with Nicholson under one cover," and, among other things, provided Caro with valuable information on Nicholson's dealings with August Eisenlohr:

And I talked to Nicholson a few days ago about Eisenlohr and his [aniline blue] patent, and I believe that Nicholson does not want to come to an arrangement. Eisenlohr is a very impractical human being who will with more experience become wise. We have heard nothing more of him. Your lecture at the Schillerverein [a German club in Manchester] was probably a success and I would like a copy of it when it is printed. It is possible that Hofmann will give a lecture about isomerism, metamerism and homology.[64]

On 21 May 1863, Martius advised Caro that "I intend to come next weekend to Manchester provided that you are there." He also reported on Hofmann's work relating to aniline dyes, particularly the outcome of experiments on Eisenlohr's aniline blue process. In this connection, Hofmann had reduced aniline blue to its colourless (leuco) form, which contributed toward establishing the constitution of the blue as a phenylated derivative of aniline red. The direct relationship between the red and the blue was also noted by Martius:

At the college we have obtained some very interesting results with the aniline blue dye. The chloride of the blue base that we have received from Nicholson needs only recrystallization in order to obtain it pure. From this chloride you can get the free base by dissolving in alcoholic ammonia, and precipitating the solid chloride with water. The free base is white or blue-white and seems to be amorphous. The solution in alcohol is colourless. The compounds with acids are blue and insoluble in water. The constitutional formulae of these bases, which are obtained by good reproducible analysis, are in a simple relation to rosaniline and [are] its three-times phenylated rosaniline.

Rosaniline $C_{20}H_{19}N_3$

Base [of aniline blue] $C_{20}H_{16}N_3,(C_6H_5)_3$

They contain one equivalent of water.

Obviously out to impress Caro, Martius added: "These results confirm my own supposition that the different aniline blue dyes differ by the extent of phenylation." This was just a few days after Hofmann, by drawing an analogy with the phenylation of aniline red, had discovered that it was possible to introduce alkyl groups into aniline red and obtained a brilliant violet colorant. Martius was fully aware that this latter discovery had immediate theoretical and industrial implications, and independently, and no doubt surreptitiously, was looking into a practical process that might be of value to Roberts, Dale & Co. Hofmann's results caused Martius to believe that if organic acids were employed in these substitution reactions, then the nature of the acid would determine whether the product was phenylated or alkylated. In this he was attempting to widen the applicability of Eisenlohr's aniline blue process:

> You can get blue and violet dyes through reaction of iodide of alcohol [alkyl] radicals on rosaniline. You have to find cheap reactions to make such substitutions. When I am in Manchester I would like to propose to you some collaborative trials in this direction. I am also of the opinion that in the method of Eisenlohr the organic acids play a very decisive role. Thus benzoic acid will give phenylated bases. Acetic acid will give methylated bases. If I can prove that such a reaction really takes place, e.g. with [formation of]
>
> benzoylated [phenylated] aniline [red] $C_{20}H_{16}(C_6H_5)_3\ N_3$ [aniline blue]
>
> acetylated [alkylated] aniline [red] $C_{20}H_{16}(CH_3)_3\ N_3$ [violet dye]
>
> then his patent cannot be disputed.[65]

Unfortunately for Martius, these reaction conditions did not afford the products that he expected. While the presence of benzoic acid did indeed facilitate phenylation of aniline red, it did not bring about the phenylation. In the same way, acetic acid did not bring about alkylation of the red.

Subsequently, Martius cancelled the projected Manchester trip, "because a friend from Göttingen has arrived and I am overworked and therefore must change the date." However, he did inform Caro of other new and vitally important progress made by Hofmann in the scientific understanding of the aniline red reaction:

> Just between us, though, I would like to tell you that trials over the last few days with aniline obtained from different sources gave the strange result that only aniline derived from coal tar, and only aniline that boils above 182°C, gives aniline red. All other anilines, for example out of indigo, benzoic acid (that is from benzene through distillation of calcium benzoylate), etc., give no aniline red. We are on the way to explain this strange observation.[66]

This "strange observation" was the important clue to the understanding and optimisation of the aniline red reaction, as well as to the constitutions of aniline dyes. Coal-tar aniline, as Hofmann had discovered, contained toluidine, which was responsible for the aniline red reaction. Aniline alone did not afford aniline red. It was now possible to draw up a useful constitutional formula. On 8 July, Martius advised Caro:

> The results we obtained during the last few days concerning the formation of dyes from the different anilines are very strange and would certainly be of interest to you. Pure aniline alone produced by all different methods and pure toluidine alone do not give dyestuffs. Instead mixtures of the two bases give immediately aniline red. All commercial anilines (even if boiling between 182-188°C) contain toluidine. We have prepared toluidine out of the commercial aniline salts through fractional crystallization of the oxalates because it is not possible to get small amounts of toluidine by fractional distillation. We are busy now with trials for the production of dyes out of the equivalent mixtures of the bases. You will agree that these results are not only of practical value but they are also of theoretical interest insofar as they explain the formula of rosaniline. This base is probably
>
> $(C_6H_4)''$
> $(C_7H_6)_2''$ } N_3
> H_3
>
> i.e. phenyleneditolylenetriamine
>
> We are busy trying the reactions leading to mauve with the different anilines.[67]

Reactions of quinone and diamino compounds were just as interesting as the further progress on the aniline red reaction. Knowledge of quinones played a role in Martius's attempt to synthezise alizarin at Roberts, Dale & Co., and would feature greatly in Caro's work from 1869.

> I hope that you have received the small package with samples that I sent to you. It contains quinone, toluyldiamine and some samples of the blue bases. You have probably found that quinone gives an analogous reaction to chloranil but neither is preferable. The diamines of the phenyl series (phenylene and toluylamine) [diamino derivatives of benzene and toluene] give with a small amount of an oxidising agent also the brown dye but they decompose too fast and it does not work so well. Also the decomposition product seems to be more close to the brown compounds that you obtained from your mauve reaction.

A package that Martius gave to Caro was lost "and we must try to get it back–the fine powdered zinc to make aniline [by reduction of nitrobenzene]–the most important ingredient in the package."

The next day, 8 July 1863, Müller-Pack of Basel and his manager Albert Schlumberger were scheduled to be in London to meet with Martius, and it was anticipated that they would "give me more exact details about the conclusion of negotiations over the [Eisenlohr] blue affair." Caro was at this time courting a local girl, Miss Edith Eaton, and Martius ended his letter: "Best wishes to all my friends and to the pretty neighbour, and greetings to yourself."[68]

Four days later, on 12 July, Martius had more to say about aromatic amino compounds, their purity, and the aniline red reaction, including experiments with iodine as oxidising agent:

> I hope that you have received the two samples of aniline and toluidine which I sent you some days ago. It is a pity that I cannot send you more because my stock is diminishing due to the many trials. The toluidine is produced from the oxalate–itself from the highest boiling fraction of commercial aniline. The aniline is from the [salts] of aniline which distil over from the production of aniline red. It boils constantly at 182°C and with sublimation there is no trace of aniline red. The relation of one equivalent (93 parts of aniline) and two equivalents (214 parts of toluidine) is the best to produce aniline red. The result of our trials with the mauve reaction is that the pure aniline gives the best results. Perkin claims the contrary. We are busy now with trials concerning the synthesis and constitution of rosaniline. Iodine when heated with aniline gives no trace of fuchsine. By contrast, aniline red is obtained immediately if aniline is replaced by toluidine. It is a very elegant experiment. Also, heating one equivalent of aniline and two equivalents of toluidine with iodine give immediately and completely aniline red and I would like to believe that this reaction could be technically relevant. Do you know who took out the patent for [oxidation with] iodine? Nicholson claims that the violet dyes Hofmann has patented, which are produced by ethylation of rosaniline, could be of practical value. In case you buy large quantities of aniline, just order some Zentner [50 kilograms] of high boiling aniline (190-205°C) so that we can produce the toluidine out of it. I have proved recently that rosaniline with aniline alone gives a good quantity of violet or blue dyestuffs and the free base works better than the chloride. Unfortunately this is the same as the recipe in the patent of Girard and de Laire [as worked by Simpson, Maule & Nicholson].

Despite Hofmann's important and far-reaching new knowledge about aniline blue and the aniline red reaction, his studies on aniline dyes were questioned by the chemist Hugo Schiff, then at the University of Berne:

> Hofmann sent eight days ago his finished manuscript about the blue to the French Academy and the Royal Society. During this time the notice by Schiff on aniline dyes was published in the Comptes Rendu giving for [aniline] blue the formula $C_{30}H_{34}N_4$, which is not in accord with our analysis. This rubbish talker should be more prudent. With this notice, which is written in an academic tone, about the

production method for rosaniline, he ridicules himself, now that it is proven [by Hofmann] that aniline alone gives no aniline red.

I have talked enough about aniline. My business here will be finished in 14 days and then I hope to see you soon in Manchester. It is possible that I shall go before then for 3 or 4 days to the Isle of Wight to get away from the London dust.[69]

On 22 July, there were more results on aniline studies, including the product of Wilson of London, its suitability for the manufacture of mauve, and on the supply of toluidine:

I have just now analysed the aniline salts of Mr. Wilson. No. 1 boils to the greater part at 181-182.5°C. The boiling point increases towards the end up to 184°C. No. 2 starts at 182°C, increases, then moves rapidly up to 183-184°C, and finally 187-190°C. I think No. 1 is especially suited to mauve production. Both samples in any case are not suitable for extraction of toluidine because they stop boiling at the point when toluidine would normally boil over. I do not understand why, if Wilson really produces aniline by himself, he cannot deliver higher boiling fractions. Mr. [Rosh] has been asked for higher boiling aniline but has not responded yet. It should be possible to get the desired product through Holliday, who offers toluidine in the Chemical News. For the production of toluidine the best procedure is to follow the recipe of [Ernst] Sell [of Offenbach], whose small publication about toluyl compounds I enclose.

In a few days the combustion apparatus which I have ordered for Manchester will be sent. The same with one of my boxes. Please receive them on my behalf.[70]

Caro recorded in his notebook that he received samples of aniline and toluidine from Martius, including the toluidine of Read Holliday.[71]

Notwithstanding the great interest in aniline red and its derivatives, Martius's principal asset when he arrived at Roberts, Dale & Co. late in 1863 was knowledge about the new reaction of amino compounds (diazotization) investigated by Peter Griess. This involved the treatment of amines with nitrous acid at low temperatures, when coloured precipitates were formed. The reaction had to be undertaken with great care, especially since certain products were explosive. What offered great potential as dyes were yellow and brown precipitates that were formed during the reaction. It is sometimes stated that Nicholson developed the yellow as a colorant during 1863, perhaps using information received from Hofmann.[72] However, no patent or published information is available to substantiate this, and there may be some confusion with Nicholson's phosphine, a by-product of his magenta manufacture. Certainly the most successful of these new dyes was phenylene or phenyl brown, later known in both England and Germany as Bismarck brown (as well as Manchester brown). The process for producing the brown was patented by Dale and Caro on 31 December 1863.

Both the brown and yellow, prepared under the same reaction conditions, were well received by dyers. They were members of a series of colorants later known as azo dyes, but in the 1860s it was impossible to decipher their constitutions, even with the availability of Kekulé's benzene ring. The yellow became a competitor to both the picric acid shades and to Nicholson's phosphine (named chrysaniline by Hofmann). A blue colorant, induline, a discovery of Caro in 1863 or 1864, was a long-lived product arising from this research, probably carried out with Martius. It was made by reacting aminoazobenzene with aniline and its hydrochloride salt at elevated temperature under alkaline conditions.[73] To develop these processes, Griess, then at Samuel Allsopp's Brewery, Burton-on-Trent, was engaged as a consultant by Caro.

Griess's studies on the reaction of nitrous acid on aromatic amines did not lead to an understanding of the process, later known as the diazo reaction, nor of the chemical constitutions of Martius's phenylene brown and the similarly obtained "aniline yellow." They were prepared by the action of sodium nitrite, the source of nitrous acid, on the aromatic amines. The nitrite was obtained at Roberts, Dale & Co. as a co-product in the manufacture of arsenic acid by passing nitrous acid into a solution of caustic soda.

"Young Germany in Manchester"

Manchester's liberal and noncomformist traditions were in full flower by the end of the 18th century, and were to find expression in the *Manchester Guardian*, founded in 1821 to support civil and religious liberty, reform, and a new political economy. Certain of these values were also resonant with the objectives of the Literary and Philosophical Society of Manchester, which, perhaps wisely, excluded religion and politics from its debates. Commercial liberalism had many ramifications, one of which was ready acceptance of foreigners whose interests were at one with those of industrial Lancashire. These foreigners included a number of Germans who had become well established as calico printers, particularly the Schwabe and Schunck families. Though united in their German origins and English trade, they did nevertheless belong to two distinct social groups, as one young Italian visitor to the Schunck family home recalled:

> They [the Schuncks] belonged to one of the two sets of German colonists in a great measure monopolising the export trade of Lancashire and Yorkshire; one of which, consisting of Jews, baptised or not, clustered around Mr. Salis Schwabe, whilst my host [Martin Schunck, father of Henry Edward], with his large clan of nephews and cousins, was at the head of the Old German and purely Christian settlement. Both colonies, but especially the latter, were a well-to-do, thoroughly educated, and more than half anglicised race, on friendly terms, yet never, or very seldom, amalgamating with the native people around them.[74]

Another, but completely impoverished, social group was that of the Irish immigrants to be found in Little Ireland, Irish Town, and the similar districts in Manchester through which Friedrich Engels was guided by young Mary Burns and found inspiration for his *The Conditions of the Working Class in England* (1845).

Then, from around 1860, there was what Carl Alexander Martius called "Young Germany in Manchester," the recently arrived and often newly qualified experts in chemistry and calico printing, such as Heinrich Caro, whose assets were their skills gained in Germany or London. The leisure hours of these men were spent at two clubs founded for the benefit of Germans–the Albert Club, opened in 1859, and the Schiller Anstalt (Schillerverein), opened in 1860 to mark the centenary of Friedrich Schiller's birth. For chemists, the Schiller appears to have been most popular, and on one occasion at least Caro lectured there on his chemical work. With their libraries, meeting places, newsrooms, and committee, smoking, card, and billiards rooms, these clubs must have reminded Caro of the associations that had been formed in Berlin during the late 1840s, particularly since a strong liberal tradition was retained, to the extent that in 1864 Engels was appointed to the executive committee of the Schiller Anstalt.

Also in 1864, when unemployment in Lancashire remained high as a result of the cotton shortage, the International Working Men's Association (the First International) was established in London. Engels became a member, though his partnership in the Manchester cotton firm of Ermen & Engels precluded his representing the association in an official capacity. It was the special climate of economic and political liberalism which existed in Manchester that permitted the openness among this heterogeneous collection of skilful Germans, such as Caro and Leonhardt, both of Jewish ancestry, and Carl Schorlemmer, consultant to Caro and close friend of Engels and Karl Marx. Perhaps it was the Caro family's involvement in the revolution of 1848 that, though different from the experiences of Engels and Marx, permitted an easygoing association between Heinrich Caro and Carl Schorlemmer.

News of the latest scientific work, new inventions, business deals, and job opportunities was exchanged at these social gatherings of the German visitors and expatriates in Manchester. The same topics were discussed at meetings in the chemistry laboratory at Owens College, and, in particular, the Saturday gatherings at the Thatched House Inn in Market Street, where the convivial atmosphere enabled the Germans to be friendly with the local people. Vocal and other entertainment was provided by Caro, Schorlemmer (nicknamed "Chlormeyer" by the chemists and "Jollymeyer" by his political friends), and Philipp Pauli. Pauli had served his apprenticeship with calico printers in northern France, acted as an assistant to R. Angus Smith at Owens College (1859-60), taken up employment at the Union Alkali Works, St. Helens, near Liverpool, until 1863, and then moved to the Sulphate of Copper Company.[75] He left for France in 1864, but not before he had made a reputation for himself by out-boxing his works foreman.

THE OLD OWENS COLLEGE, QUAY STREET, MANCHESTER.

Owens College, Quay Street, Manchester, former residence of Richard Cobden. (*The Life and Experiences of Sir Henry E. Roscoe, D.C.L., LL.D., F.R.S., Written by Himself* [London: Macmillan, 1906], opposite 102.)

On one occasion, Caro's father paid a visit to Manchester and took his son and friends on a day trip to the countryside at Knutsford. One quiet young man who particularly impressed Simon Caro turned out to be Ludwig Mond, a German emigrant who would later transform the British alkali industry.[76] In 1862, Mond worked for John Hutchinson of Widnes, and frequented the Schiller Anstalt, where he met the engineer Carl Pieper, who would also later play a role in British alkali manufacture.[77]

When there was no time to meet, news was passed on by letter. Thus on 8 February 1864, Martius advised Caro that John Dale had returned from a trip to London, where "Hofmann's lectures are under Royal Patronage," while Frederick Abel from the Royal Arsenal Woolwich, and a former student of Hofmann, was expected: "Tomorrow Abel arrives in Manchester. He wants to meet Kellner because of the position in Woolwich. Young Germany in Manchester is very happy about the things in Schleswig."[78] W. Kellner was another German chemist in Manchester, and was provided by Abel with a position at Woolwich. In the 1880s, Kellner assisted Abel in the development of the explosive cordite, and on Abel's retirement took his place as War Department Chemist. The "things in Schleswig" referred to the war of the loosely unified German states (the German Federation) against Denmark that had been launched by Bismarck a week earlier. It arose from the Danish king's attempt to control the duchy of Schleswig, which, interpreted in Germany as annexation and seen as a threat to the German minority, aroused strong nationalistic sentiments. The outcome was a victory for Prussia and the division of the newly occupied Schleswig-Holstein between Prussia and Austria, which in turn led to the war of 1866.

Martius's research in 1864

In a letter probably written in January 1864, Martius reported to Caro on progress with new dyes. These included the picric acid derivative cyan brown, phenylene brown, and the blue induline compound, also known as pseudo indigo, azo blue (probably because the conditions for its formation were similar to those employed for preparing phenylene brown), artificial indigo, or indigo substitute.

> I have sent the promised dyestuffs samples. The cyan brown has to be mixed with H_2SO_4 or oxalic acid. Too much of this acid decomposes the dyestuff. The solution of phenylene brown is a mixture of chloride of phenylenediamine with an amount of nitrite for diazotization and this is made alkaline with sodium hydro[gen]carbonate.

> In usage you boil it and mix it with acetic acid and immediately after it gives the brown colour. To steam it, it is of advantage to make the paste in the cold. The blue base [induline] is commercialised best in the form of a base. I will send you tomorrow some dry substance. Thursday, Dr. [Carl] Vogt arrives from London to inform us about new green dyes.[79]

In February, a report by Martius to Caro included details of pseudo indigo:

> Excuse my long silence. I hope you have received the 2 strands of cotton dyed with pseudo-indigo. The mordant is tannic acid and tartaric acid used in dilute form. The dyestuff is much better with cotton than with wool. I think that a pound of fibre can easily be dyed for 3d [pence]. Today, I have begun to work with a greater quantity of azo blue and cyan brown and I hope that I shall be able to send you next Wednesday several pounds of dyestuffs. The printing trials with cyan brown on delaine [a wool-cotton fabric] I shall make with the help of John Dale when we have the necessary (prepared) fabrics.
>
> What you say about phenylene brown does not surprise me. I am convinced that these colours will be of use provided that you can deliver them to the dyers in the right form. The dyeing requirement for 1 lb of wool is that you need 10 g of toluenediamine.[80]

In May 1864, Martius sent Caro details of production processes for cyan brown, aniline yellow, azo blue, and phenylene brown. Hofmann's consultancy work with Simpson, Maule & Nicholson did not prevent him from sharing information with Martius, who probably understood the reactions better than any of Hofmann's other assistants. There was, in any case, little fear of divulging trade secrets if the information was shortly to be made public. Martius advised Caro:

> Hofmann has written to me about a new reaction
>
> Rosaniline, dry distill → aniline
>
> violet → ethylaniline [*N*-alkylated]
>
> phenylrosaniline → phenylaniline [*N*-phenylated].

What Hofmann had achieved was degradation by distillation of aniline red, his violet derivative of aniline red, and aniline blue (phenylrosaniline) into aniline and its respective substituted derivatives. This offered highly important information about the constitutions of the colorants and their direct relationships. Particularly significant were the two products in which hydrogens of the amino group in aniline had been replaced by either alkyl or phenyl groups. These *N*-alkylated and *N*-phenylated derivatives would later become important dye intermediates. Of no less interest to Martius and Caro were the natures of products obtained by distilling mauve: "The question is what about mauve? What will be derived from mauve under the same conditions?"[81]

Other products included the picric acid derivative cyan brown, and the phenol and potassium cyanide required in its manufacture:

> I have sent you 7½ lb burnt cyan, prepared from [lb?] picric acid and 8 lb of potasssium cyanide. The price of this potassium cyanide is 1/6d. The price of picric acid you can ask in Cornbrook. You can easily calculate the manufacturing cost.
>
> Tomorrow I join you for going to Alderley [Alderley Edge, near Macclesfield] and I hope to meet you at 2 o'clock at London Road station. I am sending you HCl [hydrochloride] of azophenylamine for [treatment with] oleum.[82]

Martius's research included the reactions of aromatic amino compounds other than those of aniline and toluidine, such as naphthylamine, which he had already used in London. Naphthylamine was available from the Tower Chemical Works in Manchester, and there was a special interest in this amine, in part because it might offer patent-free routes to new coal-tar dyes. The outcome was the manufacture, from the summer of 1864, of a second yellow in Manchester, "chrysonaphthalic acid" made from the action of nitric acid on either alpha-diazonaphthalene (from naphthylamine [aminonaphathlene]) or alpha-naphthol. The colour was also known as Manchester yellow, and Martius yellow in Germany (and later shown to be a dinitrohydroxynaphthalene). Martius obtained other coloured products from naphthylamine (as well as from toluidine), patented jointly with Caro on 9 November 1864, though these were less successful.

A new source of aniline in Manchester

Inevitably, the rapid growth of aniline-based colorants after 1860 brought about an escalation in the price of the raw material, coal tar, the previously near-worthless by-product of the destructive distillation of coal for illuminating gas. This stimulated research into processes for optimising the extraction of hydrocarbons, particularly benzene (which was invariably mixed with toluene). An alternative approach was taken by John Leigh of Manchester, who in April 1863 suggested to John Dale that the coal gas was also a source of benzene. The coal used in Leigh's investigations was cannel coal, a compact form that burns readily with a bright flame. It was from the tar obtained by distilling cannel coal at

Gorton, near Manchester, that in 1861 Schorlemmer extracted the hydrocarbons that enabled him to prove the equivalance of the bonds attached to carbon.

In the 1830s, Leigh had taught chemistry and forensic medicine, and from the end of the decade he was analyst to the Manchester gasworks, a large supplier of illuminating gas. In 1842, he exhibited samples of benzene and its nitro products at the Manchester meeting of the British Association for the Advancement of Science, and subsequently became fully conversant with methods of gas analysis.[83] His nitrated benzenes were possibly obtained by treating the coal gas with nitric acid in an attempt to remove products that condensed in and blocked the gas distribution pipes. Certainly the information that he supplied to John Dale must have been considered reliable:

> One ton of cannel [coal] distilled in the ordinary process of gas making will yield 10 gallons of tar and 10,000 [cubic] feet of gas. The tar made at Manchester yields 5 per cent of rectified naphtha [light oil] so that the 10 gallons will give half a gallon rectified naphtha. 1 gallon rectified naphtha (that of Manchester) will give 1 pint of Benzole so that the half gallon will give half a pint of Benzole. In this way 1 ton of cannel will give at present half a pint of benzole. And as at present obtained this quantity is all the product in Benzole of a ton of cannel. Now 1,000 feet of gas (the yield of 1 ton of cannel) will give according to my experiments 1 gallon of Benzole, and as the yearly production of gas in Manchester is 800 millions of feet the quantity of Benzole obtainable from this city alone is 80,000 gallons per annum.
>
> Here then is provided at once a new and magnified source of supply and I think it may be true to say that in future Aniline may be obtained in any quantity [from benzene] that may be desired.
>
> Whatever comes of it, it is really a magnificent contribution to a falling supply of a great article. I wish you would come to see me here on Monday evening as it is necessary we should follow up so brilliant a development.[84]

Leigh probably considered that his process would bring extra revenue to the gasworks, and at the same time eliminate blocking of the pipes by hydrocarbons. Though Dale and Caro were suitably impressed by a demonstration, nothing came of its application at that time. Around 1868, however, Caro found that by treating coal gas with suitable solvents it was possible to extract liquid and solid hydrocarbons, a process later modified and put to extensive use.

Explosives

Patent literature reveals that in 1861, John Dale had undertaken an investigation of gunpowder manufacture, then much in demand for mining and railway tunnelling, not to mention its less peaceful uses. Five years later, there was renewed interest in explosives when Caro and Griess used the reaction of nitrous acid on aromatic amines to afford dyes and explosive materials.[85] Considerable interest and correspondence concerning practical applications followed. Paraf wrote from the United States, and Jules Keisser (of La Fuchsine, Renards' successor) and Lucien Picard from France.[86] Abel and Kellner at the Royal Arsenal Woolwich were also intrigued by this new reaction.[87] Caro carried a flask of his unstable new product by train to London–in the passenger compartment–for Abel's benefit. However, the interest remained academic, and Nobel's dynamite and Abel's guncotton preparations were to become the explosives of choice, later joined by coal-tar products such as picric acid. It was a massive explosion of picric acid at Roberts, Dale & Co.'s Cornbrook works in 1887 that brought dye-making there to a close.

Summary

The collaboration between Martius and Caro, and the diverse efforts of the Dale family members and their Germans and consultants, were as close as it was possible to get to an organised industrial research team in the mid-1860s. Restricted access to the main mauve and aniline red, blue, and violet processes stimulated research into alternative processes and different starting materials. Caro's contacts enabled the introduction of German-made products to Britain as early as 1862, and there was considerable interest in the contribution of German firms and inventors to new industrial developments and discoveries by that time.

Both Caro in Manchester and Hofmann in London were interested in the same types of aniline dyestuffs from their respective industrial and academic points of view. The relationship was not, however, by any means direct. Although Caro visited Hofmann's laboratory on at least one occasion, late in 1862, and worked with a number of his former assistants, there was little direct contact between the two men. The connection came about because Caro was involved, in part, in responding to Hofmann's consultancy work for Simpson, Maule & Nicholson. During 1863 and 1864, when production of aniline red in Britain was restricted as a result of Simpson, Maule & Nicholson's patent monopoly, industrial interests stimulated far-reaching scientific studies that were to bring about closure of the connections between academic and industrial organic chemistry.

The most far-reaching and profound influences on this merging of science and technology were the informal gatherings of entrepreneurs, calico printers, agents, inventors, and scientists who frequented the Thatched House Inn and the German clubs in Manchester during the first half of the 1860s, and in the case of Heinrich Caro until his departure from England late in 1866. Their common goal was shaped by the necessities of demand for, and profit from, large-scale manufacture of textile goods (and cotton in particular), and these retreats from laboratory and factory floor were ideally suited as the hubs of social and business activity. Thus at the Thatched House, Englishman and foreigner, joined if not in outlook and accent, then at least by the aromatic complexity of casks of ale and boisterous renderings by Caro and others of favourite songs, were well-disposed to discuss, exchange and trade new knowledge of scientific, technical, and commercial interest. These men, seated at benches around rough wooden tables, and warmed in the winter months by blazing fires that cast shadows on beamed ceilings, engaged in a special form of alchemy from which new inventions and enterprises emerged. They also participated freely in philosophical and political arguments, to extents that would have branded such gatherings as highly subversive in Prussia, and no doubt in France as well. Liberality, tolerance, diversity, and mechanised textile production in Manchester wove together science and technology in ways that were not possible elsewhere in Europe. Though far cries from the more genteel proceedings of the Lunar Society, 18th-century coffee houses, and the Literary and Philosophical Society of Manchester, where new technologies were also discussed, these weekend and evening meetings were no lesser sites of invention and innovation, nor of contributions to the modern enlightened industrial spirit. They certainly must have suited the temperament of Heinrich Caro, who had flourished and participated greatly in the sometimes similar environment provided by the Germania group in Berlin around 1847.

4

Negotiating Science-based Technology

Making profits from new chemical processes in the 1860s provided tough challenges that engendered both friendships and jealousies. With success came profit-sharing arrangements and new status. Failure, however, led to confrontations, clashes, and rivalries. Disgruntled employees sought out new opportunities and partnerships elsewhere. Outside of the factory walls there were drama and combat in the marketplace, discreet dealings with agents and customers, gentle persuasions in order to gain acceptance of new products, and conflicts in the courtroom. We find all these aspects of business life at Roberts, Dale & Co., including widely different attitudes towards its chief inventor, Heinrich Caro. Scheming colleagues revealed their distrust of him, while agents for chemical products barely concealed their admiration. Here, in Manchester, we have a further foretaste of Caro's later life at BASF.

Martius and Pauli

The Caro Nachlass includes correspondence between Carl Alexander Martius and Philipp Pauli that tells us a great deal about personal relationships among the Germans in Manchester, and how new chemical enterprises were planned through a blend of expertise, networks of personal contacts, clandestine meetings, and not a little espionage. The exchanges were not untypical of the dealings among aspiring entrepreneurs wishing to engage in chemical manufacture in a rapidly modernising Europe.[1] This material is significant here also because, as the Martius-Pauli plans begin to fall apart, it also reveals growing tensions between Martius and Caro, and even an anti-Semitic remark by Martius about Caro of the sort aimed at Jews of eastern European origins. (Martius, incidentally, married a Jewish woman, and entered into a business partnership with Paul Mendelssohn-Bartholdy, son of Felix.) It is indeed surprising that this correspondence, which portrays Caro as an ego-driven despot, is held with the Caro Nachlass.

In the early 1860s, the alkali industry, closely connected to textile manufacture and well established in England, held out the potential for considerable growth on mainland Europe. Philipp Pauli's employment in the profitable English industry provided him with considerable insight into the processes worked in St. Helens, Lancashire, and Widnes, Cheshire.[2] Martius at Roberts, Dale & Co. had the opportunity to examine that firm's highly praised process for manufacture of caustic soda. The scale of production, the growing demand, and the relative simplicity compared to dye invention and manufacture meant that the alkali industry appealed to both men. Thus by the spring of 1864, they were negotiating a partnership for the manufacture of alkali in Germany. Financial backing was to come from the chemical manufacturer and agent Gustav Siegle of Stuttgart, while Ostermann of St. Helens was another proposed partner. Reports on other companies engaged in this business were scrutinised, and the roles of potential partners and collaborators were outlined. The idea of the enterprise probably originated in March 1864, by which time Pauli was at the Kuhlmann & Co. factory in Lille. Pauli expressed disappointment with Kuhlmann's plant and Martius believed that most of the German companies were far more advanced. At that time Martius, who had been in touch with William Gossage at Widnes, and was preparing to depart for a business visit to Germany, had begun to lose interest with Lancashire.

> The English are sending big quantities of caustic soda to France. Even we [Roberts, Dale & Co.] are sending more tin boxes containing white caustic soda–the market is painters and book printers.
>
> A few days ago I travelled together with Gossage to Manchester. Gossage has seen the plant of Griesheim, near Frankfurt. I shall leave England at the end of March, and travel via Dover-Paris-Strasbourg-Munich. Manchester and Warrington are boring.[3]

On 15 April 1864, Martius, now returned to Warrington, advised Pauli "there is good resonance for our project from [Gustav] Siegle in Stuttgart, as well as from Gysott." He encouraged Pauli to meet with Carl Koenig, at that time technical director of a fertilizer firm in Kaiserslautern, to discuss the project.[4] Martius, who had been offered a post as assistant to Hofmann in Berlin, wanted a firm commitment from Pauli regarding their partnership: "I must know something positive by August, because I have to make my plans known to Hofmann."[5]

There was further discussion about the enterprise in May 1864. Martius considered that Pauli's employment at Kuhlmann was very good for their new project, which was planned initially for the Palatinate. However, for Pauli this was a problem, since, due to his close connection with Kuhlmann, he was anxious to avoid manufacture of caustic soda at the new company. Martius made it quite clear that he and Ostermann were intent on manufacturing caustic soda, to the extent that if Pauli is "not entirely with us then we shall break up the partnership."

> I tell you Pauli, Kuhlmann probably wants to exploit you fully in the elegant French manner, not in the English manner. So be careful and consider that the Palatinate project will have a good market in France for caustic soda. Do not tell anybody about that including Schuch. I will write to Siegle tomorrow in connection with the monthly report of Koenig.[6]

By June, they had accumulated a considerable amount of classified information on German manufacturers of alkali, and made contacts with other investors. Martius advised Pauli:

> Enclosed I send you an annual report of Rigenkuhl, close to Cassel (near Hannover) in which you can see some information about German manufacturing. This company is recognised as a well-managed one and because of that it can be profitable under relatively difficult conditions. I send you only the most important information. I have the complete report here.... In confidence, I have reports of Hafen, near Aachen ... Siegle can do nothing before we have the complete calculation. So finish this calculation as soon as possible and Koenig will give you good advice.... When I have the calculations, I will dispatch them to Fikentscher [a drugs and inorganic chemical manufacturer] who has promised to design a prospectus. Fikentscher is very competent. I shall contact Goest.

In June, Martius reported that the plans would be delayed, and also that the success of Roberts, Dale & Co.'s new caustic soda process had attracted unwelcome imitators. Martius had decided to join Hofmann,

> ... without binding myself for a considerable time. In Berlin I can maintain better contacts since we intend to start in Salzbach [Prussia]–so you can stay on longer to get more time at Kuhlmann's.
>
> Please copy the plan of Kuhlmann's plant and send it to my brother-in-law who is an official architect in Augsburg and he will redraw it for you. I have paid seven pounds sterling for the plans of the Hutchinson plant. And since we arranged for sharing this cost please send me three pounds and ten shillings, payable to Gustav Siegle, since I am in debt to him.
>
> Our [Roberts, Dale & Co.] new plant is a masterpiece of beauty.... We have been working for the past 54 weeks with the new plants in St. Helens and Runcorn. Four or five plants now use the Dale method of evaporation of caustic soda. Dale would

> like to sue them but I am afraid that that will not work because these people will pull together and we are alone. It would be a fight to the death. All these plants now start to manufacture caustic soda not only out of the red liquors but also directly out of the black ash liquor.

Martius also provided information about his phenylene brown: "Aniline brown is successful. If your former boss wants aniline brown he should contact our company."[7]

On 22 August, Martius advised Pauli that he had accepted the post of assistant to Hofmann at the University of Berlin:

> Ostermann departs to the continent. I have accepted the engagement with Hofmann in Berlin on good terms. I am no longer tied to more than one state and have a contract with the Ministry of Culture. I had in mind to go back to Germany because from England it is impossible to make contacts in Germany. It is easier to deal from Berlin. I would prefer industrial work rather than an academic career. I prefer independence. I shall visit you in Lille, then travel via Thann, Mannheim, and Munich to Berlin. Hofmann wants to be in Berlin in March 1865. Easter is his first lecture and the laboratory will open in the autumn.

The letter then drew attention to difficulties that had arisen with Caro:

> I cannot tell you how much I am looking forward to seeing Germany again. The English life is repulsive to me. "Dear Friend" Caro I really understand now. He is a very dangerous individual and is no exception to his other fellow kinsmen [i.e. Jews]. "The Friendship" is only valid as long as it is of use to Caro. More about that I'll tell you when we meet.
>
> Manchester is busy. Geiger, who does not want to go back to Berlin with Hofmann, is here from London to apply for my job, and Schorlemmer and [Wilhelm] Dittmar will go to Scotland. [Theodor] Reissig will go to Scotland on behalf of Angus Smith to do some air analysis. Prussia seems to be wishing to embark on annexations. Unity is fine when it is for the good of Germany. Until now we have shown the foreign countries what Germany can do when there is a will. What do the people in France think about the Schleswig-Holstein affair?
>
> Please meet Mr. Naumann (the designer for the alkali manufacturer in Ringhall). He is exceptionally talented. He can work well with lead [the lead chamber process].[8]

Some time later, towards the end of 1864, Martius advised Pauli of his anticipated departure from England. Pauli, still in Lille, was considering returning to England, which surprised Martius. In an undated letter, Martius wrote to Pauli:

> I do not believe that I can leave England before the end of December, because I am busy with apparatus for the new [naphthalene] yellow [Martius yellow].... Do you really want to return to England? What are the prospects? Think about St. Helens?

> You are too good a German to want to return.... Claus will perhaps go to a new copper and lead factory in Germany. On Saturday there is the festival of the German singing association.[9]

The last surviving communication is dated 10 April 1865. It recorded a decline in the relationship between Pauli and Martius, and the end of their planned partnership for the Palatinate chemical plants. Martius intended to go with August Eisenlohr to Ziegelhausen, near Heidelberg, where Pauli joined a local saltpetre factory. Caro had informed Pauli that Martius was ambiguous. Martius stated that he did not care about Caro's opinion, and despised him, defending himself against criticisms from both Pauli and Caro.[10]

Before leaving Manchester late in 1864, Martius undertook one final piece of work that resulted in publication. This was an attempt to synthesize alizarin from coal-tar naphthalene, based on the fact that the latter was known to be a product from oxidation of alizarin. Martius and Griess published details of a method for preparing what was then thought to be an isomer of alizarin from naphthalene. It was the last major investigation in this area prior to the discovery by Graebe and Liebermann in 1868 that alizarin was an anthracene, and not a naphthalene, derivative. Martius maintained contact with Roberts, Dale & Co. until late 1867, when he founded the dye-intermediates factory in Berlin.

Caro on the road

Heinrich Caro's familiarity with the dyeing and printing characteristics of both natural and synthetic dyes placed him in a position to undertake sales and service work for Roberts, Dale & Co., to keep abreast of new developments in the dye-using industries, to learn about the products of competitors, and to maintain close contact with industrial chemists. Caro's main clients were the printers and dyers in Lancashire, and the dyers in southwest Scotland.

Caro thrived in the service of his English employer. There was great variety in the activities of his laboratory and the factories, as well as in the requirements of customers and agents in England, Scotland, France, Germany, and Austria. As an expert colourist, Caro was entrusted with marketing the full range of his firm's products. He paid careful attention to the introduction of the aniline colours to dye consumers, such as Schwabe & Co., and Edmund Potter of Dinting Vale. Caro's mauve was subjected to comparative printing trials against Perkin's mauve in these works. Dale's paste was 20 shillings per lb, compared with Perkin's at 15 shillings per lb. However, as a result of Caro's efforts, and the prior contacts of Dale and Roberts, their mauve paste was brought in by Schwabe, Potter, and numerous other firms.[11] Caro's clients in Lancashire, in addition to Schwabe and Potter, were Thomas Hoyle, whose Mayfield Works was close to Cornbrook; J. & J. Worall, dyer of cord and pile fabrics, at Ordsall, Salford, in the Irwell Valley; and Isaac Bury of the Adelphi Dyeworks, Salford. His network of local and foreign correspondents enabled export during 1862 to William Meyer in Vienna, and to his former employer, the Louisenthaler works; small batches were sent to Berlin for Theodor Goldschmidt, and S[imon] Caro, Heinrich's father, acting as an agent. Pauli provided Caro with customers in northern France, and a good commission for himself.[12]

Trials were also undertaken in Scotland at the printworks of Inglis & Wakefield and at Mercer Brothers. Other Scottish buyers in 1862 included James Miller, Son & Co. of Glasgow, the sales arm of the coal-tar distillery and manufacturing concern that had sold William Perkin his first benzene around 1858, and James Laing & Co., also of Glasgow, the main Scottish agent for Caro's dyes.

As at Perkin & Sons, mauve was converted into other colorants by Roberts, Dale & Co. On 21 January 1863, John Dale and Caro filed a patent for after-treatment of magenta, mauve, and other aniline colours with acidic solutions of acrolein to give purple, blue, and green.[13] New and improved versions of mauve were developed and samples were provided to printers and dyers. From the Springfield Works, Dalmarnock, one colourist reported:

> the trial which I made with your last new paste in comparison with Perkin's last new blue shade of paste and his old No. 1 paste–There is not much distinction as to the depth between 2 new pastes.... You may depend on the trials being correctly made to the 1/20 grain.[14]

During 1862, when the Lancashire calico printing industry was adversely affected by cotton shortages caused by the American Civil War, new outlets were sought for mauve, including the colouring of and printing on paper. Close to London, a useful contact was a chemist by the name of R. Müller, who placed orders for mauve to be used in tinting paper at the Dartford Creek Paper Mill Co., Ltd, and the Ettrick Forest Paper Mills, both of Dartford, Kent.[15] There was also an order for “1 lb of magenta and 2 lbs of vermillion” from S. Royle of Royle’s “Engraving, Lithographing and General Printing, Leamington Place, Manchester.”[16] A connection with the chemist Hugo Müller at the De La Rue printing company in London, famous for bank notes, postage stamps, and other paper products, was to be more enduring, and led to the introduction of aniline dyes to postage-stamp printing in 1864.

The correspondence between Müller and Caro provides a glimpse of the technical problems encountered in applying new colorants in paper and postage-stamp printing during the early and mid-1860s, and of experiments carried out in industrial laboratories that were to become of considerable value to academic chemists. It is also the only primary source concerning the first uses of synthetic dyes in the printing of postage stamps.[17]

Hugo Müller and De La Rue & Co.

Warren De la Rue, son of the founder of De La Rue & Co., was deeply interested in chemical matters and astronomy. His chemical researches included an examination of the red colorant from the cochineal insect. In 1854, he decided to undertake an analysis of Burmese naphtha, and sought out the services of a chemist. A. W. Hofmann recommended Hugo Müller, an assistant of Liebig in Munich who had studied under Otto Linné Erdmann in Leipzig and Friedrich Wöhler in Göttingen. Müller, in common with other young German chemists, must have welcomed the opportunities, both material and intellectual, offered by entry into one of the many British industries that were becoming increasingly reliant on chemistry. He soon joined Warren De la Rue’s laboratory in the printing factory.[18]

Müller developed a close friendship with Friedrich August Kekulé, whose theories on the structures of carbon compounds became the foundations of modern organic chemistry, and also with many of Hofmann’s students and assistants, including William Perkin. Kekulé claimed that it was while returning from a visit to Müller’s Islington home to Clapham on the top deck of a horse-drawn omnibus one evening in 1854 that he first envisaged the tetravalent carbon atom.[19] His thoughts were interrupted by the conductor’s call, and the concept that was to become critical to the development of organic chemistry was not recalled until 1858.

By the early 1860s, Müller had made several improvements in the printing processes of his employer, and had also introduced versions of aniline blue (1862) and aniline green (1863) into the factory. He was especially attracted to Caro's products. Their correspondence began in July 1862 with an exchange of information about how Caro's aniline black might be used to colour paper.[20] This may have been stimulated by a French-made aniline black writing ink displayed at the 1862 London International Exhibition. Hofmann, the reporter on chemical products, noted that the ink had been examined by his "friend, Mr. Warren De La Rue, whose remarkable penetration soon recognised it as a secondary product obtained in the manufacture of aniline colors." Comparison with Roberts, Dale & Co.'s aniline black caused John Dale to advise Hofmann that Caro's product "is remarkable for the energy with which it resists the most powerful chemical agents."[21]

More traditional colorants were also discussed by Müller and Caro. In January 1863, Caro was informed that the pigment cinnabar (made from sulphur and mercury) was causing corrosion of the copper printing plates, perhaps because of the presence of free sulphur. Caro recommended use of the cinnabar available from Roberts, Dale & Co. Müller also drew Caro's attention to John Lightfoot's newly patented aniline black: "Have you heard about the new aniline black. It should be useful for cotton printing but it is different from yours. It is not produced as a by-product. Instead it is produced by a particular decomposition of aniline."[22] Lightfoot's black was produced on cotton during machine printing by direct application of aniline salts in the presence of copper compounds. Caro's by-product black, by contrast, was supplied to users in the form of a paste, and was better suited to paper tinting and printing.

In April 1863, Caro supplied Müller with Alexandria purple, a derivative of mauve. This was one month before Hofmann discovered the violet derivatives of aniline red that were later known as Hofmann's violets, and that from 1864 displaced mauve. Müller asked Caro to experiment with mauve in order to produce it in the same form as the Alexandria purple, so that it could be applied with the oil employed for printing on paper.[23] Three days later, Müller advised Caro that the Alexandria purple was not fast to light, which was a problem associated with many of the early aniline colors. However, the cinnabar of Roberts, Dale & Co. seemed to be very good, and Müller wanted to try it on a large scale. In addition he also requested "1 lb of the new [cyan?] brown."[24]

Caro had achieved considerable success in converting mauve into a lake for use in paper printing at the De La Rue factory. In July 1863, Müller referred to trials with the lake and asked for a deep colour, observing:

> These colours are so magnificent that I would make every effort to use them, and I would predict a relatively high consumption if the price was not so high. Indeed, I am at this very moment working on their application, using 30 lb of the deepest mauve lake. Could you tell me roughly if you think that you can deliver the deep mauve at a lower price, especially in view of the large purchase that I am suggesting. If so, I shall try to secure this order for you.[25]

In December, Caro informed Müller that he would be sending him a batch of "soluble aniline black."

The quest for new coal-tar dyes, novel applications, and scientific studies converged with discussions about toluidine and aromatic chlorination. Müller had used toluene supplied by Caro to prepare its amino compound, toluidine, but found the hydrocarbon to be impure, though he considered that he had found a rather easy method to produce the toluidine. They both investigated the chlorination of aniline, probably in connection with the search for patent-free routes to new colorants. However, Müller concluded, "I do not think that it would be of any use. The production is too difficult due to the fact that aniline is regenerated." Müller ended his letter: "Have you heard of Hofmann's [violet] dye and is there any news of Martius?"[26]

A few weeks later, Müller advised Caro that he had achieved chlorination of benzene in the presence of a little iodine. Caro had found this difficult, but Müller claimed that it was easy. Müller's recipe specified one pint of benzene, two ounces of iodine, and "pass chlorine through, which warms up the entire solution. The reaction is complete when a sample placed in water sinks to the bottom. Distil the product mixture, and separate chlorinated benzene from benzene. If chlorine is passed through the solution for too long then the product is dichlorinated." Later, this was to become the standard procedure for preparing aromatic chlorine-substituted derivatives. Müller also used the method to make chlor(o)acetic acid. Müller found it difficult to reduce nitrochlorophenyl (nitrochlorobenzene) to form "chloraniline," because aniline also appeared, and suggested a route via acetylated aniline that might afford the chlorinated aniline. Returning to more pressing matters of manufacture, Müller noted: "We use your mauve lake every time, and we have bought it just from you."[27]

The next item of correspondence, dated 1 February 1864, revealed that one of Müller's main interests was the printing of postage stamps:

> I am writing a few lines to you because of the mauve lake. As I advised you earlier, your colour is nice in use over a wide range. However, we need an improved quality for one purpose, the printing of postage stamps.
>
> The printing plates of postage stamps contain fine engravings. Therefore it is necessary to use a colour mixture containing a lot of oil [resin?]. In general, the method of application should be such that the dye is delivered from the ink roller to the plate in such a condition that after printing it has been completely transferred to the paper, and none must remain on the plate. If any colour remains on the plate then after a number of printings a poor quality results.
>
> All dyes behave differently under these conditions, and your mauve lake does not mix well with oil. Therefore it is difficult to use it in fine printing. First, it appears to me that the nature of the dye is the cause of this behaviour. Perhaps rapid printing or drying are responsible for the "flinty" dyestuff; possibly also the mineral components of the dye are the cause of these problems. The dye should be in the form of a fine powder, the finest possible.
>
> For example, we cannot use the hard ... Berliner [Prussian] blue. Another difficulty is the deepness of the [mauve] colour. The attached sample is an example of the deepest colour that we can obtain from your mauve lake with some consistency. I would be pleased if you could improve the dye. Perhaps if you put some aniline blue in it we can obtain a more violet shade, but not so deep as the attached sample "3."
>
> For other purposes, however, the latter would be a desired shade. Possibly the pure aniline blue can be used in the same way. I shall not burden you more today, and I am looking forward to hearing from you.[28]

Subsequent correspondence suggested that some measure of success was achieved. In general, Müller was highly satisfied with Caro's products. In March 1864, Müller requested a further supply of aniline black (perhaps for the "Royal reprint" of the original penny black which appeared in that year). A sample of mauve lake that Caro had sent earlier was considered quite good and Müller requested a few pounds in order to try it on a larger scale. Müller also asked, no doubt with paper printing in mind, "What are the methods for fixing aniline black on cotton?"[29]

Two years later, in April 1866, Müller wrote directly to Caro regarding the lack of a response to one of his orders sent to Roberts, Dale & Co., and now requested "1 oz of your aniline purple in a dry and pure form," adding: "Why have I not seen you for some time?"[30] Later in the month, Müller revealed that he had tried out some of Roberts, Dale & Co.'s new dyes and considered that they might be useful at the De La Rue factory. He requested "1 lb of the new yellow-brown [phenylene brown] in such a form as you sell it to the dyers. Also 2 lb of dinitro-naphthylalcohol [Martius yellow]."[31] In May, Müller remarked upon the "Deep colour of Manchester mauve or violet. This dye, which you have delivered often in the past, is deeper and more rich than when first produced.... It is still not useable because it is too flinty and the cause is perhaps the mineral components." This comment almost certainly related to ongoing efforts to apply aniline dyes to the specialised area of postage-stamp printing. Müller had also used the "diphenylene" red-brown and the results

> were pretty good, and we shall without any doubt want to use it. What about the chemical investigation of this dyestuff? Has Martius begun to investigate it? The ... dinitronaphthyl [Martius yellow] preparation is not of great value in printing. It is possible to produce the (free) base of diphenyl red-brown by precipitation with free ammonia. The mauve gives good results and we want to use it, despite the high price. Have you succeeded in producing naphthyl alcohol [naphthol]?[32]

In June, Müller informed Caro that he wished to make some trials with mauve pigment but required it in the form of a paste, "so send in the wet form, but not too greasy. Perhaps after pressing, but not dried out." The letter closed: "What is the best method to fix diphenylene brown? If we employ it in the common way it runs right through the paper. This means that the dye is still in solution, and we want to avoid this."[33]

More news about the mauve lake followed in August, when Müller requested a new batch,

> and sends this request direct to you because the last sample sent in July was better. You remember that I asked you in my letter that I want it to be left wet, but when I received the consignment it was rather dry. I want to make more investigations and perhaps you can send me 2 lb in the wet state (but not greasy). I shall try and incorporate the wet dye in oil and test to see if the result is smoother and better.[34]

Problems of cost were also raised again. Müller wanted to know the reason why the latest consignment of Caro's mauve lake was three times more expensive than

> in the former quality.... Since I must in every case have a better quality mauve lake I am forced to accept your price of 4s [shillings] per oz. But 5 lb will be enough since

> we cannot use such an expensive dye to a great extent. The other 5 lb could be of the quality of 20d [pence] with the improved body.[35]

Müller noted that he required these samples for comparative trials.

At this point, discussion of lakes for printing purposes came to an end. A few months later, Caro left Manchester for Germany. In 1869, Müller's friendship with both Caro and Perkin led him to act as mediator between BASF and Perkin & Sons in negotiations over rights to their alizarin processes. A decade later, in October 1879, Müller wrote to Caro with regard to the use of synthetic dyes in printing one-penny postage stamps for an International Postal Union contract. By that time, Müller was interested in testing the new azo dyes for printing on postage stamps.[36]

Commercial matters, 1864-65

The Scottish trade in Roberts, Dale & Co.'s products was handled mainly through James Laing & Co. of Glasgow. In February 1864, James Laing sent Caro a detailed list of products used by dyers in southwest Scotland. Next to the names of two firms was the comment: "You know what they use," referring to users of William Perkin's mauve. One of these firms was James Black & Co., the first major consumer of Perkin's product.

By 1864 new aniline colours were beginning to affect the popularity of mauve, and consumers were out to take advantage of the competition among colour makers. The immediate effect was reflected in the price of dyes. Roberts advised Caro, on a sales trip to Glasgow:

> I am glad to hear that Inglis & Wakefield are thinking of making us an offer for a large quantity of our mauve, perhaps it might be as well not to give them an answer at once.... should they require your answer it ought to be clearly understood to be in strict confidence for should it be allowed to transpire that we were selling to them at less price than to any one else we should give great offence and lose some of our friends, therefore you will extract a pledge from them not to disclose the transaction to Perkin's or to any party.... the transaction to be treated quite as an exceptionable one and not to be a precedent for the future.[37]

Yorkshire dyers and printers were also included in the sales ledgers of Roberts, Dale & Co. Edward Crossley of Dean Clough Mills, Halifax, an early convert to coal-tar dyes, was the first customer for magenta made by Dan Dawson of Huddersfield. In June 1864, Crossley conveyed his latest difficulties to Caro:

> We have made up a colour with the Ruby and printed a number of hanks with it but find that after the yarn is steamed and washed the colouring matter in the Ruby bleeds

Walter Crum & Co. Glasgow.
Uses mostly madder only a little mauve.

James Black & Co.
You know what they use.

Inglis & Wakefield
Delaine and garment printer's, uses large quantities of mauve and aniline colours.

A. Monteith & Co.
You know what they use.

Glen McIndoe & Hall. Barrhead.
Delaine and silk printers, use a considerable quantity of aniline colours.

J. Boyd Sons & Hamel
Garment printers, use a considerable quantity of mauve.

Z. Heys & Sons
Large garment printers, use mauve largely.

McFarlane Sigal & Craig
Garment printers, use mauve to a small extent.

Wm. Miller & Sons. Glasgow.
At present nearly all madders - at one time used a large quantity of mauve.

Muir Brown & Co.
Delaine and garment printers, use aniline colours largely.

A. C. Ducan & Co.
Garment printers, principally madder - a little mauve.

Robert McGregor
Delaine printers, use aniline colours to a small extent.

James Templeton & Co.
Carpet printers, are trying your brown and ruby.

J. Bartholomew & Co.
Fancy wool and cotton dyers.

A. Reid & Sons
Cotton dyer, use a large quantity of indigo's. This is the man for your indigo substitute.

Donald Matheson & Co.
Cotton and fancy wool dyer.

A. F. Stoddart & Co. Paisley.
Carpet printer, is trying your ruby paste.

Ferme & Murray
Cotton and fancy wool dyers.

Leckie & McGregor
do do do

Wm. Cram
do do do

McFarlane & Sigal. Paisley.
do do do

Rodger & McCallum
do do do

D. Campbell
Cotton, silk and wool dyers, small man.

James Reid
Cotton and fancy wool dyer.

John Stalker
Cotton and fancy wool dyer.

John Morgan & Co.
Wool dyer and shawl manufacturer.

Lang & Wilson
Cotton and fancy wool dyer.

Robert Kerr & Son
Wool dyer and shawl manufacturer.

Guthrie Mitchell & Co. Leven.
Delaine and garment printers, use mauve and aniline colours to a moderate extent.

Geddes & Sons. Glasgow.
Cotton and fancy wool dyers and manufacturers.

Blair & Thomson. Glasgow.
Wool dyer and manufacturer.

C. Todd & Higginbotham
Handkerchief printer, uses mauve to a moderate extent.

John Black & Co.
do do do

"All those wool dyers use Aniline Colours to a considerable extent and it is with them that we must introduce your Browns, Rubys and Blacks, also the Clan tartan Blue which you have 2 swatches. With Mr. Campbell's compliments, and hopes that you have arrived safe."

Survey of Consumers of Natural and Synthetic Dyestuffs in Southwest Scotland
adapted from James Laing & Co., 100 Virginia Place, Glasgow, to Heinrich Caro, 11 February 1864.
(Source: Caro Nachlass, Deutsches Museum, DM NL93/10)

> from the yarn and stains the whites and light colours especially when they lay one above the other (as is almost invariably the case) and also when the hanks are whizzed and thus brought into close contact. If you can suggest any firmer method of fixing the colour we shall be glad.[38]

Crossley's letter to Caro of 23 February 1865 demonstrated a strong interest in the scientific approach to dyeing:

> When you were over making those experiments on dyeing I think you said you knew someone in Manchester who had a copy of Chevreul's work on the Chemistry of Dyeing [probably *Leçons de Chimie appliquée à la Teinture*] and I would be glad to get one. I should be very glad to know if this is true and if you could by any possibility get me a copy either to purchase or lend.[39]

Laing in Glasgow and Crossley in Huddersfield both maintained contact with Caro after he left Roberts, Dale & Co., and were to become customers for BASF products. In 1869, they were among the first to try Caro's synthetic alizarin in Britain.[40]

Robert, Dale & Co.'s sales were aided by the fact that English agents from Manchester and the district also joined in the fun at the Thatched House. They included Peter Adshead of Macclesfield, as evinced by his response to Caro's request for dyed samples:

> I send them just as they are, out of the pattern drawer, with the dates of the dyes upon them, the papers you will please destroy, but keep the patterns. I send you by way of contrast, and to show the advance made, two patterns marked J. B. and dated 1860 & 1861 which are Perkin's dye. You have our Magenta and two Pinks both same dye. An opal blue called Azuline [a phenol derivative] and a darker one, not so refined.
>
> The one called violine is I think all Hoffman [*sic*], the others are mixtures of blue and Humboldt [blue]. I hope they will be satisfactory. Trusting to have the pleasure of hearing you hold forth on Saturday.[41]

Establishing the commercial viability of the new yellow (aniline yellow) and brown (phenylene brown) colorants made by the action of nitrous acid on amines required comparisons with existing natural dyes. To achieve this, Caro sought out the assistance of agents and manufacturers. J. Caldewood of Rochdale made extensive trials, and in August 1864 advised Caro:

> Enclosed I send you the result of my trials with your new yellow. I would have written to you before but my trials were not satisfactory. This yellow seems to be more stable than the Picrate of Ammonia.... you will observe that it does not separate or bleed out from the Ruby colour when mixed with it.... regarding the comparative

cost I cannot speak but when you can supply us with it in larger quantities I will give it a fair trial against the yellow we are now using.[42]

The phenylene brown was also received favourably:

Enclosed I forward you trials of Browns made from the new colouring material–as I have made these the cost will be rather more than if they had been made from Fustic yellow–Fustic yellow with mordant costing 6½d per gallon!.... Meantime I consider these results quite as good as can be got by making brown in the old way and probably they can be improved on further experience.[43]

The naphthalene-derived Manchester yellow (Martius yellow) posed serious problems with its application, as described by Peter Adshead when writing to Caro on 15 August 1865:

Regarding the yellow, it would be a very useful colour, but for two drawbacks, one the colour coming off in water, although we could manage for that. The other one is very grave, for I find that several samples I have dyed and put in paper and had them in my pocket for a few days have daubed the paper yellow. Now if this colour made into goods marked the paper it would be a serious loss to manufacturers and to us. You see I am obliged to look at the matter in all its bearings, particularly the pocket one. Will you try it, and I think you will find what I say to be correct. I wish we could find some method of making it faster.[44]

Despite Adshead's reservations, by 1866 sales were healthy, especially in France, which suggests that either Caro had to some extent overcome the problem of application of the yellow, or the novelty of the colorant compensated for its lack of fastness.

Colin Campbell, Caro's main contact at Laing of Glasgow, passed on problems from his clients. Thus in February 1865, there was a query about "your yellow paste," an unspecified dye, probably also Martius yellow: "It runs or springs at the edges, when steaming. What thickening agent would you advise?"[45] Despite the difficulties with this colour, there was a request for a further supply: "please to forward 2 lbs of the Powdered Yellow as soon as possible." The Springfield Works of T. P. Miller at Dalmarnock also conducted trials on Caro's colorants as soon as they became available.

Charles Schubert, a user of dyes in Halifax, advised Caro in October 1865 that he had entered new premises and was interested in purchasing a wide range of dyes and dyers' chemicals, including ros(e)ine (magenta), mauve, Humboldt blue, logwoods, fustic, and indigo. Caro's steaming machine for use in testing dyes and mordants attracted great interest from Schubert:

> Mr. Louis Longbottom our colour mixer informed me that you have a very neat contrivance for steaming small quantities of colours for trials. I shall be very happy if you can tell me where I could get a similar one in order to steam the colours for trials before printing.[46]

Caro's tremendous command of commercial knowledge was such that in 1865 he was asked by Charles Hanson Greville Williams, then at Perkin & Sons, for prices of chemicals in Manchester, in connection with the French government's interest in the impact on chemical manufacture of the recent Anglo-French trade agreement (1862).[47] During 1858-63, Williams had been employed at the works of George Miller & Co. in Glasgow.[48] Critics of the British dye industry's performance later drew attention to the early retirements of Perkin, Nicholson, and Williams when discussing the decline of dye-making in England after 1870.

Caro as expert witness

In 1864, Caro's combination of chemical and calico printing expertise was drawn upon by a firm of Liverpool merchants, Frederick Huth & Co., plaintiffs in a legal dispute over the cause of "tender" and "rotten calicoes" that had been "printed blue, chiefly with the pattern known as the satin stripe for the African market." The defendants were David Greenhalgh and William Rumney "who formerly carried on business in partnership at Manchester as calico printers."

In December 1864, Caro and William Dancer,

> analytical chemists, of Manchester, deposed that they had examined the goods in question and made an analysis of the dyes and chemicals which had been used in the printing and finishing. They were of the opinion that the goods had been finished with silicate of soda, and to that they had attributed the unsound state of the calicoes, owing to the influence upon them of the alkali contained in the silicate of soda.[49]

The verdict of the jury was in favour of the plaintiffs. For Caro and Dancer, the outcome of their analyses and conclusions, which proved of such great value to their client, provided an opportunity to present a communication to the Manchester Literary and Philosophical Society on 4 April 1865. In this they explained how they had established that the silicate of soda used during the finishing process had adversely affected the interior of the folded goods: "the white portions of the patterns were in a further state of decay than the blue ones, in most instances retaining only 10 per cent of their original strength." This had been caused by the use of lead sulphate as an "ingredient of the resist paste printed upon the places intended to remain white, and by the subsequent action of lime and sulphuric acid it has become fixed in the fibre. We have noticed that sulphate of lead decomposes solutions of silicate of soda very rapidly ... and we think that the mechanical effect produced by the crystallisation of the sulphate of soda formed may have caused a further and final disintegration of the fibre already weakened by the action of the alkali."[50] Through his involvement with this case, Heinrich Caro took a further step towards his mastery of the processes of science, technology, and the law, the latter both as expert witness and as a specialist in chemical patents. The knowledge gained in England would be of tremendous value to BASF, particularly in the German and British markets.

Wanklyn's violet

In 1865, Alfred Wanklyn re-entered the story as the result of his research based on the studies of Emil Erlenmeyer, an academic chemist with a private laboratory in Heidelberg. Substitutions with hydrogen iodide on glycerol and mannitol afforded alkyl iodides that were investigated as reagents for the alkylation of magenta, as a rival to the Hofmann's violets process. In 1864, Wanklyn's manna sugar process for violet had been put into production by Hugo Levinstein in London. Wanklyn also filed a patent with Wilson of London for an alkylation process that employed the dangerous reagent methyl nitrate.

From glycerol, *iso*propyl iodide was obtained, which Wanklyn used to prepare a violet derivative of magenta. Around July 1865, he sent samples to Caro, soon after asking: "How does the colour go on? Will the dyers have it?"[51] Wanklyn's patent of 26 August 1865 described the process for producing the violet, made under pressure from the reaction between *iso*propyl iodide and rosaniline in alcohol. Wanklyn worked out the large-scale production. Hydriodic acid was to be prepared in a vessel of 10 gallon capacity: "56 lbs iodine, 40 lbs water (4 gals) heat to boiling; put in 2 lbs 11½ oz of phosphorus by degrees and stir well all the time." The acid was then distilled off and used in the manufacture of the alkyl iodide: "Put in hydriodic acid boiling … boil, put in 5 lbs (measure) of glycerine, 1¼ lbs phosphorus by slow degrees – 5 lbs <u>measure</u> of C_3H_7I must distil over. 6 operations."[52] In December 1865, Wanklyn added to a letter concerning the acquisition of rare chemicals for Caro: "How does the glycerine color fare?"[53]

Wanklyn's services extended to finding out about the other violets, especially the more popular blue shades, obtained by alkylation of aniline red (rosaniline):

> I have obtained some information about the substitution colours. Manufacturers now digest together a salt of rosaniline, caustic potash or soda, alcohol and iodide of ethyl. By the use of sufficient potash they are able to obtain an ethyl colour as blue as the bluest methyl colour.

This enabled him to provide new instructions to Caro for preparing the "isopropyl" colorant:

> If you remember we were able to get isopropyl blue by using solid potash or soda along with the rosaniline and alcohol and iodide of isopropyl.
>
> I don't think you will find much advantage in adding a very large excess of alcohol.
>
> Wilson's rosaniline which I used to make the 15 lbs of colour is not to be depended upon.
>
> You will find it advantageous to redistil the iodide of isopropyl along with water or steam.
>
> The plan followed by the manufacturers for obtaining the ethyl colours in the solid state is this. The base (ethyl-rosaniline) is boiled with dilute acetic acid and then common salt is added and so the colour is precipitated and some trash remains in solution.[54]

Despite Wanklyn's optimism, attempts to commercialise the process were not successful. In the meantime, he continued to study the aniline violet reaction and was intrigued by the formation of "ether" (or, in modern terms, an ester).[55]

Caro leaves England

On 31 October 1866, Caro's agreements with Roberts, Dale & Co. came to an end. By then, chemists and colourists had achieved as much as was possible in the invention of aniline and similar dyes based on their limited conceptual tools, and several of the new colorants had begun to displace natural dyes. Caro had investigated, and where possible exploited, almost every coal-tar dye reaction, and must have considered that new innovations were limited.[56] The only exception was the recently discovered replacement of hydrogen atoms in amino groups of aniline, that afforded important intermediates, the *N*-alkylated and *N*-phenylated anilines.[57] He was also beginning to suffer poor health from bronchial catarrh, as a result of the thick sulphur-containing yellow fogs that the Manchester air was wont to throw up. It was time to seek out fresh opportunities back in his homeland, in the company of his English wife, Edith Sarah Eaton (b. 1842).

Many of Caro's English colleagues, particularly agents who valued his expertise, were saddened by the news that he intended to return to Germany. Their relationships had been both cordial and profitable, grounded as they were in discussions of costs and uses of novel products during the leisure hours spent at the Thatched House in Market Street. Peter Adshead, upon receiving notice of the intended departure, responded:

> Your letter causes me both surprise, joy, and sorrow, the joy that you will so soon be able to prove the new theory [on formation of rosolic acid; see chapters 5 and 6], the sorrow as you may suppose, that we are to lose you–I hope however you will always let me know where you will be hanging out. I am very pleased with your kind wishes.... I hope you are not going quite at once, and that I may see you to exchange ideas with you–If I had my time to do over again, I should very much like to go the same round with you.
>
> If it would be convenient or agreeable to you, I could meet you on Saturday at the Thatched House about 3 o'clock, or if not possible, then at eight o'clock, and then we can try and arrange for you to come and dine with me some day next week. My kind regards to your lady love.[58]

Late in 1866, Caro set sail for Germany. Among the novel laboratory innovations in his baggage were carpenters' glue pots that he employed as small-scale reaction setups, with the outer pot serving as a heating jacket.[59] These were the inspiration for jacketted pans used in full-size manufacturing equipment.

Caro's departure coincided with a decline in the fortunes of Roberts, Dale & Co., and was followed by an unpleasant dispute with Wanklyn over his violet process. On 27 February 1867, Richard Samuel Dale, son of John Dale senior, advised Caro of the difficulties:

> I must apologise for my long silence but as things have gone on much the same since you left, I have had little that is novel to communicate to you. You may or may not know that Wanklyn has entered an action against us for not working his [isopropyl] violet patent (laying his damages at £5,000) but such is the case. The trial if it comes off at all comes off in Liverpool, at the latter end of next month and as your evidence will, as you know, be of considerable service to us I write to prepare you for receiving an invitation from us to come over here. My father hopes that if we should have occasion for sending for you that considering how we have been served in this matter by Wanklyn, that you will have no objection to come. Mr. Kershaw our solicitor [of Kershaw & Bullock] thinks that we cannot well do without you as you know so well the state of the colour when brought to us at first.[60]

On the same day, a second letter was despatched from Cornbrook to Caro, telling an equally unhappy tale of lost trade and defective production of the phenylene brown, and bringing a further plea for assistance with the case against Wanklyn.[61] The less-successful developments, both technical and business, mirrored the decline of Roberts, Dale & Co. as an innovative British firm, and perhaps, as later commentators would surmise, were a consequence of the departure of Heinrich Caro.

The uncertainties of commercial-scale chemical synthesis included the danger of explosions, as experienced at the Warrington and Cornbrook works of Roberts, Dale & Co. This is the aftermath of a massive explosion at Cornbrook that occurred on 22 June 1887, bringing chemical manufacture there to an end. (Photo courtesy of Chris Makepeace.)

5

Chemical Theory From Chemical Industry

Introduction

The development of new dyes, as the previous two chapters have demonstrated, brought together industrial and academic chemists to engage in highly novel synthetic studies. Since the academics were particularly important as consultants, solving problems that might make dye manufacture more profitable, and as expert witnesses in cases of patent litigation, it was in their interests to undertake in-depth studies on processes and products.

The scientific foundation of the dye industry was established by the leading consultant and expert witness, August Wilhelm Hofmann, whose own academic status was considerably enhanced through this achievement. It was a logical follow-up to his research into aromatic amino compounds that commenced in the early 1840s and was continued at the Royal College of Chemistry in London. In particular, Hofmann's constitutional formulae for aniline dyes as published in 1864 received wide currency. However, the equally useful formulae of Heinrich Caro's collaborator, the cantankerous chemist James Alfred Wanklyn, did not. Wanklyn's formulae were actually announced a few weeks before those of Hofmann, and it was Caro who had provided Wanklyn with the experimental evidence. Through these revelations the dye industry made its first major contribution towards theoretical knowledge. Later, the studies and formulae of Wanklyn and Caro turned out to be important in the eventual structural elucidation of the aniline dyes. Here the industrial background to Hofmann's formulae and Wanklyn's distraction are examined.

Kekulé and chemical structures

During the years in which the synthetic dye industry first emerged, two key concepts that would transform the theoretical understanding of organic chemistry were proposed by Friedrich August Kekulé, namely the four-valent carbon atom of 1858 and the benzene ring of 1865.

The four-valent carbon atom is expressed in structural terms as shown in Figure 1a,

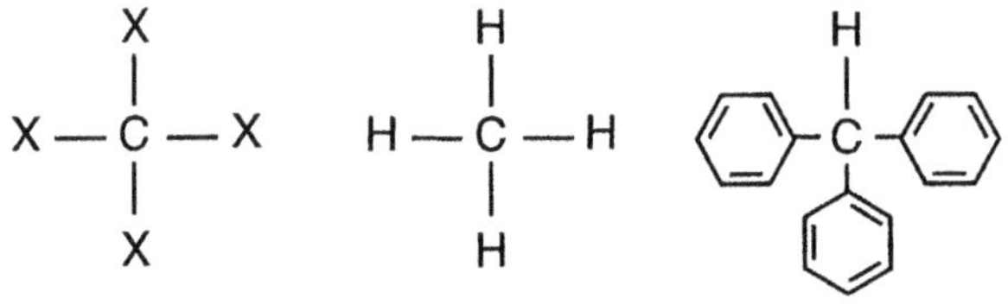

methane triphenylmethane

1a **1b** **1c**

Figure 1

where X is an element or atomic grouping. When X = H (1b), the structure is that of methane (marsh gas). Hydrocarbons such as methane form the basis of "fatty carbon" or aliphatic chemistry. The range of compounds is infinite since carbon atoms have the property of combining to form long chains as well as branch chains. Kekulé's structure explained the existence of isomers, that is, compounds with the same formulae but different structures. It was universally adopted after the equivalence of the four valencies was established in 1862 by Carl Schorlemmer, one of Caro's consultants.

Kekulé's second contribution, that of the six-membered benzene ring, enabled an understanding of the constitutions of the aromatic hydrocarbons. Complete structural diagrams of their derivatives were made possible following laboratory investigations into the assignments of substituents (functional groups or side chains), as summarised by Wilhelm (Guglielmo) Körner in 1874. Four years later, the modern structural formulae for the most important aniline dyes were elucidated by Emil and Otto Fischer, who established that they were related to methane in which three of the substituents (X's) were phenyl groups (benzene less one carbon atom), that is, they were derivatives of triphenylmethane (1c). The Fischers' starting point had been Caro and Wanklyn's work on rosaniline and rosolic acid.

Aniline red

Hofmann's constitutional formulae were modifications of his ammonia type formula of 1850. Type formulae were useful for establishing relationships between compounds that displayed similar reaction patterns. In particular, Hofmann had anticipated that the study of amino compounds would suggest routes to artificial drugs, such as quinine. His hopes were confounded until the discovery of aniline purple (mauve) by his student William Perkin, who had started out by attempting to synthesize quinine.

The services of Hofmann were first sought out by the dye industry in 1860, by which time he had studied aniline and other amino compounds for almost two decades. His prior knowledge enabled him to become the most important expert witness in cases of patent litigation between 1860 and 1865, especially his defence of the patents of Simpson, Maule & Nicholson. During 1862-63, and as a result of the commercial importance of aniline red, Hofmann isolated, analyzed and characterized its free base, which he called rosaniline. Hofmann also had access to other dye products, in particular the aniline blue of Charles Girard and Georges de Laire (1861), made by heating aniline with aniline red. Renards owned the French and British patents, and licensed the process to Simpson, Maule & Nicholson.

Hofmann brought notice of the growing economic contribution of the synthetic dye industry to the world's attention through his role as a juror and reporter on chemical products at the 1862 London International Exhibition. This provided him with an opportunity to acquire samples for analysis from the various European exhibitors, and during the following two years he made available to the scientific public the results of his major discoveries in the field of aniline dyes. Hofmann derived empirical formulae and balanced equations, and, as Martius revealed exhaustively to Caro in 1863, established the nature of the reaction mixture for producing the red. In particular, he demonstrated a direct relationship between the red and the blue when he proved that the blue was formed by introduction of phenyl groups into the red.

Reasoning by analogy, Hofmann predicted that novel colorants might be possible if, instead of phenyl groups, other groups of atoms were introduced into rosaniline. His first successful experiments, achieved in May 1863, led to replacement of hydrogens by alkyl groups to afford blue and violet solutions. The new products were the Hofmann's violets, which became highly profitable commercial colorants. The fact that the red was shown to be related to the blue and blue-violet dyes by simply replacing (unspecified) hydrogens, as established by Hofmann, proved that they were members of a family of compounds. In October 1864, Hofmann adapted his ammonia type formula to express these dyes as a family in which "typical [ammonia type] hydrogens" of amino groups in rosaniline were replaced during the formation of aniline blue and violet (Figure 2). Analyses showed that the aniline dyes were condensation products of three amino compounds (triamines).

Though these modified ammonia type constitutions were incorrect, and misled Hofmann in his later research, in the 1860s they were very serviceable models for both academic and industrial chemists and acted as useful guides for further research. Moreover, in 1864 type formulae were the sole means for expressing constitutions, and could accomodate both aliphatic and aromatic compounds. New information appeared in the literature only after it was established that publication did not threaten the interests of Hofmann's clients, Simpson Maule & Nicholson, and the Renards. Through Hofmann's role as expert witness, these firms maintained their patent monopolies, and remained the largest manufacturers of aniline dyes in the early 1860s. This situation was the principal stimulus that drove Heinrich Caro to consider different approaches to the invention of novel coal-tar dyes. He was greatly aided by the results of Hofmann's research, provided direct from Hofmann's laboratory by Martius. During 1863, another German-born industrial chemist was independently engaged in the study of coal-tar products in London, Hugo Müller at De La Rue & Co. Though Müller's position as a participant was more neutral, his correspondence with Caro contributes considerably to the contemporary background of the new discoveries.

Hugo Müller's network

Müller, following up his earlier experiments jointly with Warren De la Rue, took a special interest in the aromatic hydrocarbons and their derivatives that were available from Roberts, Dale & Co. The letters Caro received from Müller provide the main clues to the latter's industrial and academic research interests and his network of contacts. They are of interest here for what they do, and what they do not, reveal. The earliest surviving communication concerning relevant results is dated 10 January 1863, on which date Müller ordered from Caro a supply of hydrocarbons for his investigations.[1]

Three months later, on 10 April, in a letter that acknowledged receipt of naphthalene and dyestuffs, Müller exposed, through his own contact with August Eisenlohr, the close involvement of Hofmann in industrial matters. At the end of March 1863, Eisenlohr had failed in his efforts to conclude a contract with Roberts, Dale & Co. for supply of his aniline blue. It was in this connection that Caro had undertaken experiments with the blue colorant of Simpson, Maule & Nicholson. Müller was surprised to hear directly from Eisenlohr that negotiations with Roberts, Dale & Co. had collapsed.

Müller advised Caro: "I am very curious to hear about how this matter will develop in the future. Howevcr, if Nicholson says that the patent [for Eisenlohr's process] is not valid then nobody will buy it."[2] A few weeks later, on 13 May 1863, Hofmann established that aniline blue was triphenylated rosaniline, that is, rosaniline in which three hydrogen atoms had each been replaced by a phenyl (C_6H_5) group. This work was, as Martius's correspondence with Caro revealed, encouraged by the threat posed to Simpson, Maule & Nicholson by Eisenlohr's process. Hofmann's equation and constitutional formula for aniline blue subsequently had some considerable bearing on the commercial standing of Eisenlohr's process after it was adopted by the dye manufacturer and merchant Hugo Levinstein in London. In 1865, Levinstein lost a case of patent infringement brought by Simpson, Maule & Nicholson.

Hofmann's findings led Müller to continue with investigations of coal-tar hydrocarbons, especially toluene, as well as naphthalene, of which 10 pounds weight was ordered from Roberts, Dale & Co. in July 1863.[3] At the same time, Martius, still in London, was investigating toluene and naphthalene derivatives for the benefit of Caro. On 19 January 1864, Müller acknowledged receipt of a batch of naphthylamine from Caro.[4] Two months later, on 20 March 1864, he requested a further 10 lb of naphthalene from Roberts, Dale & Co. because the price was lower than in London. His letter noted that "Martius seems occupied with production of pure toluene," a response, no doubt, to Müller's complaint about its quality.[5]

Despite the wealth of detail in the correspondence between Müller and Caro, there is no mention of one coal-tar product that was known to be of great importance to both men at different times, namely phenol, as well as its derivatives. This implies that Caro did not wish to reveal his interest in them, which, as is shown here, was considerable.

$$\left.\begin{array}{c} C_6H_4 \\ (C_7H_6)_2 \\ H_3 \end{array}\right\} N_3,H_2O$$

aniline red
(Verguin, 1859)

$$\left.\begin{array}{c} C_6H_4 \\ (C_7H_6)_2 \\ (C_6H_5)_3 \end{array}\right\} N_3,H_2O$$

aniline blue
(Girard and de Laire, 1861)

$$\left.\begin{array}{c} C_6H_4 \\ (C_7H_6)_2 \\ (C_2H_5)_3 \end{array}\right\} N_3,H_2O$$

aniline violet
(Hofmann, 1863)

Figure 2

<u>Rosolic acid and its derivatives.</u>

phenol + oxalic acid + sulphuric acid → yellow coralline, or rosolic acid

yellow coralline + ammonia → red coralline, or péonine

red coralline + aniline → azuline

rosolic acid, $C_{20}H_{16}O_3$
[from condensation of one molecule of phenol and two molecules of *para* cresol]

aurin(e) = pararosolic acid, $C_{19}H_{14}O_3$
[from condensation of two molecules of phenol and one molecule of *para* cresol]

Figure 3

$$C_2\left\{\begin{array}{l} HNC_6H_5 \\ HNC_6H_5 \\ HNC_6H_5 \\ H \end{array}\right.$$

rosaniline

$$C_2\left\{\begin{array}{l} H \\ H \\ H \\ H \end{array}\right.$$

ethylene (type)

$$C_2\left\{\begin{array}{l} HNC_6H_5 \\ HNC_6H_5 \\ HNC_6H_5 \\ H \\ H \\ H \end{array}\right.$$

leucaniline

$$C_2\left\{\begin{array}{l} H \\ H \\ H \\ H \\ H \\ H \end{array}\right.$$

hydride of ethyl (ethane)

Figure 4

One reason, almost certainly the main one, was to ensure that details would not become available to Hofmann, who in 1864 was working on the constitutions of the new synthetic dyes, as was Caro's consultant and close collaborator, James Alfred Wanklyn. Wanklyn's studies, unlike those of Hofmann, included a colorant made from phenol.

Caro and the phenol colours

From the late 1840s, phenol was nitrated to afford the useful yellow dye known as picric acid. The first company to manufacture the dye was Guinon, Marnas & Bonnet of Lyon. The original source of phenol used in the process was an Australian plant. Colour-producing reactions from phenol had earlier been investigated by Friedlieb Ferdinand Runge who in the 1830s used the impure product available from coal tar. One of Runge's products was a compound known as rosolic acid.

Rosolic acid was reinvestigated in 1859 by Hugo Müller in London, and by Hermann Kolbe and Rudolf Schmitt in Germany. It is likely that Müller's research was motivated by an interest in novel colorants for use in the printing factory.[6] Kolbe and Schmitt had obtained the acid, which, they stated, was a red dye, by oxidation of commercial phenol with a mixture of oxalic and sulphuric acids. They did not patent this process, which was discovered in February 1859, but published details two years later.[7]

Rosolic acid and its derivatives were probably prepared in Manchester from 1862-63. The stimulus for their manufacture there was the availability of phenol from local coal-tar distilleries, and the restrictions placed on the manufacture of aniline colours by the monopolistic aspirations of Simpson, Maule & Nicholson. An improved grade of phenol was available from 1862, when Frederick Crace Calvert, Manchester manufacturer and lecturer at the Manchester Royal Institution, obtained it in the form of a readily crystallizable hydrate (details were published in 1865). This enabled the production of pure phenol (carbolic acid) for use as a disinfectant. Another local manufacturer of phenol, and also of its coloured derivatives, was Charles Lowe.

At Roberts, Dale & Co., Heinrich Caro made a major investigation into the possibilities for creating multi-purpose phenol-based colours, employing reactions involving the firm's oxalic acid. Caro's phenol studies at Roberts, Dale & Co. began in 1862, probably using Charles

Lowe's product.[8]

Caro devoted a small section of his monumental and pioneering history of the dye industry to the phenol compounds, and, because of his own close involvement in their development, he can be considered a reliable source. According to Caro, Marnas manufactured the dye péonine from rosolic acid by reaction with ammonia under pressure, and converted péonine into another dye, azuline. Significantly, the latter was the first light-fast coal-tar blue dye and was marketed in 1861, even before aniline blue. The stable rosolic acid became the basis of "a new branch of the [coal-tar dye] industry, especially after it was successful as a pigment for wallpaper printing in the form of the fiery Turkey red lake."[9] A 1943 inventory of samples held in the Caro Nachlass reveals that the products investigated and produced at Roberts, Dale & Co. included rosolic acid, aurin(e), jaune phenique (probably picric acid), and "coralline-lake," the pigment otherwise known as Turkey red lake.[10]

The constitutions of these phenol dyes provided chemists with a not-inconsiderable challenge. In Manchester, R. Angus Smith suggested that rosolic acid was formed by a condensation of two molecules of phenol, while the French chemist Edmond Willm expressed the constitution of azuline using Hofmann's ammonia type formula, and described the product as a "dioxyphenylamide."[11]

Caro, through his close familiarity with rosolic acid, aniline dyes, and the diazo reaction, was able to make a singularly major contribution to the chemical understanding of the constitutions of both aniline and phenol dyes. Though there was, by common admission, some uncertainty over the exact formulae of the compounds Caro and Wanklyn were working with, the results showed unequivocally that the constitutions of rosaniline and rosolic acid were similar. Wanklyn speculated that both aniline red and rosolic acid (and their derivatives) belonged to what he called the "ethylene type."

The ethylene type

In 1864, ethylene was expressed graphically in its modern form with a double bond connecting the two carbon atoms ($CH_2{=}CH_2$). This was adopted by Alfred Wanklyn to represent the constitutional formula of aniline red, and made public in September of that year at the annual meeting of the British Association for the Advancement of Science, held in Bath. Wanklyn's ethylene type formula showed two carbon atoms separated from the four hydrogen atoms by a bracket. The ethylene type, unlike other type formulae, performed a single function, that of expressing the constitutions of coal-tar dyes. Wanklyn argued that the constitution of the rosaniline series could be expressed by the ethylene type by virtue of known reduction and replacement reactions. Thus he compared the ready reduction of ethylene to ethane with the conversion of rosaniline into colourless leucaniline, both of which involved the addition of two hydrogen atoms. This enabled him to propose the formulae as shown in Figure 4.[12]

At the time of the Bath meeting, Hofmann had not yet published his results on the alkylation of rosaniline (the reaction that afforded Hofmann's violets). He had proposed a modified ammonia type formula for rosaniline "which appears to be adopted by some chemists" with two toluyl (tolyl, C_7H_7) groups and one phenyl (C_6H_5) group separated by a bracket from three nitrogens (Figure 5). Martius used such constitutional formulae in his correspondence with Caro during 1863. These formulae did not, however, indicate how the important reactions of rosaniline (aniline red) leading to blue and violet colorants might occur. It was the facile replacement of three hydrogen atoms in rosaniline that provided Wanklyn with the clue to a more rational formula. Thus "Hofmann's beautiful research relating to this transformation of aniline red into aniline blue leaves no doubt that three atoms of hydrogen are concerned." Similarly, during the formation of aniline violet "there can be little doubt that substitution goes on to the length of three [hydrogen] atoms." This enabled Wanklyn to state, as would Hofmann a few weeks later, that these replaceable hydrogens were attached to nitrogen, that is, "the rational formula of rosaniline must display three atoms of hydrogen in association with nitrogen" (Figure 4).

It was in the following presentation that Wanklyn suggested how his ethylene type could also be used to express the constitution of rosolic acid, such that three molecules of the phenol condensed through the uptake of two carbon atoms from oxalic acid (Figure 6). This constitution was in agreement with the observation by Kolbe and Schmitt that rosolic acid was decolorised, or reduced, to the leuco form with "nascent hydrogen." Further, the use of the ethylene type was extended by an equation (Figure 7) which expressed the action of aniline on rosolic acid in the formation of a blue dye (although this was not the process normally

$$C_{20}H_{19}N_3 = N_3 \left\{ \begin{array}{l} C_7H_7 \\ C_7H_7 \\ C_6H_5 \end{array} \right.$$

Figure 5

$$4 \times C_5H_4O = C_{20}H_{16}O_4 = C_2 \left\{ \begin{array}{l} C_6H_5O \\ C_6H_5O \\ C_6H_5O \\ HO \end{array} \right.$$

Kolbe and Schmitt, 1859 — Wanklyn, 1864

Figure 6

$$C_2 \left\{ \begin{array}{l} C_6H_5O \\ C_6H_5O \\ C_6H_5O \\ H \end{array} \right. + \begin{array}{l} H_2C_6H_5N \\ H_2C_6H_5N \\ H_2C_6H_5N \end{array} = C_2 \left\{ \begin{array}{l} C_6H_5C_6H_5N \\ C_6H_5C_6H_5N \\ C_6H_5C_6H_5N \\ H \end{array} \right. + \begin{array}{l} H_2O \\ H_2O \\ H_2O \end{array}$$

rosolic acid — "blue dye"

Figure 7

$$C_2 \left\{ \begin{array}{l} NC_6H_5H \\ NC_6H_5H \\ NC_6H_5H \\ H \end{array} \right. \xrightarrow{\text{nitrous acid}} C_2 \left\{ \begin{array}{l} N_2C_6H_3 \\ N_2C_6H_3 \\ N_2C_6H_3 \\ H \end{array} \right. \xrightarrow{\text{water}} C_2 \left\{ \begin{array}{l} C_6H_5O \\ C_6H_5O \\ C_6H_5O \\ H \end{array} \right.$$

rosaniline — azo-rosaniline — rosolic acid

Figure 8

$$C_2 \left\{ \begin{array}{l} OC_6H_5 \\ OC_6H_5 \\ OC_6H_5 \\ HO \end{array} \right. \qquad C_2 \left\{ \begin{array}{l} OC_6H_5 \\ OC_6H_5 \\ OC_6H_5 \\ H \end{array} \right. \qquad C_2 \left\{ \begin{array}{l} OC_6H_5 \\ OC_6H_5 \\ OC_6H_5 \\ H \\ H \\ HO \end{array} \right.$$

rosolic acid Wanklyn's interpretation of Kolbe and Schmitt's empirical formula, 1864 — rosolic acid Caro and Wanklyn, 1866 — reduced (leuco) rosolic acid from Kolbe and Schmitt's process, according to Caro and Wanklyn, 1866

Figure 9

used to produce azuline).[13] Alfred Wanklyn, therefore, is to be credited with priority for the first useful formulae that expressed the constitutions of both aniline- and phenol-derived dyes.

On 19 October 1864, not long after the Bath meeting, Hofmann's paper in which he suggested a modified ammonia type formula for rosaniline, with three hydrogens shown as separated from the tolyl and phenyl groups of the earlier formula (Figure 5), was received at the offices of the Royal Society of London. By replacement of these three hydrogens with three phenyl or alkyl groups, respectively, Hofmann indicated how aniline blue and violet were formed. Undoubtedly, these renderings of Hofmann's modified ammonia type were inspired by the type formulae of Wanklyn, much as Hofmann's most important work on the constitution of aniline blue in May 1863 was stimulated by the industrial interest in Eisenlohr's blue. By the end of 1864, the formulae of Wanklyn and Hofmann were in print.

Wanklyn's constitutional formulae were the direct outcomes of research in a nonacademic setting, the Manchester factory laboratory of Roberts, Dale & Co. Wanklyn had been in continuous contact with Caro, whose quest for novel inventions forced the need for a new theoretical basis for coal-tar dyes, one that extended beyond aniline red and its derivatives. Since, as Hofmann himself had admitted, the dye industry proceeded in advance of chemical theory, there was plenty of scope for the intrepid researcher to come up with bold new theories. Wanklyn's main contribution was in suggesting, in two separate presentations at Bath, the rosolic acid-rosaniline relationship. Further, there was only one place where this relationship could have been established: in a laboratory where aniline and phenol colours were being studied. Hofmann's industrial clients were interested only in aniline dyes, and so there was no motivation for him to look beyond the compositions of these products.[14]

It is probable that by the summer of 1864, Wanklyn was in possession of the most persuasive evidence for his announcements at Bath. The crucial reaction was the decomposition of diazo compounds with water, which took place if the temperature was allowed to rise above 10°C. Instead of the usual nitrogen-containing coloured precipitates, nitrogen-free compounds were obtained. Hofmann had investigated the reaction of nitrous acid on rosaniline, but his diazo product was unstable and explosive, and the reaction was not followed up. This acted as a signal to others, including Alfred Paraf at Roberts, Dale & Co., who converted rosaniline into what he thought might be rosolic acid under similar conditions (Figure 8).

Paraf must have made this observation not long before he left Manchester for the United States early in 1864. Details were given to Caro, who later followed up a chance observation, the formation of a crystalline chromic acid salt of a diazo compound, during an investigation into the technical preparation of dinitronaphthol (Martius yellow). The same conditions were applied to the product of the reaction of nitrous acid on rosaniline, whereupon the crystalline salt of its diazo compound was obtained.[15] The product of decomposition of this salt with water showed features common with rosolic acid: "So we recognised that it was rosolic acid ... and we went on to state the relation to rosaniline with formulae."[16]

In 1866, Wanklyn and Caro first made public the experimental evidence for the connection between rosaniline and rosolic acid, through the ethylene type, in a paper submitted to the Royal Society. Wanklyn informed Caro: "Our paper has been presented by Frankland to the R.S. [Royal Society]. I was at the Chemical [Society] last night and saw Perkin. He is very much pleased with our result and I don't think we shall be at all disappointed with the reception we shall meet with."[17] In the same letter, Wanklyn drew ethylene type formulae for "ethyl hydride hydrated rosaniline," and rosolic acid. The joint paper was published in the *Proceedings of the Royal Society of London*, and details also appeared in *Chemical News*.[18] Caro and Wanklyn amended Wanklyn's 1864 constitutional formula for rosolic acid, based on Kolbe and Schmitt's empirical formula, by dropping one of the four oxygens. Also, since the two parties had obtained rosolic acid under different conditions, Caro and Wanklyn suggested that the Kolbe and Schmitt product had been obtained as the leuco (reduced) form, in which case there would be two additional hydrogens in the colorant. (The product of Wanklyn and Caro was essentially free of the leuco acid.) The published elemental analyses permitted this juggling of formulae, according to Caro and Wanklyn (Figure 9).

Caro independently published a paper on the constitution of rosolic acid in the *Philosophical Magazine*. Caro did not use type formulae, but he did discuss the important question of the origins of the two "fatty carbons" (corresponding to the ethylene carbons). He obtained samples of pure phenol from Charles Lowe, and also by distilling the calcium salt of salicylic acid, a carboxylic acid derivative of phenol. Upon treatment with a selection of oxidising agents, these pure products did not afford rosolic acid. When mixed with "cressylic alcohol" (cresylic alcohol, or cresol, the higher homologue of phenol–that is, phenol with a methyl side chain), rosolic acid appeared. This was a situation analogous to that found by Hofmann when investigating aniline red; oxidation of pure aniline alone did not give aniline red. Further, Caro found that pure phenol, on treatment with sulphuric and oxalic acids, the industrial conditions, did afford rosolic acid. Apart from the fact that a mixture of phenol and cresol gave a poor yield of rosolic acid, and the observation that pure cresol alone gave no colouring matter, Caro's conclusion was that the fatty carbons in the rosolic acid formula came in the first case from the methyl of the cresol, and in the second case from the oxalic acid.

Caro reported similar results if pure aniline was treated with reagents containing fatty carbons: "The bearing of these experimental results on the theory of the constitution of rosolic acid will be obvious. Both of these substances appear to contain aromatic and fatty carbon ... in order to form either of them, it is necessary to have both a phenyle-compound [aromatic] and a fatty-carbon [aliphatic] compound present."[19] The importance of Caro's results was acknowledged by Hugo Müller in London. Despite their close contact, and Müller's interest in phenolic products, even in 1866 he had no prior knowledge of Caro's interest in rosolic acid.[20] On 18 October, Müller wrote to Caro:

> I have received the Zeitschrift fur Chemie. I found a review of your nice work on rosolic acid. This is the first time that I have seen it mentioned since I do not get the Philosophical Magazine. This work was entirely new to me. I do not have to tell you how much I am interested in it. Please send me a reprint. I hear that you are working on a number of things and for this purpose you are in alliance with Griess and Wanklyn.

Müller's interest in cresol and other phenolic compounds led him to enquire of Caro:

> Could you send me a sample of pure cresol? Have you got it in solid form? I have worked the last time with cresol from coal tar but I could not get it solid. Perhaps it crystallises after you just add some small crystals in the same way as is done with phenol alcohol [phenol]. Did you obtain the product of naphthyl alcohol [naphthol]

successfully?.... it is not easy to produce it in such large quantities.[21]

Müller's letter therefore poses an intriguing question concerning the extent to which Caro and Wanklyn maintained secrecy about their research on rosolic acid prior to publication. Caro's need to publish might even be considered surprising, especially since at one stage the rosolic acid work must have been classified information at Roberts, Dale & Co. The deliberate withholding of information prior to publication is evinced by Müller's sudden interest upon reading the report in the *Zeitschrift für Chemie*, especially as he had previously freely exchanged all manner of research results with Caro, and retained an interest in phenolic compounds following his 1859 publication. Further, Müller knew about the connection between Caro and Wanklyn from April 1863, if not earlier, because of his own contact with Eisenlohr.

There are no clear answers to this question. Perhaps silence was maintained because Caro and Wanklyn realised the impact that publication of their work would have on both industrial and academic studies. The need to render public experimental results was important to both men, especially in the case of Caro because of uncertainty about his future career. Despite his acceptance, and achievements, in Lancashire, he was still a foreigner working in England. In Caro's homeland, the German dye industry was beginning to make its presence felt, which must have suggested new opportunities. Caro was also anxious to establish his reputation across the boundaries of science and technology, which would enable him to advance his academic studies. Publication, therefore, of the results of his collaboration with Wanklyn would provide much-needed academic recognition. Moreover, the information was appreciated by fellow industrialists, although the secrets of manufacturing processes were not divulged. In any case, Caro's days in Manchester were numbered.

Summary

The industrial investigation carried out by Caro that contributed to the ethylene type was a critical component in the events leading towards final structural elucidation of aniline dyes. The role of the modified ammonia type has long been recognised, perhaps because it emanated from the laboratory of the leading academic chemist in London and, later, Berlin. The important role of the ethylene type has, however, rarely been recognised, perhaps in part because Wanklyn, its originator, was, from the year after he and Caro published together, "ignored and despised by British academic chemists."[22] Also, in 1867 Wanklyn had moved from organic synthesis to water analysis. His contact with Caro came to an end with the latter's departure from Roberts, Dale & Co. (although it would be revived later in the century).[23]

In Berlin, again during 1867, and with Hofmann as his consultant, C. A. Martius continued at his newly opened intermediates factory to exploit the reactions of aromatic amines with nitrous acid, now that Caro and Wanklyn had shown them to be of value to theoretical studies, and Caro and Griess had published on phenylene brown.[24]

The development of both the ethylene and modified ammonia types for expressing the constitutions of coal-tar dyes was a feature of the complex interplay between private and public chemical knowledge during the 1860s. In the world of industrial chemistry, any disparity between secrecy, for financial gain, and publication, for intellectual status, was not problematic as long as the latter was not a threat to the former. On the contrary, publication by key workers gave favourable exposure and prestige to manufacturers of novel products, and served to enhance academic-industrial collaboration.

The publications on ethylene and modified ammonia types followed the discoveries, and availability of pure products, from different industrial settings each with different needs. These theoretical models served important roles insofar as they were persuasive devices for correctly predicting, classifying, and relating products that were of interest to both academic and industrial chemists. Although the types of Wanklyn and Hofmann as used for dyes were incorrect, they were not displaced until 1878.

Finally, this case study demonstrates the way in which major areas of organic chemistry developed after 1860. Incorrect or partially correct theories that appeared in response to the challenges of dye technologies, and were sometimes the outcomes of industrial research, became the foundations upon which new and more correct theories were constructed. After the 1870s, when a wider body of relevant and reliable knowledge was available, the theoretical developments, frequently driven by the needs of the dye industry, became increasingly confined to the academic setting. Only then did the dye industry come to be based on discoveries made in academic laboratories.

6
The Chemist as Inventor

Hofmann did not actually return to Germany till 1865 the year after the defeat of Schleswig-Holstein. Caro, Martius ... returned in 1866, lit with the same flame, eager to take their share for the Fatherland of both the work and the glory. The Germans, after their defeats by Napoleon and the riots of 1848, turned to Bismarck ... Caro, although he had married a Salford girl, threw up his partnership with Roberts, Dale ... and took his young wife to Ludwigshafen to join the B.A.S.F. They, like the Agfa, had a lot of money behind them. Here you have the beginning of the powerful Badische, Bayer, and Berlin firms, later on to form the combine of the "3 B's" which was the predecessor of the I. G. [Farbenindustrie].

Herbert Levinstein, 1949.[1]

At the close of the 19th century, the German synthetic dye industry was the undisputed world leader. It had become a symbol not just of Germany's industrial prowess but also of its mastery of organic chemistry. This was recognised at home and abroad, particularly in England, where the dye industry was founded. During the 20th century there were moments of acute interest in how this had occurred, most particularly at the outbreak of World War I, when Britain found itself without a strategic dye industry–whose intermediates and processes were the sources of modern explosives and poison gas–and in the aftermath of World War II when, especially in the United States, new paradigms of technological revolutions were invoked. The latter was to be the stimulus for the classic study, John J. Beer's *The Emergence of the German Dye Industry*, published in 1959.[2] Beer's volume reviewed the history of the German synthetic dye industry prior to the formation of I. G. Farbenindustrie in 1925, and though it remains the most readable introduction to the subject, it does not address many important aspects of the key relationships between chemistry and technology, and of corporate structure and innovation. Beer readily admitted an important lacuna, namely the precise nature of the connections between academic chemists and the dye firms, particularly royalties and contractual arrangements.[3] Even Caro's involvement with academic chemists received short shrift.[4]

Only after 1980 did a new generation of historians, often with different agendas, critically engage these and similar issues, and offer new interpretations and perspectives. Thus Georg Meyer-Thurow, like Beer, concentrated on the introduction of formal scientific knowledge into the Bayer factory, which, however, only began research in the mid-1880s and was therefore a latecomer in the process started by Heinrich Caro during the 1870s. More wide-ranging and balanced was Ernst Homburg, who investigated the seven most important German dyestuff companies and underscored the importance of management decisions on the beginning of industrial research. Peter Borscheid and Walter Wetzel assigned, respectively, two and three phases to the development of industrial research as it shifted from academic-industrial contacts to in-house industrial research. Henk van den Belt and Arie Rip, in building on Thomas Kuhn's *Structure of Scientific Revolutions* and evolutionary economics, described the changeover of technological paradigms in the dyestuff industry, commencing with a trial-and-error period, then moving through a scientific phase towards industry-generated inventions stimulated by patent law and the availability of technical dyeing facilities at the firms.[5]

Prevalent in all the earlier studies has been a great emphasis on the emergence of structural organic chemistry as a precondition for science-based technological developments. They also emphasised the importance of azo dyes and their influence on the German patent law, often excluding other equally important products and strategies. Here we provide new and very different perspectives based on a more comprehensive overview and analysis of the 1868-90 period. And because of the centrality of Heinrich Caro, as founding father of industrial research in the German chemical industry, he is to be our cicerone as we follow the often winding, and sometimes rough and uneven, paths in the history of actual developments.

The two product groups most closely associated with the emergence of the German dye industry as a major economic force were alizarin and azo dyes. However, though Heinrich Caro at BASF pioneered their developments, the alizarin technology achieved at other firms, both English and German, was at first way ahead, as was commercial progress in azo colorants made at Bayer and AGFA. Caro's success with alizarin arose mainly from his clever strategy of getting his own discovery into the key patents and filing these patents for BASF outside of Germany. This enabled the creation of a vital strategic alliance with William Perkin's firm that, once technical problems at BASF were resolved, gave the German firm control of the largest slice of the alizarin market. The technical delay did, however, encourage fundamental studies at BASF into the chemistry of the alizarin process. Similar in-depth studies were made on azo dyes, but while few new colorants arose from this endeavour, the enormity of Heinrich Caro's labours was to have considerable academic repercussions that would later be turned to tremendous advantage at BASF. It is for this reason that the latter part of this chapter emphasises the scientific development of alizarin and azo dyes and related products. But first we describe Caro's return to his homeland, and the economic situation there, and then review the early years of the German dye industry, introducing not only BASF, but the other major players, particularly AGFA, Bayer, and Hoechst.

The return to Germany

When Caro left Manchester for Germany at the end of 1866, he returned to a country engaged in far-reaching political and economic changes. Prussia, recently emerged victorious from war against Austria, had established a near-total hegemony in Germany, a development that foreshadowed the foundation of the Kaiserreich (1871). Events in Germany were observed closely by its neighbours as well as by Germans abroad, including those who, in common with Caro and others among the expatriate German community in Manchester, held increasingly strong patriotic feelings for their homeland. Most significant to Caro's future, and the futures of many of his colleagues, was the tremendous social and economic transformation of the country, the increasing influence of the well-educated upper middle class, the emancipation of the Jews, and the takeoff of the much-delayed industrial revolution in the German states. All these, and particularly industrialisation, were in the process of transforming the previously distinct and agrarian-dominated economies of thirty-four independent and sometimes disparate principalities–kingdoms, grand duchies, and electorates–into a nation that aggressively aspired towards industrial and political power. Little wonder then that Caro, as well as August Wilhelm Hofmann, August Leonhardt, Carl Alexander Martius, and many other Germans in England, having advanced their careers as much as was possible, welcomed new opportunities in the emerging German Empire. For Caro this was also an opportunity to escape from the heavily polluted airs of Manchester that had taken a toll on his health.

In the 1860s, the German states experienced an unprecedented economic boom. At the forefront of these advances were the coal, iron, and steel industries. Thus, for example, iron production grew from 220,000 tons in 1850 to 1,413,000 tons in 1867, while available machine power increased from roughly 260,000 horsepower in 1850 to 2,480,000 horsepower in 1870.[6] Moreover, developments in the machine tool, chemical, and textile industries had enabled Germany to catch up with France and Belgium. The delayed industrialisation led to distinct advantages through access to mature technologies, permitting growth of large, modern enterprises that were favoured by sympathetic governments and administrations and sustained by a pool of low-cost labour. More liberal economic legislation from the 1850s facilitated the formation of industrial enterprises, especially joint-stock companies, and new types of banks, also organised on a joint-stock basis and modelled after the Crédit mobilier of France. The centres of industrialisation were the coal mines and iron works in the Ruhr area and Upper Silesia, and the textile industry in the Rhine-Main district and in Berlin. Nevertheless, and despite these advances, in 1867 more than 50 per cent of German workers were still occupied in the agrarian sector, compared with just over 25 per cent in manufacturing, and 20 per cent in the service industries.[7] The dominance of the agrarian sector was enforced through the political influence of the gentry, of which Otto von Bismarck, Chancellor and builder of the Empire, was a prominent descendant. But Bismarck and his fellow Junkers could hardly ignore the changes taking place in their midst. Engineering and chemicals were economic forces to be reckoned with, especially in areas where they converged, such as in textile production. The German chemical industry, in particular that based on coal-tar products, was about to secure for itself a unique place in the transformation of Germany society.

The German coal-tar dye industry emerged after 1860 through imitation of foreign inventions, aided by the absence of patent laws that in France and England were used to create powerful monopolies and stifle competition. Through aggressive marketing of its products, which were of good quality and keenly priced, the German dye industry achieved a number of rapid and striking successes. At the end of the 1860s, around twelve dyestuff companies existed in the various states,[8] and by the mid 1870s they had managed to control one half of the world market in synthetic colorants. Probably the first German manufacturer of synthetic dyestuffs was Karl G. R. Oehler's firm in Offenbach.[9] Oehler had purchased the coal-tar distillery of Ernst Sell in 1850, and one year later produced the yellow coal-tar dye picric acid, followed in 1860 with mauve. During the 1860s several other dye-making companies came into existence.[10] Those that flourished during the subsequent decades of intense growth were the Badische Anilin- & Soda-Fabrik (the "Badische," or BASF), of Ludwigshafen, whose forerunner was established in 1861; Hoechst, of Höchst am Main, which originally traded as Meister, Lucius & Co. (founded in 1863);[11] Farbenfabriken vorm. Friedrich Bayer & Co., of Barmen and Elberfeld (founded in 1863);[12] Kalle & Co., of Biebrich am Rhein (also founded in 1863);[13] and Gesellschaft für Anilinfabrikation, of Rummelsburg, near Berlin (1867, as manufacturer of intermediates; from 1873 also of dyestuffs, and known as AGFA).[14] Two important firms were founded in the 1870s, Frankfurter Anilinfarbenfabrik von Gans und Leonhardt, of Mainkur, near Frankfurt (1870);[15] and Farbwerke E. ter Meer, of Uerdingen (1877).[16] Most of the new companies emerged in the western parts of Germany, along the rivers Rhine and Main, that provided good transport facilities and sinks for disposal of waste. Typically, the founders of the companies were chemists and businessmen. Very often they already had experience in the processing of, and trade in, natural dyestuffs or the production of raw materials and intermediates. By the end of the 1860s academic chemists managed the production departments in most of the firms.

Late in 1866, Caro and his English-born wife made their way to Berlin, capital of the Prussian kingdom. As an accomplished chemical inventor, he was already known to the founders of pioneering German dye firms. However, he did not at first seek out a position in industry and investigated the possibility of an academic post. Early in 1867, the Caros moved on to Heidelberg, attracted by the warm climate of this city in the Grand-Duchy of Baden, and, for Heinrich, the chemical laboratory of the University of Heidelberg, then directed by Robert Bunsen. Caro's wish to enter Bunsen's laboratory was supported with a letter of recommendation from Philipp Pauli,[17] who on his return to Germany, and following the failure of his negotiations with Martius over the alkali venture, embarked on a career in the German chemical industry.[18] Caro must have had little cause to regret his departure from Manchester. The University of Heidelberg provided an atmosphere that was highly conducive to his newfound status among academic chemists. Moreover, in the 1860s Baden was renowned for its policy of encouragement of the sciences and technology. Since the revolution of 1848 the study of chemistry and its application to agriculture had received considerable emphasis.[19] Robert Bunsen's laboratory was an acknowledged leading educational centre, turning out large numbers of highly trained chemists.[20] August Kekulé, among others, had studied for his Habilitation in Heidelberg.

In the 1860s, Bunsen was one of the most celebrated of German chemists, with an international reputation. From 1859 he developed spectral analysis, jointly with the physicist Gustav Kirchhoff, and collaborated in this work with Henry Roscoe. Bunsen was aware of the significance of industrial developments on his science, and together with Kirchhoff and Roscoe had visited the Warrington factory of Roberts, Dale & Co., in 1862. Probably of greater interest to Caro than spectra were Bunsen's studies on gas analysis, first published in 1857. Though Bunsen specialised in physical and inorganic chemistry, Heidelberg also attracted young and promising organic chemists, including August Eisenlohr. Emil Erlenmeyer, an early proponent of structural chemistry, occupied a private laboratory in Heidelberg, taught chemical theory at the university, and acted as a consultant to industrial enterprises. His work had provided the experimental basis for Alfred Wanklyn's aniline violet process that was tried at Roberts, Dale & Co.[21] Caro may well have had similar plans for combining an academic career in chemistry with consultancy. Certainly, his industrial connections also kept him busy in Heidelberg. Through correspondence with British, German, and French manufacturers and agents he negotiated licensing and other arrangements for the inventions that he had patented with Dale and others.[22]

There was still much other business to be done relating to affairs in England, including the securing of patents and the matter of the Dales' litigation with Wanklyn concerning the aniline violet process.[23] In March 1867, the Dales were advised that ill health would prevent Caro from attending the court hearing in England. Their solicitor, Kershaw & Bullock, asked Caro to find a suitable advocate in Heidelberg to conduct his examination by a special commission to be sent out from England.[24] There was some considerable urgency, since the trial had been delayed for just fourteen days. Early in 1868, Caro was advised of the outcome of the trial, but from a different quarter, the phenol specialist Charles Lowe: "You will be interested to learn that Wanklyn has won his case against Messrs. Roberts, Dale & Co. with costs, damages to be assessed."[25] This was another severe blow for Roberts, Dale & Co.

Lowe and other British manufacturers made considerable efforts to maintain contact with Caro, and praised the quality of his published work on rosolic acid. From around 1867, Frederick Crace Calvert and Lowe applied the results in their factories, acknowledging Caro's contribution. Crace Calvert noted of Caro's publications: "I have read your excellent reports with great care and ... we agree and come to the same conclusion."[26] Interest in the reactions of phenol was responsible for the continued correspondence, and in March 1867, Lowe advised Caro that he was exhibiting carbolic, picric, and rosolic acids at the 1867 Paris International Exhibition. Lowe was anxious to gain Caro's assistance in finding new markets for his phenol products in Germany: "We propose establishing an agency in each of the large manufacturing districts of Germany. Can you amongst your numerous friends give us a name or two who might probably be interested to act for us."[27] Caro recommended Philipp Pauli, and Lowe responded: "I am writing to your friend Dr. Pauli. We are much obliged to you for his name."[28]

Caro's studies on the formation of rosolic acid might well have remained a mere curiosity, but for the fact that from this work, and by an accidental confluence of interests in it, he succeeded in May 1869 in resolving the main scientific problem associated with manufacture of synthetic alizarin. Moreover, it was probably in March 1867 that he communicated to Lowe details of Adolf Baeyer's new method for reducing phenol to benzene, a method that would within twelve months contribute to the elucidation of the constitution of alizarin. On 1 April 1867, Lowe replied:

> I have not heard of Baeyer's method of producing benzol [benzene] from phenol, but I have had for some time in my note book an experiment ... somewhat bearing on the point ... Try the influence of heat and zinc powder on a solution of ammoniacal gas in phenol ... I will send you a good specimen of the pure [carbolic] acid to be able to work with and should your researches lead to the discovery of any new useful colouring matter I shall be most happy to work the matter out for you practically.[29]

On 13 January 1868, Lowe provided Caro with further encouragement in the pursuit of rosolic acid-type products.

> Since the publication of your [1866] paper on rosolic acid you will be glad to know

> acting on the theory you therein developed we have much improved the quality of our aurine and altho' from mechanical causes the theoretical proportions cannot be employed yet our results show that the theory is undoubtedly correct. If you think it is worth while we will forward you a sample. We shall be glad to receive any suggestions as regards the proportions of these products and if you in the course of your researches should hit upon any new colour or other saleable products to make arrangements with you for making same.[30]

Caro's contribution to chemical theory, and its use in the improvement of manufacturing processes, having gained the acknowledgement of English dye-makers, was now to benefit German manufacturers.

Badische Anilin- & Soda-Fabrik

In order to further exploit the discoveries made in Manchester, Caro renewed contacts with the expanding German organic chemical industry. The most important firm for Caro was the Badische Anilin- & Soda-Fabrik (BASF), originally of Mannheim, Baden, on the east side of the Rhine and some 20 km from Heidelberg. Around 1865 the company was in the process of moving to Ludwigshafen, on the opposite side of the Rhine in the Bavarian Palatinate. In 1862, on his visit to Germany, Caro had become acquainted with the forerunner, Chemische Fabrik Dyckerhoff, Clemm & Comp., established in Mannheim during 1861 to manufacture aniline dyes. The partners were two merchants, Friedrich Sonntag and Otto Dyckerhoff, the chemist Carl Clemm, and the entrepreneur Friedrich Engelhorn.[31] From the start, Carl Clemm, who had studied at the Karlsruhe Polytechnic and the University of Giessen, and then engaged in fertiliser manufacture, was the technical manager of the company.[32] In 1862, his brother August Clemm joined the factory. August had a similar background in chemistry, and had been an assistant of Carl Weltzien at the Karlsruhe Polytechnic.[33] The Clemms were nephews of Carl Clemm-Lennig, who in 1851 had purchased a Leblanc alkali works near Mannheim. In 1854, at around the time he was in contact with the partners in Roberts, Dale & Co., Clemm-Lennig merged with two other firms to create Germany's main producer of heavy chemicals, the Verein Chemischer Fabriken in Mannheim. Clemm-Lennig later parted company with this concern.

In 1863, Chemische Fabrik Dyckerhoff became known as Sonntag, Engelhorn & Clemm. Since the Verein's prices were much too expensive, the partners agreed to embark on the manufacture of inorganic chemicals, which in 1865 led to the founding of the Badische Anilin- & Soda-Fabrik, a name that reflected both of its principal activities. Undoubtedly Engelhorn was the leading figure in the new concern. Born in 1821, he made his fortune as a goldsmith and jeweller prior to establishing a factory for the production of illuminating coal gas. As a result of this activity, Engelhorn, energetic and restless, but also rash and flighty, became familiar with the raw material of novel artificial dyestuffs, namely coal tar. Another incentive for the founding of the new dye-making company was probably Engelhorn's acquaintance with Rudolph Knosp, of Stuttgart, an important German sales agent, who also marketed William Henry Perkin's mauve. The site of the new company was near the rural town of Ludwigshafen, almost opposite Mannheim across the Rhine.

Ludwigshafen was founded in 1843 on the site of a Rhine redoubt, and in 1853 the village became a town, with around 1,500 inhabitants. By 1867, just two years after the establishment of BASF, there were 4,850 inhabitants. A number of factors had caused the transfer of BASF to the left bank of the Rhine, including the unfriendly behaviour of Verein Chemischer Fabriken, environmental problems (the aniline red process employed arsenic acid), and the more liberal and pro-entrepreneurial policy of the Bavarian government in providing authorisations for chemical manufacture.[34] Furthermore, Ludwigshafen had an excellent railway connection with the newly opened Ludwig Railway, from which sidings were laid down into the BASF factory. River transport had been improved in 1863 as a result of the straightening of the Rhine, as planned by the civil engineer Johann Gottfried Tulla. Close to Ludwigshafen, a bridge was constructed across the Rhine, and within a few years the town had one of the largest harbours on the German section of the Rhine.[35] Another significant factor in the re-siting of the factory was the employment situation of the inhabitants of the Palatinate. Due to overpopulation (this was one of the largest groups of Germans to emigrate, mainly to the United States, in the mid-19th century), BASF had a substantial pool of labour to hand. In addition, the wide, fast-flowing Rhine was used for waste disposal, particularly the mixtures of aromatics and arsenic compounds employed in the production of aniline dyes.

Through the support of the banker Seligmann Ladenburg, BASF was backed by one of the largest finance houses in Germany, W. H. Ladenburg Söhne, also of Mannheim.[36] From the outset, BASF was a joint-stock company, and was fully integrated. Engelhorn and the Clemm brothers produced all the inorganic chemicals and organic intermediates necessary for the manufacture of coal-tar dyestuffs, as well as the finished dyestuffs. Knosp in Stuttgart and Dahl & Co. in Barmen were the sales agencies for BASF products, and their successes were reflected in the factory's turnover, which increased from one million marks in 1865-66 to more than three million marks in 1868-69 (despite falling prices for the products), and four-and-a-half million marks in 1872-73. The massive increase in production was accompanied by a rise in the number of workers, from around 130 in 1866, to 310 in 1867, and 615 in 1872. Overall, BASF was by far the largest coal-tar dye factory in Germany. Second in size was Hoechst, which employed 250 workers in 1872; and third was Bayer, which had only 119 workers in 1875.[37] The preeminence of BASF was partly due to the fact that until the early 1880s it was the only coal-tar factory that produced synthetic dyes and the inorganic chemicals required in their manufacture.

During the critical and formative years from 1865 to 1877 the German dye firms benefited greatly from the absence of a comprehensive German patent law. Though Caro later opined that the period was marked by a "miserable and unprofitable imitative industry,"[38] this was an exaggeration influenced by his own later adherence to the patent system and his contributions towards its improvement. Imitation certainly characterized German industrial strategy in the 1860s, and was enhanced by technology transfer that was achieved through the migration of technical experts, mainly from England.

The situation at BASF was little different from elsewhere in the German coal-tar dye industry. Before 1868 there was no sign of any inventive activity. Typical of the approach to the acquisition of new knowledge was a failed attempt at industrial espionage by Carl Clemm in London during 1860 (one year before he co-founded Dyckerhoff, Clemm & Co.). Clemm was forcibly thrown out of the works of Simpson, Maule & Nicholson while attempting to acquire confidential information about the manufacture of magenta by the newly invented arsenic acid process.[39] In 1867, BASF imitated the main aniline dyestuffs, magenta (aniline red), aniline blue, and Hofmann's violets, all of which were invented in Britain and France. The situation was little different in the inorganic section. The poaching by BASF of workers with experience in the production of inorganic chemicals from rival firms was deemed a necessity, though sometimes it was costly. Thus Julius Giese, first manager of the inorganic chemicals department at

BASF, was induced to leave Verein Chemischer Fabriken in Mannheim, but Engelhorn had to pay a substantial fine since Giese had left the Verein without its approval.[40] Gradually, however, BASF came to terms with the fact that piracy was not always the most desirable course of action, nor even the most successful, though some of the partners had to be convinced of this. When, for alkali production, Engelhorn acquired a license to work a sodium and potassium carbonate manufacturing process invented by Heinrich Keßler, he covered the expense of the first trials out of his own pocket.[41] Only later did BASF agree to reimburse him the cost of this exercise.[42] In 1868, negotiations were completed with Jean Théodore Coupier for operation of his distillation apparatus that separated aniline and toluidine,[43] and his nitrobenzene process for the production of aniline red.[44] The latter overcame the use of the toxic arsenic acid, and disposal of its waste. In the same year another arsenic acid-free manufacturing process for aniline red was offered to BASF by J. J. Müller-Pack, whose own business in Basel had collapsed because of well contamination from releases at one of his two factories.[45] Aniline dye production at BASF was extended to methyl green and safranine dyes, the latter developed for the firm by Félix Duprey, a French expert.[46]

Since the development of new products and processes was not carried out at BASF prior to 1868, there was no perceived requirement for research facilities at Mannheim or Ludwigshafen. Carl and August Clemm, the firm's chemists, were responsible only for the works management, and not for invention and innovation.[47] They acquired knowledge and technical know-how through licensing arrangements, imitation, espionage, and a network of technical experts. Heinrich Caro impressed the Clemms and partners more than any other of their experts. They also realised that his rich experience in the English dye industry was a tremendous asset.

In the summer of 1867, Caro came to an arrangement with BASF over the recipes for three colorants–phenylene brown, naphthalene yellow, and induline–that he had developed in Manchester, jointly with Martius. The agreement stipulated that Caro was to receive a ten per cent share of the profits or a two per cent share of turnover, according to the level of sales. Furthermore, in return for a payment of 500 guilders, he agreed not to make his recipes available to any other German dyestuff producer. BASF also agreed to purchase the German rights to Caro's future inventions.[48] His

Friedrich Engelhorn (1821-1902), the energetic and tireless entrepreneur who led BASF for almost two decades from 1865. (BASF Archives.)

Carl Clemm (1836-99), co-founder of BASF, head of the workshops, and after 1871 technical director of the inorganic department. He retired in 1883. (BASF Archives.)

August Clemm (1837-1910), co-founder of BASF and first technical director of the dye manufacturing departments. He retired in 1882. (BASF Archives.)

The first train to cross the new bridge across the Rhine, at Ludwigshafen station, 25 February 1867. (BASF Archives.)

Ludwigshafen in 1869. The bridge across the Rhine is at lower left, and Ludwigshafen and the BASF factory at right, on the west bank. (BASF Archives.)

relationship with BASF was, as an independent consultant, not untypical of the time. In general, a consultant would develop new processes and products, sell the recipes and other details, and move on when the work was done, or when other, more lucrative, opportunities became available. In the case of Caro, however, there was to be no parting of ways. In November 1868, following the proven successes of his inventions, he accepted the post of a deputy, or joint managing, technical director at BASF, equivalent to the positions held by Carl and August Clemm, and with an annual income of 2,000 guilders. Caro also received a royalty based on the profits of the company, and a special royalty of five per cent on any cost-saving process improvements that he introduced.[49] According to the original contractual agreement

> Mr. H. Caro is to undertake, in particular, tasks in the laboratory that are necessary from both a theoretical and practical point of view–but he is obliged to manage production departments (especially in the aniline line of business), if it is necessary, because of travel, death, illness or other disruptive causes.[50]

The inclusion "from both a theoretical and practical point of view" affords clear evidence of the level to which academic chemistry had made inroads, and in particular through Caro, into the practice of industrial organic chemistry. This is the first formal document that assigned a research function to a technical director. Indeed, in accord with this clause in the contract, Caro soon invented in his laboratory at BASF a new dyestuff, Palatine orange, the product of the reaction of nitric acid on benzidine (itself made from nitrobenzene).[51] Moreover, with this document, science-based industry had been formalised.

In addition, Caro, jointly with the Clemm brothers and Engelhorn, in 1869 filed a British patent for obtaining benzene and other hydrocarbons from coal gas by extraction with high-boiling oils, followed by distillation and recovery of the solvents.[52] In Prussia, the patent application for the same process was rejected. The development of this extraction process was based on investigations Caro had made in Manchester not long after John Leigh demonstrated his method of extracting benzene. In the winter of 1868-69, a modification designed by Caro was introduced that later enabled the development of solvent-based extractions of benzene from coal gas and also brought about a considerable fall in the price of benzene. In the 1880s, it formed the basis of the successful extraction of benzene during coke production, thereby reducing German dependency on British supplies.

Within a year of joining BASF, Caro was provided with an opportunity for demonstrating that he was thoroughly adept in dealing with academic chemists working at the cutting edge of their science, and in adapting their practical and theoretical chemistry to useful inventions. Indeed, Caro's genius at combining science, technology, and the law would find its greatest and most enduring expression in his work on the industrial synthesis of alizarin, the dyestuff of the madder root. This work commenced early in 1869 and lasted, with interruptions, until the end of 1876. During 1873-74, it took on a distinctly academic aspect.

It was on the strength of his successes with alizarin during the spring and summer of 1869 that in July of that year Caro negotiated with Friedrich Engelhorn a royalty agreement on the alizarin, Palatine orange, and benzene-from-coal gas processes, and also on future inventions, that gave him a five per cent royalty on new inventions. An important outcome was that the new arrangement became valid for all technical directors, and the royalties were to be shared equally among them. The same provision applied to all inventions made by any one of them after the date of the agreement.[53] The implications were enormous. By personally initiating the steps leading to the royalty agreement, Caro was responsible for elevating the business of, and rewards for, chemical invention to new levels in Germany. His motivation was the type of arrangement earlier negotiated in England with Roberts, Dale & Co., and directed towards the exploitation and discovery of useful processes and products, though then there was no emphasis on theoretical studies. By the late 1860s, however, and as Caro demonstrated, the theoretical aspect was beginning to take on a new, and industrially relevant, meaning.

Ironically, and soon after completing these negotiations, Caro's creativity as an inventor became almost completely blocked, and was to remain so until 1873. In part this was because immediately following his discovery of a viable process for the production of alizarin he became so preoccupied with the technical development of this difficult reaction that he had no time for new inventions. Nevertheless, during 1870 he also undertook work on the production of chloral hydrate (an anaesthetic and hypnotic), the dyeing properties of the indulines, and research into chrysaniline (phosphine, a by-product of the synthesis of magenta), as well as analysis of a rival product known as "Aecht Scharlach."[54] One area of activity, however, had enormous implications for academic chemistry, a return in 1870 to the rosolic acid work.[55] This was because Caro's new situation at BASF allowed him to pursue more fundamental studies, particularly if they held out possibilities for new industrial discoveries. Accordingly, he collaborated with the academic inventors of the alizarin process, Carl Liebermann and Carl Graebe, on research that did not result in immediate useful inventions but certainly did enhance his standing among academics.[56]

Caro's contributions to the profitability of BASF encouraged him to negotiate for, and probably acquire, shares in BASF during 1873.[57] His alizarin synthesis had already laid the foundations for the future development of the company, and no doubt his newly acquired wealth, tied to the performance and assets of BASF, helped to ensure that his subsequent discoveries and inventions would be more closely connected to the firm's needs.

The technical development of the alizarin synthesis was one of the most important scientific-technical innovations of the 1870s, and certainly the most important innovation at BASF. It enabled the rapid changeover from England to Germany as the leading nation in the field of synthetic dyestuffs. It was also to become the model for the future relationship between science and technology, especially after the mid-1870s, from which time sales of artificial alizarin accounted for more than half of BASF turnover. Because of this, the background behind the industrial manufacture of alizarin at BASF deserves close scrutiny.

The alizarin synthesis

That the highly competitive business of alizarin was greatly dependent upon intensive and ongoing laboratory research extending over several years was made abundantly clear by Engelhorn in an 1876 memorandum to the BASF sales agency in New York:

> For the manufacturer of alizarin, the optimisation derives from two things: 1) as perfect as possible products; and 2) minimal manufacturing costs. Concerning the first point it is necessary to produce all dyestuffs that occur in the manufacture of artificial alizarin so that they are as pure as possible. ... More than 100 chemists (and certainly not the worst ones) are trying to outdo each other and the whole development of this industry stands without comparison, and with the help of the most complex chemical processes it will finally succeed.[58]

Progress depended on the availability of more "refined" raw materials and intermediates, and advanced manufacturing processes that gave better quality products and optimum yields. This, as Engelhorn recorded with obvious pride, was being realised after considerable scientific and technical efforts by Caro and colleagues.

But minimal manufacturing costs and, therefore, economic success was also a question of scale, and not necessarily of the very best quality product, as was made clear in the reminiscences of Carl Glaser:

> Engelhorn always advised me when new manufacturing equipment was installed, to think about the challenge, how to manufacture twenty times the quantity, and always to bear in mind that alizarin is a large-volume product that would be sent away in goods wagons. It was not the purest product that was important, but comparatively the cheapest, and our aim should be to dominate the market by production of immense quantities.[59]

The endeavour aimed at achieving these economies of scale and scope had commenced just seven years before Engelhorn made his confident pronouncements. The success of the alizarin synthesis changed not only the structure and the strategies of BASF, but also of the entire German chemical industry. Moreover, the technical development of alizarin brought rapid international fame to Caro during his early years at BASF.[60] Alizarin was to become the outstanding example of the complexity and success of the science-technology relationship in 19th-century chemistry.[61]

Caro's own involvement with alizarin had begun long before he joined BASF. In Mülheim during the 1850s he had worked with the natural dyestuff of the madder root and no doubt became aware of the many attempts to determine its constitution, all of which, before the late 1860s, failed. The puzzle posed by alizarin was finally solved at the institution where Caro had studied in Berlin, the Gewerbeinstitut (from 1866 the Gewerbeakademie). There were two main figures, Carl Graebe and Carl Liebermann, both chemists with rich experience, not only in the textile and allied chemical industries, but also in the most modern organic chemistry of the time, based on the benzene theory put forward during 1865-66 by August Kekulé, then professor of chemistry at the University of Ghent in Belgium.[62]

Kekulé had extended his 1858 structure theory for aliphatic compounds to the chemistry of the so-called aromatic compounds. The latter, with benzene as the "mother-substance," possessed a high carbon-to-hydrogen ratio. In this they were similar to unsaturated aliphatic compounds, but exhibited totally different chemical behaviour, particularly great stability. To overcome this anomaly, Kekulé proposed a closed chain of six carbon atoms, with each carbon bonded to a hydrogen atom, expressed in his first publication on the topic by so-called sausage formulae. Subsequently he introduced the modern hexagon ring formula for benzene and the concept of alternating single and double bonds between the carbons in the ring. Kekulé's benzene theory was accepted by almost all chemists within a decade, and became the foundation of the greatest part of classical organic chemistry during the 19th century.[63] Nevertheless, support for the benzene ring theory had at first to await the establishment of sufficient, and corroborative, experimental data based particularly on isomerism, the chemistry of fused rings and, later, heteroaromatic compounds (that contain elements other than carbon in the ring structure, especially nitrogen, oxygen, and sulphur).[64] Invariably, historical accounts have described the verification of Kekulé's theory mainly within the academic context and afforded prominence to the fact that scientific theories, in this case the structural chemistry of aromatic substances, were behind technical innovations, above all dyestuffs and pharmaceuticals.[65] It is certainly true that much of the empirical testing of Kekulé's theories was undertaken at universities. But there is another side to the story, namely the role of industrial chemistry in bringing about the rapid acceptance of structural theory. This came about in three ways: through the collaboration of academic chemists with industry; through research done in industrial laboratories; and, above all, through the tremendous success of structural theory in enabling the invention and development of coal-tar products, the dyestuffs, their intermediates, and pharmaceuticals. Successful industrial chemistry confirmed the validity of a scientific theory. The starting point was alizarin, and the place the Gewerbeakademie in Berlin where, since October 1860, Adolf Baeyer was lecturer in organic chemistry and director of the new organic chemical laboratory.

The Gewerbeakademie, because of the then great interest in the industrial application of natural products, provided an ideal environment for Baeyer's research, which in the 1860s was mainly related to the chemistry of uric acid and indigo. His uric acid studies were the outcome of investigations into the murexide purple dyestuff started by the calico printer Adolph Schlieper, of Elberfeld.[66] Baeyer's indigo work began in 1865 and at the end of the following year he achieved the difficult conversion of oxindole, a degradation product of indigo, to indole, using zinc dust for the

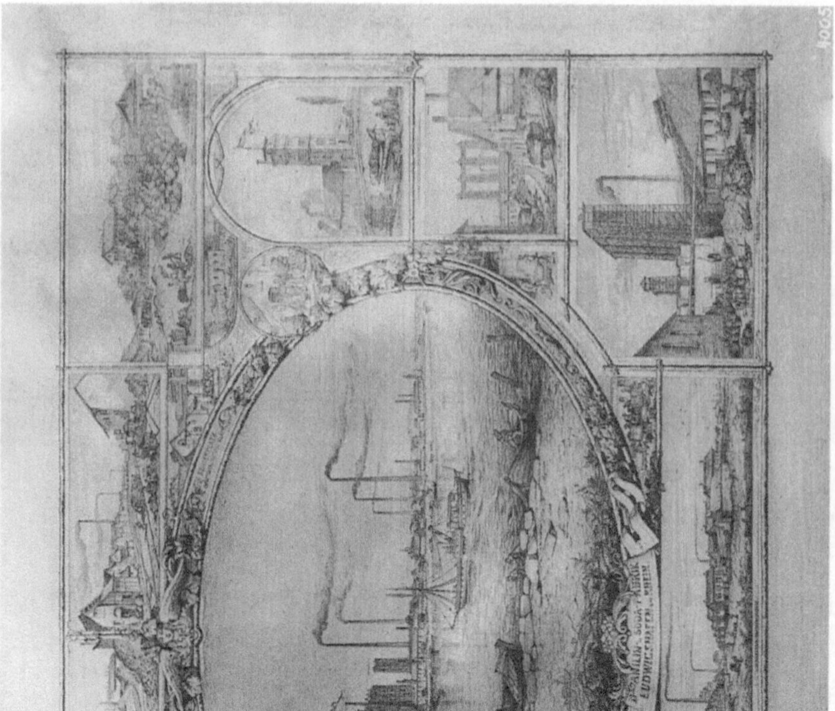

View of the BASF factory in 1873, seen from the opposite side of the Rhine. The insets show the various inorganic manufacturing facilities and workshops of BASF. Drawn by Karl Jauslin. (BASF Archives.)

Typical primitive works laboratory in the early days of BASF at Ludwigshafen. (BASF Archives.)

Detail of the so-called acid square (Säure Platz) at BASF. In the foreground are glass jars (carboys) for storage of hydrochloric acid, by-product of the Leblanc process for manufacture of soda. To the left is part of the sulphuric acid plant. (BASF Archives.)

reductive distillation. This reaction method was suggested by Johann Carl Friedrich Stahlschmidt, from 1860 until 1870 Baeyer's colleague at the Gewerbeakademie, and deputy director of the organic chemical laboratory.[67] Stahlschmidt specialised in technical chemistry, and with this background he was aware of the potential of reductions with zinc dust, as used in industrial chemistry since the 1850s.[68] In 1866, the year in which Baeyer successfully employed the zinc reduction, Emil Erlenmeyer in Heidelberg made what would be another critical contribution to the alizarin story. He suggested how Kekulé's benzene ring theory could be related to larger, and related, aromatic hydrocarbons when he drew naphthalene as two fused rings.[69] Shortly afterwards, the significance of this was picked up by Carl Graebe, a former collaborator of Erlenmeyer and now an assistant of Baeyer at the Gewerbeakademie in Berlin.

Since the topics explored in Baeyer's laboratory were in part related to the practical application of science, Graebe studied the reactions of phthalic acid–the oxidation product of both naphthalene and alizarin–almost certainly because the researches of Julius Wolff and Adolph Strecker had suggested that alizarin was a derivative of naphthalene.[70] Accordingly, Graebe wisely embarked on a research topic that was important to industry, as well as of great academic interest. He focused on quinones, compounds that were found to have chemical properties similar to those of alizarin. Beside their potential industrial significance, quinones posed interesting structural questions that were related closely to the establishment of Kekulé's benzene theory.[71] Based on the outcomes of these investigations, Graebe and his colleague Carl Liebermann early in 1868 used Baeyer's zinc dust method to establish that alizarin was a derivative of anthracene, and not, as previously believed, of naphthalene. Following Erlenmeyer's fused ring structure for naphthalene, they proposed a structure of three fused aromatic rings for the fourteen-carbon anthracene. They soon established that alizarin was a dihydroxyanthraquinone. A three-step synthesis of alizarin from anthracene was achieved at the end of 1868, and involved the oxidation of anthracene to anthraquinone with nitric acid, bromination of the quinone, and displacement of the two bromine atoms by hydroxyl groups with boiling potassium hydroxide solution. Though this synthetic pathway had a low yield, and bromine was an expensive commercial product, for the first time a complex natural product of enormous economic value had been created in the laboratory. The two inventors embarked on patent protection in Europe, most especially in France, Great Britain, and Prussia.

After abandoning plans to establish manufacturing facilities on their own, Graebe and Liebermann decided to sell the rights to their invention. English as well as German companies were approached, and it was possibly from the negotiations with Perkin & Sons that William Perkin was alerted to the fact that alizarin was an anthracene derivative. There was also contact with the calico printer Edmund Potter & Co., no doubt through Henry Roscoe, who was married to the youngest daughter (Lucy Potter) of the proprietor, and perhaps even with Roberts, Dale & Co. However, these came to nothing, though Schorlemmer immediately investigated alizarin for Roberts, Dale & Co.

Graebe and Liebermann rejected an offer from Hoechst (where Graebe had been employed prior to joining Baeyer), which was prepared to pay a percentage of profits, not of turnover, as the academic inventors had demanded. After extended negotiations, BASF finally took up the process. The connection with BASF had come about through Liebermann's father, who was a good friend of Heinrich Caro. On 29 May 1869, Graebe and Liebermann agreed to hand over patent rights to BASF in exchange for a fourteen-year contract that would provide the inventors with three per cent of the turnover on alizarin sales. As part of the contractual arrangements, the two inventors agreed to assist the company with the technical development.[72] For this purpose, Carl Graebe was to work with Caro at BASF in Ludwigshafen and Mannheim during the summer of 1869.[73]

One reaction seemed to be critical for the technical success: The sulphonation (replacement of hydrogen by the sulphonic acid group) of anthraquinone. Since this reaction required only sulphuric acid, it would overcome problems associated with the great expense of bromine, and also, hopefully, the low yield of the bromine route. In 1867, Kekulé and Adolphe Wurtz had independently described a similar sulphonation reaction, using benzene. The product, on hydrolysis, then afforded phenol.[74] Graebe and Liebermann found during their earlier research in Berlin that in the case of anthraquinone this did not work, but they agreed while completing negotiations with BASF to pursue the topic further jointly with Caro.[75] It was probably in May 1869 that Caro independently achieved the critical sulphonation of anthraquinone when he applied the same reaction conditions–heating with a mixture of sulphuric and oxalic acids–that he had used for formation of rosolic acid at Roberts, Dale & Co.[76] Caro's

Adolf Baeyer (standing, second from left) and assistants at the Gewerbeakademie, Berlin, ca. 1868. Seated are Carl Graebe (at left) and Carl Liebermann (at right). (Deutsches Museum.)

Carl Glaser (1841-1935), probably mid-mid-1880s, when he was, with Heinrich Caro, a member of the BASF board. (BASF Archives.)

sulphonation worked not because of the presence of the oxalic acid, which was actually superfluous, but because he allowed the temperature to rise above 200°C, conditions that were never tried by Graebe and Liebermann. As a result, Caro gained credit as co-inventor, which also entitled him to a share of the profits, though this was not to the liking of the two academic inventors.[77] They soon had to accept, however, that the technically feasible reaction had become available only as a result of Caro's discovery. Caro's improvement became the basis of new patent applications bearing the names of Caro, Graebe, and Liebermann, and filed in London and Berlin. The timing of patent filing was critical, since almost simultaneously Ferdinand Riese at Hoechst and William Perkin in London succeeded in mastering the sulphonation of anthraquinone, both probably drawing on information gleaned from the patentees during earlier negotiations. Hoechst did not file a patent, but registered its invention on 19 May at the Höchst magistrate's office, in the form of a *pli cacheté*.

The British patent application of Perkin was filed in London on 26 June, just one day after the British patent of Caro, Graebe, and Liebermann arrived at the patent office.[78] This close timing was a source of potential conflict between Perkin and BASF, and was soon aggravated by the fact that Perkin's patent was sealed in August 1869, at which time the Germans had not yet completed their specification. The two firms were brought together through the help of Hugo Müller, and the outcome was a contract between Perkin and BASF for division of most of the international market in artificial alizarin.[79] Perkin and BASF maintained a joint monopoly in Britain, while BASF controlled most of mainland Europe, the United States, and elsewhere.[80]

This complex background may explain why Caro alone later sought full credit for the discovery of the sulphonation of anthraquinone, and, in order to do so, he suggested that it was an invention he was not able to foresee. This is in accord with the fact that the surviving accounts of Caro's achievement, based on his own reminiscences, stress the strong element of serendipity in his discovery and the inspiration of his earlier work in Manchester.[81] Nevertheless, a single item of correspondence from Liebermann to Caro shows that the sulphonation was investigated as part of the common research programme agreed between Caro, Graebe, and Liebermann during May 1869.[82] Heinrich Caro was fortunate that he was the first to succeed, which not only enabled him to participate in the patent and royalty arrangements, but, perhaps more importantly, also provided him with a strong personal incentive to ensure that those arrangements were made concrete, especially through the English patent. This is where Graebe and Liebermann, and the principles of BASF (apart from Caro) and Hoechst, lacked sufficient experience and knowledge of the English patent system.

The English patent became even more critical after BASF was refused the Prussian patent for the sulphonation process, because, according to the interpretation of the patent officers, the description was too close to the original Graebe and Liebermann patent to suggest any originality. As a consequence of this decision, there was no monopoly for the manufacture of alizarin by sulphonation of anthraquinone in Prussia, the largest and economically the strongest of the German states. At this time, in June 1869, Caro had already prepared a design for the technical synthesis of alizarin. Graebe's correspondence with Liebermann described progress at BASF, though his optimism was tempered with an equal measure of pessimism. In particular, Graebe was highly critical of Caro, who refused to apply his full energies to the development work until he received a guarantee of a more substantial share of the anticipated profits.[83]

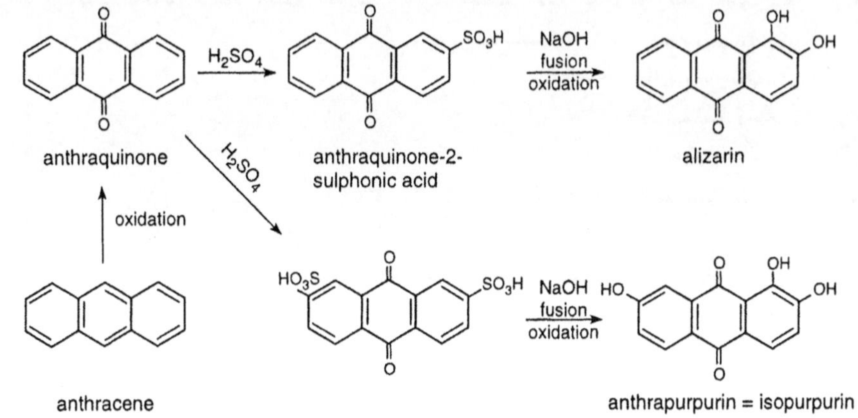

Manufacture of alizarin and the hydroxyanthraquinone anthrapurpurin (modern formulae)

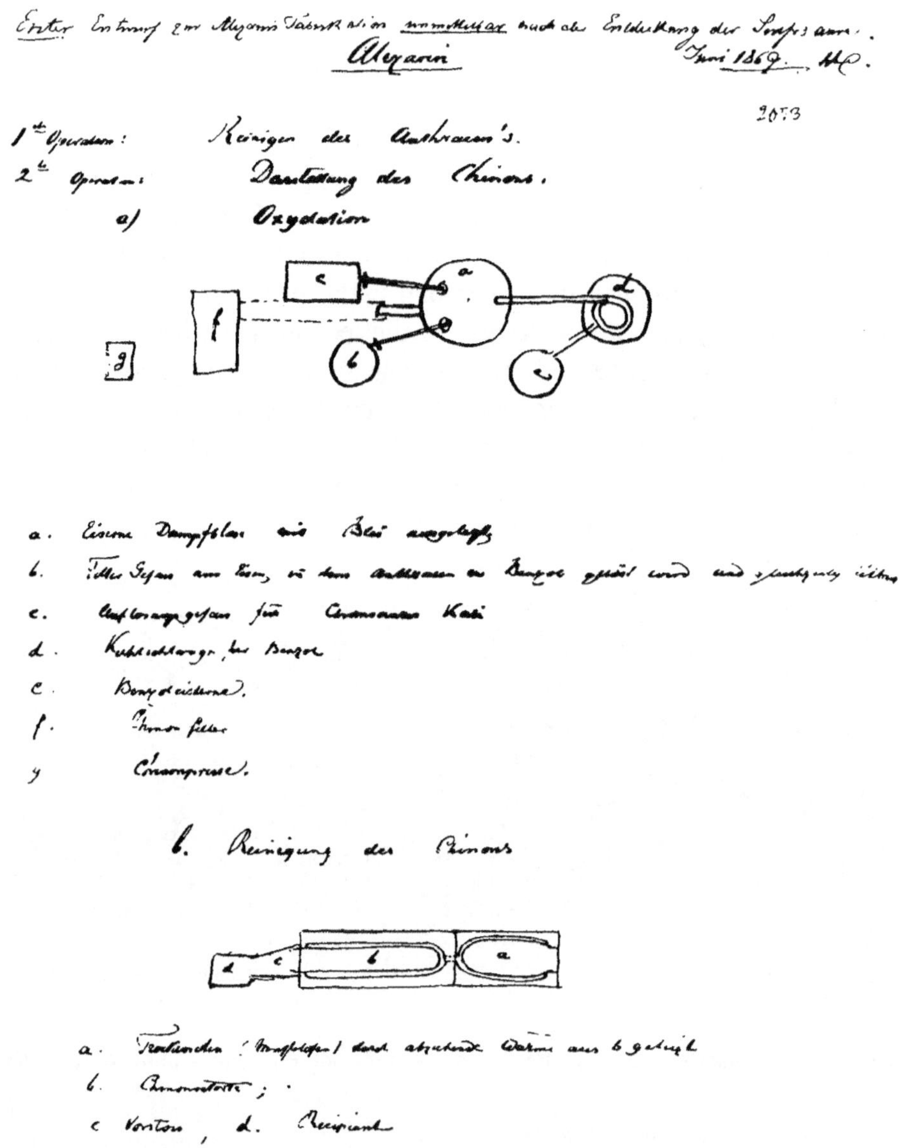

Page from Heinrich Caro's notes on the manufacture of alizarin, June 1869. (Deutsches Museum.)

From a technical point of view, the years 1869 and 1870 were not very successful for the alizarin synthesis at BASF. Besides difficulties created and experienced by Caro in 1869, he and Graebe put much effort into developing the technically worthless alizarin synthesis based on bromine, mostly for reasons of securing strong patent protection for the original patent.[84] Moreover, and unlike at Perkin & Sons and Hoechst, investigations into the manufacturing process employing the sulphonation of anthraquinone were not tackled seriously prior to the spring of 1870. Thus Perkin, Hoechst, and Gebrüder Gessert (of Elberfeld) were far more advanced in the production of good quality alizarin, and were able to deliver substantial amounts of the dye during the latter part of 1869.

In the summer of 1869, Engelhorn had agreed to allocate 10,000 guilders for the combined development of manufacturing processes for alizarin, induline, and Palatine orange.[85] Though this was a very substantial sum, it was not sufficient. It is apparent that Engelhorn, the Clemm brothers, and Caro severely underestimated the enormous difficulties that they would soon confront. In the autumn, shortly after Graebe had returned to his academic post, his place was taken by Carl Glaser, a former assistant of Kekulé in Ghent. In 1868 Glaser had followed Kekulé to Bonn, where he took his Habilitation, and was one of the closest collaborators of Kekulé during the years crucial to the development of the benzene theory. Glaser had studied for his doctorate under Adolph Strecker in Tübingen, and worked on the synthesis of alizarin from naphthalene, and therefore had good experience in alizarin chemistry. Glaser was, therefore, an ideal candidate for taking on the difficult job of the alizarin synthesis, though for a short time at first he was assigned to the development of the manufacturing processes for the more minor products induline and Palatine orange. In this connection he was also well qualified, since he had worked on azobenzene. Glaser was not looking for an industrial post, but his friendship with Graebe, and a visit to his sisters in Mannheim, brought him to BASF at an opportune moment.

Glaser and Caro were transferred from Ludwigshafen to the old manufacturing department of BASF in Mannheim, for reasons of both secrecy and the need to work in a well equipped laboratory, which was set up under the instructions of Glaser.[86] During the first half of 1870, as a result of the agreements with Perkin, there was close technical and scientific cooperation between BASF and Perkin's firm, which was more advanced in engineering technology.[87] BASF now benefited considerably from the experience of its English partner. Indeed, Glaser in his memoirs drew attention to the great difficulties confronted by BASF in acquiring the necessary engineering know-how, which had not been the case in Britain, at least at Perkin & Sons.[88]

Scaling up: Manufacture of alizarin begins

It was only towards the end of 1871 that BASF was capable of producing alizarin at levels similar to its German competitors and Perkin & Sons. Even then, it took until 1876 before all difficulties were finally overcome. To understand the reasons for this astonishing delay, despite the fact that at BASF two highly experienced chemists, Caro and Glaser, with the help of the academic inventors, were involved in research and development, it is necessary to consider the somewhat complex technology and chemistry of the separations and reactions.[89] As a result of this, and of the delay at BASF, there was to be one positive outcome. BASF chemists and their academic collaborators made important new theoretical contributions to the chemistry of alizarin and its derivatives.

When Glaser began to work with Caro on the alizarin synthesis in the spring of 1870, the first challenge was to purify the raw material, anthracene. This was extracted from the residue of pitch delivered from British, French, and German coal-tar distilleries. Caro had visited England late in 1869 to meet up with Perkin and discuss business matters, and travelled to firms who were working on the distillation of pitch for obtaining anthracene. These included Thomas & Henry Metcalf of Manchester.[90] However, the purity of the anthracene was perhaps no more than twenty per cent, at least before the mid 1870s, when a percentage of fifty was achieved. During the first half of 1870, the period of closest technical cooperation between BASF and Perkin, Caro made another visit to London, probably in order to examine the Perkin & Sons plant, and sent to Glaser some highly purified anthracene. The Perkin brothers distilled impure anthracene with potassium hydroxide to obtain a good feedstock for their alternative route to an alizarin product, which began with chlorination of anthracene. Glaser and Caro managed to repeat the success of their British colleagues in purifying anthracene, despite engineering difficulties.

Distillation of the anthracene with alkali, however, was far too expensive to become the starting point for the BASF sulphonation route. It was later used for the production of the so-called alizarin R (a BASF brand mark), a highly purified dyestuff that afforded reddish-blue shades when dyed or printed. For this purpose, BASF used the chlorination route invented by Perkin.[91] In the commercially more important sulphonation process, anthracene was mixed with petroleum spirit and pressed. The resulting mixture, containing about 40 to 50 per cent of anthracene, was purified by sublimation with water vapour or superheated steam.[92] The next step was oxidation of the anthracene to anthraquinone with potassium dichromate. That was straightforward, and resulted in a product of around 95 per cent purity. The quinone was then sulphonated. During 1870, several chemists, including Caro, Glaser, and their academic counterparts Graebe and Liebermann, found that sulphonation resulted in a mixture of monosulphonic and disulphonic acids of anthraquinone. They mistakenly believed that both the mono- and disulphonic acids of anthraquinone yielded the same product, alizarin. This was based on analogy with the fusion of the monosulphonic acid derivative of benzene with alkali, which gave phenol. Accordingly, BASF chemists did not bother to separate the mixed sulphonic acids prior to commencing the alkali fusion that brought about hydroxylation to afford alizarin. On a laboratory scale, Caro and Glaser used small open silver pans for the fusion, with considerable success, but when they changed to a pilot-plant scale, the end product was a very impure alizarin. It was not then known that hydroxylation was both a substitution of one sulphonic acid group and the oxidative introduction of a second hydroxyl group, brought about either in the presence of air or an oxidising agent. The amount of atmospheric oxygen present on the pilot-plant scale of working was insufficient to bring about completion of the reaction.

The competitors of BASF, above all Hoechst and Gebrüder Gessert, through empirical studies overcame the difficulties much earlier.[93] From the moment when, early in 1871, BASF realised that these firms produced good-quality alizarin, Caro and Glaser began to devise a fusion process that took place in trays, most probably imitating a similar arrangement developed at Hoechst. The delicate and difficult fusion required highly trained workers whose job it was to maintain the correct temperature and operating time.[94] With this procedure, which was in use by the end of 1871,[95] BASF manufactured alizarin that was commercially competitive until the mid-1870s. In 1872 or 1873, an alizarin department devoted to improvements in large-scale production was created, and managed by Glaser.

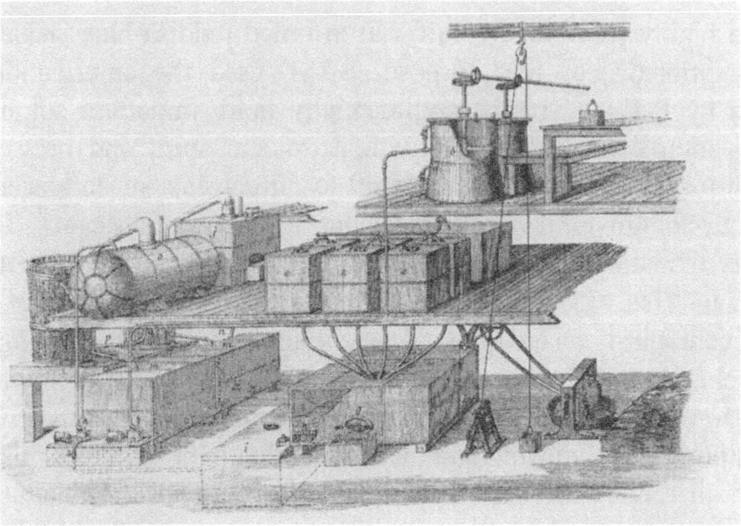

Purification of anthracene (top) and fusion of sulphonated anthraquinone with alkali (bottom), the first and final stages in the manufacture of alizarin as carried out at Perkin & Sons, Greenford Green, near London. During 1869 and 1870, Heinrich Caro visited the Perkin factory and received technical information about these and other alizarin-related processes that was put to good use at Ludwigshafen. (William H. Perkin, *The History of Alizarin and Allied Colouring Matters and Their Production from Coal-Tar* [London: Printed by William Trounce, 1879], figures 1 and 7.)

Caro, however, remained assigned to laboratory work, most likely because that was his wish.

It was probably in 1872 that BASF chemists managed to separate the salts of the mono- and disulphonic acids of anthraquinone. On cooling down the boiling reaction mixture, the sodium salt of the 2-monosulphonic acid precipitated out first, and because of the appearance of the small crystals was called silver-salt. After fusion with alkali the silver-salt yielded alizarin, called by BASF alizarin V 1. The disulphonic acids resulted in a mixture of anthra- and flavopurpurin (both trihydroxy compounds), named alizarin V 3. The dyestuff made from the unseparated salts was called alizarin V 2. Thus, including alizarin R, BASF had on offer at least four different kinds of alizarin in 1873, which was probably a greater range than any of its competitors. Further advances took place during 1874 and 1875, following the merger of BASF with Rudolph Knosp and Heinrich Siegle, both of Stuttgart. The now greatly expanded BASF assigned additional chemists to the alizarin department to assist Glaser. The outcomes were various advances in production processes, most notably purification of anthracene and production of alizarin R. Anthracene purification was achieved by Sigmund Vischer, previously a chemist at Siegle. An improved alizarin R process was due to the efforts of Heinrich Appenzeller, formerly at Bindschedler & Busch of Basel. For the first time, and for production of alizarin R, BASF employed an oxidising agent, saltpetre (potassium nitrate), in the alkali fusion step. Later it was learned by Glaser from a former employee of Gebrüder Gessert that the oxidant prevented reversible reactions. Gessert (which around 1873 was acquired by Bayer)[96] used potassium chlorate in stirred pressure vessels. After Glaser was advised of the importance of adding oxidant, he immediately realised why BASF had been unable to optimise the fusion step for its various alizarin products. The result of this was that from 1876, BASF employed a production process that rivaled those of other firms, both in respect to quality and quantity.[97] The success of BASF in alizarin manufacture from the mid-1870s is demonstrated in Table 1.

The scale of output ensured the firm's overriding economic muscle as a founding member of the Alizarine Convention in 1881, from which time eight companies, seven German and one British, agreed to share the market and fix prices.[98] Despite all the progress in understanding the alizarin process, manufacture required great skill and care, particularly when carried out under pressure. This made it necessary to use equipment that could be worked safely. The dangers inherent in early alizarin manufacture were highlighted in Glaser's reminiscences, where he described how on 15 August 1878 a pressure vessel used in the alkali fusion process exploded and was cut in two pieces. Though Glaser, Appenzeller, and one worker were nearby, they escaped unharmed.[99] An investigation into the causes of this accident revealed that Carl Clemm, who was responsible for the acquisition of apparatus at BASF, had bargained over the price with the supplier of the reaction vessels, and, as a result of the lower price that was agreed upon, iron of inferior quality was used in their construction.

Table 1. Production of alizarin at BASF, 1870-1888 (in tons, 100%)[100]

Year	BASF	Year	BASF
1870	Ca. 0.25	1880	280
1871	2.2	1881	323
1872	7.7	1882	411
1873	13	1883	305
1874	45	1884	437
1875	94	1885	531
1876	137	1886	603
1877	225	1887	681
1878	296	1888	788
1879	208		

Technology and science

The foregoing account makes clear that the industrial alizarin synthesis owed much of its success to enhanced knowledge about the constitutions and structures of organic substances. But as much as science contributed to the progress of industry, so too did technology decisively influence the course of theoretical chemistry. The key figures in this transfer of knowledge were Carl Graebe, during 1870-75 at the University of Königsberg (Prussia) and after 1878 at the University of Geneva (Switzerland), and Heinrich Caro.[101] Until 1876, Graebe had a tight contractual commitment with BASF, and even after the termination of this contract, he, along with Liebermann, agreed to support BASF "with advice and information."[102] After 1876, however, there was probably no specific arrangement with BASF that prevented Graebe from working with other firms. Indeed, he had contacts with many German, Swiss, and French dyestuff producers. Nevertheless, BASF was his preferred partner, and both he and his client profited from this collaboration.[103] A most important aspect of this relationship between science and industry was the supply by the Luwigshafen factory of chemical substances to the academic chemist, and their confidential investigation by the chemist for the benefit of the factory. Industry thus gained through its access to a strong theoretical foundation for existing manufacturing processes, as well as to potentially useful new products and processes. Moreover, dye companies increasingly used academic institutions as external laboratories, both for analysis and synthesis, and, prior to the establishment of industrial research and development laboratories, they depended to a considerable extent on academic assistance. In this way the academic chemist profited from access to chemicals that were rare, completely new or expensive, and, in particular, often difficult to synthesize. He also profited financially if his discoveries led to industrially useful products. Leading academic chemists were thus enabled to assign to their doctoral candidates a wide range of research topics based on industrial problem-solving, as well as opportunities for employment in the expanding dye industry. For this the academic chemist was more than willing to surrender a part of his independence, and even accepted self-censorship and non-disclosure conditions dictated by his industrial sponsors.

An outstanding example of this type of relationship was the investigation of new products found in crude anthracene. It was sold as an oil, a partially refined residue of pitch, and contained many impurities. Glaser and Caro discovered three hitherto unknown substances in the anthracene oil, and Graebe was their academic collaborator in characterization and elucidation of structural formulae. These substances were acridine, carbazole, and phenanthrene. Acridine and carbazole belong to the so-called heteroaromatic substances, and contain nitrogen atoms in their ring structures. The former was discovered by Caro in crude anthracene in 1870 and isolated in an impure form.[104] He assigned the task of structural elucidation to Graebe and together they chose the name acridine because of the itching and inflammatory properties of the new compound (acriter = sharp, strong, acrid, painful). Since established degradation reactions, such as the distillation with zinc dust, did not yield identifiable products, Caro and Graebe had to rely on derivatives of acridine and their properties in order to characterize the new compound. They made an erroneous assumption concerning the number of carbon atoms, which led them to believe that acridine was an isomer of carbazole, isolated from the residue of anthracene purification by Carl Glaser in 1871. Investigations into acridine were continued at the end of the 1870s after new dyestuff inventions suggested that acridine might be of interest as a raw material for dyes and pharmaceuticals. Thus, Graebe and Caro established that quinoline-2,3-dicarbonic acid was a degradation product of acridine and, following Baeyer's 1879 structural elucidation of quinoline (a nitrogen-containing aromatic compound with a naphthalene-like structure), it was possible to arrive at a probable structure of acridine. But the wrong elemental analysis–which gave twelve carbon atoms for acridine instead of thirteen–still prevented complete structural elucidation, despite the involvement of both Baeyer and Graebe. The correct structure became available only in 1883 when BASF chemist Carl Riedel published an account based on his previous work at the University of Munich.[105] He had established the relationships between acridine, quinoline, and pyridine, and opened the way to the synthesis of acridine, accomplished independently in 1883 by August Bernthsen and Otto Fischer. Competition among the academic chemists in these studies became so intense that Caro–in one case at least–was obliged to act as mediator between Bernthsen and Graebe.[106] Here, it was Caro's prerogative to decide who investigated and published on a specific scientific question.

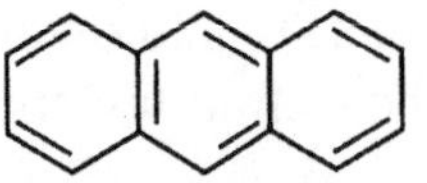
anthracene

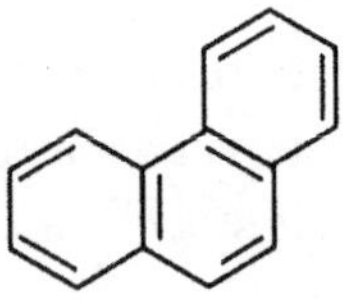
phenanthrene

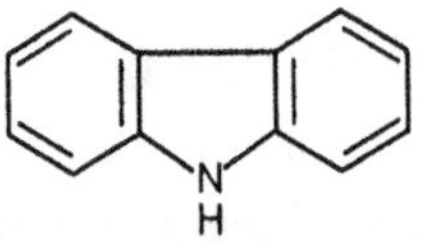
carbazole

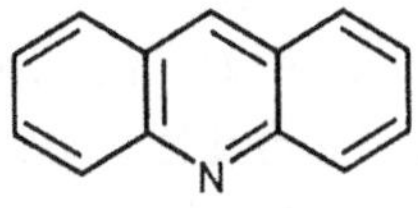
acridine

Graebe and Glaser chose the name carbazole for the second compound discovered in crude anthracene because its reactions were similar to those of aromatic hydrocarbons ("carb-"), though the new compound contained nitrogen ("azo-").[107] They did not publish their method for isolation of carbazole until after Perkin had published details of the distillation of anthracene with alkali.[108] This costly, but effective, method led to a very pure anthracene and was reported to Caro by Perkin in 1870 during their cooperation on alizarin production. It was held to be highly confidential to the extent that even when Graebe and Glaser in 1872 published on carbazole they did not mention the purification steps that had led to the isolation of the new compound. Graebe, in 1872 and 1873, used pyrogenic synthetic methods to establish the correct formula for carbazole, a method introduced by Marcelin Berthelot in 1866, and that was very fashionable in the 1870s. For this purpose, Graebe passed diphenylamine and aniline through red-hot tubes, which yielded carbazole. Both acridine and carbazole were important for theoretical chemistry, and not only because they were previously unknown substances. They were examples of nitrogen-containing aromatic compounds, and important stepping stones in the elucidation of the structures of their congeners.

The structure of anthracene also required clarification. Graebe and Liebermann preferred an angular structure for anthracene on the basis of its syntheses reported by Heinrich Limpricht (1866) and Berthelot (1867). The angular structure was also supported by Graebe's opinion that the two oxygens in anthraquinone should be assigned to contiguous carbon atoms in the inner ring. In 1872, new scientific discoveries led to a major revision of this structure. Glaser discovered a new compound, phenanthrene, in anthracene oil, and oxidative degradation showed that phenanthrene had the angular structure of three fused rings. Anthracene, therefore, had to be a linear fusion of three rings. This was supported by a new synthesis of anthracene by Willem van Dorp, and of anthraquinone by Kekulé and Antoine Franchimont, both of which clearly indicated a linear structure for these compounds.[109] Phenanthrene was also investigated by Graebe, and by Rudolf Fittig in Tübingen.[110] This shed important new light on the structure of quinones, and in 1874 it was shown by Arno Behr and van Dorp, through intramolecular condensation of 1,2-benzylbenzoic acid, that anthraquinone is a 9,10 derivative (modern nomenclature).[111]

One final challenge remained, the exact positions of the two hydroxyls in alizarin. To resolve this problem, Caro in 1873 joined forces with Adolf Baeyer, then at Strasbourg, and their work on alizarin and its derivatives was to inaugurate a decade-long collaboration. They exchanged information about novel reactions they had independently discovered for the formation of quinizarin, an isomer of alizarin. Baeyer was interested in this reaction because of its similarity to another reaction used in the synthesis of phthaleins, compounds produced by heating phthalic anhydride and phenols in the presence of sulphuric acid, and one of his favourite research themes.[112] Caro had a special interest in this work as a possible route to related, and novel, compounds, as well as in the elucidation of the structure of alizarin, since this was now the BASF product with the highest turnover.

In 1874, not long after Baeyer and Caro decided to collaborate, their first joint publication appeared in print; it dealt with the structure of alizarin.[113] They described how by using the phthalein synthesis with phenol they obtained a mixture of two monohydroxyanthraquinones, both of which gave alizarin when fused with potassium hydroxide. The same condensation was also carried out with isomers of dihydroxybenzene, followed by subsequent introduction of a third hydroxyl group. This made possible the unequivocal structural determination of alizarin as 1,2-dihydroxyanthraquinone, and the isomeric quinizarin as 1,4-dihydroxyanthraquinone. From a scientific point of view, the elucidations of the structures of alizarin and quinizarin were of the highest order.[114] Caro and Baeyer's elegant synthetic work and reasoning were based on the most recent theoretical work of Graebe, Theodor Petersen, and Wilhelm Körner, as published in 1873 and 1874.[115] In addition, purpurin, one of the natural dyestuffs of the madder root, was now within reach of artificial synthesis.[116]

These developments were closely followed, and supported, by the management of BASF. In 1875, just before the improved fusion process was achieved, Engelhorn wrote to Gustav Siegle, who since the merger had become a member of the board and was responsible for the sales department in Stuttgart:

> Concerning alizarin, we have not yet achieved the hoped-for results; but we are busy and Caro tells me that the results of the laboratory work will certainly improve the manufacture, and I shall double underline in red ink the day in my calendar when we can say that nobody produces alizarin better than us.[117]

At this time Caro and the chemists in his laboratory were deeply involved in research into hydroxyanthraquinones. Surviving laboratory reports show that in August 1875 Caro assigned to his assistant August Burghard the investigation of the reaction conditions for the production of alizarin V 3a (obtained from the sodium salt of a disulphonic acid of anthraquinone),[118] and also the synthesis and analysis of a trihydroxyanthraquinone, probably flavopurpurin.[119] In December 1875, Burghard was instructed to undertake a comparison of a dihydroxyanthraquinone by-product of alizarin V 3a synthesis with anthraflavic acid, discovered in 1871 by the English chemist Edward Schunck (who collaborated with Perkin).[120] Caro's private assistant, Robert Holdmann, investigated a mononitroanthraquinone and its possible conversion into alizarin.[121] In the spring of 1876, Ernst Mylius, who had worked during 1874-76 in the alizarin production department and was now in Caro's laboratory, was instructed to investigate an unknown by-product resulting from direct oxidation of the monosulphonic acid of anthraquinone.[122] Throughout 1876, Caro's laboratory was kept busy with the study of the formation of alizarin from sulphonic acids of anthracene,[123] which was found to be not technically feasible, and the manufacture of purpurin from alizarin, with the aid of arsenic acid as oxidant, in an attempt to imitate natural products similar to garancine.[124] In an effort to widen the application of alizarin products, Burghard studied the dyeing characteristics of dry alizarin, which were found to be poor.[125] Theodor Reissig, who had known Caro in Manchester, undertook a comparative investigation of the products of the sulphonation and bromine processes. This arose from the fact that the British patent for the latter process had been declared invalid and it was considered prudent to prepare for possible threats to the June 1869 sulphonic acid patent of Caro, Graebe, and Liebermann.[126] In summary, during 1875 and 1876 Caro's laboratory was engaged in studying the alizarin process for theoretical, technical, and patent reasons. However, the decisive progress in the production process was achieved by the application of outside knowledge, particularly the secret process of Gessert, and not through industrial research at BASF.

Caro's last discovery in the field of alizarin dyes, alizarin orange, is a particularly good example of his genius at recognising the potential of new products. In January 1876, he received a sample of a new dyestuff from Charles Müller, the BASF agent in Mulhouse, Alsace. The dye, orange d'alizarine, had been discovered by Charles Strobel, at Henry Haeffely & Co. of Mulhouse, when he treated alizarin-dyed fabrics with nitrous acid vapour. Caro's own investigation showed that the dye was a mononitro-derivative of alizarin. Furthermore, Caro managed to establish the correct structure of alizarin orange (1,2-dihydroxy-3-nitroanthraquinone) and to distinguish it from another mononitro-derivative of alizarin obtained by William Henry Perkin in 1875.[127] In October 1875, the Alsatian chemist Daniel-Auguste Rosenstiehl independently started his own investigation of the orange colorant. He reported his results on 27 October 1875 and 29 March 1876 to the Société Industrielle de Mulhouse, but could not establish a production process that brought all the chemicals together in solution, a necessary precondition for industrial manufacture.[128] Caro probably knew of Rosenstiehl's work, though he never admitted it, and eventually succeeded in discovering a solvent-based manufacturing process after extensive trials with several nitration methods and solvents. It was not by chance that Caro filed a *pli cacheté* for this reaction with the Société Industrielle de Mulhouse on 22 March 1876, shortly before Rosenstiehl published his second contribution on the orange in the journal of the very same society.[129] Meanwhile, Caro and three assistants developed a manufacturing process for the production of alizarin orange.[130] In May 1877, Rosenstiehl left the further development work to Caro.[131] Though the dye was not a big seller, it later gained considerable importance as an intermediate for the production of alizarin blue, a dye developed at the BASF alizarin department by Heinrich Brunck and Carl Glaser. Subsequently, Glaser and his works chemists took on increasingly greater responsibilities in studies on alizarin, as a report by Glaser in 1878 concerning the American alizarin patent demonstrates.[132] In this and other alizarin investigations, Caro was not willing to invest too much effort into research.[133] As a result, the alizarin department achieved independence from Caro in technical and scientific matters and, it seems, required less support from Caro.

Another outcome of Baeyer's phthalein work was Caro's discovery in 1874 of a colorant known as eosin, which, because of its wide ramifications, is discussed in chapter 7.

Azo dyes

After 1877, azo dyestuffs took on an increasing importance for the development of the coal-tar dyestuff industry, to the extent that by the end of the 19th century the greater part of all artificial dyestuffs belonged to this class. Caro recorded that already around 1884, seven years after the inauguration of the German patent law, 9,000 azo dyestuffs were covered by German patents–though only a few were commercially successful.[134]

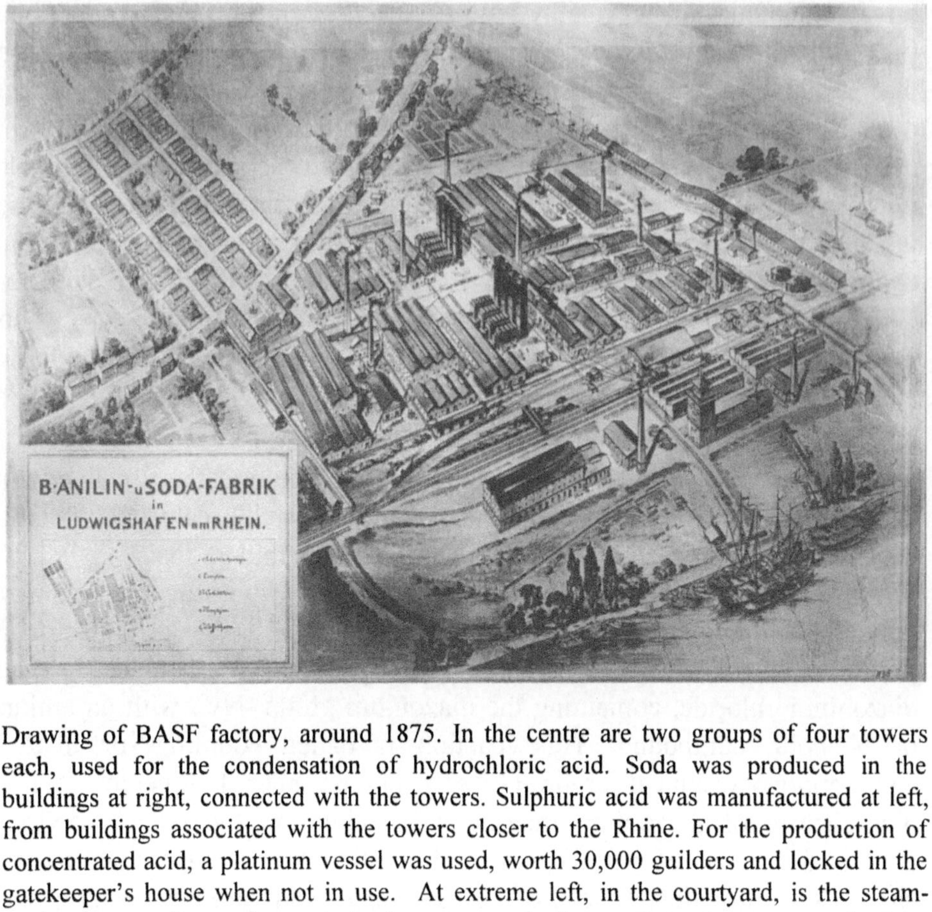

Drawing of BASF factory, around 1875. In the centre are two groups of four towers each, used for the condensation of hydrochloric acid. Soda was produced in the buildings at right, connected with the towers. Sulphuric acid was manufactured at left, from buildings associated with the towers closer to the Rhine. For the production of concentrated acid, a platinum vessel was used, worth 30,000 guilders and locked in the gatekeeper's house when not in use. At extreme left, in the courtyard, is the steam-engine house. Power for control of reactors and other equipment was transmitted by overhead belts. To the right of the towers near the Rhine is the plant for the production of dyestuffs. Aniline red was produced in the upper part of this area, in a building next to the river. The primitive laboratory shown earlier was probably located here. Further to the right is the nitrobenzene and aniline manufacturing area, including equipment for distillation of aniline. Alizarin dyes were produced in the lower part of this area. Closer to the Rhine is the water tower and workshops and an additional steam-engine house. At upper left are residential buildings, including a building with courtyard. The road leads to two larger buildings, one the gatekeeper's house (later the site of the central research laboratory), and the other the administration building. Beyond these buildings are more dwellings along the street. (BASF Archives.)

This was a result of their tremendous diversity, the relative ease of manufacture, and reasonable profitability. It is in this rapid growth that many historians of science and technology see a major impetus for the institutionalisation of industrial research, perhaps following Caro's often-quoted statement that it mainly amounted to "scientific mass production" (*wissenschaftliche Massenarbeit*). However, this is misleading in the sense that he almost certainly did not mean just routine. Research for new azo dyestuffs was as demanding as research in the field of aniline and alizarin dyes; and the most important endeavour involved the synthesis of suitable intermediates, mostly derivatives of naphthalene. Caro was a crucial figure in the first years of the history of azo dyes and made important contributions to this field, partially in collaboration with his friend Peter Griess, the inventor of the diazo reaction, and collaborator with Caro when the latter was in Manchester. Nevertheless, other companies, most notably Hoechst, Bayer, and AGFA, invented better products and therefore made more profits from the azo dye business. Caro–apart from a brief period of very intense activity around 1877-78–was not greatly involved in subsequent azo dye research. To understand how this came about it is necessary to review azo dye developments until the mid-1880s.

Azo compounds contain an atomic grouping of two nitrogen atoms that acts as a "bridge" between two components. This bridge is built-up by joining what we now call a diazonium intermediate (for example, benzene diazonium chloride, containing the diazonium group $-N_2^+$) with an amino or phenolic compound. This reaction is called coupling, or in the contemporary technical jargon, Griess's method, after its inventor.[135] The manufacture of diazonium intermediates relied on the diazo reaction, namely the action of nitrous acid on aromatic amino compounds, known since 1858 through the work of Griess. Since many aromatic amino and phenolic compounds were available by the 1870s, it was possible to synthesize a myriad of combinations, which explains in part the diversity of azo dye chemistry. This was enhanced by the coupling of more than two components to generate large molecules containing two or more azo groups. But the potential of Griess's method for the rational synthesis of artificial dyes was not realised before 1876. One reason for this was the fact that Griess's views did not allow for a clear differentiation between what were then called diazo compounds, and the azo, or coupled, compounds. It was Kekulé who made the most important contributions to the practice and theory of diazo and azo compounds, and succeeded to establish the correct structural formula for the azo grouping, as early as 1866. However, Griess did not immediately accept this, and for him and chemists involved in technical exploitation of the reaction, the theoretical problems were still not solved. Moreover, practical reasons, for example the explosive properties of diazo compounds, made research complicated and dangerous, and prevented the use of Griess's method in technical preparations.

Prior to the mid-1870s, a different process was used for the manufacture of the two azo compounds that were marketed as dyes, namely phenylene brown and aniline yellow, and developed by Caro and C. A. Martius at Roberts, Dale & Co. Both dyes were produced by the reaction of nitrous acid on amino compounds, either *m*-phenylenediamine (to afford phenylene brown, triaminoazobenzene) or aniline (to afford aniline yellow, aminoazobenzene). With this process it was only possible to produce azo compounds from the single aromatic substances. The real potential of Griess's method, that is the coupling of different molecules, was neither understood nor realised. This was despite the fact that August Kekulé had, on the basis of his own theory, converted diazoaminobenzene (C_6H_5-N=N-NH-C_6H_5) into aniline yellow, that is, aminoazobenzene (C_6H_5-N=N-$C_6H_5NH_2$), speculated that this change involved coupling of two components, and proposed that azo compounds could be synthesized from two different starting amino compounds.[136]

Practical reasons were probably the barrier to the use of this reaction for the production of other azo compounds, and Kekulé never reported his efforts, if any, in this direction. Nevertheless, in 1870, Kekulé and his collaborator Coleman Hidegh used phenolic compounds as coupling components, and succeeded in the production of hydroxyazobenzene by adding phenol to diazotized aniline.[137] This was a clear indication that the potential existed for producing a wide variety of azo compounds by Griess's method. It was for this very reason that in November 1874, Caro decided to try the method in his laboratory. He obtained a mass of red crystals through the reaction of diazotoluene, a congener of diazobenzene, and resorcinol, and shared his results with Adolf Baeyer, who answered enthusiastically:

> Following our latest discussion I have been busy with the formation of azo derivatives from the reaction between diazo compounds and phenol compounds. You can obtain them easily in a pure state by addition of phenol to diazobenzene in nitric acid and neutralisation with alkali. I have obtained the resorcinol compound as

> magnificent vermilion needles. What about the further pursuit of this extensive field? I intended to assign it to a graduate student, but, because you are working now on it, I would like to ask about your opinion.[138]

Caro's opinion, no doubt, was to keep the results secret. When Baeyer published details of the reaction, he did not expand on or extend the knowledge published by Kekulé and Hidegh five years before.[139]

It is thus obvious that in 1875 all the necessary theoretical information for the production of azo dyes was at hand. Despite the fact that Griess opposed Kekulé's structural theory for diazo and azo compounds until 1877, it was nevertheless known from 1866 that the possibility existed for synthesizing azo compounds from two different molecules. This was proved in 1870 by Kekulé and Hidegh and again in 1875 by Baeyer and Carl Jäger, though the reactions were difficult and did not result in commercial dyes. However, in 1876 attention was again directed to the reaction of diazo- with amino-compounds, when Caro asked Griess to study the reaction of diazotoluene with *m*-phenylenediamine, the amino analogue of resorcinol. Late in 1875, however, the twenty-two-year-old chemist Otto N. Witt, at Williams, Thomas & Dower, of Brentford, near London, had undertaken a similar reaction between diazobenzene and *m*-phenylenediamine and obtained an orange precipitate that offered potential as a dye.[140] Because the history of these events was later somewhat distorted by the participants–Caro, Griess, and Witt–to suit their claims for priority in the discovery of the first commercial azo dye made by direct and designed coupling, it is necessary to digress briefly in order to provide an account of events as they probably occurred in 1875-76.

Otto N. Witt was born in Moscow to German parents. He completed his chemical education in Zurich during 1875, whereupon he joined a local calico printing factory. It was in Zurich in 1875 that Witt met Heinrich Caro, and soon after he travelled to Mannheim where they exchanged information on carbazole and diphenylaminenitrosoamine. They met again in Mannheim, and Caro provided Witt with letters of introduction to English chemists, including Müller and Wanklyn. Caro's recommendation helped Witt obtain a post at Charles Hanson Greville Williams's firm, Williams, Thomas & Dower, of Brentford and Fulham. There, late in 1875, Witt worked on a theory of colour and constitution that, he claimed, led him to predict that an orange dye lay between phenylene brown and aniline yellow.[141] To test the theory he undertook the coupling that afforded the orange product. The starting materials were aniline and the diaminobenzene compound *m*-phenylenediamine.

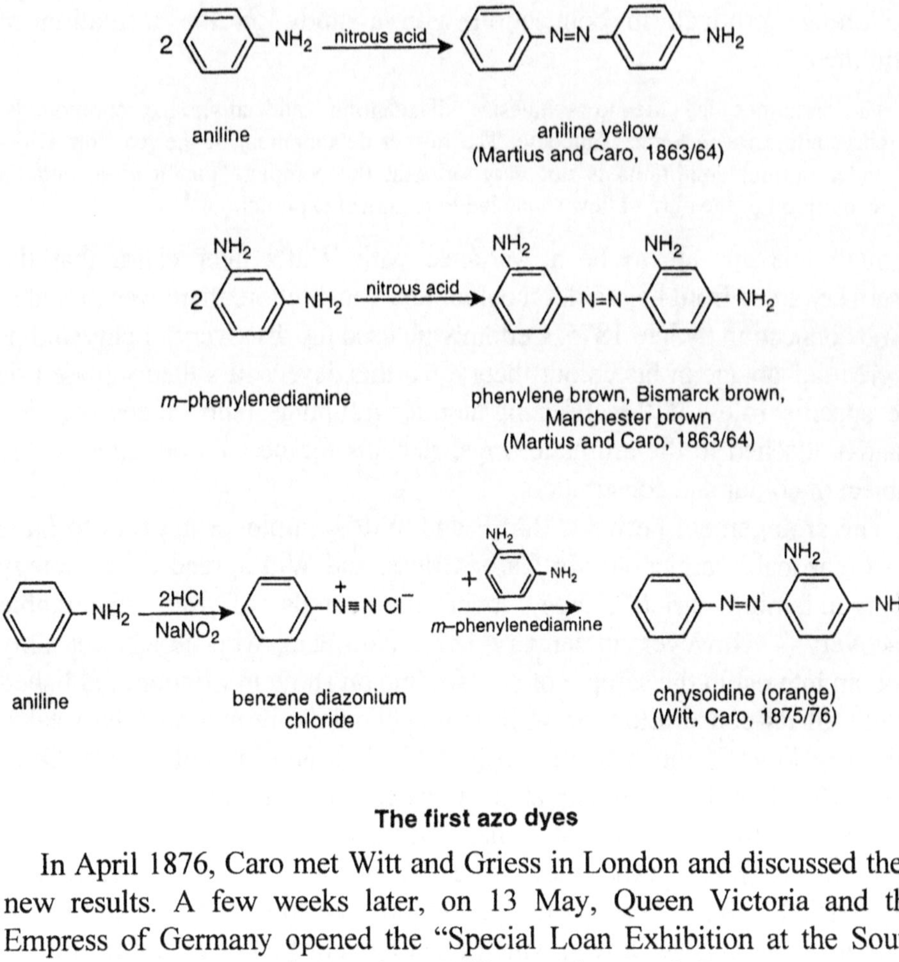

The first azo dyes

In April 1876, Caro met Witt and Griess in London and discussed their new results. A few weeks later, on 13 May, Queen Victoria and the Empress of Germany opened the "Special Loan Exhibition at the South Kensington Museum," in London. Williams, Thomas & Dower was one of the exhibitors, and placed on display a sample of Witt's "new basic orange dye," called chrysoidine. Probably because Hofmann and Martius were on the German committee, AGFA was the only German commercial exhibitor of dyes in evidence at the exhibition. On May 8, Witt had sent a sample of his product to Caro, probably anticipating that BASF would be interested in drawing up a licensing arrangement with Williams, Thomas & Dower.[142] Caro, however, immediately analyzed the product and identified it as diaminoazobenzene, an asymmetric azo compound, which was almost identical to Caro's product that Griess had investigated. This enabled BASF to introduce chrysoidine without a licensing arrangement with the English firm. In June 1876, Witt described how he had first come across the orange product, in connection with a study on the formation of indulines:

> The indulines led me to synthesize diazoamino- and aminoazo compounds–chrysoidine was a logical outcome. The further development of the reaction, which under normal conditions is not very smooth, the complete purification, and the recognition of the pure yellow shade led to technical exploitation.[143]

Though this appears to be at variance with Witt's later claim that the discovery arose from his work on colour and constitution, there was probably some connection by late 1875. Certainly he used his discovery of chrysoidine to great advantage in his colour theory. To this day, Witt's theory, based on the specific roles of the different atomic groupings (substituents or side chains) attached to the aromatic rings, remains the best introduction to the subject of colour and constitution.

The arrangement between BASF and Witt's employer appears to have been reasonably amicable, for Caro, Griess, and Witt agreed on a strategy of maintaining strict secrecy over the details of this remarkable discovery.[144] However, in January 1877, Hofmann, who almost certainly took an interest in the sample of chrysoidine on show in London, published details of its constitution, as well as of phenylene brown and the related aniline yellow,[145] much to the chagrin of Caro and his colleagues. Once more, Hofmann had demonstrated the existence of a family of dyestuffs, though this time the constitutional formulae were in accord with the structural formulae. And they were for all the world, academic and industrial, to share. Perhaps the revelation contributed to the demise of Williams, Thomas & Dower, which must have lost a considerable amount of business once the recipe was made public, and became bankrupt in 1877.

Following Hofmann's publication, Witt attempted to claim priority for inventing chrysoidine by citing the brief description of his product in the London exhibition catalogue.[146] But Hofmann would have none of it. Defending patents over secrecy, he responded: "The time of the Arcanists is over. Whoever, in the last quarter of the nineteenth century provides his colleagues with a chemical puzzle must be prepared to see it solved, sooner or later."[147]

August Wilhelm Hofmann in his laboratory at the University of Berlin, 1870. (Deutsches Museum.)

In 1874, Hofmann and Martius had joined the Vorstand of the Deutscher Patentschutz-Verein, chaired by Werner Siemens, and in the following year Hofmann through publication disclosed the constitution of Caro's dye eosin. Hofmann's interest in publishing structural and other information about eosin and chrysoidine was an outcome of his ardent lobbying for patent protection, and of his consultancy work for Martius, that began in 1867 with a partnership in the latter's intermediates firm. But now, in 1877, the matter was given far greater import, since the Reichstag was in the process of approving a patent law, one that covered chemical processes (rejecting an earlier proposal for product protection alone).

Chrysoidine, however, was not the reason for the takeoff of azo dyes. It was notable for the first use of Griess's method (of obtaining asymmetric azo compounds) in technical chemistry, but there was no real potential for extending its application. The availability of soluble sulphonic acid derivatives of azo dyes was the technological breakthrough. In 1875, Griess had prepared helianthine by coupling the diazo compound of sulphanilic acid with dimethylaniline, which meant that the use of sulphonated compounds in the synthesis of azo products was known.[148] However, this was not commercialised.

Independently, François Zacharie Roussin, a French pharmacist, had prepared azo compounds based on sulphanilic acid, naphthol, and dimethylaniline and obtained yellow dyes.[149] These so-called "Roussin oranges" were also unpatented and caused a sensation when sold in France in 1876-77 by the Poirrier firm in Paris. According to Caro, and by comparison with chrysoidine, the products of Roussin were shown to be acid dyestuffs of pathbreaking "new technical effect." Immediately they were shown to be successful opponents of natural dyestuffs.[150]

This was to be the reason for the massive expansion of azo dye research in the German chemical industry. With hindsight, it was indeed what Caro called "wissenschaftliche Massenarbeit"–scientific mass production.[151] Though this might bring to mind images of large numbers of trained technicians attempting to achieve every possible combination of aromatic components, the reality was quite different. The most important activity was the invention of key compounds for use in the coupling reaction, and for this endeavour structural studies were essential.[152] German companies and chemists reacted immediately when new products from rival firms appeared. Hofmann moved fast in his attempt to tackle the structural elucidation of Roussin's Orange II, though he failed.[153] It was Conrad Schraube in Caro's laboratory who succeeded with this problem in June 1877 when he established that the dye was based on diazotized sulphanilic acid and α-naphthol.[154] Soon after, German companies were imitating the unpatented inventions of Roussin. Caro extended the range of the new azo dyes into the reds with his invention of fast red (AV) in July 1877.[155] This was based on his reasoning that two naphthalene-based components in the azo compound would give a red, and to achieve this he used diazotized 4-amino-1-naphthalenesulphonic acid (naphthionic acid), coupled with β-naphthol. Up to this time, only yellow, orange, and brown azo dyes were known. It was characteristic of Caro's semi-intuitive style that he was very aware of the potential uses of the reaction, and assigned his assistant Holdmann to undertake the necessary experiments. (Using α-naphthol, a brown dye was formed.) Fast red was an immensely important dye for wool and replaced a host of natural dyes, in particular cochineal and orseille.

By 1879, this semi-intuitive style of working was replaced by more thorough methodological and theory-based reasoning, greatly influenced by developments during the two previous years. This is strikingly apparent from a letter that Caro wrote to his academic colleague and close friend Victor Meyer on 16 July, and in which Caro's approach to azo dye invention, and other areas of dyestuff chemistry, was shown to be nothing less than state of the art. Meyer had requested Caro's opinion on the potential of certain reddish-violet dyestuffs that he and a collaborator had synthesized during the summer of 1879. Meyer's objective was to establish a route to blue azo dyes, which at the time were much sought for, through the introduction of methoxy-groups. The objective was the same that Caro had used in the invention of fast red AV, namely to create heavier molecules to afford bluer shades of dyestuffs. In particular, Meyer had used an analogy with triphenylmethane dyes, based on Hofmann's demonstration that introduction of the methoxy grouping into derivatives of rosaniline and rosolic acid led to bluer colours.[156]

Caro's answer made clear that the age of tinkering and simple analogies had passed. He pointed out that the introduction of large atomic groupings into dyestuffs of different classes, such as azo, aniline, induline, and anthraquinone dyes, had given different results. Thus while it was true that there was a general correlation between molecular size and shade, there were several exceptions. In this connection, Caro emphasized the role of molecular structure, and for this he used Witt's recent (1876) theory of colour and constitution. Moreover, he explained his own views concerning the physical causes of the colour of certain molecules, using clearly atomistic and mechanistic language:

> The outcomes [the different colours of molecules] depend only upon the molecular architecture, and you can no doubt (entre nous!) understand this if you make a pictorial representation, or imagine one–bearing in mind that through the alteration of the gravitating atoms the inter-atomic distance in the resulting molecular group (the atomic spacing) must also be be increased or diminished. It is well-known how you can either open or close such a gap, and this relates only to how it is constructed, and the direction of the force applied.[157]

What is remarkable here is that Caro shows himself to be a physical atomist, through his ability to relate the colour of molecules to their architecture. The inclusion of "entre nous" indicates that such speculation was not well received, or probably not even raised, in public discussion, though many chemists, particularly Baeyer and Kekulé, adopted this way of thinking. Caro's model bears a direct relationship to Kekulé's 1872 oscillation hypothesis that explained the equivalence of all carbon-carbon bonds in the benzene ring.

Caro then moved from reasoning based on physical causes to a wider-ranging discussion of the colour-and-constitution relationships of known azo dyestuffs. In his view, the main hindrance to the construction of blue azo dystuffs through simply increasing the size of the molecule was the fact that light absorption increased with size, and, for azo dyes, this invariably resulted in very dark shades, approaching black, but certainly not blue. Additionally, the influences of mordants had to be counted in. Thus, according to Caro's point of view, the shades of Meyer's dyestuffs were dependent not only on the introduction of the methoxy group but also on other features. This discussion was impressive proof of the complexities of azo dye research, both practical and theoretical, at the end of the 1870s and during the 1880s.

Caro also became engaged in more public aspects of theoretical azo dye chemistry. With Schraube, he described the reactive properties of the diazo compounds of aminoazobenzene in Munich at the 1877 annual assembly of the Gesellschaft Deutscher Naturforscher und Ärzte (Society of German Natural Scientists and Physicians) and contributed substantially to the establishment of the disazo dyestuffs.[158] At BASF, Julius Schuncke and Glaser later found the dyes Orseilleroth and Blauschwarz, the latter being the first black disazo dyestuff. But the most important development at the end of the 1870s was the separation of the various isomers of sulphonated naphthol compounds by Heinrich Baum at Hoechst.[159] The outcome of the isolation of the isomeric disulphonic acids of β-naphthol, R and G acids, and the separate use of them as intermediates for azo dyestuffs was a much clearer shade, known as "Höchster Ponceaux." Once again, and as had been the case with the alizarin dyes, the importance of understanding isomerism in technical work was demonstrated. Then in 1884, Paul Böttiger, while employed at Bayer, invented a red disazo dyestuff synthesized from benzidine and naphthionic acid.[160] Böttiger, however, kept the details to himself, and after leaving Bayer filed a patent for his new process. This was the first member of a new class of dyestuffs not requiring mordants, and known as direct or substantive dyes. Many companies, including Hoechst and BASF, missed the opportunity to exploit the new range from the start because of the poor acid fastness of this first member. However, direct dyeing, a much easier dyeing process, made the fortunes of Bayer and AGFA, which exploited Böttiger's invention.[161] This first product, named Congo red, marked the decisive beginning of modern azo dye chemistry.

There was thus, and inevitably, some "scientific mass production," even if not of the type suggested by Caro. This was in addition to the synthesis of large numbers of new potential colorants, all of which had to be tested for their dyeing capabilities. Many intermediates were naphthalene derivatives, often based on β-naphthol and requiring several steps and careful control of the reaction conditions. Structural studies required elegant procedures that enabled unambiguous assignment of substituents in the aromatic rings. While in the mid-1880s these compounds were of no scientific interest, they were to become technically important later in the decade. Moreover, the technical development of the reactions used for the synthesis of such intermediates was often difficult. As Herbert Levinstein pointed out:

> These new azo dyes–oranges, scarlets, reds and bordeaux–were simple dyes requiring, like most azo dyes, only simple plant. But the intermediates–(1) β-naphthol and its sulphonic acids and their amino derivatives, and (2) α-naphthylamine and naphthionate–involved quite a formidable plant, including novel stills.[162]

Apart from new plant, the two aspects of technical azo dye chemistry that contributed most to the establishment of industrial research laboratories in the German chemical industry were structure and synthesis. Research into azo dyestuffs was one of the leading topics in industrial laboratories, and in the case of BASF this research even led to an unexpected innovation in aniline dyes, as well as important discoveries in the field of intermediates. This was through two of Caro's most outstanding inventions: acid magenta and conversion of naphthols into naphthylamines.

Edward Chambers Nicholson had demonstrated in the early 1860s that the water solubility of dyestuffs was enhanced by the introduction of the sulphonic acid group. An example of a sulphonated colorant was Roussin's orange. Sulphonation to improve solubility was widely used in the 1870s. However, sulphonation seemed useless for magenta, because it was supplied as a salt, and was thus water-soluble. Caro attempted to synthesize sulphonated magenta as an intermediate in the production of azo dyes, in this case an analogue of the sulphanilic acid used by Roussin. Though this failed, Caro noted that the new substance was fast to acids. Since the magenta derivative could be dyed in an acid bath, this had the advantage that it could be employed in admixture with certain natural wood dyes as a

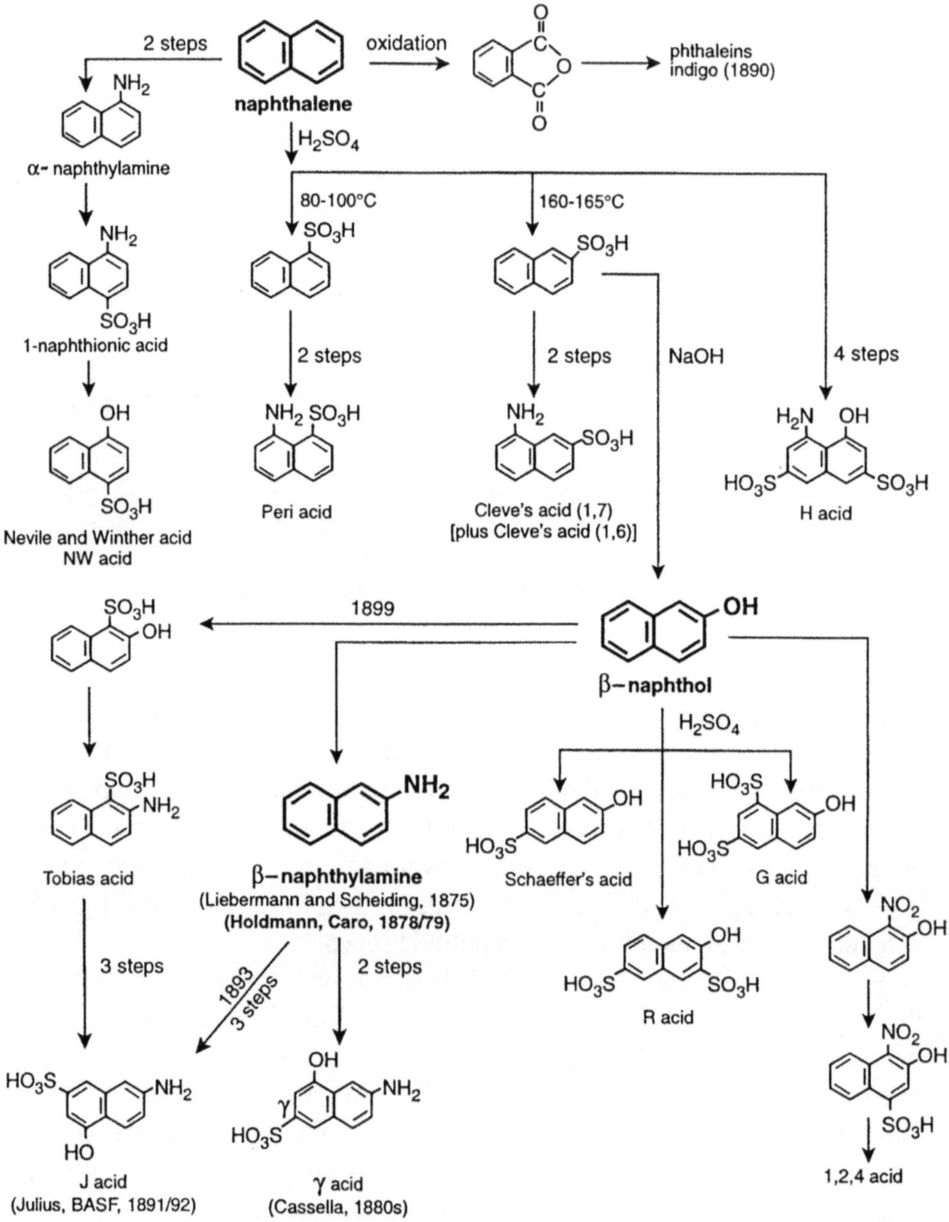

Naphthalene-derived intermediates

novel colorant. On 16 December 1877, BASF registered its second German patent, this time for acid magenta.[163] Moreover, Caro introduced with this sulphonation a new technical effect to dyestuff technology, and BASF extended it to azo dyes, other triphenylmethane dyestuffs, and even to the alizarin dyes.[164] Sulphonation was also relevant to Caro's invention of the dye naphthol yellow, or acid yellow, patented in December 1879.[165] This product was closely related to the dinitronaphthol colorant that Martius had invented at Roberts, Dale & Co. in the 1860s (Manchester or Martius yellow). The presence of the sulphonic acid grouping improved applicability tremendously, and naphthol yellow became an important dye for wool and silk.

One particularly important pathway to the production of azo dye intermediates was a reaction discovered by Caro and his assistant Robert Holdmann during 1879. This brought the hitherto industrially elusive β-naphthylamine, first reported by Liebermann and Scheiding in 1875, within reach.[166] Caro described the invention in his history of the dyestuff industry as an example of serendipity: "The method owes its origin ... to one of those risky conclusions based on analogy, which in most cases leads the empiricist to surprising discoveries."[167] In order to replicate the synthesis of the valuable Ponceaux azo dyes produced by Hoechst, Caro instructed Holdmann to try the reaction of β-naphthol on diazotized aniline. But instead of getting an azo dye, Holdmann obtained β-naphthylphenylamine in which the hydroxy group of naphthol had been replaced by aniline. Later, they tried ammonia instead of aniline and obtained β-naphthylamine. Suddenly, an important new intermediate was accessible. As a consequence, there was a conflict between Caro and Holdmann over credit for the original discovery. Correspondence over this discovery and the dispute enables a reconstruction of the circumstances under which it was made.

According to Holdmann, he had come across the reaction while Caro was absent through illness in England during the winter of 1878-79 (and when he was cared for by Griess).[168] Upon Caro's return, they together investigated the reaction of β-naphthol and ammonia.[169] During December 1879, Caro succeeded in the development of the technically feasible process, based on the reaction of ammonium chloride on the sodium salt of β-naphthol. This was also achieved simultaneously by Caro's former assistant Eduard Hepp, then with Oehler & Co., who had some knowledge of the method and invented a technically viable process independently of Caro.[170] The outcome was that both firms produced the intermediate, though the patent was filed under the name of BASF. Carl Graebe undertook the scientific investigation for Caro and BASF,[171] and it is a sign of the precarious position of Holdmann that Graebe left it to Caro to decide whether or not Holdmann's name should appear in print as that of the inventor of the method.[172]

Summary

In this chapter we have, through following Caro's work at BASF and its ramifications beyond the factory walls, examined the relevance of both technological know-how and scientific knowledge for the successful invention of novel artificial dyestuffs. Caro transferred his English experience to Germany as a first step, and then applied his knowledge of the English patent system to secure for BASF a key alizarin patent, though only in the nick of time. The outcome was a strategic alliance between BASF and Perkin that was to ensure for the Ludwigshafen factory the largest market for synthetic alizarin. This brought tremendous prestige to Caro. His personal wealth was also considerably enhanced, albeit after some delay, due to the technical challenges of the alizarin synthesis. Caro's success, and interest in the scientific side of his alizarin work, brought about a strong and enduring connection with academic chemistry, especially between Caro and the research school of Adolf Baeyer. This, and Hofmann's publications on the constitutions of azo dyes, that Caro and colleagues had tried to keep secret, fundamentally changed the character of industrial research. In the next chapter, Caro's academic network from the late 1870s to the end of the 1880s will be described, with Baeyer and his colleagues in Munich at centre stage.

7

Academic-Industrial Collaboration

So much was desired by me, but has not been achieved; so much have I gained, but was once more snatched from me! But, above all else, there is the same old question: Why did that wonderful and productive personal contact with you come to an end before its time? What rough hand was capable of tearing asunder the fragile bond between science and technology?

Heinrich Caro to Adolf von Baeyer, 1902.

With these bitter words of self-recrimination, Heinrich Caro responded to Adolf von Baeyer's note of congratulation on the occasion of the 25th anniversary of the award of Ph.D. *honoris causa* to Caro from the University of Munich.[1] While Caro acknowledged the importance of the academic-industrial relationship, he also struggled to understand how changing and unfavourable circumstances could cause it to fall apart. It was during the decade commencing 1873, when Caro first began to collaborate with Baeyer, that Caro was most successful in terms of his dyestuff inventions at BASF, and that he made substantial contributions to chemical industry through the creation of a unique network of links with academics. Though Caro's academic network was to collapse in the mid-1880s, the foundations that he laid flourished and endured into the 20th century, evolving smoothly from dyestuffs to pharmaceuticals, then to high-pressure chemistry, synthetic polymers, and, finally, the life sciences.

It was through Caro that a new system of using contractual arrangements between firms and academic scientists as consultants to the chemical industry originated. The academic scientist was an external collaborator, though bound to the firm by a contract that–most commonly–entitled the manufacturer to exploit exclusively and for its own benefit the inventions that arose from the work of the consultant. The reward was a royalty on profits, support from the company in terms of chemicals and reagents, and, in certain cases, a retainer or salary.[2] At first, and this referred especially to Caro's network, these conditions were subject to wide variation, according to the status of the academic and the needs of the firm.

Caro's engagement with academic chemistry reached back to his English period when he cooperated with Peter Griess and Carl Schorlemmer and in particular to his collaboration in the early 1860s with James Alfred Wanklyn on the constitutional formula of rosolic acid. Then, at BASF during 1869-70, he was placed in charge of the development of alizarin through cooperation with the academic inventors Carl Graebe and Carl Liebermann. Graebe retained close connections with BASF during the next two decades, and maintained an extensive correspondence with Caro on further studies into rosolic acid, which led to the structural elucidation of aniline dyes.[3] It was Caro's interest in academic chemistry that enabled him to forge a strong link with Adolf Baeyer from the end of 1873, shortly after Baeyer had moved to Strasbourg. Their cooperation soon proved to be of crucial importance for the careers of both men, as well as for BASF. Within two years, Baeyer and Caro began to tackle the synthesis of indigo, the most important natural dyestuff. Caro's access to Baeyer's research school also brought about his collaboration with Emil and Otto Fischer on the constitution of rosaniline. However, Caro's network of contacts, both academic and industrial, was not restricted to Baeyer and his assistants. Thus August Bernthsen, later Caro's successor as manager of the BASF central research laboratory, was prominent in the elucidation of the structure of Caro's methylene blue, while Caro's friendship with Victor Meyer led to a decade-long exchange of research results.

These academic connections included occasional contacts, a network of correspondents, short-term cooperations in research and development projects, and non-specific contractual arrangements. This pattern of working became quite normal in the late 19th-century German dyestuff and pharmaceutical industries.

Certainly, there were widespread academic-industrial contractual and other arrangements even before the chemical industry became extensively science-based through Caro's involvement. Thus, scientific entrepreneurs such as Justus Liebig,[4] Hermann Kolbe[5] and August Wilhelm Hofmann[6] participated in the foundation of industrial enterprises while retaining their academic positions. Indeed, the scientific work that underpinned their industrial interests enhanced their standings as academics. Significantly, all were founders of or partners in companies. In sharp contrast, chemists and entrepreneurs of the post-1860 period, particularly those interested in dyestuff manufacture, were prevented from founding enterprises, because either there was little room for new openings or insufficient capital to permit the sort of sophisticated research and development that might lead to novel products and processes. This explains why in general academic chemists from around 1870 found it more convenient to cooperate with well-established firms through arrangements that gave them royalties on profits, retainers, or salaries.[7]

The benefits of academic-industrial partnerships went both ways, and academic chemists profited in an important and far-reaching manner from these connections. Indeed they would have achieved much less in their researches without the material support of, and the abundance of research chemicals supplied by, industry. Invariably, it became a symbiotic relationship, one that even determined the focus of academic research.

To develop these themes, this chapter looks at Caro's network of academic consultants that emerged during the early 1870s and culminated with the indigo work at the beginning of the 1880s.[8] We deliberately focus on Caro's work with Adolf Baeyer, especially the indigo synthesis, and on Caro's strategy for establishing the constitutions of aniline dyes with Emil and Otto Fischer. The reason is that the former is a further example of the way in which Caro used his knowledge of calico printing to tackle industrial problems, and the latter is a demonstration of continuity with work that he started in Manchester during the 1860s. Both indigo and the structures of aniline dyes received the greatest impetus in the period immediately following the success of alizarin and the development of azo dyes based on the coupling reaction. Finally, we embark on a survey of the wider network of Heinrich Caro's academic connections.

Baeyer, Caro, and BASF

Caro's reputation as the most prolific and successful inventor of coal-tar dyestuffs in the 1870s was the direct consequence of his self-appointed role as a principal mediator between science and industry and the style of working that he had established in Manchester. Academic-industrial collaborations furnished new dyestuffs and guided much of the theoretical direction and practice of aromatic organic chemistry that dominated academic research until the first decades of the 20th century. Adolf Baeyer, who was to become one of the most prominent organic chemists of his time, and the leading academic collaborator with BASF, was introduced to dye and colour chemistry from a different direction, but not without an interest in relevant products.[9]

Baeyer was the son of Johann Jacob Baeyer, a military officer in charge of the Prussian land survey, and Eugenie Baeyer, née Hitzig. He studied natural sciences at the University of Berlin and received his doctorate in 1858 from the same institution, though it was based on work done at Heidelberg under August Kekulé, whom he later followed to Ghent. In 1860, Baeyer was appointed a lecturer at the Gewerbeinstitut in Berlin, and remained there until 1872 when he received an appointment at the new, and prestigious, German University of Strasbourg, established following the Franco-Prussian War of 1870-71, and the subsequent annexation of Alsace-Lorraine. The rulers of the newly unified German Empire created a university in Strasbourg endowed with excellent resources, including the most modern laboratories and equipment, as part of the cultural policy aimed at bringing about Germanisation of the former French territories. It replaced the original French institution in the capital of Alsace.[10] At Strasbourg, Baeyer founded his famous research school in organic chemistry, where many well-known organic chemists commenced their careers, and it was during his short stay there that the collaboration with Caro and BASF was commenced.

Only towards the end of his life did Caro record the beginning of his cooperation with Baeyer.[11] The first time they met was in September 1862 during Caro's journey to Germany on behalf of Roberts, Dale & Co. This brought him to Berlin and, briefly, to the Gewerbeinstitut. They were next in touch in December 1866, soon after Caro returned to Germany, and again in 1869 during the negotiations between BASF and Graebe and Liebermann over alizarin. Significantly, around that time BASF supported Baeyer with samples of substances, in this case quinoline (a decomposition product of quinine) and picoline (methylpyridine), that he used in research that was related to their use as possible dye intermediates.[12] But the real collaboration started in September 1873 when Baeyer and Caro met at the meeting of the Gesellschaft Deutscher Naturforscher und Ärzte (Society of German Natural Scientists and Physicians) in Wiesbaden. This was soon followed with their joint work on the structure of alizarin, published in 1874, and which established the modern structural formulae of alizarin and certain congeners.

Closely connected to the theoretical work on the structure of alizarin was Baeyer's study of the reaction leading to phthaleins. At the end of the 1870s this had a tremendous bearing on the eventual structural elucidation of the early aniline dyes, particularly aniline red. Baeyer's work on the phthaleins commenced in 1871, when he heated the anhydride of phthalic acid with phenols and sulphuric acid, and discovered the first representatives of the class, namely gallein, fluorescein, phenolphthalein, and coerulein. Since they so closely resembled natural wood dyes, particularly brasilein and hematoxylin, Baeyer was convinced of their potential value as dyestuffs. At that time, however, little information on their structures was available. This situation would change after the meeting in Wiesbaden, when Baeyer handed over to Caro a sample of fluorescein. Caro succeeded in obtaining a yellow-red dye by introducing four bromine atoms into the fluorescein molecule. This tetrabromo derivative showed itself to be an excellent dyestuff, especially for silk. Caro named it eosin, following the nickname Eos of the girl he had admired in his youth, Anna Peters, the sister of his friend Richard Peters.[13] In the summer of 1874, Caro carried to Baeyer's Strasbourg laboratory a sample of eosin, which deeply impressed the research students there, among whom was Emil Fischer. The outcome was that eosin became one of Fischer's first research topics in organic chemistry, and the topic of his doctoral thesis. Eosin was the basis of a whole series of commercial products, first marketed by BASF in the summer of 1874, and for which Baeyer had provided extensive analytical support.

Before the phthaleins could be commercialised, the intermediates had to be made available in bulk, particularly resorcinol, an expensive laboratory product isolated from galbanum resin, and phthalic acid.[14] Almost simultaneously, Caro and Baeyer achieved success. Caro synthesized resorcinol from the disulphonic acid of benzene and also resolved the scaling-up difficulties, while Baeyer established a new process for the production of phthalic acid through the oxidation of naphthalene with dilute nitric acid and potassium dichromate.[15] The latter was to become an industrial process of exceptional importance.

Baeyer and Caro agreed to keep the eosin recipe secret, reflecting, perhaps, lack of confidence in the Prussian Patent Office's ability to evaluate new chemical patents, particularly since only a few years earlier, in 1869, the office had rejected the important sulphonation patent for the synthesis of alizarin. When first introduced to the market, the price of eosin was exorbitant, as much as 800 marks per kilogram.[16] Nevertheless, dyers purchased the product, which demonstrated its great popularity, and the high price that it commanded generated interest at other dye-making firms. In 1875, A. W. Hofmann analyzed a sample of eosin, and then published its constitution which revealed the method of synthesis and made it public property.[17] Hofmann, as a supporter of the patent system, published this information not only to demonstrate his aversion towards secrecy as a means for protecting chemical inventions. He was also acting to protect his own interests, that were closely related to the fortunes of Carl Martius and AGFA.

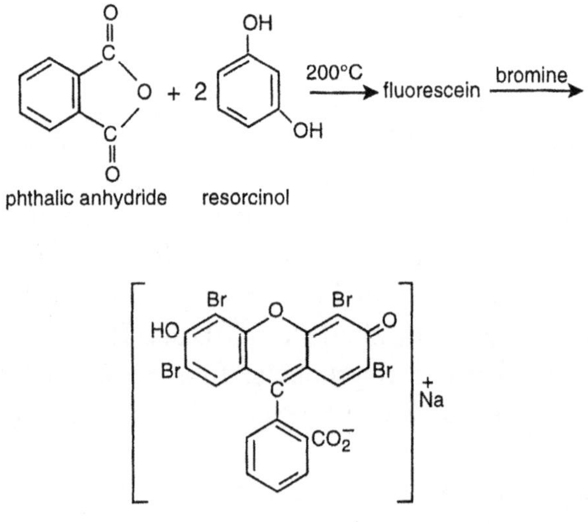

eosin, tetrabromo fluorescein, Caro, 1874

Baeyer's research group investigated the structural formulae (as opposed to constitutions) of the phthaleins between 1876 and 1880.[18] Originally, Baeyer had assumed a close relationship to anthraquinone derivatives. Following the synthesis by Charles Friedel and James Mason Crafts in 1878 of phthalophenone, Baeyer succeeded in establishing that this was the mother substance of the phthalein group. In this endeavour he was assisted by a number of his research students, three of whom, Johann Baptist Burkhardt, Albin Schillinger, and Conrad Schraube, later joined Caro at BASF.[19]

Another family of compounds investigated by Baeyer and Caro was that containing the nitroso group, and which, in common with alizarin and the phthaleins, became important for both theoretical and practical reasons. Baeyer had investigated the nitroso reaction in the mid-1860s, but then dropped this work, until after he obtained a nitroso salt from dimethylaniline, and Caro encouraged him to resume work on the topic.[20] In the words of Baeyer:

> I did not pursue this topic, because of overwork, until Mr. Caro brought me back to it in 1874. He passed on to me a sample of the chlorine salt of nitrosodimethylaniline, which he had obtained by the action of amyl nitrite on a hydrochloric acid solution of dimethylaniline.[21]

The existence of nitrosodimethylaniline, a stable nitroso compound of a tertiary amine, was completely unexpected, and surprised both academic and industrial chemists.[22] Initially, the newly-discovered product was mainly of academic interest, which was certainly the reason why Caro encouraged further research into the nitroso group in Baeyer's laboratory. Baeyer accepted the challenge and with his students he was able to synthesize new and long-sought-for substances, especially nitrosophenol and nitrosobenzene. The possibilities seemed to be endless, as Baeyer recorded: "Sometimes my head reels, when I think about the vast area that is in front of us."[23] To exploit this new area of enquiry quickly, Baeyer devoted his own efforts and almost the full strength of his institute to the nitroso compounds during the winter of 1874-75.[24] The academic chemists enhanced knowledge of reduction and oxidation of nitroso and amino compounds and in so doing contributed substantially to the stock of industrially relevant basic chemistry. Within two years of Caro's first discovery, nitrosodimethylaniline was the starting point of a new and very successful dyestuff, his methylene blue.

Baeyer rarely discussed his own direct involvement in these industrial-academic endeavours. It was only in 1905, on the occasion of his 70th birthday, that he even described his first contact with the world of applied science:

> Some time after the commencement of my scientific career I came into touch with technology. The first technologists that I met were Messrs. Engelhorn, Clemm and Caro, who came to Berlin to negotiate with Gräbe [*sic*] and Liebermann over alizarin. I was amazed because I had never seen a technologist in my life. In Straßburg it happened that I came into a close relationship with my friend Caro, and

> with him I undertook a large number of studies. Through indigo my friendship with the technologists became even closer.[25]

It is remarkable that Baeyer, who taught at an institution whose very function was to educate future engineers and technicians, claimed that he had never before seen a technologist or engineer. Probably he was here referring to the origins of his own involvement with industrial chemistry, namely the BASF connection, particularly since there is no evidence that Baeyer had close contacts to industry during his years at the Gewerbeinstitut. It was Heinrich Caro who introduced Baeyer to the realm of chemical technology.

Their common research programme was strongly coordinated, as their voluminous correspondence demonstrates. Thus Baeyer relied upon Caro for advice concerning technical and patent affairs.[26] In addition he was supplied with valuable raw materials for research in organic chemistry, and he often offered to pay for these substances.[27] Baeyer also undertook analyses and structural elucidations of industrial products and intermediates,[28] and was sometimes involved in technical developments, especially in the case of eosin. Quite apart from technical products and processes, the related issues concerning patents, and the need to maintain strict secrecy, there was the question of what could be revealed through scientific publication without compromising BASF.[29] Publication was subject to prior consent from BASF, which at first relied on Caro's judgement. Thus in June 1874, Baeyer wrote to Caro about their work on the structure of alizarin and hydroxyanthraquinone congeners:

> I intend to write up the results of our work this week and I will send you the manuscript as soon as possible ... and I request that you inform me as to what extent the isomerism of the alizarins is publishable, or if I should omit this point altogether.[30]

Baeyer maintained a strict policy of informing Caro about any of his new research results that might have industrial application, including full experimental details and the structures and constitutions of products, as well as their chemical properties.[31] The cooperation of Baeyer with Caro was at the same time a collaborative venture between two scientists and an alliance involving an academic scientist and an industrial enterprise. The two chemists published jointly, and their research programme was both technical and scientific in scope, with Baeyer always showing an intense interest in technical matters, and Caro holding academic research in the highest esteem. There was another important benefit for BASF, since in the mid-1870s it did not possess sufficient resources to undertake research on the scale possible in Baeyer's university laboratories, at first in Strasbourg, and from 1875 in Munich. Moreover, as a consequence of the hierarchical structure of command and control in the universities, the collaboration with Baeyer was a cooperation with the complete institute. This meant that BASF was, through the connection between Caro and Baeyer, always well-informed about new knowledge emerging from what was almost certainly the world's largest and most successful research school in organic chemistry during the 1870s and 1880s.

It was from thc success of the alliance between science and industry that in 1875 the management of BASF proposed a contractual agreement with Baeyer.[32] Directors Engelhorn and August Clemm no doubt wished to enhance collaboration following the outcomes of investigations into the phthaleins and the structure of alizarin. Though Baeyer was not willing to accept a regular salary (which was the original intention), he did agree to formalise the already well-established cooperation with the firm. Baeyer proposed that he would receive royalties on his inventions, as was already the case, and in return he would agree

> to report all my observations, which in my opinion appear to be of potential technical value, firstly to BASF. This initial report can be supplied with or without restriction. If the report is unrestricted, the information is passed over to the ownership of the company. Otherwise the company acquires ownership only following a specific agreement over royalties, patents, and licenses.[33]

Baeyer suggested that if there was no agreement over conditions, then he would retain the rights to the discoveries, including publication. In those cases where the partners had signed a contract, Baeyer would be obliged to accept the veto by BASF of any publication:

> With regard to scientific publication, I would act only following agreement with the company, in all cases of a tacit or a specific agreement.[34]

These conditions were not totally acceptable to BASF, where directors Engelhorn and August Clemm wanted Baeyer to pass over exclusively to BASF all his discoveries and experimental details, without any negotiations over royalties. On this one crucial issue there was strong disagreement, as made clear by Baeyer in July 1875:

> That is the point to which I must take exception to, and I would ask you to take into consideration an arrangement, according to which I would be allowed to participate

> in any discussion concerning conditions in the case of a discovery made independently of any prior arrangement with the company. I wish to express my greatest wish that my relationship with the company, which has been for me both pleasant and helpful, will become even more fruitful for both parties as a result of such negotiations.[35]

In November 1875, the management of BASF provisionally agreed to Baeyer's terms, and existing records indicate that both parties signed a contract at Easter 1876.[36] Remarkably, Baeyer retained his independent status to a considerable extent. Only he would decide which part of his work was technically valuable, and, as previously, he was free to choose his research topics. The nature of the cooperation was not specified, but was to include all the work of Baeyer and his dependent assistants and co-workers. Moreover, the material benefits for Baeyer were not particularly great. Why then was the contact with BASF, and with Caro, of such great value for him?

The answer is that Baeyer received tremendous scientific advantages from his collaboration with Caro, to the extent that even while establishing his research groups in Strasbourg and Munich he was still able to maintain a high scientific output. Caro provided him with invaluable details of an enormous number of interesting reactions, synthetic pathways, and new compounds, which were topics for highly novel academic research. Both men invariably had common goals that were totally in accord with academic and industrial interests. These included structural elucidation of a host of complex organic compounds, the most important of which, both in scientific and commercial terms, was indigo. This was generally agreed to be one of the greatest scientific problems of the time, that once resolved would bring unprecedented prestige and open the way to commercial synthesis, and destruction of the British monopoly of the natural product, known as the "king of dyestuffs."

Hunting for Indigo

Artificial indigo made by BASF was first shipped to consumers in 1897, almost thirty years after alizarin was first manufactured. It was based on researches that Baeyer had commenced at the Gewerbeinstitut in the 1860s, on encouragement from and collaboration with Caro in the mid-1870s, on Baeyer's agreements with both BASF and Hoechst at the beginning of the 1880s, and, finally, on the processes developed by Carl

Heumann in 1890.[37] Until the early 1880s, Caro was the principal industrial participant, even though the process he scaled up on the basis of Baeyer's research was a commercial failure. It was, nevertheless, part of the tremendous science-based commitment towards the industrial replication of natural products. Certainly the manufacture of synthetic indigo would not have been so readily realised but for the joint work of Baeyer and Caro, which also contributed towards Baeyer's Nobel Prize (1905).

Indigo occupied a major place in the world of fashion, colonial trade, science and technology throughout the 19th century, and was the inspiration for Johann Strauss Junior's operetta, *Indigo und die vierzig Räuber*, first performed in Vienna during 1871. (BASF Archives.)

The sources of the ancient blue colorant were plants, most notably *indigofera tinctoria*, cultivated on a vast scale in plantations in British colonial India.[38] During the years from 1880 to 1896 the average annual world market of the natural product was worth 80 million marks, equal to the combined turnover of all the European coal-tar dye factories. Indigo had played an important role in the development of organic chemistry during the first half of the 19th century, and was long known to be chemically complex. In 1826, Otto Unverdorben distilled indigo and obtained an oil, later named aniline (from the Portuguese for indigo, anil).[39] Fifteen years later, Jean Baptiste André Dumas established a formula for indigo (C_8H_5NO), and Auguste Laurent and Otto Linné Erdmann independently isolated the oxidation products isatin and isatic acid.[40]

This was the starting point in 1865 for the work of Baeyer, following his investigations of uric acid, the basis of his doctoral dissertation. The latter had been a research project that arose from industrial interest in novel synthetic dyes, in this case the purple known as murexide, though it was not based on coal tar, but Peruvian guano. Baeyer sought to establish the simplest compound from which indigo was derived, and it was for this purpose that he distilled indigo with zinc dust.[41] He established that indole was the mother substance of indigo, and synthesized indigo from the oxidation product of indole, isatin. However, the only source of indole was indigo itself. In 1869, Baeyer recognized that "if you want to synthesize indole you have, according to the foregoing formula, to introduce into benzene a two-membered carbon chain and a nitrogen atom and then combine them."[42] There was no way then of achieving this. One year later, Baeyer was forced to interrupt his indigo investigations, in deference to the wishes of the more-eminent August Kekulé, who thought he was close to solving the riddle of its constitution. Kekulé, however, came no closer to a solution of the constitution. If nothing else, this episode certainly demonstrates the great prestige that was attached to resolving the constitution and synthesis of indigo.

During the winter of 1876-77, Caro supplied Baeyer with information about a new pathway to indole. Caro had managed to synthesize indole from the dye intermediate diethylaniline, after drawing an analogy with Graebe's synthesis of carbazole from diphenylamine, and bringing about a pyrochemical reaction in a hot tube.[43] Baeyer sent a note of congratulation to Caro and requested details of the yield of the reaction.[44] Though the synthesis of indole was still a topic of academic interest, with little possibility of offering a pathway to the dyestuff, Baeyer's interest in indigo was revived. Since Caro was busy with the development of newly discovered azo dyestuffs, he entrusted the investigation of indole to Baeyer, and they published their findings jointly in 1877.[45] Subsequently, Baeyer reinvestigated the synthetic route to indigo that he had worked on in 1869. The outcome was that in May 1878 he achieved the first total synthesis of indigo. However, in this case he published his results instead of taking out a patent, much to the annoyance of his colleagues at BASF. Baeyer apologised for his apparent oversight:

> I did not think about a patent, because the price of indigo blue is so low.... With tremendous pleasure I gave a lecture about the synthesis of isatin at the academy [the Royal Bavarian Academy of the Sciences] and shortly afterwards I sent the manuscript to Berlin [for publication]. It seemed to be understood throughout the work that this could not be exploited in a technical way.... Do not be angry about it, it is better to do something new.[46]

When Baeyer's first contract expired in 1878 it was not renewed, and from then on BASF's links with Baeyer were through Caro's personal connections. Caro managed to lure Baeyer back to the investigation of indigo, though at first the work was of purely academic interest. In December 1879, Baeyer sent Caro a structural formula of indigo not unlike the modern one, though without experimental evidence, and it was never published. By then, the lack of technical application caused Caro to become somewhat concerned over the future usefulness of Baeyer to BASF. However, at the beginning of 1880, Baeyer succeeded in achieving something new for industry. Starting with the coal-tar product toluene he synthesized indigo. The main intermediate was *ortho*-nitrocinnamic acid.

> Since Christmas the manufacture of new things is proceeding better again and the indigo affair especially has entered a new phase. There is nothing spectacular, the technical indigo is not yet there, but at least a process which uses readily available auxiliary agents has been achieved. Now I must decide as to whether I should publish that immediately, or file a patent.[47]

Caro urged Baeyer to develop this reaction for technical purposes, and Baeyer came to an agreement with BASF, signed on 16 March 1880, that provided Baeyer with 100,000 marks and a share of 20 per cent of the profits on synthetic indigo, with a maximum of one million marks. In return, Baeyer agreed to deliver his patent rights to BASF and to support a policy of "mutual energetic support."[48] In May 1880, Baeyer sent two of his research assistants, Paul Friedlaender and Albert Hehner, to Ludwigshafen to assist with development of the reaction.

Moreover, Baeyer was appointed overall head of the indigo research work done at both Ludwigshafen and Munich, according to a May 1880 memorandum sent to him from the BASF management: "Hereafter you assume full leadership of all operations on artificial indigo that are done in our laboratory–especially under the guidance of Dr. Caro."[49] The agreement specified that all letters from Caro to Baeyer concerning artificial indigo were to be stored in a special copybook, which was always accessible to the BASF management. Baeyer probably did not realise that with his control of the research work for artificial indigo he would become, for a short time, not only the leader of the research effort, but the effective head of the main research laboratory at BASF. On 7 May 1880, the management of BASF wrote to Caro: "We cordially request you ... to engage the staff of the laboratory immediately and exclusively with the indigo-work."[50] On 16 June, three months after the initial contract was concluded with Baeyer, BASF joined with Hoechst to form a research and marketing cartel, probably because both parties feared external competition.[51] The research work carried out at Hoechst was also supervised by Baeyer. Hoechst's task in 1880 was the development of production processes for cinnamic acid.[52] On 14 July 1882, BASF and Hoechst together signed a second contract that covered their mutual interests in the indigo processes.[53] The cartel remained intact until 1897.

Baeyer's original process started with *o*-nitrocinnamic acid and led, via the intermediates *o*-nitrocinnamic acid dibromide and *o*-nitrophenyl-propiolic acid, to indigo.[54] Caro succeeded in the development of a cinnamic acid process that employed benzal chloride and sodium acetate,[55] drawing upon his great experience in the synthesis of triphenyl-methane dyes, such as malachite green. Baeyer was successful in increasing the yield of the desired *ortho*-product of nitrocinnamic acid by employing esters. Even then the yield of *ortho*-compound, the isomer suited to production of indigo, did not exceed 50 per cent. The further development of this reaction was Caro's principal task in the summer of 1880.[56] The *ortho*-isomer, following bromination and treatment with alkali, yielded *o*-nitrophenlypropiolic acid, which was treated with a reducing agent and then, via the intermediates indoxylcarbonic acid and indoxyl, the desired indigo was obtained. Because the chemistry of these stages was poorly understood, the scaling-up of laboratory methods was not successful. In November 1880, Baeyer decided to proceed with a more systematic scientific investigation:

> Concerning my experiments and operations, I must change something. With the everlasting trials there is a waste of valuable time, and it is better to proceed systematically with the numerous workers I have. In the beginning it will be slower, but we have the advantage of being able to move on secure ground.[57]

It was in the same month that Caro established a novel way of producing indigo-printed cloth. This relied on application to the cloth during the printing process of the intermediate *o*-nitrophenylpropiolic acid, which afforded indigo directly by reduction with sodium xanthate. This turned out to be the only commercial application of artificial indigo prior to the first complete synthesis of indigo (though a similar process was introduced by one or two other dye manufacturers). How did the discovery take place? According to Ernest Ehrhardt, and reminiscent of Kekulé,

> Dr. Caro one night in a dream saw in letters of a flame before him the words "xanthate of soda," and tried the next day xanthate of soda. It worked perfectly, and the "propiolic acid" was put into the market for indigo printing.[58]

More likely, however, was Caro's superb command of calico printing science and technology. It was certainly followed closely by the chemical world. From London, Henry E. Armstrong at the London Institution asked

> ... if you will give me some idea of the cost of the pure indigo and the probability of your being able to make it in large quantity. The commercial world here is much excited in the question. What prospect is there that the use of indigo will be rendered unnecessary by the employment of the (1)-[*ortho*-]nitrophenylpropiolic acid for dyeing?[59]

The most detailed account of Caro's work on artificial indigo appears in a letter that he wrote to Henry Roscoe on 11 May 1881. Roscoe had visited the BASF factory in the summer of 1880, and his correspondence with Caro about artificial indigo was considerable.[60] This particular response demonstrates not only Caro's remarkable level of knowledge of both calico printing and applied chemistry, but also Roscoe's own standing at the interface of science and technology, in part as a leading Mancunian academic and in part as son-in-law to Edmund Potter, the calico printer. Caro's artificial indigo was aimed principally at the printing of calico and not at dyeing. It is interesting that Caro did not foresee a threat to natural indigo, which, in his view, would remain essential for dyeing purposes. There were of course difficulties, that Caro readily admitted. Thus, apart from the fact that this was an indirect process, and not based on a particularly abundant starting material, there was also the problem of finding uses for the co-product, *para*-nitrocinnamic acid, which appeared with the desired *ortho*-nitrocinnamic acid. Nevertheless, Caro expressed considerable optimism:

> As far as regards the past and the present of Artificial Indigo I presume that you are in possession of Baeyer's English patent specifications (1880: March 18th, no. 1177; April 30th, no. 1771) which contain a very accurate outline of the process actually in use for the manufacture of Orthonitrophenylpropiolic Acid. It is not saying too much, that a manufacture of the mother substance of Artificial Indigo does in reality now exist. The laboratory-work has been completely finished, and all the obstacles being fully conquered, operations on a manufacturing scale have been successfully carried on in our works during the last two months.[61]

Caro then outlined the manufacturing process, starting with dichloride of benzylene (benzal chloride). This was based on his English patent no. 3,330, of 1880, "a practical modification of Perkin's beautiful synthesis of Cinnamic Acid from Benzoic Aldehyde [benzaldehyde], Acetic Anhydride and Acetate of Sodium." It had been developed during 1878 in Caro's laboratory for his "oil of bitter almonds green" (malachite green, BASF Victoria green) process. The *ortho*-nitrophenylpropiolic acid was delivered "to the trade in the form of a 25% paste, and at a preliminary price of 50sh [shillings] per 1 kilo of the dry acid contained therein." He then went on to explain that the cost of this synthetic indigo was more than twice the price of natural indigo, and

> [c]ompetition with the natural dye-stuff is therefore not to be thought of, until we arrive at a selling price of about 20sh per kilo of the dry Nitro Acid, and at a theoretical yield of Indigo from the Acid. It is not impossible that these stern demands may in some future days be fulfilled–at present we cannot think of manufacturing indigo from Nitrophenylpropiolic Acid.

However, the acid, as Caro had discovered, did show considerable potential for direct printing on cotton when his reducing agent, the "xanthate of soda," was employed. He described this in his letter to Roscoe, which included a comprehensive technical review of progress in printing with natural indigo, as well as of the choice of reducing agents:

> But there is an immediate prospect for turning Baeyer's discovery into practical account. As you are aware of, a great loss of coloring matter is connected with the process hitherto in use for dyeing and printing with Indigo. In the "blue vats" a large percentage of Indigo is lost in the sediment, another portion is washed off and wasted after the dipping, which in order to produce a pattern, Indigo has to be

destroyed before or after it has entered into the fibre of the cloth. Moreover the "back" of the pieces gets needlessly loaded with the coloring matter. The losses are still greater in the printing with indigo. The old "Navy blue style" (Bleu foyence) has ceased to exist on account of the great difficulties, which it presents to the printer; the printing with Indigopulp (Bleu Solide) or Indigo white and Stannous Oxide is of very limited application; Schutzenberger's hydrosulphite process has been abandoned; and only a few printing firms (Grafton, Schlieper in Elberfeld) have lately succeeded in printing Indigo somewhat largely. But no printing process exists, which allows indigo to be used in combination with other colours and mordants, and without the requirement of any special mode of fixing after the printing. The weak point of natural Indigo lies therefore at present yet in the absence of a good process for utilising the whole of its coloring matter or for employing it in the principal styles of Calico Printing. Could indigo be used as freely as Alizarine by the Calico Printer, there would be little doubt that its consumption might be vastly increased. Now, the facility with which Orthonitrophenylpropiolic Acid in alkaline solution may be changed into Indigo blue at once suggested the idea of establishing the reaction within the fibre of the cloth, and experiment proved that Indigo could thus be printed. The first method tried (as fully described in patent no. 1771) was based upon the employment of Grape Sugar [glucose] as a reducing agent. This reaction does not proceed in the cold; upon long standing only minute amounts of Indigo are formed–but at an elevated temperature, from 70° upwards–the change takes place. Unfortunately the production of Indigo blue is rapidly followed by its reduction into Indigo white. It is hardly possible to seize the proper moment, when the coloring matter is fully developed before reduction, [and] ... decomposition, begins to set in. (Indigo white does not stand steaming). Steaming at low pressure and of from 1 to 2 minutes duration gives the best results–and the continuous steaming apparatus (Mather & Platt's) seems to be specially adapted for this purpose–nevertheless our experiments on the large scale were gladly discontinued in this direction, when in November last I succeeded in finding the Xanthate process (Messrs Schott & Segner [BASF agent] can supply you with Directions to use the Xanthate process), which allows the Blue to be formed in the cold. Moreover the Indigo blue is apparently produced in a considerably larger proportion than by the Glucose-process, and absolutely free from its Isomer, Indirubine or Indigopurpurine. An Alkaline Xanthate may be mixed with a solution of neutral salt of Orthonitrophenylpropiolic Acid without producing any considerable change during several hours. Then gradually decomposition sets in accompanied by the formation of Indigo blue and Indirubin. But on allowing the mixed solutions to evaporate, Indigo blue is rapidly developed. Alumina and Iron mordants may be printed at the same time and afterwards dyed in Alizarine, etc. The ready formed Blue stands steaming to a moderate extent, and sufficiently so to allow Alizarine Reds or other steam colours to be fixed at the same time. As the printing colour gets gradually weakened by decomposition it is better to prepare the cloth first with Xanthate of Soda, and then to print upon it the alkaline Propiolate.

So far this process promises well and seems to be a step into the right direction. Several printers have already adopted it, and at present your Manchester Calico

> printers are trying it everywhere. Improvements are sure to follow, both in the economy of the manufacture of Nitrophenylpropiolic Acid and in the printing process. So we may say, that Baeyer's discovery has–within less than a year's time–been rendered of practical or industrial application.

Caro continued to justify his considerable optimism by again drawing attention to the different applications of natural indigo and the cinnamic acid derivative: Natural indigo was for dyeing; the cinnamic acid product was restricted to printing. Furthermore, to dispel any doubt about the potential of the latter it was necessary to look no further than the successes of mauve and aniline black in displacing natural products. In any case, there were other, more viable, threats to natural indigo in the form of newly discovered synthetic dyes:

> I am now hesitatingly entering upon the question, whether artificial Indigo is likely to interfere with, or even to supersede the natural product. It is boldness to prophecy when facts now-a-days travel faster than thoughts. So I can only state what my own impressions are. I never yet for a moment consulted the statistics of the Indigo growth and Trade in reference to what ultimately may become of artificial Indigo. It never troubled my mind, whether the Indigo planter may still exist at 5 shillings the pound of 85 per cent Indigo blue, or what else may be the greatest richness of the natural dye and the lowest possible cost of its remunerative production. I considered natural Indigo and Orthonitrophenylpropiolic Acid as two things bearing no comparison to one another. From the fact, that the one would do what the other could not do, I concluded that there would be no competition between the two, and plenty of room for improvement on either side. Orthonitrophenylpropiolic Acid appeared to me as a new product, endowed with properties so valuable as to render its manufacture imperative. First of all, because the acid allows the formation of a fast Blue colour within the textile fibre, a wish cherished by the Printer–then bearing upon entering into the Chemistry of the Cinnamic Series a new conquest was to be made of a new territory, the importance of which cannot be doubted. Did Perkin consider the price of Archill or of any other Purple Dye, when he originated the vast manufacture of Aniline with no other prospect then before him besides the Mauve or Aniline Purple? Were ever the experiments on Aniline Black abandoned because people prophesised, that a Logwood Black would for ever remain cheaper?
>
> Even at the present prices of Orthonitrophenylpropiolic Acid Printers will be able to use it for light patterns and for new combinations-styles.... [once] its price can be lowered, the printer will be able to use it for heavy patterns or for imitating the blue-vat style. It is of no use thinking at the present of the time when yarns or piece-goods may be uniformly printed or dyed with Nitrophenylpropiolic Acid, nor when Artificial Indigo blue may be used for the manufacture of its Sulpho acid or for the dyeing of wool. It is questionable whether that time will ever arrive before more formidable rivals with natural Indigo blue will have sprung up from our laboratories. Coloring matters of the Methylene-Blue-, the Induline-, or the Azo-Series are more

likely to make an inroad into these present applications of the natural Dye-Stuff.

But the question may be here discussed, whether it is at all probable that Orthonitrophenylpropiolic Acid may in some future time be brought nearer to the present price of Indigo from the plant.

The main setback to the production of artificial indigo was the scarcity of the starting material, toluene, which could then be produced only out of coal-tar benzene rich in toluene. The need for large quantities of toluene would have meant that production of benzene had to be increased, with a consequent drop in its price. But Caro was also optimistic that toluene would become abundant and inexpensive, and that the coal-tar supplies might be supplemented by petroleum-derived aromatic products. As for the by-products of the indigo production–the *para-* derivatives–Caro anticipated that future demand for them might be in the manufacture of aniline and other dyestuffs.

When Baeyer discovered the Indigo, Cinnamic Acid was a laboratory-product, costing about 150 shillings for 1 kilo–now it can be manufactured at the fifteenth part of that price, and in any quantity provided there is enough Toluol to be had. In this respect we need not fear. There is yet more coal tar wasted, than recovered. The regenerative furnaces are beginning to appear upon the scene, the coking ovens will in no distant day be producers of coal tar–even the conversion of Petroleum residues into benzolic hydrocarbons is not to be lost sight of. Then the paranitrocinnamic acid is by no means to be considered as a hopeless waste-product. We shall not succeed in preventing its simultaneous production, but we shall have to find some proper use for it. It is a remarkable fact, that the coloring matters of the Rosaniline group are belonging to the Para series. There may be an outlet for paranitrocinnamic acid.

But the principal thing to be expected is that Baeyer's researches in the field of Indigo will not stop at the present beginning, and that the flow of progress will not reverse its course.

Caro's lengthy and valuable report–which displayed all the optimism and confidence of a man at the pinnacle of his career–was provided to assist Roscoe prepare for a lecture that he was scheduled to give in Manchester on 27 May 1881. By the beginning of May, Roscoe had received samples of the BASF propiolic acid paste from the calico printer Grafton & Co.[62] On 16 May, the day that Roscoe replied to Caro,

Mr. Schott was kind enough to call this morning and brought me a good supply of propiolic acid paste and also the directions for printing. Messrs. Edmund Potter & Co. and Messrs. Grafton & Co. sent me samples to show off their printing.

I congratulate you most heartily on your well-deserved success.

Your name will be welcomed as a member of our new Society [of Chemical Industry].[63]

On 4 June, Henry Roscoe sent Caro page proofs of the complete lecture, in which credit in equal measure was given to Baeyer and Caro. Roscoe observed:

> For as to Baeyer is due all the credit of the discovery, to you is (so far as I can see) due that of its commercial application. Therefore unless you think that the statement will injure you, I beg you will allow it to stand as a true statement of fact.[64]

This was a tremendous source of embarrassment to Caro, perhaps because in his subordinate role to Baeyer he felt that the credit should go to his academic colleague and BASF:

> My Dear Professor Roscoe,
>
> A day or two ago I received the Manchester Guardian containing an extract of your admirable lecture on Artificial Indigo. I need not tell you with what intense interest I read your statements, which–coming from you–claim the full weight of authority. Your views on the present and future of Baeyer's discovery cannot fail to inspire every worker in the new field with confidence and hope of ultimate success. Your lecture has indeed done great service to the case of Artificial Indigo in as much as it has calmed down the too sanguine expectations on the one side, and the derogatory opinions on the other side. Thus you have rendered the atmosphere clear, in which chemists and printers may now go on to work. Allow me, now, my Dear Sir, to thank you for the very kind manner with which you acknowledged the share taken by the Badische Aniline & Soda Works and by myself in the practically carrying out of Baeyer's inventions. Judging impartially, I should certainly say, that great praise is due to the Directors of Our Company for the enterprising spirit, with which at a time, when Artificial Indigo appeared to be solely of scientific interest, they endeavoured, regardless of any pecuniary sacrifice, to found a new manufacture upon the latest results of the laboratory.
>
> But at the same time, my Dear Sir, allow me to confess candidly, that I quite blushed at the overpraise, which You–too kindly–have bestowed upon me. I cannot admit that I have done more, than what any other Chemist in my position and with my means at his command could certainly have done. Constantly advised by Professor Baeyer, and ably assisted by my devoted and thoroughly efficient assistants I have done little else but to conduct the work, entrusted to my hands. I cannot admit, that my name should be placed into undeserved prominence besides Baeyer's name in the history of Artificial Indigo. Let me do more than hitting upon one or two practical steps in the new manufacture before I shall consider myself worthy of such kind remarks, as I hardly dared to read in the concluding sentence of your lecture. Allow me earnestly to beseech you, my Dear Professor Roscoe, that, in the event of your lecture being printed in full, that last sentence may only acknowledge the surpassing merits of Baeyer–and, if you like–the share taken by the Badische Aniline and Soda Works in the practically carrying out of his invention.
>
> With many thanks and kindest regards.
>
> I remain, My Dear Sir, Yours very truly, H. Caro.[65]

While Caro readily discussed the scientific side of indigo work, and the prestige associated with Baeyer's connections, he did not wish to reveal details of the technology, apart from a rebuttal of reports that had appeared in the press concerning difficulties in production of the *ortho*-nitrophenylpropiolic acid. To set the matter straight, Roscoe asked Caro to prepare a statement on the state of artificial indigo for publication in the new *Journal of the Society of Chemical Industry.* Caro decided that this was a job that Baeyer was best qualified to undertake, though he summarised the position for Roscoe.

> My Dear Professor Roscoe,
>
> Immediately after receipt of your kind note I have sent the same with its contents to Professor Baeyer and requested him to do the work which you were so kind as to ask from me. I thought that nobody would be so competent to say a word about the present state and the future prospects of Artificial Indigo as Baeyer himself, and that you would feel anything but displeased to receive a communication for your new journal from Baeyer's pen. On the other hand I feel myself fettered as to any publication of my own disclosing the manufacturing process and actual sales of Propiolic Acid, as well as the improvements which we are trying to arrive at.
>
> Pending Baeyer's decision I hardly need tell you that the statement in the Manchester Papers–taken from a similar article in the "Frankfurter Zeitung"–is entirely untrue. On the contrary, the manufacture of Orthonitrophenylpropiolic Acid is carried out in our works on the large scale and without any interruption. We have succeeded in overcoming all difficulties with which that manufacture was amply surrounded at the beginning. There is hardly any process in the whole range of chemical processes known to me which is so beautifully within the control of the manufacturer as the preparation of propiolic acid from the purification of Toluol down to the last product. We have already been lowering the price of Propiolic Acid from 50 marks to 40 marks the kilogramm of the dry acid, and if we feel sure to increase the consumption by a further reduction of price, we might be able to do so.
>
> The great problem to be solved now, is to obtain the theoretical yield of Indigo from Propiolic Acid–which by-the-by Baeyer has already solved by his latest researches but in a roundabout manner, which however proves that it can be done. If such a process could be found, which ensures the direct and complete conversion of Propiolic Acid into Indigo blue, then I do not see the reason why we should not begin to compete with Refined Indigo, in a similar manner as Artificial Alizarine had to make first its way against Madder Extracts.

Caro also suggested that even if problems persisted with propiolic acid then in the meantime BASF's new alizarine blue would prove a "formidable rival" to indigo in certain applications, particularly the darker shades:

> At all events, you see that I am not disheartened. It cannot be denied that our new Alizarine Blue–on account of its fastness and the great facility with which it can be

> fixed and applied to all sorts of styles–proves a formidable rival of Propiolic acid. But only for dark and full shades. For medium and light blues the tint of Alizarine Blue is too purplish and cannot interfere with Propiolic acid.

Caro closed his response with an observation on the patent section of the *Journal of the Society of Chemical Industry*:

> In my next letter I shall have great pleasure in sending you Baeyer's reply to my note, and a somewhat different extract from the Patent, [that] you wish me to report upon. Do you not contemplate to publish in the New Journal not merely extracts, but critical accounts and full explanations to the General Reader of all Chemical Patents –in a similar way as Emile Kopp used to do in the Moniteur scient.[ifique]–classed according to the special manufacture and to the subject, and written by your members?[66]

In a sense, much of what Caro had predicted to Roscoe in May 1881 turned out to be correct. During 1882, Baeyer and his collaborator Viggo Beutner Drewsen managed to find a second method for the artificial production of indigo, this time using *o*-nitrobenzaldehyde and acetone.[67] However because of the low yield during the nitration, this method did not reach the commercial stage.[68]

Although Baeyer was in control of all the work done at BASF, the division of labour between Baeyer and Caro, representing science and industry, respectively, was apparently not always smooth nor clear. Previously they had equal rights. Now Baeyer was in charge and it must have been difficult for him to head an industrial research and development enterprise at a distance. Baeyer respected Caro greatly as a colleague with equal rights, and highly valued the friendly cooperation with industry. But he was very much aware that in technology, collaborations could be more problematic than in the world of academe.[69] There were also demarcation problems concerning the nature of the indigo cooperation. For example, when one of Baeyer's assistants at Ludwigshafen, Paul Friedlaender, found how to use *para*-nitrocinnamic acid, the useless isomer of the indigo process, for the synthesis of triphenylmethane dyes,[70] the question was raised of to whom did the rights of the invention belong. Was it to Baeyer, since Friedlaender was his assistant, or to BASF, which was, according to the contract, the owner of all inventions made in the context of the indigo work? BASF claimed, and won, control, but Baeyer received his share of the profits on this process.[71]

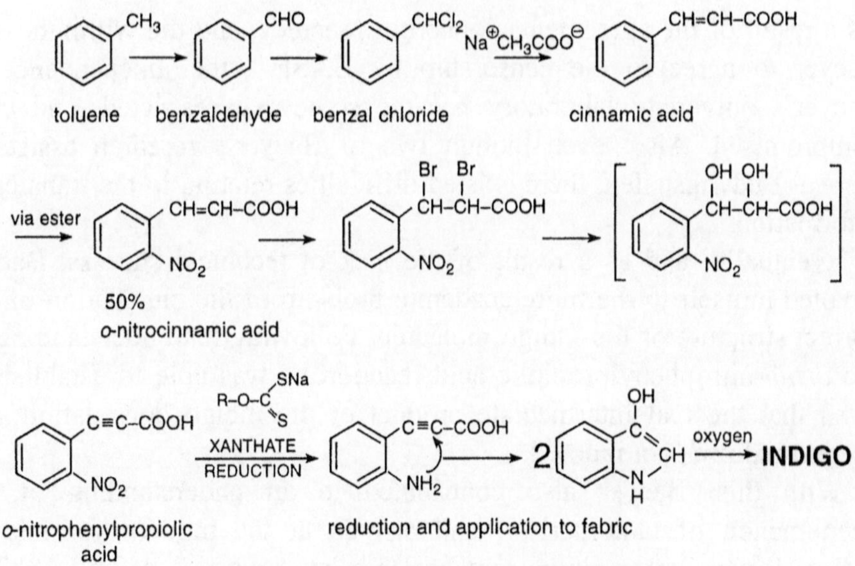

Caro and Baeyer's route to indigo, 1880.

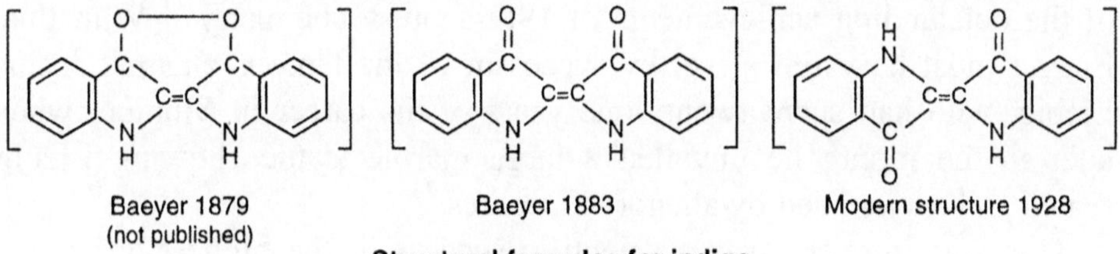

Structural formulae for indigo

As a result of the agreements concerning secrecy, and the willingness of Baeyer to agree to the censorship by BASF,[72] the independence of Baeyer's university laboratory became somewhat restricted, and even compromised. Also, even though two of Baeyer's research assistants were at Ludwigshafen, there existed difficulties relating to the transfer of information.

Eventually, and as a result of the lack of technical success, Baeyer devoted himself to the more academic problem of the elucidation of the correct structure of the indigo molecule. Following his understanding of the *ortho*-nitrophenylpropiolic acid reaction he was able to establish in 1883 that the real intermediate product of the indigo degradation was pseudo-indoxyl, not indoxyl.

With this, Baeyer also contributed to an understanding of the phenomenon of tautomerism, and arrived at the modern formula of indigo. It was with a single sentence in a letter dated 3 August 1883 to Caro, accompanying small talk about the forthcoming Liebig ceremony in Munich, that Baeyer announced the result of years of hard work and one of the outstanding achievements of 19th-century chemistry.[73] With this, Baeyer must have felt a worthy successor of the famous chemist Justus Liebig, who had spent twenty-one years of his career in Munich, when later in the month he unveiled a large marble statue showing Liebig seated and surrounded by allegorical figures.[74]

This was in every way a scientific success of the highest order that arose from academic-industrial collaboration, even though the economic implications were marginal at that time. To arrive at the structure of indigo, the university scientist Baeyer readily accepted the constraints imposed by technical interests: secrecy, emphasis on the investigation of yields, and the search for new production methods. However, the manufacture of *ortho*-nitrophenylpropiolic acid was a minor and short-lived production process; the costs of research and development had been much too high for such a product. The failure of the remarkable pioneering cooperation aimed at replacement of natural indigo with a synthetic product foreshadowed the end of an era at BASF.

Wide-ranging changes in the managing board of BASF at the beginning of 1884 also modified the attitude of the management towards research and development. The new directors emphasised the importance of in-house research, and the strengthening of technical development work. Heinrich Brunck, from 1884 managing director of BASF, had good reasons for his criticism of the indigo synthesis: "In industry, methods are not enough, there is the need for processes, in fact workable processes."[75]

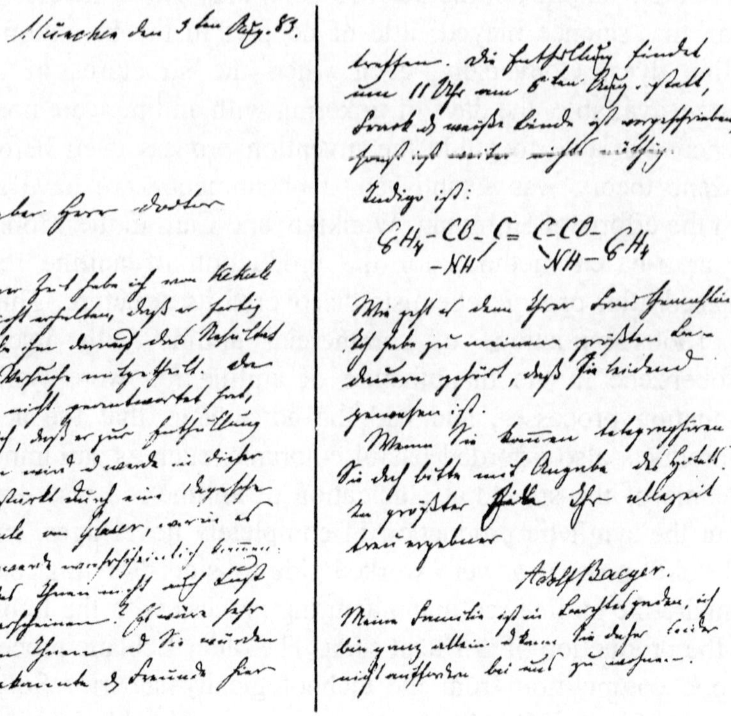

$C_6H_4-CO-C=C-CO-C_6H_4$
$-NH$ $NH-$

Adolf Baeyer.

Adolf Baeyer's letter to Heinrich Caro, 3 August 1883, in which Baeyer includes, for the first time, the most important scientific outcome of their cooperation, the modern structural formula of indigo. (BASF Archives, from an original in the Caro Nachlass, Deutsches Museum.)

No new threats to natural indigo appeared until 1890, when Carl Heumann at Zurich Polytechnic discovered what would eventually become the commercial routes to artificial indigo. They were based on naphthalene (converted to phthalic acid) and benzene (converted to aniline and then phenylglycine). In 1909, at a time when synthetic indigo had already displaced much of the trade in the natural product, Caro's former assistant Ernest Ehrhardt could, with considerable justification, declare the triumph of long-term research and development and massive investment that was only within the means of large and powerful companies.[76]

Aniline red and the structures of the aniline dyes

Despite the economic importance of aniline red (magenta) and its derivatives during the 1860s and after, there was no clear structural information about aniline-derived colorants. Nevertheless, this did not mean that science played little or no part in the invention of the first aniline dyes. Conversely, even when the structures of aniline dyes became available, the days of tinkering with aniline were not over. Thus, science was able to guide the invention process even before Kekulé's benzene theory was established, a phenomenon we have already seen with the efforts of Hofmann, Wanklyn, and Caro in the 1860s. Moreover, the craft-based methods for the production of aniline red were not replaced after organic chemists discovered its structure. This is because the 1860s oxidations of commercial aniline with arsenic acid or nitrobenzene in the manufacture of aniline red were well-established production processes, and had the advantages that the accompanying by-products also afforded useful colorants, such as safranine. The main outcome of the structural elucidation of aniline red was that it brought about the synthetic production of completely novel dyes, and "modern" and "old" processes were worked side-by-side. For this reason we can compare the aniline red manufacturing process with the Leblanc process for the production of artificial soda. The older Leblanc process survived, despite competition from the technologically superior Solvay process, because of its valuable by-products, most notably chlorine.

At the end of the 1870s, through the work of Emil and Otto Fischer, the search for the parent compound of aniline red was successfully concluded. Caro was the crucial figure in this endeavour, though more in his function as a manager of science than through his own investigations. He was intimately aware of how complex and difficult the structural elucidation of aniline red would be and relied for its resolution on his connections to academic chemists, whom he favoured with ideas, compounds, and proposals for investigations. Following Caro's work on the alizarin synthesis, he collaborated with Graebe and Liebermann, especially Graebe, on various scientific problems, which led him back to the study of the constitutions of rosolic acid and rosaniline.[77] The relationship that had been established between these two compounds by Caro and Wanklyn in Manchester was the essential starting point. Further conversions on rosaniline and rosolic acid were achieved by Liebermann with Caro's help and by Caro and Graebe, who in 1873 described their results at the annual meeting of the Gesellschaft Deutscher Naturforscher und Ärzte, held in Wiesbaden.[78] It was on the same occasion that Caro began to discuss academic-industrial collaborations with Adolf Baeyer, and rosolic acid became a subject of mutual interest, especially in connection with the phthaleins and their leuco derivatives, the phthalines. By analogy with Wanklyn's representation of rosolic acid as a triphenylethylene derivative, Baeyer expressed the structures of phthalines in terms of tetraphenylethylene in his correspondence with Caro.[79] Indeed, as late as 1878, he used the ethylene type to express the structures of rosaniline and rosolic acid.[80]

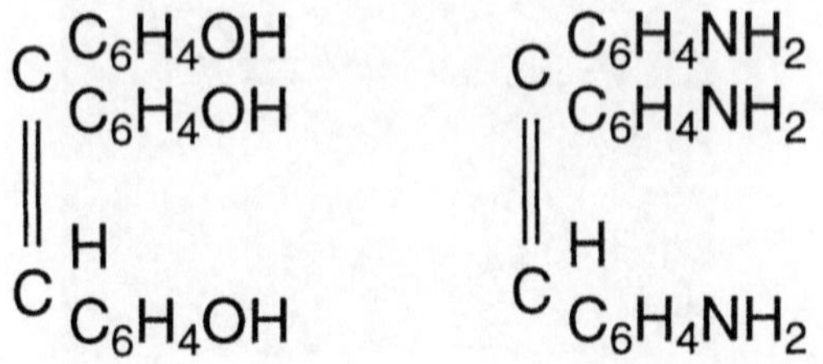

Baeyer's rosolic acid   Baeyer's rosaniline

A little later in the same year, Emil and Otto Fischer published the modern structure for pararosaniline, which they had reduced to triphenylmethane by reaction with nitrous acid and alcohol. Caro and Graebe almost immediately after published details of the closely related structure of rosolic acid, while Baeyer published similar structures for phthaleins.

Caro and Graebe, in their 1875 publication on rosolic acid, rosaniline, and their respective leuco compounds, had suggested that the three phenyl groups in these compounds were connected by two carbon atoms, and not by nitrogen.[81] This was remarkably reminiscent of the ethylene type. The main point, however, was their claim that there existed a common hydrocarbon skeleton for both the rosolic acid and the rosaniline molecules. What they could not explain was the existence of the diazonium compound of rosaniline, which was the link with rosolic acid. Furthermore, Caro and Graebe were not able to synthesize the postulated hydrocarbon precursor by reduction with zinc of rosolic acid, since to their annoyance this destroyed the molecule. At this stage, their joint work was interrupted when Graebe suffered from a nervous breakdown during the winter of 1875.[82] By the time the effort was renewed in 1878, Emil and Otto Fischer had almost finished the job.

Emil Fischer. (Deutsches Museum.)

Emil Fischer was about to embark on a career in organic chemistry that would lead to an appointment as professor of chemistry at the University of Berlin as successor in 1892 of A. W. Hofmann, and the Nobel Prize (1902). Though he is remembered mainly for his investigations of the carbohydrates, amino acids, and peptides, and his mastery of stereochemistry, in the late 1870s he was noted for his research, as a student of Adolf Baeyer in Strasbourg and Munich, on dyestuffs. Fischer's doctoral thesis covered the phthalein compound fluorescein, and was related to Baeyer's and Caro's work on phthaleins and the dyestuff eosin.[83] Otto Fischer, Emil's cousin, also took his Ph.D. with Baeyer at Strasbourg and worked with Emil at Munich. Otto eventually succeeded Emil as professor of chemistry at the University of Erlangen.[84] Both men were among the original members of Baeyer's research school at the time of the close collaboration of Baeyer with Caro and BASF.

In 1876, Emil Fischer discovered phenylhydrazine, later his favoured reagent for structural elucidation of sugar molecules, and with which, jointly with Otto, he synthezised the hydrazine derivative of rosaniline. Then, via the diazo intermediate, they established the formula of the hydrocarbon "mother substance" of rosaniline. This unknown compound, $C_{20}H_{18}$, had eluded Graebe and Caro. Only after the Fischers synthesized the pararosaniline from pure aniline and *p*-toluidine and systematically degraded it did they obtain triphenylmethane, $C_{19}H_{16}$ (a compound known since 1872). From this they established that rosaniline was the methyl homologue of triaminotriphenylmethane (pararosaniline). Two years later, in 1878, the Fischers produced pararosaniline from triphenylmethanc, and this was final proof for the correctness of their structural formula. Otto, especially, used this knowledge for establishing new pathways to dyestuffs. In 1877, he had achieved the synthesis of malachite green (BASF's Victoria green) from benzaldehyde and dimethylaniline, and in 1880 he succeeded with the synthesis of aniline red from *para*-nitrobenzaldehyde. The latter process was never commercialised because of immense difficulties involved in converting the colourless, reduced leuco intermediate into the dyestuff. This was to be a problem in all new syntheses of aniline red until the end of the century.

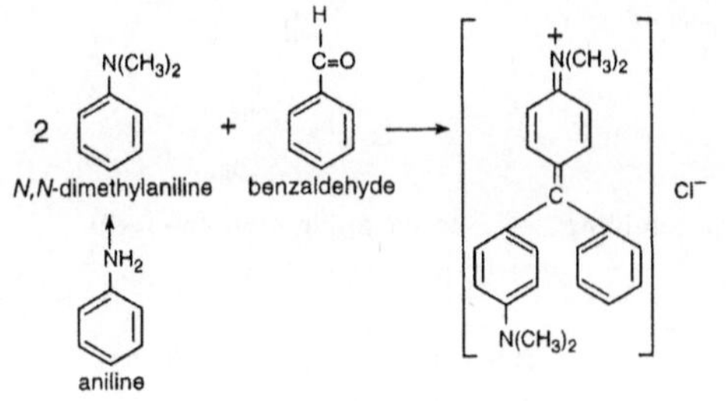

Caro's bitter-almond-oil green
(Malachite green, AGFA; Victoria green, BASF).

Caro's role as manager of science was in facilitating the studies of the two cousins, including with research chemicals. Before the Fischers began their investigations they requested Caro's permission,[85] following an old academic tradition of respecting the topics of other scientists. Caro gave his permission and encouragement, since he knew that Graebe would be removed from the investigation through illness. Emil and Otto Fischer worked under the supervision of Baeyer, who probably had just signed his contract with BASF, and in 1877, Baeyer informed Caro and BASF as soon as his young collaborators achieved their results:

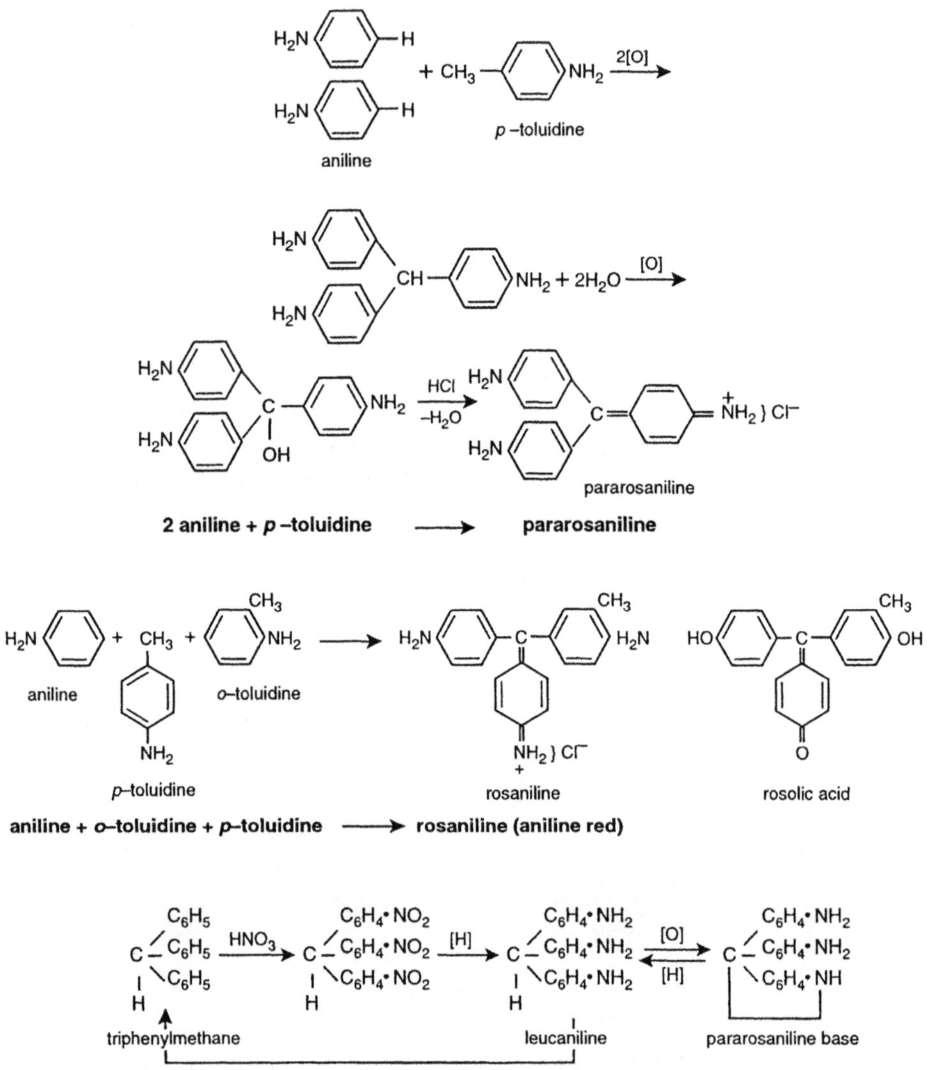

Structure of rosaniline dyes (E. and O. Fischer, 1878)

> Today Fischer has made a discovery of first rank. The hydrocarbon of rosaniline yields through nitration and reduction leucaniline, and the latter can be converted again into rosaniline through heating.... The technical importance of this discovery cannot be realised now, because we do not know if the hydrocarbon can be produced directly and how much the costs would be. However, we have so many excellent synthetic methods at our disposal, and therefore we can also anticipate the technical solution of this problem. I would like to ask you for your opinion on this. Please inform Messrs. Engelhorn and Clemm immediately about this discovery which is so important for the history of aniline red, and give them my best wishes. Apart from them, it would be wise to keep it secret.[86]

In accord with his verbal and contractual obligations, Baeyer always advised Caro and BASF of the results of work that was directly or indirectly supported by BASF, and commented on potential technical applications. In this case the publication strategy was based on strict adherence to theoretical implications alone, and, deliberately, absence of credit to either Caro or BASF for any form of support. Both Caro and the Fischers emphasised, for different reasons, the theoretical character of the researches, and concealed the potential technical applications.

While the Fischers stressed the theoretical importance of the synthesis of rosaniline,[87] and Caro was highly satisfied with this, he was anxious that they did not investigate derivatives of technical interest. This is why in the public domain there was no mention of the fact that Caro had strongly supported Emil and Otto Fischer with information and new substances, nor that Caro took up his studies on rosolic acid again during the first half of 1878. Fischer advised Caro:

> Your investigations into this substance are more suitable to eliminate any doubt about the nature of aurin, far better than the theoretical thoughts we have made on this subject and the, unfortunately, difficult transformation into the hydrocarbon.... Even though it is painful for us to conceal your part in our work, we fully respect your reasons for that requirement and we shall avoid mention in our publications of anything relating to your studies and to any technical purposes, and we shall bear that in mind in the future as well. I promised you last autumn that our research is exclusively for scientific purposes and that nothing would be more agreeable for me than if we could bring an end to the work with an experiment that proves the constitution of rosaniline. A further, more comprehensive investigation of the derivatives of rosaniline is far beyond my time and working powers and, in addition, I agree with your opinion that these investigations will be carried out by others.[88]

Once Graebe and Caro returned to their work on rosolic acid and aurin, they came to an arrangement with Emil and Otto Fischer in which there would be clear separation of their spheres of interest. Graebe and Caro were especially interested in the nature of the dyestuff salts, which they envisaged as molecules containing two amino and one imino group.[89] In connection with this work they succeeded with a new synthesis of aurin from benzophenone.[90] However, the work remained mainly of scientific interest. As for aniline red (magenta), it was commercially available until the end of the century only through the processes dating from the 1860s. Modern synthetic chemistry was useful for production of other dyes. Emil Fischer, who also undertook some work on the second indigo synthesis of Baeyer and Drewsen, maintained his close contacts with Caro and BASF until 1883.

RETORTS FOR THE DISTILLATION OF METHYL-ANILINE.

Distillation following alkylation of aniline. The products, such as *N,N*-dimethylaniline, were important intermediates from the late 1860s. (William Crookes, *A Practical Handbook of Dyeing and Calico-Printing* [London: Longmans, Green & Co., 1874], opposite 192.)

Caro contributed most notably to the synthesis of new and hitherto inaccessible aniline dyes, through his joint studies with the Swiss-based chemist Alfred Kern,[91] at Bindschedler & Busch of Basel. In 1883, the latter enterprise exhibited at the Swiss Federal Exhibition in Zurich large samples of a violet dyestuff called crystal violet. Kern, manager of the aniline dyes department at Bindschedler & Busch, had employed the highly toxic gas phosgene ($COCl_2$) in the synthesis of aniline dyes, though the process was complicated and not yet fully mastered. In part to overcome this technical and scientific difficulty, the Swiss company joined forces with BASF, and for a short period during 1883-84, Kern and Caro worked together. There were two reasons for the involvement of the Swiss: Their great need for inexpensive raw materials and intermediates, available only from the German dye industry, and expertise in patent affairs. Both companies created a research and marketing cartel and arranged prices for products; BASF agreed to pay Bindschedler & Busch ten per cent of profits on dyes developed jointly. The contract was tied to the duration of the patents.[92]

With his background in the production of aurin from phenol and dihydroxybenzophenonechloride, Caro improved on Kern's synthesis substantially during the winter of 1883-84. The new process, developed in 1884, involved the combination of one molecule of phosgene with two molecules of *N,N*-dimethylaniline. The resulting intermediate, Michler's ketone, yielded, with phosphorus oxychloride ($POCl_3$) and one molecule of *N,N*-dimethylaniline, crystal violet (hexamethylpararosaniline). This was immediately recognised as offering a new direction in dye synthesis:

> At this stage the period of joint work in the field of phosgene dyestuffs really began. We finally abandoned the old route involving the condensation of hydrols, which had hardly encouraged us to start the manufacture of phosgene. Firstly, Messrs. Carl Clemm and Jacobsen developed the technical side of phosgene production, while you [Kern] and I, supported by able chemists, investigated the uses of the new possibilities in dyestuff manufacturing.[93]

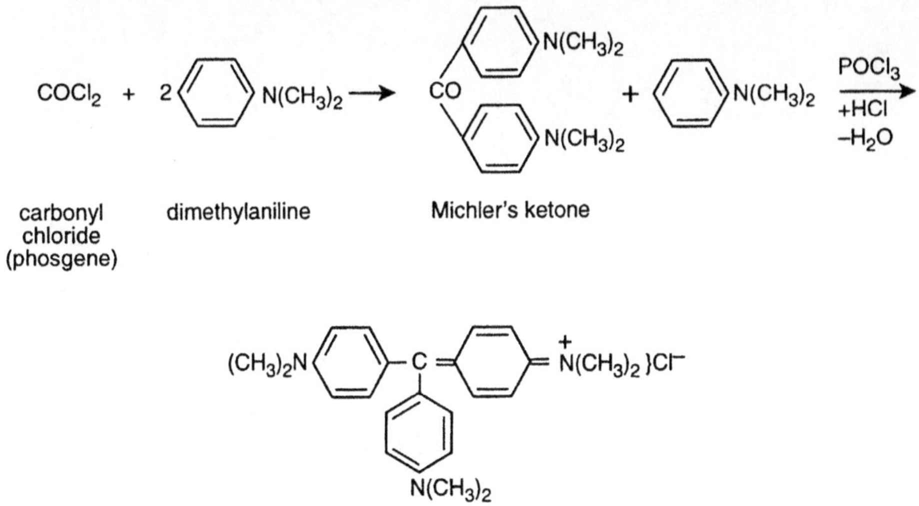

Caro's process for crystal violet, 1884.

BASF in 1881, painted by Eugen Stieler. By this time a second water tower had been erected and buildings for production of intermediates near the harbour, as well as the harbour itself, had been enlarged. Note how loading and unloading were done without the aid of cranes, and the large amounts of steam, smoke, and fumes. (BASF Archives.)

The factory courtyard of BASF, again by Eugen Stieler (1881). In the centre is the soda plant; to the right are the condensation towers for hydrochloric acid, with water tower behind. The white powder in the middle of the courtyard is sodium sulphate, an intermediate product of the Leblanc process for the manufacture of soda. (BASF Archives.)

Because this production process could easily be broken down into identifiable steps, the synthesis of many different intermediates, each dependent on the nature of the starting aromatic amine, was possible. The extent to which Caro realised the value of the new method is indicated in a letter to William Perkin written in April 1884, in which he declared "an endless variety of Rosaniline-analogues may now be built up with the same certainty and ease as Azo-compounds."[94] The collaboration with Kern and Bindschedler & Busch also opened the way to an entirely new dyestuff class, the diphenylmethane dyes, most notably the yellow auramine.[95] BASF and Bindschedler & Busch also reached agreements over indigo and the hydrazone dye tartrazine during the 1880s.[96]

For BASF, the connection with Bindschedler & Busch was important, since even though Caro and BASF were at the forefront of theoretical chemistry in their work on the structural elucidation of the aniline dyes they were unable to attain the technical targets. This was achieved at the Swiss company by Kern working in the manufacturing department, and not in a dedicated research laboratory. Thus while the benefits of structural organic chemistry were open to all capable of realising the opportunities, in this case results were more readily achieved on the factory floor than in a laboratory, as Caro and his academic network discovered when Kern turned to syntheses based on phosgene. BASF was able to exploit the new opportunity by using Caro's competence in patent law, and skills in the production of intermediates. However, BASF was also ahead in other ways, including in the use of alternative syntheses. With the strength of Caro's development work, and his industrial use of phosphorus oxychloride, BASF was even able to circumvent the contractual arrangement with Bindschedler & Busch, and to avoid paying the ten per cent profit share to the Swiss company. Yet again, Caro and his laboratory proved to be a lucrative investment for BASF.

Personal relationships and academic consultants

There were several other important chemists in Caro's academic network.[97] They ranged from occasional contacts and personal friends to academic consultants. Caro's contacts were widespread in the sense that he very often sent samples of compounds, intermediates, reagents, and auxiliary agents to academic chemists. Caro's ability to make fruitful connections with academia was of tremendous value to BASF, and was a model for other profitable cooperations involving BASF and external chemists. This included René Bohn, chief chemist in the BASF alizarin laboratory, and his collaboration with Carl Graebe during the 1880s and 1890s.[98]

The influence of academic research on dye invention at BASF is demonstrated through the distribution pattern for the origins of patents filed by BASF and its consultants from 1877 to 1883. Most prominent was the indigo work of Baeyer for BASF, and the patents on the quinoline synthesis, filed by Zdenko H. Skraup. It is clear that in the early 1880s, BASF's inventive capabilities relied on external contacts as well as on in-house research. This situation would change considerably in the mid-1880s when in-house scientific and technical capabilities exceeded those of any academic chemistry department.

Table 1. German patent applications of BASF and its academic collaborators, 1877 to 1883

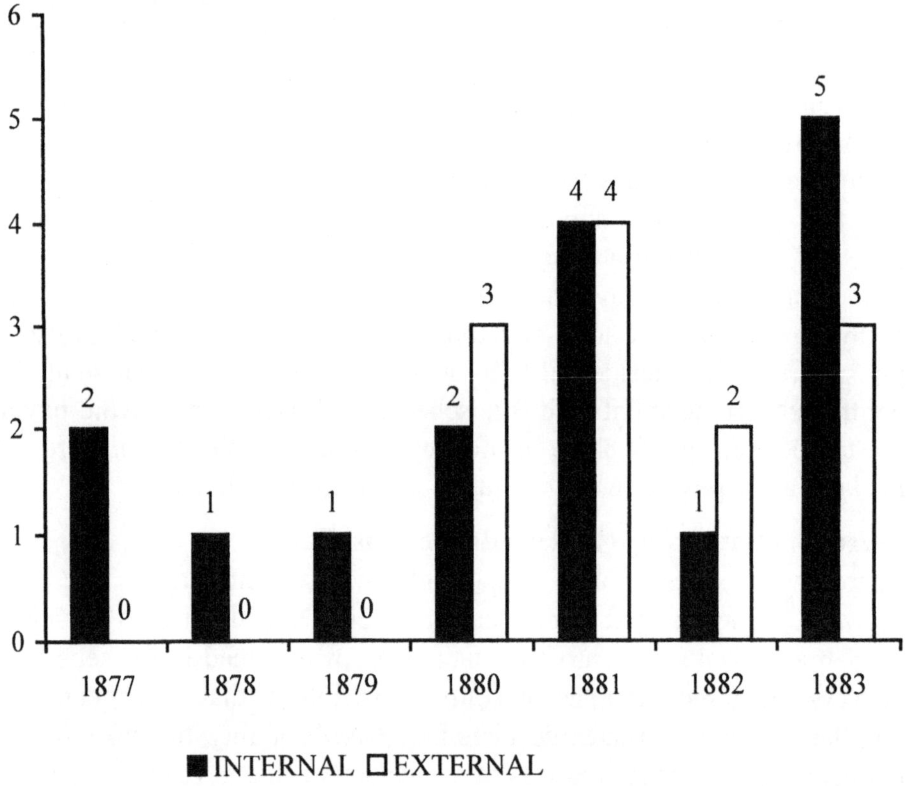

Caro's broad style of contact with the academics ensured that BASF remained the most innovative of the dye-making companies. Thus with close personal contacts, such as with Peter Griess and Victor Meyer, both of whom sent Caro their latest products and details of reactions for joint exploitation, it was the relationship with Caro, and not with BASF, that counted. The more occasional contacts with university chemists were also important to Caro. In addition, important studies for the theoretical understanding of dye chemistry were undertaken in close cooperation with academic chemists, as the work of Emil and Otto Fischer and August Bernthsen demonstrates.

Table 2. External/academic contacts of Heinrich Caro at BASF. This table includes only long-term contacts.

Name	Affiliation	Projects	Duration of cooperation
Adolf Baeyer	Universities of Strasbourg and Munich	Structure of alizarin, phthaleins, nitroso compounds, indigo, etc.	1873-83
August Bernthsen	University of Heidelberg	Methylene blue	1882-87
Carl Engler[99]	Karlsruhe Polytechnic	Methylene blue, patent affairs	1879-84
Emil Fischer	Universities of Munich and Erlangen	Structure of triphenylmethane dyes, indigo	1876-83
Otto Fischer	University of Munich	Structure of triphenylmethane dyes	1876-78
Carl Graebe	Universities of Königsberg and Geneva	Alizarin, acridine, structure of triphenylmethane dyes	1869-83
Peter Griess[100]	Allsopp's Brewery, Burton-on-Trent	Azo dyestuffs	1875-83
Carl Liebermann	Berlin Polytechnic	Alizarin	1869-70
Victor Meyer	Zurich Polytechnic, University of Göttingen	Azo dyestuffs, thiophene, phenylhydrazine	1875-87
Emilio Noelting[101]	Monnet & Co., La Plaine, near Geneva	Eosin, azo dyestuffs	1876-78
Zdenko H. Skraup[102]	University of Vienna	Pharmaceuticals, quinoline synthesis	1882-86
Otto N. Witt	Berlin Polytechnic	Sulphonic acids of β-naphthol, indulines	1885-91

Among various academics, the relationships with Victor Meyer, August Bernthsen, and Otto N. Witt deserve more than a passing mention, because they represent the range of contacts through which new knowledge was shared. Victor Meyer was one of the leading German organic chemists of the second half of the 19th century.[103] Caro had developed a close friendship with the Meyer family when he was in Berlin in the 1850s, and this had turned to joint research activities and other business dealings with the calico printing factory of Victor's father. The main feature of the correspondence between Victor Meyer and Caro is that it covers academic matters alone, and there is no hint of Caro's encouraging Meyer to divert his attentions to applied and technical chemistry. Nevertheless, Meyer did independently investigate blue azo dyes, as possible competitors of indigo, in 1879.[104] He also adopted certain reactions that Caro had discovered at BASF (particularly a carbonyl reaction that was used to establish the ketone structures of sugars) and sent Caro novel products to investigate.[105] In 1883, Meyer discovered a molecule with a ring structure based on four carbon atoms and one sulphur atom. Surprisingly, the new compound, thiophene, showed aromatic behaviour, and therefore was of great interest from theoretical and practical standpoints. Caro supplied Meyer with the starting material required for this work, methylthiophene, extracted from toluene.[106] In return, Meyer informed his industrial friend of progress and especially the possible use of thiophene in the manufacture of dyes.[107] Meyer also conferred with BASF about the possibility of registering a patent on a newly discovered reaction used in the synthesis of phenylhydrazine.[108] The correspondence was continued until 1889, when Caro left BASF and Meyer moved to Heidelberg. Caro, incidentally, assisted Meyer to plan his new laboratory at Heidelberg, which was based closely on BASF practice. This was another important contribution of industrial chemistry to academic science, though, once again, based on friendship rather than on an attempt by BASF to gain further inroads into academe.

A complete contrast was the contact with August Bernthsen, professor of chemistry at the University of Heidelberg.[109] The start of Bernthsen's close connection with Caro, in 1882, arose from his interest in establishing the structure of one of Caro's most important inventions, methylene blue.[110] (See also chapter 8.) Caro was flattered that an academic chemist was willing to tackle this topic, and even supplied

Bernthsen with internal BASF laboratory reports based on his own research.[111] Almost certainly, the cooperation between Bernthsen and BASF was from the start a formal arrangement in which Bernthsen's role was as a project or research consultant. The first collaboration was highly successful: Bernthsen succeeded with the structural elucidation of methylene blue and even discovered a new pathway to the dyestuff,[112] which he protected with a patent:

> As soon as I was confident enough I considered registering a patent, and, in any case with your agreement, I have already tried to protect my findings with the filing of a patent. According to our agreement I will not withhold it from your esteemed factory.[113]

However, this first synthesis was not a technical success. The last stage of the reaction failed, and Bernthsen was at that time not very enthusiastic about concentrating on solving technical problems. In 1884 he wrote to Caro:

> I have not seriously tackled a scientific investigation of the new patents related to nitrosodimethylaniline.... As a whole, I have the feeling that the scientific results of these trials do not justify the effort.... Similarly, I do not lay great stress on further work concerning the transformation of Lauth's violet into methylene blue, and particularly because I do not know if my findings would be publishable.[114]

Since this last reaction step was critical to industrial production of methylene blue, it was of great interest to Caro. To get Bernthsen to work on it, Caro had to remind him of the arrangement with BASF:

> I mention on this occasion that I attach great importance to the organisation of your already established cooperation in the future through continuous investigations of minor importance, that are both of interest for, and do not distract you from, your scientific aims, and are for mutual benefit.[115]

This strategy worked and Bernthsen agreed to discuss research that was for the benefit of both sides,[116] at the same time accepting the conditions of BASF's protective order.[117] There was a good reason for this, since Bernthsen, as a professor without tenure and without a state-sponsored laboratory, relied heavily on support from BASF.[118] During late 1885 and early 1886, Bernthsen was at BASF to make use of its facilities for his scientific investigations.[119] He was supplied with chemicals, and also with Caro's advice concerning suitable assistants.[120] Because of the common interests, the question of secrecy was not usually a problem. Three years after his failure to realise a new technical synthesis for methylene blue, Bernthsen discovered another method, and this time the reaction was commercially feasible. It came just in time, since Hoechst discovered a similar route to the same dyestuff and patented it. With Bernthsen's expertise, and his correct interpretation of the course of the reaction, BASF was enabled to sign a contract with Hoechst and the manufacturer Georg Carl Zimmer of Mannheim that secured BASF the greater part of the market.[121] Heinrich Caro's collaboration with Bernthsen had tremendous implications for the future development of the BASF research organisation, particularly from 1887, in which year Bernthsen replaced Caro as head of research.

Otto N. Witt's connection with Caro and BASF is of particular interest. He had moved from England to Germany in 1879, and joined the Leopold Cassella firm, and then Emilio Noelting in Mulhouse. His next and last factory position demonstrated the difficulty of entry into dye-making by both new and well-established chemical firms after around 1880. From 1882 to 1885, Witt held a senior post at the Verein Chemischer Fabriken in Mannheim with special responsibility for installation of dye-making plant. After sustaining tremendous losses, the Verein pulled out of this activity, and in 1885 Witt moved to the Berlin Polytechnic, successor of the Gewerbeakademie. At about the same time he entered into a contract with both BASF and AGFA, a joint venture in which both firms shared his inventions. This arrangement lasted until around 1891, and possibly longer. Though the results were of little industrial value (Witt worked on the sulphonic acids of β-naphthol, a topic closely related to naphthol yellow, and indulines, an important dyestuff class), Witt's cooperation was rewarded with a regular annual income, though later reduced, probably as a result of his poor performance in 1889.[122]

Summary

In this chapter we have examined a variety of academic-industrial collaborations. These range from Adolf Baeyer's strong influence during the entire period under consideration, even in matters of general research policy at BASF; Otto N. Witt's contractual agreement with BASF commencing in 1885; the project-type cooperation of Caro with Carl Graebe and the Fischers on the structural elucidation of aniline red, and with Bernthsen on methylene blue; and finally the close personal friendship of Caro with the brilliant scientist Victor Meyer. This is comparable to John P. Swann's analysis of the American pharmaceutical industry in the first half of the 20th century, where he differentiated between the general collaboration of a scientist with industry (involving matters of research policy and management of the firm), the contract-bound external scientist who was obliged to deliver his inventions to the company, and the limited cooperation that was restricted to a specific project and time period.[123]

It was the strong charismatic personality of Caro that enabled him to guard the often-fragile bond between science and technology. He was extremely versatile in adapting the forms of cooperation to the changing circumstances and personalities involved, and directing the course of the science-technology relationships in their first and decisive phases. Prior to the mid-1880s, Caro was able to give the contacts a strong personal emphasis, and often his private contacts replaced business contracts and agreements. What becomes clear from this and other studies[124] is that the enduring form of cooperation of academic chemists with industry involved a contract that required the scientist to hand over all inventions of technical value to the firm, very often in return for a royalty on profits and a fixed salary, or retainer. In this connection, it is interesting to note that at the rival Hoechst, the research strategy, directed by Eduard von Gerichten and Wilhelm Roser, was to maintain a network of contacts to external scientists in both dyestuff and pharmaceutical research until the turn of the century.[125] Then the management decided to cut back on the number of outside collaborators, mainly in the dyestuff field, and probably because of their poor performance. For academic chemists, it became more and more difficult to follow the technological momentum of dyestuff chemistry without the access to internal technical knowledge and without the close contact to the research, development, patent, testing, and marketing organisation of a big dyestuff company. With the major exception of Witt, BASF decided to abandon the strong dependence on external inventiveness as early as 1885. For this, it relied on an elaborate in-house research organisation, whose development originated with Heinrich Caro in the mid-1870s.

Heinrich Caro, probably 1879. (Deutsches Museum.)

8
The Industrial Research Laboratory

I think it is desirable to make an attempt to show the inner mechanism by which chemical science has been and is being so successfully adjusted to commercial wants by our continental neighbours.

Raphael Meldola, 1886.[1]

With these words, the British chemist Raphael Meldola, in his 1886 lecture before the Society of Arts in London, commenced a review of the influence of the German dye industry on industrial progress. That influence was hardly more tellingly invoked than by its impact on British chemists, particularly those with industrial experience, such as Meldola, who invented an important colorant, Meldola's blue, similar to Caro's methylene blue, when employed at Brooke, Simpson & Spiller of London. Meldola and others were not slow in recognising the weaknesses of the British dye-making firms, whose decline had started in the mid-1860s, around the time when Caro and other Germans returned to their homeland. It was a few years later, in the aftermath of the Franco-Prussian war of 1870-71, that German hegemony in dye manufacture became anchored in mastery of aromatic organic chemistry to an extent that was not to be achieved elsewhere. This at first took place through academic-industrial research alliances of the sort exemplified by the alizarin work of Caro, Graebe, and Liebermann during 1869-70, and formalised by Caro and Baeyer from 1874. The endeavour was soon woven into the fabric of factory life by the assignment of chemists to laboratories that were increasingly given over to research and development tasks. Thus by the mid-1870s, Caro's research laboratory, dedicated almost entirely to invention, had come into existence at BASF, and by the time that Meldola gave his lecture it had evolved into the central research laboratory. Similar research laboratories became essential features of all major German dye-making firms before the turn of the century.

This institutionalisation of research, apart from one or two short-lived exceptions, was not adopted by the French and British. At La Fuchsine, the Renard successor, Girard and de Laire engaged in research into new aniline dyes during the mid-1860s, but the firm's complacency and poor quality control, encouraged by the monopoly over aniline red, brought about its early demise. At Roberts, Dale & Co., highly novel research was carried out mainly by Caro, with the aid of Martius and other German chemists, but the limited progress was in part due to the lack of reliable explanations of how aromatic compounds underwent reactions. William Perkin had more success in industrial research than the Manchester firm when he tackled the alizarin synthesis, though he was also confronted with considerable uncertainty, and probably relied on clues coming out of Germany after Graebe and Liebermann made their first public announcement concerning the constitution of alizarin. In any case, Perkin worked almost alone in what was really a private laboratory, quite separate from the factory, and which was not included in the 1874 sale agreement of his firm to Brooke, Simpson & Spiller, which two years later sold its alizarin interests to Burt, Boulton & Haywood.

According to Meldola, who had been greatly discouraged by the attitude of the management at Brooke, Simpson & Spiller, scientific discovery based on aromatic–or coal-tar–products provided an opportunity never before available to chemical technology:

> It will, I think, be conceded that the manufacture of coal-tar products is *par excellence* the most scientific of the chemical industries. This high position may fairly be claimed for the industry when we consider the number and complexity of the products, the delicacy of many of the reactions employed, the special arrangements of plant required, and the intimate knowledge of the chemistry of the aromatic compounds which the colour chemist must at the present time possess.[2]

Meldola understood that there were distinct differences between the way that industrial invention was achieved and managed in Germany and England, and by the turn of the century British chemists were aware that success in Germany lay in the modern, dedicated, industrial research laboratory, and in particular the central research laboratory, as prevalent in Germany but absent in Britain. The central research laboratory was an organisational innovation in its own right and by 1900 an important component of all leading science-based dye firms. It was directed by highly qualified chemists (after the 1880s invariably at Ph.D. level), sometimes including members of the board of directors, and was supervised by and directly responsible to the senior management of the firm. The range of activities pursued by the central research laboratory included all established product lines, especially dyes and intermediates, though it was kept quite separate from the day-to-day work of the manufacturing departments. During the 1880s, the central research laboratory evolved into a complex structure, with special sub-departments for patent-related work, a library, an analytical laboratory, a pilot plant, and in some cases a small facility for coloristic studies.

It was not, however, the only laboratory in a typical dyestuff company engaged in research for new products and processes. At BASF, for example, the alizarin and aniline dyes manufacturing departments, two important divisions in the company, were each sub-divided into separate units that catered for particular classes of dyes. The sub-divisions were equipped with works laboratories where routine testing and analytical work was carried out, and in many cases the chemists in charge and their assistants undertook research, and, especially, development work. The heads of the BASF alizarin and aniline dyes departments eventually established their own research laboratories, in 1878-82 and 1884, respectively. These departmental laboratories, as they were called, were much smaller than the central research laboratory, and concentrated on their respective product lines. However, the style of working, and the impact, were comparable to that of the central research laboratory. Complementing this research organisation was the technical dyeing department, a sales and servicing organisation that assisted dyers and printers in the use of dyestuffs, and later increasingly became engaged in new applications research. Through the technical dyeing department, chemists in research and production departments learned about problems and the needs of dye users, and were better able to formulate new products that met the needs of customers.

Though the organisation of the 19th-century research laboratory in the German dye industry–mainly using the example of Bayer–has been explored by historians of science and technology,[3] the way in which Heinrich Caro at BASF became prime mover in its inception, as described in this chapter, has not. Here we show how the various activities that he merged together spawned three distinct organisational units: the central research laboratory, the patent department, and the technical dyeing facility.

Notwithstanding this focus on the BASF laboratories–the constructs of bricks, benches, shelves, ovens, and sinks–there is, surprisingly, a dearth of information about their locations, sizes, and facilities throughout almost the whole time that Heinrich Caro was active at Ludwigshafen. Accordingly, information about the existence of the earliest laboratories has been obtained indirectly, using in particular salary and employment documents in BASF archives. For example, the recorded dates of engagements of chemists and the natures of their assignments has provided much useful information, summarised as follows.

Right from the start, there were separate laboratories in the BASF production plants. They were, as elsewhere in the chemical industry, concerned with analyses and general tests associated with checking the quality of materials and monitoring production processes. Thus, when the newly founded BASF applied in 1866 for authorisation to manufacture aniline and aniline dyes, its prospectus mentioned a laboratory (Versuchslaboratorium).[4] In 1868, on joining BASF, Caro worked in a laboratory at Ludwigshafen, but moved to Mannheim with his assistant, Carl Glaser, in 1869 once the special laboratory for development of the alizarin process was completed at the site of the earlier Sonntag, Engelhorn & Clemm works. The Mannheim factory was sold in 1870, at which time Caro and Glaser returned with their laboratory equipment to Ludwigshafen. When, in 1872 or 1873, Glaser became head of the newly founded alizarin department, he always had a "Betriebslaboratorium" at his disposal, as must also have been the case for other chemists in charge of departments at Ludwigshafen. But even in the big manufacturing units, these early laboratories were mainly concerned with the improvement of existing processes and routine analytical work on raw materials and products. This changed during 1878-84, when research laboratories appeared in each of the production departments, at first in the aniline dye department, followed by the alizarin department. Probably, as was the case in the alizarin department, the research laboratory grew out of the works laboratory.

Caro's laboratory in the 1870s was probably located close to the administration building, and was called simply Laboratorium, but after the founding of the aniline and alizarin departmental research laboratories it was referred to as the Hauptlaboratorium, the main or central research laboratory. This name was subsequently given to a substantial purpose-built building, constructed during 1887-89, which was a complete division in its own right, with scientific and patent departments.

It is significant that in the inorganic department, one of the three large divisions of BASF during its first two decades, there was no research laboratory. This was due to the fact that inorganic production processes were well-established and routine. When, around 1890, BASF did begin research in inorganic chemistry, in connection with the indigo programme, the investigations were conducted in manufacturing laboratories due to the large-scale nature of the work.

Research laboratory beginnings

The formal beginnings of organised industrial research at BASF followed the February 1873 merger with Rudolph Knosp and Heinrich Siegle, both of Stuttgart.[5] Through this merger, BASF acquired a successful marketing organization, and, on the basis of size alone, immediately secured leadership in the international dye-making industry. The Knosp company had long been the principal sales outlet for BASF, and Rudolph Knosp was appointed to the highly influential position of chairman of the supervisory board of BASF.

The firm of Heinrich Siegle manufactured aniline dyes from 1867, in a department run by the then proprietor, Gustav Siegle, son of the founder. Heinrich Siegle specialised in lake dyes, prepared mainly from natural products. Gustav Siegle, educated as a technical chemist at Stuttgart Polytechnic, played a crucial role in the management of BASF as a member of the board during the sixteen years following the merger.[6]

BASF now had two production sites, Ludwigshafen and Stuttgart, with the latter as the centre for pigments and natural products, the location of the main commercial administrative offices, and, most important for Caro's activities, the technical dyeing department, where dyes were tested and customers' problems in application were handled. This arrangement survived until 1889, when the merger with Siegle's company was dissolved and the Stuttgart facilities of BASF were moved to Ludwigshafen, most notably the technical dyeing department.

The merger with Knosp and Siegle had a far-reaching impact on Caro's contractual arrangements with BASF. In 1874, he retained his position as deputy (joint managing) director, though only after protracted negotiations over his status and benefits. The new contract was retroactive to 1 January 1873, just a few weeks before the merger.[7] From that date, in addition to his salary, Caro received two per cent of the annual profits of the whole company. These conditions also applied to deputy director Carl Clemm, though Caro demanded an extra one per cent on profits from alizarin, based on the argument that he was the inventor of the technically feasible route to this important dye.[8]

Caro was obliged to maintain secrecy over all business matters throughout the period of employment, as well as for a further five years following the termination of the contract in 1878. Such protective clauses were normal in contracts between dyestuff firms and their employees, especially chemists, particularly at a time when there was little recourse to patent protection. However, in this case the period of required secrecy following the expiry of the contract was unusually long. This stipulation ensured that in the event of Caro parting company with BASF, he would not be allowed to use his knowledge at competing companies, at least until such time as it would have become somewhat dated. At first there was some concern as to whether or not this specification also applied to inventions Caro might make after he left BASF. However, Caro negotiated successfully for the addition of a rider that would free him to exploit his inventions made after 1878, if he left BASF, without any commitment to the firm.[9] Caro, it is abundantly clear, regarded inventive activity as the most important of his various endeavours, and his greatest personal asset. Certainly this was confirmed by his achievements during the tenure of the 1874 contract, namely inventions among the classes of phthalein, azo, and triphenylmethane dyestuffs. These included the azo colorants chrysoidine and fast red AV, the dimethylaniline derivative methylene blue, and the sulphonated naphthol derivative, naphthol yellow, also known as acid yellow.

It was from 1874 that Caro's role as inventor was to find expression in a distinct organisational unit that evolved around him and would eventually make necessary the construction of the central research laboratory building at Ludwigshafen. Furthermore, through the success of his inventions Caro was in an even stronger position to demand better conditions in 1877, at the time when his earlier (1874) contract came up for review. During the negotiations Caro made clear his considerable dissatisfaction with existing conditions, to the extent that he threatened to sever his connections with BASF altogether. This was, perhaps, no idle threat. Not long before, during the winter of 1875-76, he had seriously considered the offer, initiated by Victor Meyer at Zurich Polytechnic, of a professorship in technical chemistry there, but declined, probably because he still felt bound by his contract to BASF. Caro recommended Hugo

Müller, who also declined for contractual reasons, in this case with Warren De la Rue. Eventually, Georg Lunge, an expert in inorganic chemical technology, and like Meyer a good friend of Caro, received the post.[10] According to Bernthsen, in 1877 Caro considered leaving Germany and setting up in business as an independent consulting chemist in London.[11] This was certainly a serious option, one followed by other chemists with considerable knowledge and experience of the dye industry, particularly the alizarin processes. Thus, in 1879, Benjamin Nickels, formerly of Brooke, Simpson & Spiller, and who had worked at what was once Perkin's Greenford Green site, opened in London an "Analytical and Technical Laboratory," not long after asking Caro for a sample of anthracene for use in a test of its oxidation to anthraquinone.[12]

The BASF management finally induced Caro to stay on, but only by acquiescing to almost all of his conditions. Apart from the financial matters, Caro demanded that he be freed of all managerial responsibilities and given a completely free hand with chemical research, providing that it was directed towards the firm's interests. This was also accepted by the management, as is borne out by the wording of a single paragraph in the supplement to Caro's third contract with BASF:

> The understanding of your duties for the company of the B. Anilin Sodafabrik remains the same as in the previous contract and supplement of 12 October 1874. That is, all inventions that you make in the course of the contractual period and all patents taken out by you pass into the ownership of the company and are to be handed over by you to the company for this purpose. For the specification of your position the following remark is made: You enjoy the right to examine all business affairs of the B. Anilin Sodafabrik; your duty is to pursue the purely chemical part into the details and, above all, to contribute through this to the prosperity of the company.[13]

"To pursue the purely chemical part into the details" was nothing less than a specific instruction to engage in research and development work, probably based on Caro's own demands. Caro had undertaken this, along with his other functions, since 1874, as his many profitable inventions demonstrated. But now there was a distinct difference. It became his full-time occupation. This was further emphasised, according to the terms of the 1878 contract, by the fact that Caro was no longer burdened with managerial responsibilities, even though it was his right as a deputy member of the board to have free access to the firm's business records and to participate in the administration. The mention of a supplement dated 12 October 1874 attached to the contract of 21 May 1874 demonstrates clearly that inventive activities were a recognisable part of the job description even in 1874. In 1878, the arrangement was formalised, and invention was the principal function. Thus, whatever the range of responsibilities in 1874, the new contract, dated 6 February 1878, was unambiguous: At some time between May 1874 and February 1878, Caro received the position of research leader.[14]

Notable is the fact that the number of chemists in Caro's laboratory underwent a considerable increase between 1873 and 1876. These were the years immediately prior to the passing of the German patent law and large-scale industrial research into azo dyes. The expansion in manpower was primarily due to the wide-ranging investigations on alizarin that Caro was following up during 1875-76. Overall, 20 to 25 per cent of all chemists at BASF in the decade commencing 1874 were employed in Caro's research laboratory. The peak year was 1876. After 1880, in absolute terms, the number of chemists employed at what had become the central research laboratory remained constant, and eventually fell to 11.5 per cent of all the chemists employed at Ludwigshafen.

Additional evidence that Caro's laboratory was considered to be a distinct division, and integrated into the firm prior to 1877, can be found in the surviving salary list (Salairkonto) of the clerks and chemists at BASF during 1873-99. Here Caro is recorded for salary purposes under the heading of "laboratory" right from the beginning, even in 1873.[15] The laboratory equipment included high-pressure autoclaves based on English models. At around that time his laboratory was not unlike the "Chemical Laboratory" at the London factory of Brooke, Simpson & Spiller, which "in 1876, was a unique feature in an industrial enterprise. Although very simple compared with modern standards, it may be noted that it contained several interesting items."[16] Whatever the similarities, or differences, in the facilities and functions of these laboratories, that in London would hardly change during the following decades, nor would it be followed with anything much better elsewhere in the British dye industry. The main reason was the absence of the organisational structure and system of hierarchy found in German firms that favoured the creation of formal business units or divisions.

The qualifications of staff also suggest the likely dates when research laboratories came into existence at BASF.[17] Thus the first academically

Table 1. BASF workers, total chemists, and chemists in Caro's laboratory/the central research laboratory (CRL) from 1865 to 1889[18]
Numbers are based on data for the end of the year.

Year	Workers	Chemists	Chemists in Caro's lab./CRL
1865	135	2	0
1866	310	2	0
1867	432	2	0
1868	470	3	1
1869	520	5	1
1870	470	5	1
1871	665	6	1
1872	615	6	1
1873	722	10	1
1874	835	16	3
1875	940	20	4
1876	1,123	19	5
1877	1,244	20	5
1878	1,427	22	5
1879	1,534	27	5
1880	1,922	29	6
1881	2,110	31	6
1882	2,378	34	8
1883	2,423	40	9
1884	2,330	48	9
1885	2,402	49	8
1886	2,628	53	7
1887	2,993	59	8
1888	3,401	66	8
1889	3,596	69	8

educated assistant to join Caro's laboratory was Richard Wienand, a student of Hermann Kolbe at the University of Leipzig, who arrived in August 1874.[19] Within a few weeks a second chemist, Friedrich Köhler, entered Caro's laboratory. Wienand left BASF early in January 1875 and there is no record of his subsequent career. In April 1876, Köhler was transferred to the aniline dyes department, where he was described as an "independent theoretical chemist engaged in the manufacture of aniline dyes, for which he made many improvements."[20]

Köhler was the first research chemist in any production department at BASF, available "to support the manager of the aniline dyes department."[21]

The fact that he was trained by Caro underscores the organisational importance of the latter's laboratory. Moreover, Köhler's work in the aniline department was closely connected to Caro's activities. Thus Köhler invented the aniline dye Lichtgrün S by adopting the sulphonation step that Caro had used in the invention of acid magenta (acid fuchsine, Fuchsin S). Both chemists used the valuable theoretical knowledge that became available with Emil and Otto Fischer's demonstration that aniline dyes were triphenylmethane derivatives. Köhler also undertook research into azo dyestuffs, including his Echtgelb, and these again were studied concurrently by Caro. By the time that Köhler left the Ludwigshafen factory in 1882, twelve chemists were employed in the aniline department, most of them as heads of manufacturing units or as their assistants.[22] Köhler, incidentally, moved to the BASF production site at Neuville, near Lyon, France, and later joined the Schoellkopf firm, based at Buffalo, in the United States. Wienand's replacement at the beginning of 1875 was August Burghard, a pharmacist who had studied in Stuttgart and Göttingen. Burghard remained in Caro's laboratory until 1878, and then moved on to the aniline-dye manufacturing department as works chemist, where he remained until reaching retirement in 1914.[23] Köhler's successor in Caro's laboratory was Edmund ter Meer, a graduate from Baeyer's research school, and who was later a well-known industrialist, following the foundation in 1877 of the dye-making company E. ter Meer, at Uerdingen.[24]

By around 1877, Caro usually had at his disposal two Ph.D. chemists at any one time. An indication of the type of chemist Caro was seeking out in the mid-1870s is provided in a letter he received from Victor Meyer at Zurich Polytechnic, a few months before Meyer tried to lure Caro to join his institution:

> As I see it, you need a young chemist, who works well, reliably and with exactness in the field of organic chemistry and who is obedient and gladly willing to work under your guidance and instruction.[25]

From 1875, Caro's private assistant was Robert Holdmann, who had received a vocational education, and whom Caro later described as "Hülfsarbeiter" [Hilfsarbeiter] (manual worker, labourer). Holdmann joined the predecessor of BASF, Sonntag, Engelhorn & Clemm, in 1864 at the age of fourteen. His laboratory journals for the period between 1875 and 1879 show that despite his inferior position and title, he made a number of important discoveries, especially the conversion of naphthol compounds into the corresponding amino-derivatives, the naphthylamines, and particularly, as seen in chapter 6, β-naphthylamine. These were discovered in the winter of 1878-79 when Caro was in England.[26] In 1885, Holdmann left Caro's laboratory and joined the inorganic department of BASF.

Robert Holdmann (1850-1917), shown here on the occasion of his 50th anniversary at BASF in 1915, one of four employees honoured in this way. Holdmann joined Caro's laboratory around 1875, and became his private assistant. From 1885 Holdmann was in the inorganic department of BASF. (BASF Archives.)

In commercial terms, the best indicator of the importance to BASF of Caro's laboratory is the level of investment in it, as compared with investments in production departments. From 1 January 1873 to 1 July 1876, over 34,000 marks were assigned to the research laboratory, quite a substantial sum if we consider that 250,000 marks went to the huge alizarin manufacturing department. By way of contrast, the small safranine dyes department received just 14,000 marks.[27] The result of this investment in research was that during the nine years commencing 1874, Caro's laboratory was responsible for some 40 per cent of all newly introduced dyestuffs at BASF.[28] In all, seventeen dyes originated in Caro's laboratory, and five and three, respectively, in the aniline and alizarin departments. A further nineteen inventions came from outside the firm, either from other companies or from external academic inventors. While this demonstrates the considerable dependence of BASF on external innovations, as would be expected during that early period, it also emphasises the growing importance of, and reliance upon, Caro and his collaborators engaging in in-house research and development.

Table 2. Research chemists in Caro's laboratory at BASF, 1874 to 1883[29]

Name	*Last place(s) of study*	*Started*	*Left*
Richard Wienand(t)	Leipzig	1874 (?)	1875 (?)
Friedrich Köhler	Giessen	1874	1876
August Burghard	Göttingen	1875	1877/78
Edmund ter Meer	Strasbourg	1876	1877
Ernst Mylius	Berlin/Göttingen	1876	1876
Theodor Reissig	[unknown]	1876	1877
Edmund Chambon	[unknown]	1877	1878
Conrad Schraube	Munich	1877	1882
Eduard Hepp	Munich	1878	1879
Johann Burkhardt	Munich	1878	1879
Friedrich Müller	Munich (not Baeyer)	1879	1880
Paul Friedlaender	Munich	1880	1880
Albert Hehner	Munich	1880	1881
Albin Schillinger	Freiburg i. Br.	1881	1882
Magnus Bösler	Munich	1881	1883
Heinrich Boner	Zurich	1882	1883
Carl Riedel	Munich	1882	1888
Carl Müller	Freiburg i. Br.	1882	1884
Henri Schaeppi	Zurich	1882	1884
Bruno Beyer	Leipzig	1883	1916
Carl Langer	Zurich	1883	1884
Eugen Sapper	Tübingen	1883	1884

By the end of 1883, some twenty-two chemists had passed through Caro's laboratory, eight of whom had completed their studies with Adolf Baeyer in either Strasbourg or Munich. Only four of these chemists remained in Caro's laboratory for two or more years, while four left BASF within two years. Most of the others joined production departments of the company. From 1879 there was also an analytical specialist in Caro's laboratory, the pharmacist Friedrich Feez. General coloristic investigations at BASF were undertaken by Hermann

Spannagel, who worked principally for Caro from 1877 to 1880. It is thus clear that Caro received support in routine analytical and coloristic studies. Spannagel had previously been assigned to the aniline dyestuffs department, to which he returned for the remainder of his career. There he was responsible both for daily control of dyestuffs production and evaluation of new dyestuffs emanating from Caro's laboratory. Caro had one other important responsibility, namely all work related to patent matters, as described later in this chapter.

The connection with Baeyer's research school remained crucial for the supply of qualified personnel to Caro's laboratory. During the years from 1877 to 1880 all but one of the newly engaged chemists came from Baeyer's laboratories, of which the most noteworthy were Conrad Schraube and Paul Friedlaender. Schraube joined Caro's laboratory in 1877 after completing studies in Leipzig, Strasbourg, and Munich, and in his first years with Caro worked on azo and disazo dyes.[30] After five years with Caro, an unusually long period, Schraube then continued research as successor to Köhler in the important aniline department, until retirement in 1911. Friedlaender, another outstanding 19th-century chemist, assisted Caro in the indigo work during the time that it was under the control of Baeyer. Later Friedlaender continued his distinguished career as editor of the standard patent compendium *Fortschritte der Theerfarbenfabrikation und verwandter Industriezweige*, and, successively, as director of the research laboratory at Oehler & Co., and professor of chemistry at Karlsruhe, and Vienna. He was also consultant to Cassella & Co. and Hoechst.[31] Schraube and Friedlaender highlight both the stability and the fragility of Caro's newly founded laboratory. Schraube's career developed entirely with BASF in-house research, firstly under the supervision of Caro, and then as director of his own research laboratory. Friedlaender never joined the ranks of BASF chemists and his involvement in the indigo project was an outcome of the collaboration between BASF and Baeyer. The fact that Baeyer's role in this was as an external research leader emphasises the uncertainties of the BASF research organisation in 1880. Indeed, during the following decade the importance of the central research laboratory waned considerably, and the direction and leadership of the laboratory became increasingly insecure. Only after 1890 did the central research laboratory revert to its former importance.

Over the four-year period 1874-78 that Caro's research programme became established–in its formal, organisational, personal, and financial respects–the industrial research laboratory, whose sole task was invention and innovation, became a characteristic feature of the German chemical industry. That the tasks of the industrial research laboratory were clear as early as 1879 is indicated in a letter from Rudolf Nietzki to Caro, in which Nietzki described his responsibilities at the German dye company Kalle & Co.:

> I have my own small but nice laboratory and nothing to do with the manufacturing; moreover I shall have the same position as you have in Ludwigshafen: That of an inventor![32]

Critical years

Changes in the composition of the BASF management board at the beginning of 1884 led to replacement of Friedrich Engelhorn and Carl Clemm by Heinrich Brunck and Carl Glaser, elevating the latter two men to the same level as Heinrich Caro, who continued to be responsible for both research and, increasingly, patents. However, decisions related specifically to cooperation in research with other companies, and also the general direction of internal research and development at BASF, were from now on made by the entire general management of BASF. Up to 1884, Caro's laboratory had been the principal instrument for engaging and executing the strategic decisions of the company, notwithstanding the activities of the dedicated research laboratories in the aniline and alizarin departments. In addition, some significant research was now undertaken in the inorganic department, although in this case not in a dedicated research laboratory.

During the five years commencing 1884, Caro's inventive activity was to decline as a result of the organisational changes, the substantial inventive successes in the departmental laboratories, and his increasing involvement with patents, both in screening the inventions of competitors, and, most notably, the defence of BASF patents in court. The outcome was that during the critical years from 1884 to 1889, when an important new line of azo dyes emerged, only three of BASF's twenty-six newly introduced dyestuffs originated in Caro's laboratory, compared with seven from external sources, seven from the alizarin laboratory, where the talented chemist René Bohn was in charge from 1884, four from the aniline laboratory (under the supervision of

Schraube), and five from the various manufacturing units.[33] Throughout these final years of Caro's career at BASF, the central research laboratory was to become the least important source of innovation, at least on the basis of the number of viable dyestuff inventions providing a reliable indicator of innovative activity. However, it would take on tremendous significance in the technical preparations for patent battles, the most important activity for Caro at BASF during the latter half of the 1880s.

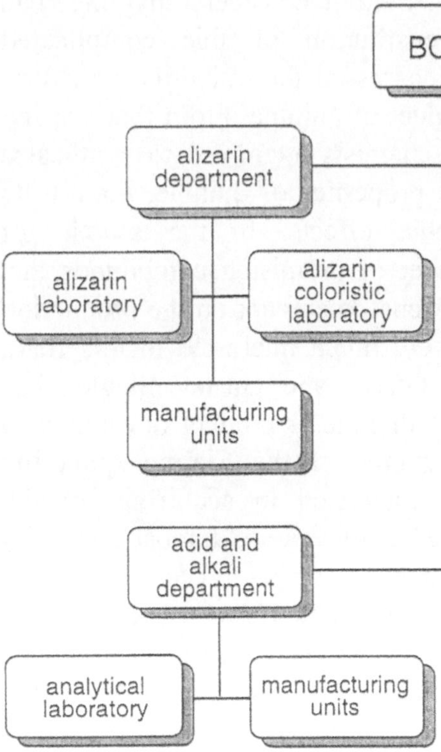

Organisation of the technical departments of BASF, 1890.

From the beginning of the 1880s it had become increasingly clear that Caro alone was not capable of handling the entire responsibilities of both research and patent matters. A new research leader was required. This appointment was recognised to be of such crucial importance that the review and selection process was allocated to the supervisory board.[34] During 1882-83, the management of BASF had sought out a first-rate academic chemist, either an organic dyestuff chemist or a specialist in heterocyclic organic chemistry, to head the research department. While this effort failed, partly because of the management changes during 1883 and 1884, it is also an important indicator of the growing connection between science and industry.

This connection is shown by the interest in heterocyclic chemistry at the beginning of the 1880s, which was mainly focused on nitrogen-containing ring compounds, certain of which showed a structural relationship to quinine. A number of chemists, including Wilhelm Koenig, Otto Fischer, and Zdenko Hans Skraup, considered that they had come close to establishing the constitution of this complicated compound. It was clear that quinine possessed the quinoline structure, since quinoline was a degradation product of quinine. From that starting point, many academic and industrial chemists attempted to synthesize substances that exhibited the curative properties of quinine, mainly its anti-malarial, but also its antipyretic, effects. In the search for antipyretics, they came across a number of promising compounds that encouraged dye companies such as Hoechst to embark on the production of pharmaceuticals. BASF was also very much interested in this field, mainly through the efforts of Carl Glaser and Gustav Siegle. The outcome was the synthesis in 1885 of thalline, a product developed in collaboration with Skraup, the discoverer of the Skraup quinoline synthesis.[35] In addition, BASF was interested in acquiring broader expertise by taking on specialists in the heterocycle field, most especially Eduard von Gerichten and Hermann Ost.

In 1882, von Gerichten (later Vongerichten) was professor in Erlangen, but was closely connected with the Baeyer research group in Munich, an important centre of quinine-related research. Von Gerichten's interest at that time was mainly in morphine, and this obviously interested Caro, who in the summer of 1882 invited him to join BASF. Later in the year, von Gerichten responded:

> On the basis of your kind offer last summer to help me in the transition to industry I advise you that I have now decided to establish whether I am of any use in industry. You know as well as I do that the alkaloid question is now reaching the industrial scale, and eventually I hope to achieve something there. At least I know the field well.[36]

Caro, urged on by Gustav Siegle, who was anxious to employ the alkaloid specialist, again encouraged von Gerichten to consider joining

BASF.[37] But it was in vain, since he had already accepted a position at Hoechst, where he later founded the central research laboratory.[38] Ost,[39] best known for his textbook of chemical technology, contacted Caro at the beginning of 1884, when he was still an assistant of Kolbe in Leipzig.[40] Shortly thereafter he became lecturer in organic chemistry at Hanover Polytechnic. Dissatisfied with inadequate funding for laboratory equipment, Ost sought out a post in industry, where he could make better use of his knowledge and experience than was possible in Hanover.[41] Caro was delighted when he received Ost's application, and immediately proposed that Ost should continue his researches in organic chemistry at BASF.[42] But Ost withdrew his application in February 1885 after he received the title of professor at Hanover and sufficient funding for his laboratory there. He did, however, establish a shortlived alliance with BASF, with himself as external collaborator;[43] this was terminated by the end of 1885. With the failure of BASF to attract a specialist in the newly emerging field of synthetic pharmaceutical chemistry, the endeavours that had started with thalline soon came to an end. In contrast to Hoechst, Bayer, Kalle & Co., and other dyestuff companies, BASF did not continuously engage in production of pharmaceutical compounds.

Nevertheless, the experience of Hoechst, where a specialist in alkaloid chemistry became the founder of the central research laboratory at that company–and where dye research was also continued alongside pharmaceutical research–demonstrates that such a specialist could have played an important role in supporting Caro as director of research and patent affairs. The problem was that the management at Ludwigshafen, which included Caro, was continuously on the lookout for a scientist for that purpose in the very period, 1882 to 1887, when upheavals and abrupt changes in personnel and policy were taking place at the most senior level of BASF.

Failure, however, was not for want of trying. There were even attempts to lure Emil Fischer away from his promising academic career. In May 1883, Gustav Siegle tried to hire him, but without sucess despite the offer of a very high salary.[44] Notwithstanding his decline of the BASF post, Fischer used the summer of 1883 to synthesize at Ludwigshafen compounds he needed for his research.[45] Friedrich Engelhorn made a second attempt to bring about a permanent association by suggesting that Emil Fischer and his academic colleagues Adolf Baeyer and Victor

Meyer should become scientific consultants for the company. A letter from Victor Meyer to Baeyer reveals that the offer included the substantial sum of 5,000 marks a year, with the stipulation that they should visit the factory once or twice a year in order to provide advice, and hand over to BASF their inventions. Following the management changes at BASF this proposal did not materialise.[46] At the same time, during 1883 and 1884, BASF tried to hire Carl Engler,[47] Otto Fischer, Peter Griess,[48] and Richard Meyer[49] (the brother of Victor), but was unable to do so. Caro's response to Otto Fischer, following the collapse of negotiations, may well have been typical.

> Today I received your notice rejecting the job offer we have made you in our enterprise, which I deeply regret. I had hoped to win over a faithful colleague and collaborator with you, and to solve the great and beautiful tasks of dye practice. Naturally I cannot change your decision, and I am afraid that you appeared to be more concerned with the difficulties and shady sides of the practical profession than with its high value and incomparable advantages over the teaching profession.[50]

Heinrich Caro, at age 45. (Deutsches Museum.)

Gustav Siegle (1840-1905) in 1872, one year before he merged his Stuttgart-based dye-manufacturing and trading business with BASF. (BASF Archives.)

The change in the management at BASF continued to affect Caro's situation. Now that he had lost his favourite patron, Engelhorn, on the latter's retirement, he was forced to accept the burden of more managerial tasks than he was previously accustomed to, especially in connection with patents.[51] In addition, he was uncertain as to how the collaboration with his new colleagues on the board of BASF, Carl Glaser and Heinrich Brunck, would develop. Cautiously, he renewed his contract in 1884, but only for one year, since he was not convinced that he was suited to the new style of working.

Indeed, in 1885 he remained at BASF only following difficult negotiations, the outcome of which was a contract for the four-year period commencing May 1885 that gave him an annual income of 15,000 marks, two per cent of the profits (a minimum of 20,000 marks was guaranteed), and an additional commitment that he would receive 10,000 marks per annum during the five years after his contract expired. With these stipulations, Caro was at the same senior level as Brunck and Glaser, in keeping with his 1884 requirement that nobody at BASF should have a higher income than he did.[52] Because of the guarantee, Caro's annual income was more consistent than during 1878-83, when each year he received 14,580 marks plus profits. This was the same as Carl Clemm's remuneration (during this period August Clemm and Engelhorn received 20,580 marks per annum). During 1873-77 Caro's annual income was 12,000 marks, plus profits.

In order to lighten the burden of his patent work, Caro proposed that an assistant be appointed to support him for a short period during 1885.[53] This was Henri Schaeppi, who had first entered Caro's laboratory in December 1882 after completing his studies at Zurich Polytechnic. In 1884 Schaeppi left Caro, and by the following year was described as a "technical-chemical employee." In a letter to the BASF management, Caro described the new role he had in mind for Schaeppi as assistant in patent affairs, and explained that with this appointment he would be enabled to maintain better contact with the research laboratory. This would be difficult, in Caro's view, if he continued to bear the burden of what he described as unproductive patent work.[54] In patent matters, which included the preparation of court demonstrations, experiments, and technical trials, Caro proposed that Schaeppi should work independently.

In the scientific field, however, Schaeppi would be under the close supervision of Caro. Though nothing came out of this proposal, it does indicate that at the time even Caro underestimated the importance of patent protection, which he considered unproductive, but which was in every respect as valuable to the firm as the process of invention. A few years later, Heinrich Caro would demonstrate this decisively in both England and Germany.

As for Schaeppi, he accepted a position as representative of BASF in Manchester and returned to Ludwigshafen in 1886 to take charge of important patent litigation then taking place in England. He left BASF in 1888.[55]

Eventually, in November 1887, BASF succeeded in acquiring an experienced research chemist for the central research laboratory. He was August Bernthsen,[56] then assistant professor at the University of Heidelberg and who had maintained close contact with Caro from 1882. They had cooperated in research on methylene blue, and Bernthsen was successful in both determining the structure of this important dyestuff and in providing BASF with an alternative synthetic pathway. Caro was particularly keen to hire Bernthsen, who had certainly proved his worth to BASF. Caro acted as mediator when differences arose between Brunck, Glaser, and Bernthsen over patent royalties on inventions that Bernthsen had made during his time as external collaborator with BASF.[57] Despite the fact that BASF offered Bernthsen an annual salary of 20,000 marks (double the average income of a professor), and that his position at the University of Heidelberg was insecure, he at first hesitated, and considered other options. However, after the Ministry of Education of the Grand-Duchy of Baden refused to pay him a fixed income and negotiations with the Polytechnic in Graz, Austria, failed because the salary offered was considered too low, Bernthsen agreed to accept the post at BASF.[58] He began work at Ludwigshafen on 15 November 1887.

Following Bernthsen's appointment, the central research laboratory was divided into two departments, one headed by Caro, the patent laboratory, and the other headed by Bernthsen, the scientific-chemical department. There was room for about five chemists in each of Bernthsen's and Caro's departments.[59] Though the laboratory facilities were excellent, Bernthsen was highly disappointed that he could not gain direct access to information about the production departments at BASF, mainly to establish possible research topics. This information was highly classified, even within the factory, where the management followed a policy of maintaining strict secrecy about production matters. After Bernthsen complained, he was told to review the patent applications of competitors in order to provide guides to his research.[60] This also highlights the sort of conditions that Caro had to endure.[61] Paul Julius, one of Bernthsen's closest collaborators, and his eventual successor, wrote that the young August Bernthsen had a hard time gaining acceptance. He was looked upon as an unwelcome scientific intruder by the old practical chemists of the factory. Even Caro did nothing to make Bernthsen's initial steps smoother.[62]

Caro remained the leader of research and patent affairs on the management board, and Bernthsen was subordinate to him. In a letter to the management Bernthsen described his future tasks:

> Therefore I am to be head of the scientific-chemical department of the main laboratory and receive my instructions from the management. I shall direct work on topics that will be given to me by the management, dealing with the creation of new, or the improvement of existing, branches of manufacture. I shall also support the scientific investigations of the various departmental laboratories on demand and provide advice to the work of the department of patent affairs at the request of the management. Furthermore, I am to deal with the establishment of new manufacturing branches and processes on my own initiative, based on the scientific and technical literature.[63]

Independent research was just one of the regular tasks of the scientific department, which dealt also with the planned expansion of existing processes and products, and their improvement, though only at the management's instructions and not from dealing with individual divisions. It was also a reservoir of knowledge, always at the disposal of the management. The tasks of the scientific department of the central research laboratory were mainly related to the rhodamines, discovered in 1887, and direct azo dyestuffs, such as Arthur G. Green's primuline. Green had followed Meldola at Brooke, Simpson & Spiller, and, also in 1887, discovered primuline, which, despite its importance, as was immediately recognised by German companies, including BASF, was not patented by his somewhat apathetic employer.[64]

Bernthsen also oversaw the last stages of a project that Caro had been prominent in bringing about, the construction of the new central research laboratory building (Hauptlaboratorium), started in 1887 and completed in 1889. The two-storey building incorporated several departments and laboratories, including the patent department, assigned to Caro, and stood next to the main management building at the works entrance. With its various sections and laboratories, the central research laboratory was the largest research unit at BASF. From 1888 it was equipped with a pilot plant (Technikum), whose head was Bruno Beyer, and an analytical laboratory, whose first head was Friedrich Feez, followed by Richard Fink.[65] In addition there was a well-stocked library, a large and comprehensive collection of samples, and the patent office. From 1891 to 1895, the technical dyeing department occupied a part of the same building.[66]

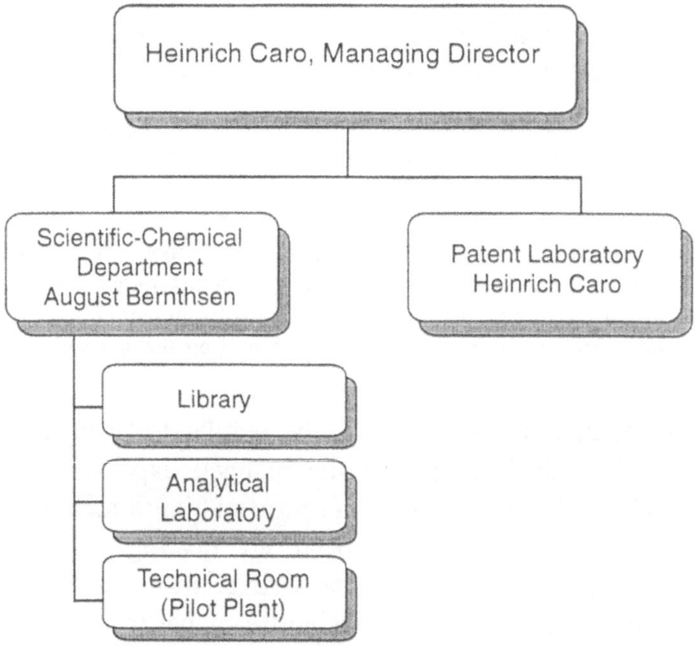

Organisation of the central research laboratory at BASF, 1888.

Patent affairs

From the moment that Caro joined BASF, his special responsibility was patent affairs, no doubt as a result of his experience in England and his multilingual talents. Caro drew up most of the patent specifications during his time at BASF, including those destined for the American and English patent offices, and probably the French ones as well. The main emphasis of his later patent work, however, was not in the writing up of patents, but in their protection. It was, in particular, necessary to defend them in court, through scientific argument, demonstration experiments, and the opinions of expert witnesses. In the late 1880s about half of the research chemists in the central research laboratory worked in the patent department, such was its importance to the continued profitability of the firm.[67]

The screening of competitors' patents was the task of every chemist at BASF who did research in his specific field. The work necessary prior to filing patents was the duty of the research or works chemist who had made an invention, involving drawing up of specifications in collaboration with a lawyer and Caro or Bernthsen. These activities, however, were not the only functions of Caro's patent laboratory. Its principal purpose was the experimental underpinning of the patents prior to litigation, an endeavour often requiring far more work than the original invention.[68]

When litigation was the only course of action, it had to be in accord with the laws and customs of different countries, the most important of which were Germany, Great Britain, and the United States, each of which had a different patent system and law. In Germany there was a mechanism that allowed opposition to a patent application at the patent office if a party with rival interests considered the application to be unjustified or invalid. There were also increasing numbers of cases of litigation in the civil courts, generally involving actions directed against unauthorised or unlicensed use of patents. The scientific preparations for these civil actions were a major task of the central research laboratory. Lengthy, comprehensive reports had to be drawn up and instructions for experts and lawyers carefully prepared, in addition to demonstration experiments.

Particularly important was a series of patent suits over Caro's methylene blue, patented in 1877. This provides examples of the directions that disputes and litigation took, and of how these were affected by new knowledge that became available after patents for new processes were filed. At first, the structure of the blue dye was not known, nor were the natures of the intermediates, and, therefore, the mechanism of the reaction was unclear. With this limited knowledge it was difficult to defend Caro's patent against circumvention, since it would have been impossible to show that changed reaction conditions did not amount to a different process.

The basis for Caro's discovery of methylene blue was his collaboration with Baeyer on nitroso compounds, that were prepared by the action of nitrous acid on imino compounds. Caro's invention was suggested by the work of the French chemist Charles Lauth, who in 1876 succeeded in the synthesis of a new colorant, soon known as Lauth's violet. For his process, Lauth treated *p*-phenylenediamine with hydrogen sulphide and ferric chloride. The problem with this synthesis was that in 1876 *p*-phenylenediamine was not an industrial product, and the yield of the dyestuff was not high. With a thorough grounding in nitroso compounds, and an understanding of the potential of Lauth's work, Caro immediately synthesized, starting with *p*-nitroso-*N,N*-dimethylaniline, a derivative, *p*-amino-*N,N*-dimethylaniline, or 4-(dimethylamino)-aniline. This was similar to Lauth's intermediate, and Caro succeeded in producing a dyestuff with a different shade but in a much better yield. This was Caro's methylene blue, for which in December 1877, BASF obtained its first German patent (number 1,886) following the introduction of the new German patent law in that year.[69] Despite its commercial success and many circumvential patents, the structure of methylene blue was established only in 1884 by August Bernthsen. Thereafter, nitrosodimethylaniline, the intermediate for methylene blue, became important in the production of dyestuffs such as toluylene blue, Meldola blue, indophenol, gallocyanine, and the indamines class.[70]

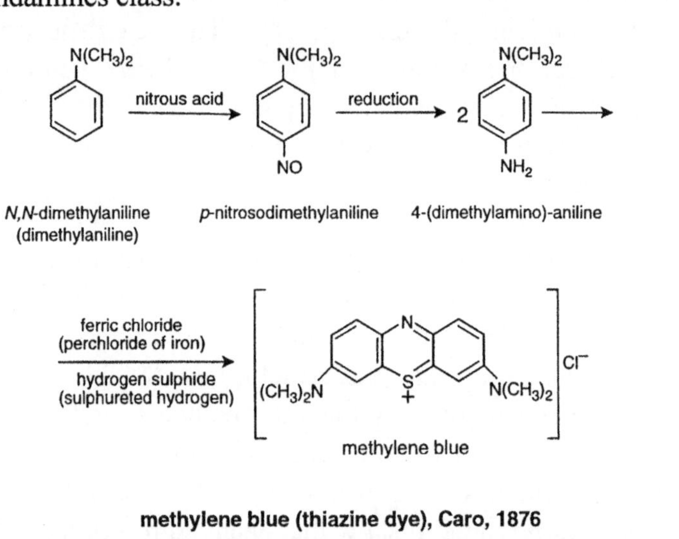

methylene blue (thiazine dye), Caro, 1876

(4-(dimethylamino)aniline = *N,N*-dimethyl-*p*-phenylenediamine = *p*-aminodimethylaniline)

PATENT-URKUNDE

№ 1886.

AUF GRUND DER ANGEHEFTETEN BESCHREIBUNG UND ZEICHNUNG IST DURCH BESCHLUSS DES KAISERLICHEN PATENTAMTES

Badische Anilin- & Soda-Fabrik in Mannheim

EIN PATENT ERTHEILT WORDEN.

GEGENSTAND DES PATENTES IST:

Verfahren zur Darstellung blauer Farbstoffe aus Dimethylanilin und anderen tertiären aromatischen Monaminen

GESETZ v. 25. MAI 1877.

ANFANG DES PATENTES: 15 December 1877

DIE RECHTE UND PFLICHTEN DES PATENT-INHABERS SIND DURCH DAS PATENT-GESETZ VOM 25. MAI 1877 BESTIMMT.

ZU URKUND DER ERTHEILUNG DES PATENTES IST DIESE AUSFERTIGUNG ERFOLGT.

Berlin, den 7 August 1878

KAISERLICHES PATENTAMT.

Beglaubigt durch

Sekretär des Kaiserlichen Patentamtes.

Cover page of Heinrich Caro's methylene blue patent, DRP no. 1,886, accepted on 15 December 1877. This was the first dyestuff process to be patented following the passage of the German patent law of 25 May 1877. (BASF Archives.)

UNITED STATES PATENT OFFICE.

HEINRICH CARO, OF MANNHEIM, GRAND DUCHY OF BADEN, GERMANY.

IMPROVEMENT IN THE PRODUCTION OF DYE-STUFFS FROM METHYL-ANILINE.

Specification forming part of Letters Patent No. **204,796**, dated June 11, 1878; application filed March 28, 1878.

To all whom it may concern:

Be it known that I, HEINRICH CARO, of Mannheim, in the Grand Duchy of Baden, in the Empire of Germany, have invented a new and useful Improvement in Dye-Stuffs or Coloring-Matters, which improvement is fully described in the following specification.

The object of my invention is the production of a blue dye-stuff or coloring-matter, which is derived from tertiary monamines, and particularly from dimethyl-aniline.

My invention is based on suggestions made by Charles Lauth, (Bericht der Deutschen Chemischen Gesellschaft, 1876, page 1035; Bulletin de la Société Chimique de Paris, 1876, II Sem., page 422,) who obtained a purple coloring-matter by the action of sulphureted hydrogen and of oxidizing bodies upon the para-diamido compounds of benzole or its homologues. This reaction, however, has not yet received any practical or industrial application, chiefly because the purple coloring-matters thus obtained offer neither in point of quality nor of economy any advantage, when compared with the already existing coloring-matters of a similar tint.

By using, among others, the chemical agents indicated by Lauth, I have succeeded in producing from dimethyl-aniline, and some other tertiary monamines, in a direct and economical manner, a blue dye-stuff or coloring-matter, which forms the subject of my present invention.

The process of producing this blue dye-stuff or coloring-matter is divided into three successive steps: first, production of nitroso-dimethylaniline; second, reduction of this substance into amido-dimethylaniline; third, transformation of the latter into the blue dye-stuff or coloring-matter which I have termed "Methylene-Blue."

First step: For the purpose of producing nitroso-dimethylaniline, I prepare a cold solution of ten kilograms dimethyl-aniline in thirty kilograms concentrated muriatic acid and two hundred liters water. To this mixture I add a solution of 5.7 kilograms pure nitrite of soda (one atom) by allowing it to run in slowly, while constantly agitating the mixture, for from four to five hours. The mixture assumes a yellow color, and it contains crystals and a solution of the muriate of nitroso-dimethylaniline. Instead of using the pure nitrite of soda, an equivalent quantity of free nitrous acid or other compounds of this acid may be used.

Second step: For the purpose of reducing the nitroso-dimethylaniline into amido-dimethylaniline, the ordinary agents may be used, such as metals—viz., iron, tin, or zinc; but I prefer to use for this purpose sulphureted hydrogen in the following manner: I place the solution of muriate of nitroso-dimethylaniline, obtained as above stated, into a wooden tank, which is closed, and provided with a mechanical agitating device, and with an escape for the surplus sulphureted hydrogen, and I add to said solution five hundred liters of water and fifty kilograms of concentrated muriatic acid. Then I inject a stream of sulphureted hydrogen until the yellow color of the solution disappears entirely. During the reduction the liquid assumes for a time a red color, and finally it becomes colorless, while its surface is covered with a blue froth or scum. In this stage the solution contains muriate of amido-dimethylaniline, and already a portion of the new sulphureted coloring-matter in the form of a colorless compound. Instead of gaseous sulphureted hydrogen, I can use in the same manner sulphuret of sodium, sulphuret of ammonium, or other sulphurets which are decomposed by muriatic acid, to be added successively to the solution.

Third step: The formation of the blue coloring-matter requires the addition of an oxidizing agent to the solution, which is obtained under the second step, and which is colorless and saturated with sulphureted hydrogen. For this purpose I add to the same slowly two hundred liters of a solution of perchloride of iron, (specific gravity 1.07,) or a sufficient quantity of the same until the odor of sulphureted hydrogen disappears, and a small surplus of the oxidizing agent is present. Instead of perchloride of iron, I can use an equivalent quantity of bichromate of potash, or of a similar oxidizing agent; but I prefer the perchloride of iron on account of its cheapness. Instead of causing the oxidizing agent to act on the solution of amido-dimethylaniline containing sulphureted hydrogen, I can reverse the

Text of Heinrich Caro's United States patent for methylene blue, no. 204,796, of 11 June 1878. (BASF Archives.)

operation by treating the amido-dimethylaniline first with the oxidizing agent, and then converting the colorless and inconstant oxidized product thus formed and contained in a strongly acid solution into the blue coloring matter. In this case it is requisite that the oxidation and the introduction of sulphureted hydrogen shall follow each other rapidly, and the introduction of the sulphureted hydrogen must be stopped as soon as this gas slightly predominates. For this reason the last-named process is more difficult than that first described.

The separation of my blue coloring-matter is effected as follows: The mixture is saturated with common salt, and a sufficient quantity of an aqueous solution of chloride of zinc is added until the coloring-matter appears completely precipitated. Then the mass is filtered, and from the substance remaining on the filter the blue coloring-matter, which is easily soluble in water, is separated by successive treatment with water. The filtered solutions of the same are again saturated with common salt, and by the addition of chloride of zinc, and by filtering, pressing, and drying, the desired coloring-matter is obtained as a compound with chloride of zinc in the form of a brown bronze-powder. In this form the new coloring-matter is easily soluble in water and adapted for technical use. For this reason the chloride of zinc is used in preference to other metallic salts and precipitating agents, which also allow of bringing the new coloring-matter in a marketable condition; but I do not confine myself to the use of chloride of zinc.

The production of amido-dimethylaniline can also, as is well known, be effected by the reduction of mono-nitro-dimethylaniline; and, furthermore, this base is also formed when any diazo compound is transformed into an azo compound of dimethyl-aniline, by bringing it together in its atomic proportion with dimethyl-aniline, and such azo compound is treated with reducing agents.

For the practical manufacture of my blue coloring-matter, however, I consider the transition through the nitroso-dimethylaniline, as above described, the most advantageous.

By the process above described blue coloring-matter can also be produced out of dimethyl-aniline, dimethyl-orthotoluidine, methyl and ethyl diphenylamine, and analogous tertiary monamines, the same as out of dimethyl-aniline. Such coloring-matters, however, possess no superiority over the coloring-matter produced from dimethyl-aniline, either as regards the cost of their production or their coloring properties.

The proportions which I have given for mixing the different substances together give a satisfactory result; but they can be changed within wide limits, and I do not limit myself, therefore, to the exact proportions above stated.

My new dye-stuff or coloring-matter, "methylene-blue," when produced in the form of a powder, has a dark-bluish color, not dichroic; it is easily soluble in water; it is but very slightly affected by acids or alkalies; by reducing agents, such as zinc-dust, it is decolorized, and when brought in contact with air it will reassume its color; when it is brought together with metallic tannates, insoluble blue compounds are formed; and in dyeing and printing, this property is employed by forming said insoluble compounds in the fiber of the fabric.

In these points my methylene blue differs essentially from the so-called "methyl-blue," and from all aniline-blues known to me, since these coloring-matters are reduced by alkalies, and they do not form insoluble blue compounds when brought together with metallic tannates, which facts are well known to practical dyers, and to dealers in coloring-matters and dye-stuffs.

What I claim as new, and desire to secure by Letters Patent, is—

As a new manufacture, a dye-stuff or coloring-matter having the characteristics above described, and produced by means substantially such as herein set forth, or by any other means which will produce a like result.

In testimony that I claim the foregoing I have hereunto set my hand and seal this 22d day of February, 1878.

HEINRICH CARO. [L. S.]

Witnesses:
WM. PICKHARDT,
C. GLASER.

Up to 1883, this lack of understanding became highly problematic once new methylene blue processes were patented. In one instance, an 1881 patent of AGFA, BASF was supported by two highly respected scientists, Baeyer and Kekulé. Their opinions on the invalidness of the AGFA patent was accepted by both sides without engaging in litigation. Rival inventors, however, were not always so judicious. "Speculative" patentees, particularly Wilhelm Majert of Berlin, were Caro's main concern. The Berlin-based dye-making firm Ewer & Pick used certain of Majert's processes, and had taken out patents for processes that gave the BASF dyes methylene blue and auramine. This resulted, in 1886, in the purchase by BASF, for a considerable amount of cash, of the Ewer & Pick patents. In June 1886, Caro asked Raphael Meldola in London to undertake laboratory experiments based on one of the Ewer & Pick patents:

> Did you ever obtain any results whatsoever by the patented method of Ewer & Pick? We never succeeded in doing so. According to my opinion the said patent–the author of which is Dr. Majert, a well-known schemer–has never sprung from the laboratory. Patents of that class are highly detrimental to the progress of industry on account of their impeding the work of legitimate investigators.
>
> Whichever way we turn we find ourselves already blocked up by similar speculative claims as those, as Dr. Majert is framing immediately after the appearance of every noteworthy discovery.
>
> I only make these remarks in order to point out to you, that there are two sides to the question of raising the scientific standards of manufacturing chemists. Whilst providing them with the means of understanding the scientific principles of their manufacturing operations, we likewise open the seductive road of speculative labour, unless we ingraft into their minds, more than before, the love of truth.[71]

Another German competitor of BASF, Oehler, had a valid patent for a different process that yielded the same end product, methylene blue. Oehler's brand name was ethylene blue, and in Germany there was no way for BASF to halt its production, since under German patent law a patent protected only the process, and not the product. However, the situation was different in the United States, where only a substance could be claimed under a patent. To prevent the sale of ethylene blue in the United States, BASF had to prove that Oehler's product was identical to its own. For that purpose, BASF sent a former employee of Caro's laboratory, Magnus Bösler, to America, and supported him with analytical work that was done during February 1884 in Ludwigshafen.[72]

In the meantime, the patent situation over methylene blue had changed again, this time, in 1883, through research at BASF, Hoechst, and by

August Bernthsen, then an external collaborator of BASF. Bernthsen established that methylene blue was a phenothiazine derivative, but a new technical synthesis based on this failed because the yield was too low. Nevertheless, Bernthsen's work established the close relationship of the phenothiazine dyes to the indamines, dyestuffs that contained no sulphur atom but otherwise had a very similar structural basis. With that knowledge, Carl Roth was able to find a new pathway to methylene blue. This was patented by Hoechst, which now threatened BASF's methylene blue market. Shortly afterwards, research done by Bernthsen afforded another synthesis for methylene blue, based on the structural elucidation of methylene red, a co-product of the methylene blue production process.

Bernthsen's new pathway involved well-characterized intermediate compounds, instead of Caro's empirical process, and he also corrected the supposition by Roth and Hoechst that the sulphur atom entered during the final stage of the reaction. Furthermore, Bernthsen's knowledge allowed the preparation of many isomers and homologues of methylene blue almost at will. The patent based on this research was attacked by Hoechst. In the resulting litigation, August Kekulé was an expert witness for BASF and Johannes Wislicenus and Emil Fischer for the plaintiffs (Hoechst).[73] The outcome was an agreement involving Hoechst and Georg Carl Zimmer of Mannheim, in which BASF negotiated 55 per cent of the market share.[74] This particular example demonstrates the importance of both scientific knowledge and Caro's patent laboratory to the defense of patents in court. Despite the fact that the patent of Hoechst was filed at an earlier date, BASF was able to obtain the greater part of the market share, through applying the detailed knowledge available from Bernthsen's research.

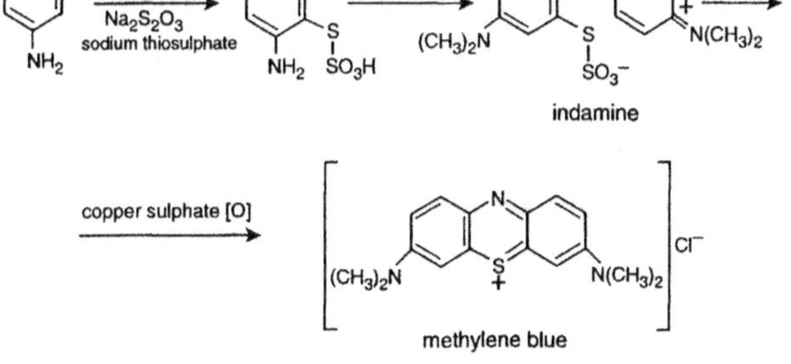

Pathway to methylene blue, Bernthsen, 1884

During the second half of the 1880s, Caro's workload increased substantially as BASF attacked rival products in court, and its own patents on profitable products were assailed.[75] In 1886, at the same time as BASF was fighting Ivan Levinstein in England over its fast red AV (see chapter 9), Caro advised the management on litigation concerning naphthol yellow against Levinstein, and A. Leonhardt & Co. in Germany, England, and the United States.[76] Litigation involving more than two parties was especially difficult, and the outcomes involved considerable uncertainty. For this reason, Caro recommended that BASF should not engage in litigation against Levinstein and Leonhardt over unlicensed manufacture and sale of naphthol yellow by the former, and the validity of the rival English naphthol yellow patent of the latter.[77] A pertinent reason why litigation was to be avoided, if possible, was the large amount of time and money that had to be invested, not only in the courtroom but also in the laboratory.

In preparing for the naphthol yellow court cases, Caro investigated in detail the reaction steps involved in the production process during the winter of 1885-86.[78] At the same time he was busy with litigation against Geigy of Basel over the French auramine patent. With his wide-ranging international background in protection of BASF patents, Caro would later be the principal expert court witness in patent suits that did not involve BASF. The most famous of these was the Congo red case (chapter 9).[79]

Patents, and their support, were certainly extraordinary influences for stimulating research in the industrial laboratories. And much more so than is suggested by the standard explanation that invention in industry became important as a result of the German patent law of 1877, which forced firms to cease imitation and commence their own research. The very placement of a novel dye into the market provided the stimulus for a competing firm to establish its constitution and often, also by analysis, the production process, which endangered the product's value. Piracy was aided by the fact that analytical methods at the end of the 1870s were so advanced that there was rarely a dye recipe that could not be worked out from routine laboratory studies. Therefore, the inventor of a new dye had to patent it, with a carefully worded description, prior to embarking on licensing arrangements, in order to fully safeguard his interests.[80]

These activities led to the mushrooming of a complex and vast patent literature. As a result, research leadership came to rely as much upon a thorough knowledge of the patent literature as it did on the scientific literature. Screening and reworking of patents constituted a major function of the industrial research laboratory in the dye industry.[81]

The importance of Caro's role as patent expert for BASF is further indicated by what transpired after he decided to leave the firm in 1889, the same year in which the association between Gustav Siegle and BASF was dissolved, and the marketing and technical dyeing departments were transferred to Ludwigshafen. Caro did not announce his intentions before October of that year, much to the distress of his colleagues on the management board, Glaser and Brunck. They knew that it would be extremely difficult to replace him as patent expert at such short notice, if at all. In the event, Glaser and Brunck put a lawyer, Max Hecht, in charge of patent affairs,[82] assisted by chemists, "who, because of their duties in our company come into contact with patent matters."[83] Explicitly, the chemists' collaboration involved patent support work for new patents, and litigation over existing patents. Glaser became supervisor of the newly established patent office, though this organisational restructuring turned out to be a provisional solution.

In actual fact, the counseling with Hecht became increasingly the duty of August Bernthsen, who also took over legal affairs. That the position of Caro had to be taken by both a lawyer and a team of highly skilled and innovative chemists points to the relevance and breadth of his duties in the years before he left BASF. Moreover, Glaser and Brunck could not afford to lose Caro's expertise altogether. They attempted to hold him to a consultancy agreement, which would bind him close to BASF.[84] Caro tried to avoid this, and Brunck and Glaser had to ask the supervisory board for assistance in their negotiations with him.[85] Knosp, chairman of the supervisory board, arranged a position for Caro on the board and on the "Engere Commission" (Inner Committee, the executive committee unit of the supervisory board), and, finally, Caro came to an agreement. His exit contract with BASF gave him 20,000 marks a year and it obliged him to deliver all his inventions to BASF and to be available as an expert, especially in patent matters. His role was that of a "berathender Sachverständiger der Direction" (consulting expert of the management). He was obliged to undertake special investigations on request, to give advice for ongoing patent litigations, and to support BASF in the handling of new patent applications. Moreover, rights for Caro's future inventions that were connected to established BASF products were to be transferred to the company without any special reward. Only in the case of entirely new inventions was BASF obliged to make payments, though the amount was to be determined by the supervisory board.[86]

Caro accepted the contract in the spring of 1890, and continued to keep in touch with BASF until his death in September 1910. In this period he made two notable discoveries, a new production process for rhodamine dyes in 1894,[87] and in 1898 Caro's acid, mono-persulphuric acid,[88] employed extensively in the following years by Baeyer, Eugen Bamberger, and other academic chemists.

After the departure of Caro, Bernthsen received a more senior appointment, and was placed in full charge of the central research laboratory, including the chemists in Caro's former patent laboratory. Glaser was Bernthsen's supervisor at the board level.[89] The main problem experienced by Bernthsen was his ongoing poor relationship with the production departments, and the weak connection to the "scientific side of the business."[90] As late as October 1889 he was investigating employment outside of BASF, in this case at the University of Göttingen.[91]

Bernthsen's only way of acquiring information about BASF's business affairs was indirect, and mainly through his work for the patent lawyer Max Hecht. As Bernthsen advised Kekulé:

> I am involved in the sense that I have to check most patent documents before they are delivered to Dr. Glaser and that means hopefully a more active contribution by me to the tempo of the company.[92]

Caro's resignation provided Bernthsen with the opportunity to develop his own career at BASF,[93] which actually followed a similar path. Hecht commited suicide in 1897, and Bernthsen, who had, prior to this date, been involved as a consultant on patents, took over the BASF patent office and merged it with the rest of the central research laboratory. Thus from 1897, Bernthsen was director of the entire central research laboratory.[94] Paul Julius was head of the scientific section and Julius Abel head of the patent laboratory. Bernthsen became increasingly responsible for patent applications and litigation that involved all departments at BASF.[95] It was the nature of the business rather than sheer coincidence that caused both heads of research at BASF during the 19th century, Caro and Bernthsen, to move over to patent work in the course of their careers.

The research tasks of the central laboratory at BASF between 1890 and 1914 were related mainly to the well-established requirements of the dye-using industries. Direct azo dyes and the rhodamines continued to be major research fields. The difficulties of finding top-level scientific staff for this work, even in Germany, caused the management to make enquiries elsewhere. Around 1894, the Englishman Arthur Green was offered "through the good offices of Dr. Heinrich Caro, a post in the Central Research Laboratory at Ludwigshafen, at an adequate salary but with unsatisfactory prospects in view of my nationality."[96] Green's reputation derived from his discovery of primuline and related products. He declined the BASF offer, and moved from London to the Clayton Aniline Company of Manchester, where he introduced dye manufacture, aided by "my staff, [which] though small and mainly composed of Alsatian and German elements [including relatives of the owner, Charles Dreyfus], was a loyal and capable one, and we were quite a happy family."[97] In 1901, Green left for a post at the University of Leeds.

Summary: Research at BASF, 1870-1914

The origins of the central research laboratory at BASF can be found in the demand for increased technical expertise once the company recognised the need to introduce new dyestuffs and processes in order to make full use of its production capacity. It is noteworthy that as early as 1870, BASF was a highly integrated company and produced its requirements in inorganic reagents and organic intermediates on-site. The discovery of novel recipes for dyes shifted the emphasis away from imitation towards invention from the early 1870s, increasingly through collaborations with academic chemists. The research programmes undertaken by academic chemists brought about strong connections between science and industry. This background was responsible for a steady flow of compounds and reactions in both directions, and for mutual benefits. The research laboratory was the lens of the firm within its sphere of influence, screening dyes and patents, maintaining contact with the academic world, and developing new products and processes in specific fields.

In the same way that they had created synthetic alizarin, academic and industrial chemists pursued new and major strategic goals, notably the synthesis of the natural dyestuff indigo. For this purpose, around 1880, BASF was willing to put its resources into the research work of Adolf Baeyer, a leading academic chemist. Notwithstanding these ambitious and far-reaching goals, it was also important to pursue the more mundane needs of the existing dyestuffs market in order to generate profits that sustained research. This was another feature of the research process, involving routine screening of competitors' dyestuff samples, and was continued, often with increasing intensity, even after the passing of the German patent law. However, from around 1880, it was the screening of patent literature that became more and more complex, and important, for research chemists. Little wonder then that in patent matters it was necessary to replace Caro by one lawyer and several chemists! There must have been times when his experience was sorely missed.

After 1890, research on artificial dyestuffs was conducted independently of academic chemistry and shop-floor practice. Dyestuff research now had its own institutional and almost exclusive setting, the industrial research laboratory, with closely defined objectives, the invention of commercially useful products, and a system of publication, namely, the patent recipes for specific products or groups of products.

Although the central research laboratory had become an integral part of the strategy and structure of BASF, contact with the production departments was weak, such that routine investigations and research were done in their own laboratories. The outcome was that research for the development of the two most important dyestuff classes, the aniline and alizarin dyes, was undertaken in departmental research laboratories. Strategic goals were pursued by specific chemists located at different sites within the factory, though under the close control of the management. Following the failure of the strongly academic-directed indigo programme in the early 1880s, research at the central research laboratory of BASF moved away from novel innovations.

In 1897, the year in which synthetic indigo was first produced commercially, studies at the central research laboratory into azo dyes and rhodamines were supplemented by the sulphur dyes, at that time also a major research area. In 1899, azo lake dyes were a new and very successful form of application. The start of the 20th century witnessed novel research into the anthraquinones, until then completely dominated by the alizarin laboratory. This widened the potential for research into the important indanthrene-type vat dyes. Just before World War I, the central research laboratory diversified into the development of catalytic hydrogenation and the invention of synthetic tanning agents. In this period, the central research laboratory controlled the core technology, and the most important market of BASF, namely the dyestuff business. The research laboratories of the aniline and alizarin departments continued with the same tasks in their respective fields.

Increasingly, innovations that were responsible for the wider diversification of BASF were not made in the central research laboratory but elsewhere in the company. The successful indigo synthesis of 1897 was realised in the aniline and the inorganic departments. The liquefaction of chlorine and the contact process for the production of sulphuric acid were developed in the inorganic department. Research and development work for the synthesis of nitric acid was carried out in the indigo department, as was research for synthetic rubber. The high-pressure synthetic ammonia process was also developed in the inorganic department. Therefore, strategic research for technological goals in the long run was decentralized at BASF. Increasingly, the inorganic section became the focal point. The almost total absence of the central research laboratory in these endeavours was quite remarkable, though perhaps an outcome of the previously exclusive emphasis on aromatic chemistry.

BASF factory, Ludwigshafen, by Weeser-Avell, 1889. In the middle background are the new central research laboratory and the administration buildings. By this time, loading and unloading of ships on the Rhine had become more mechanised. (BASF Archives.)

The central research laboratory (Hauptlaboratorium) of BASF, built in 1887-89, in around 1910. (BASF Archives.)

The former central research laboratory building in 1999. (A. S. Travis.)

Interior photographs of dyestuffs factories in the 19th century are rare. These two were taken around 1895 at the BASF Ludwigshafen works. The upper view shows manufacture of azo dyestuffs. The products are Diaminogen and Echtgelb, “fast yellow.” (The Diaminogens were introduced by Cassella in 1895.) Production of the fast yellow was based on the disulphonated derivative of Caro and Martius’s aniline yellow. The lower view shows dyestuff crushing mills. In the foreground is a barrel for anthracene yellow. (BASF Archives.)

The BASF Ludwigshafen factory in 1893. The central research laboratory is at upper left, near the main entrance. To its right is the administration building. (BASF Archives.)

9

Patents and Agreements

The beneficial effects of the German patent laws on the development especially of the chemical industries have been simply incalculable.

Otto N. Witt, on German exhibits at the 1897 Paris International Exhibition.[1]

Counsel who can grasp chemical facts and present them to a judge effectively from a legal point of view are scarce. Witnesses who know the law and can modulate the tones in which they express chemical facts according to their legal, not their chemical, significance are few. They do and always will command high fees.

Herbert Levinstein.[2]

Introduction

The emergence of the synthetic dyestuff industry during the second half of the 19th century is often presented as a tale of poorly exploited British inventiveness, followed by smooth and unhindered German successes. According to this standard story, the British failed because they neglected appropriate education and legislation, were incompetent, and preferred to invest in profitable heavy manufacturing and colonial enterprises.[3] The Germans succeeded because of their mastery of the use of formal knowledge, the introduction in 1877 of a comprehensive patent system, the inauguration of dedicated industrial research laboratories, and the application of business strategies based increasingly upon the monopoly power of "conventions," or cartels, and "communities of interests."[4] Such clear-cut conclusions are invariably supported by the accounts of participants. The Germans used the situation to promote increased funding for education and research. On the British side the conclusions were often meant as warnings of the failure to invest in scientific education and basic research. This was the message of Raphael Meldola's 1886 lecture before the Society of Arts in London in which he advised his audience that a survey of British dye users had revealed that over 80 per cent of the colorants they employed were "Made in Germany."

The rhetoric of Meldola and other leading British chemists reinforced the idea that there was a conflict between the British and German dye industries. This, however, was not always the case. Cooperation between British and German firms, as well as the well-known cooperation between leading German firms, was commonplace. These cooperations were invariably encouraged by the outcomes of negotiations over patents, starting with the 1870 alliance between BASF and Perkin over alizarin. The patent systems, in turn, played major roles in stimulating innovation, and also in bringing about some quite unexpected attempts at collaboration. The influence of the patent systems of Germany and Britain, and of litigation in the two countries, on the dynamics of cooperation and collaboration will be explored here mainly through the changing relationship between Caro and the Manchester dye-maker Ivan Levinstein. This also highlights some of the most important aspects of Caro's work for BASF as a patent expert, and his own contributions to German patent law.

Starting in the early 1860s, Caro had acquired considerable knowledge of the working of the British patent system as it applied to chemical inventions. At BASF he wrote up patent applications in German, English, and, probably, French, with each application modulated to the relevant country's patent system. It is hardly surprising, then, that Meldola, in preparing his lecture, had corresponded with Caro on all aspects of both the British and German dye industries, including education and business ethics as they applied to intellectual property rights. On 8 June 1886, Caro congratulated Meldola on a splendid lecture which "forcibly points to the necessity of a thorough training in chemistry. The beautiful results would never have been achieved by anyone, who did not command a similar knowledge of the entire range both of facts and methods accumulated by previous investigators."[5] It was in the same letter that Caro also drew Meldola's attention to the nuisance value of the "speculative" patentees, particularly Wilhelm Majert of Berlin, who collaborated with Ewer & Pick, also of Berlin. This firm undertook some manufacture, and was particularly interested in filing patents for processes that afforded colorants already produced by other manufacturers.

Meldola responded:

> I am much interested in what you say about the "speculative" patentees. We suffer a great deal from these kind of people here, but not as much in chemical patents as you do. I must confess that I have only made one experiment with the Ewer & Pick patent and that was unsuccessful. I did not do the experiment very carefully however and attributed the failure to my carelessness.[6]

Particularly problematic in this "speculative" context were the so-called benzopurpurine dyes. These were a range of azo dyes that possessed the then-remarkable property of not requiring mordants for fixing them to cotton. In 1884, AGFA had purchased rights to the first patent for these substantive dyes. The AGFA dye was known as Congo red, and was soon followed by Bayer's version, called benzopurpurine.

The benzopurpurines were to become the main topic of industrial research into new dyes for over a decade (though at BASF only from 1889). The reason was, simply, the economic significance, since cotton dyeing and printing were the most important applications of dyes. The benzopurpurines were investigated by inventors in Germany and, to a lesser extent, in England (as well as in the United States), who filed patents for processes that specified a variety of coupling components. The latter included homologues and isomers of known or newly discovered compounds, but, because blanket coverage was often claimed for a particular type of intermediate, the patents made claim on members not yet prepared, or known. In addition, mixed products resulted from many of the processes specified, which created considerable confusion. This left the patent system open to abuse or, at best, uncertainty. Moreover, chemical inventors understood the German law of 1877 to mean that a process could be patented but a product could not.

It was at the 1879 patent congress of the two-year-old Verein zur Wahrung der Interessen der chemischen Industrie Deutschlands (Association for the Protection of the Interests of the German Chemical Industry) in Baden-Baden, that Caro, a co-founder and representing BASF, proposed that the Verein establish a patent committee. This committee came into existence soon after, with Caro as its chairman from 1885 to 1898. One of the committee's first moves was to lobby for patent protection of products and the processes for their synthesis.[7] A principal reason was that the main threat to the German dye industry at that time, especially in view of the deteriorating economic situation, was the unlicensed import from Switzerland, where there was no patent coverage for chemical inventions, of dyes made by processes described in German patents. Protection of both products and processes would have been effective in preventing these imports. By 1885, the situation had become so difficult that the Verein appealed to Bismarck to issue a circular proposing widening of the interpretation of the law such that a product became incorporated into the patented process. The Chancellor issued a circular in August 1886, recommending that courts enforce this view.[8]

The general patent situation, including for mechanical devices, was so unclear in Germany that an Imperial Commission was charged with revising the patent law. The commission appointed Heinrich Caro as its expert in chemistry. The *Patentblatt* of 11 August 1886 included a list of twenty-two questions to be addressed by the commission, the seventh of which dealt with the linking of a chemical product to the process from which it was made.

On 8 November, Caro informed BASF's London patent agent, John Henry Johnson: "As you are probably aware the German Patent-Law is going to be revised.... The Imperial Commission will shortly–(and probably on the 19th of this month)–assemble in Berlin and I have been called upon to take part in the Proceedings."[9] Caro passed on to Johnson, and probably other English patent agents and legal experts, a number of outstanding questions that the commission had raised in connection with the English patent system.[10]

At the November 1886 assembly, Heinrich Caro strongly supported product protection.[11] The final recommendation of the commission was that process and product protection should be linked in patent law. This would allow the discovery and protection of completely new processes for known products, and would retain the much-cherished advantages of German patent law. However, it would prohibit the filing of a patent for a product alone. Since the product was covered under the process patent, it would be fully protected.

Caro suggested that patentees should be quite specific about the products claimed, and should also supply samples to the patent office. The 1886 Imperial Commission also proposed a more flexible approach to what constituted novelty, one that avoided a too-restrictive legal definition but that permitted technically acceptable variance and came within the domain of what it called the "culturally fluid and mutable concept of invention." In 1887 a sample regulation was introduced, though this was opposed by Otto N. Witt,[12] because, in his view, it would put the independent inventors, which included himself and other academics, at a major disadvantage when compared with the big companies. However, the days of independent chemical inventors were drawing to a close, as the reviewer of Witt's 1889 book on chemicals and patents in the industry-friendly journal *Die Chemische Industrie* reminded readers: This change was natural and in full accord with the modern mode of production.[13]

Revision of the patent law to include both products and processes did not take place until 1891, and in the interim the courts had to confront the uncertainties of product protection. The main lawsuit that tested the law regarding chemical patents was conducted in Leipzig, Saxony, where imported methylene blue produced by the Swiss Geigy & Co. took a large slice out of BASF's profits. The litigation went through three stages, ending up at the Reichsgericht (Imperial Court), which in March 1888 ruled that the product was included in the patented process. Sales of the Geigy methylene blue ceased in Germany.[14]

Heinrich Caro's second main contribution to the change in the patent situation was made three years later in 1889, and almost at the end of his career at BASF. He was called upon to act as an independent expert witness in a case of patent litigation in which Ewer & Pick attacked the Congo red patent. Many commentators have wondered why Caro was involved in this case, especially since it appeared to have nothing to do with BASF.[15]

Caro appeared in court as an independent expert, and presented a very specific viewpoint on the validity of the Congo red patent. He advocated product protection in order to restrict the scope of the Congo red patent. Though Caro's opinion was ostensibly neutral, it was in keeping with the interests of BASF, which was anxious to grab a stake in the direct dye business. One hoped-for outcome was an alliance between BASF and its erstwhile rival in England, Ivan Levinstein. The story of how this happened also reveals the great competence of Ivan Levinstein and his chemists in Manchester. This made Levinstein a formidable rival, or ally, in his dealings with German companies. It also provides a clearer picture of how, and why, Levinstein became involved with AGFA and Bayer for a period of five years commencing January 1890, at the same time that Caro left BASF.[16]

Ivan Levinstein in Lancashire

Ivan Levinstein was born in Berlin in 1845, and his early years had much in common with those of Heinrich Caro. As with the Caro family, music and politics impacted upon the Levinstein home, where during Ivan's early childhood the young Russian pianist Anton Rubinstein had received support, and in 1864 the socialist leader Ferdinand Lassalle spent his last hours, following a fatal duelling incident. Levinstein's father, Levin Jacob, once owned a calico printing factory, but when that venture failed he turned, among other things, to political and financial journalism, and then to assignments for the Rothschild banking house. It was while working for the latter around 1859 that he attempted to offer Bismarck, the newly appointed Prussian ambassador to St. Petersburg, a financial incentive for representing the interests of both Austria and Prussia. When they were unable to agree over the terms, Bismarck threatened to throw Levinstein down the stairs leading from his office.[17]

Like Caro, Ivan Levinstein was educated at the Gewerbeinstitut, where he studied chemistry and in 1863-64, as assistant to F. R. Weber, lecturer in chemical technology, came to appreciate the new coal-tar dyes. He also attended lectures at the University of Berlin. According to Ivan, his father set up a factory in Berlin for the manufacture of synthetic dyes, in which the teenaged son played a role. However, in 1864 Ivan Levinstein arrived in Salford, next to Manchester, and was soon preparing magenta on a small scale.[18] In 1865, he moved to Blackley, near Manchester, and during the following years he built up a reputation for the manufacture of aniline, its salts (used in aniline black printing), and aniline dyes.

The failure of his brother Hugo to secure a process for aniline blue when sued in a case of patent infringement in 1865 led Ivan to consider new patent-free processes and starting materials for preparing dyes, notably the use of toluene derivatives.[19] Aniline and toluidine dyes, aniline salts, and Bismarck brown carried Levinstein's firm into the early 1870s. At the end of the decade, the range was extended with the availability of new azo dyes, following the work of Griess, Witt, Caro, and Roussin. With Hofmann's publication in 1877 of the constitutions of azo dyes based on derivatives of benzene, the formation of these colorants was clearly recognised to take place by the coupling of diazo intermediates with aromatic compounds, notably those containing amino and, in the case of Roussin's product, hydroxyl groups. Hofmann's work in making public the modes of formation of azo dyes introduced a new dimension to chemical analysis and synthesis as applied to industrial organic chemistry, while his failure to establish the constitutions of Roussin's oranges afforded new opportunities for Heinrich Caro and Ivan Levinstein.

Ivan Levinstein (1845-1916). (Zeneca Archives.)

Roccelline and Caro's fast red AV

In 1877, Roussin discovered a new azo dye produced from diazotized naphthylamine. It was called roccelline, and was made, as were his other azo dyes, by the Parisian-based firm of Poirrier. Ivan Levinstein took a more-than-passing interest in roccelline on display at the 1878 Paris International Exhibition, and was soon ordering consignments for resale in Manchester.

Caro established the constitution of Poirrier's colorant in 1877 and embarked on various syntheses of naphthalene-based azo dyes containing the sulphonic acid grouping.[20] The outcome was that in February and March 1878, respectively, Heinrich Caro patented in England and Germany a process for red and brown acidic azo dyes, the soluble "sulpho-acids" of "oxyazonaphthaline" (hydroxyazonaphthalene sulphonic acids) prepared from diazotized naphthylamine and naphthalene-derived coupling components.[21] The naphthylamine was the alpha isomer, the only one then available commercially. The most important of Caro's products was known as fast red AV and was well suited to the dyeing of wool.

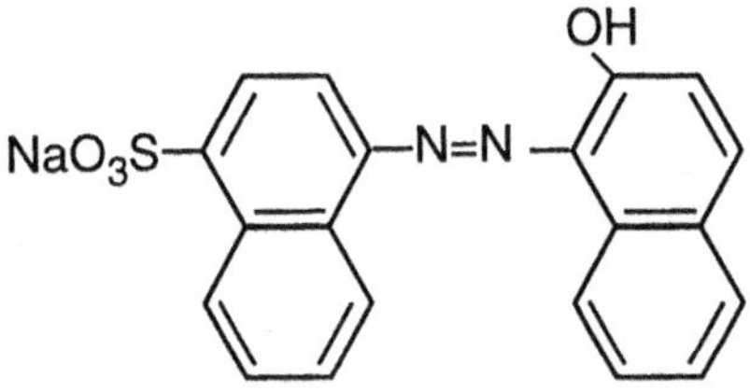

fast red AV, Caro, 1877

Two years later, in 1880, Levinstein began the manufacture in Manchester of a colorant similar to roccelline (which he later called fast Blackley red and Blackley red). BASF established that Levinstein's product was closely related to Caro's fast red AV, and in September 1881 began a legal action in London claiming infringement by Levinstein. Henri Schaeppi, Caro's assistant in patent matters at that time, was placed in charge of the case. His witnesses included Peter Griess, and British academic chemists James Dewar, Henry E. Armstrong–both leading experts in aromatic chemistry–and William Odling. A major difficulty arose over what was meant by "naphthylamine" as specified in Caro's patent. The naphthylamine of the specification was, the BASF witnesses declared, understood to be the alpha (α-) isomer ("ordinary naphthylamine"). Also, although the court was made aware that the β-isomer had been discovered in 1875, it was accepted that this was a scientific curiosity and not an industrial product at the time of the invention. Armstrong pointed out that in 1878 β-naphthylamine "could only be procured by a special order from certain chemists who would procure it, from such persons as *Kahlbaum* of Berlin."[22]

The commercial naphthylamine was probably sufficiently homogenous to ensure that the proportions of isomers, of which the alpha was the major, were consistent and suited to dye manufacture. Disputes over naphthylamine apart, however, the court did tacitly acknowledge that BASF was confronted with a worthy opponent in Ivan Levinstein, "evidently a gentleman of much intelligence, and possessed of considerable chemical knowledge."[23]

The court also noted that Heinrich Caro was conspicuous by his absence from most, if not all, of the proceedings:

> The course pursued by the Plaintiffs [BASF] has made the answer to these queries very difficult; for the first thing to know is, what in fact was the inventor's invention; and yet Plaintiffs have not put into the box *Dr. Caro* or any witness to prove what the real invention was, or to show that the patent has been worked by the Plaintiffs' works or anyone else, although *Dr. Glaser*, one of the principles connected with the Plaintiffs' works, and *Dr. Schraube*, also from the same works,–and, both, according to *Dr. Griess*, gentlemen familiar with manufacture of the sulpho-acids of naphthylamine by the Plaintiffs, –were in Court during the trial, and the Defendants invited the Plaintiffs to call some witness from their works … In making these observations we do not forget that *Dr. Caro* was said to have been unwell; that the Defendants' solicitors were anxious, as appears from a letter written by them, that the trial should not be delayed for his appearance.[24]

This subsequently led to considerable speculation about Caro's non-appearance, with suggestions that he was somehow too ill to attend at critical moments, made drunk with champagne one day before he was due to appear in court, or embarrassed by, or told to stay away because of, an error in the BASF patent description. Herbert Levinstein, Ivan's son, observed: "Caro, who loved patent actions with their subtle dialect and rapid thrust of wits, was careful to keep out of England while this case was being heard."[25] Maybe, however, Caro just could not find time to get away from the laboratory bench, and left deliberations to his patent agent, John Henry Johnson, and partners, particularly George Beloe Ellis. Other stories connected with the case dealt with the outcomes of different experiments carried out in court before the judge, and questions never completely resolved, in part because Levinstein claimed a secret process, which, it was later revealed, had nothing to do with the steps described in the patent. The various versions of events described by three English chemists, Arthur G. Green, Ernest F. Ehrhardt, and the Swiss-born Max Wyler (of Levinstein's firm), though anecdotal, are of considerable interest because they provide perceptions on Caro and his inventions in the 1920s and 1930s. Ehrhardt, incidentally was Birmingham-educated and in March 1889, just after completing his doctoral studies in Munich, joined Caro as assistant in the patent laboratory. His mother tongue and understanding of both chemistry and chemical patents would prove invaluable in recording and evaluating the intricacies and intrigues of patent disputes.

According to Green, experiments were carried out for the court on α-naphthylamine, which was treated with 80 per cent sulphuric acid as specified in the patent ("fuming sulphuric acid containing 80 per cent anhydride"). The results, if not spectacular, were at least unforgettable. Green

> remembered being told about the way in which it was sought to convince the Judge in the Fast Red case that the method of sulphonating α-naphthylamines, as described in the patent, was not practicable. The Judge was invited into a small back room, and a pound of α-naphthylamine was placed in a big pot and 4 or 5 pounds of 80 per cent. fuming sulphuric acid was poured on to it. There was a frightful commotion at once. In one moment the room was full of SO_3 fumes, and the Judge and everybody else got away as quick as they could. The Judge declined to see any more experiments.[26]

However, at a later date there was a further demonstration experiment. This time Justice Pearson ordered an independent expert to sulphonate the azo dye and not the naphthylamine (the direct precursor of the naphthionic acid). The expert appointed was Henry E. Roscoe, who performed the experiment in the presence of Thomas Carnelly, representing Levinstein, and Peter Griess, representing BASF. Roscoe undertook one of his demonstration experiments on the roof of his chemistry laboratory. The sulphonation of the azo dye ("naphthylamine-azonaphthol") was "effected with perfect success by Sir Henry Roscoe, which gave the Badische Fabrik their victory."[27] Justice Pearson's verdict was that the BASF patent was valid.

As for Levinstein's secret process, this, it appears, was in the preparation of naphthionic acid from naphthylamine: "as a matter of fact the secret process did not refer to the patented step, it related to the manufacture of naphthionic acid. After this sulpho acid of naphthylamine had been made by the secret process the treatment was just as claimed in the specification, so it is clear why this defence failed." It was in 1889, when Levinstein was in alliance with BASF, that Ehrhardt

> learned this from Mr. Levinstein's own lips in the old Gambrinus in Glasshouse Street. Dr. Caro, Mr. Levinstein and I had been at a long consultation with Professor Dewar at the Royal Institution. When we came out Dr. Caro called out that he would like a glass of German beer, which in those days was more difficult to get in London than in more recent times prior to 1914. During my visits to London University for examination purposes I had frequently passed the Gambrinus in Glasshouse Street–it was not then extended to Regent Street as it is now–and I took Caro and Levinstein into this replica of a Bavarian beer cellar as it then was with its bare wooden tables, deeply carved with initials and devices by the customers who patronised the place.

> Caro was delighted at the Bohemian atmosphere and here the talk drifted to the Fast Red case and I obtained the information that I have given above.[28]

More objective, no doubt, was Henry E. Armstrong's description to Caro of the announcement of the secret process:

> Levinstein disclosed his secret process to-day and as I anticipated it is in the main identical with your method of manufacturing. He adds 300 lbs. naphthylamine to 1200 lbs. ordinary oil of vitriol and takes about 2 hours to do this, then a fire is lighted under the pan and the temperature raised to a point far beyond any mentioned in the patent until the separation of the sulpho-acid takes place. This takes altogether about 4½ hours. The product consists he says practically of a single sulpho acid. He then washes away a part of the excess of sulphuric acid and reduces the sulpho acid to a fine state of division by agitating it in a "smasher" with water, next he adds an excess of nitrite of soda and so converts the sulfo-acid into the diazo-compound. The naphthol he prepares himself and takes the finely divided body as precipitated from the "soda-melt," I presume adds this to carbonate of soda solution, and then introduces the diazo-body. Afterwards the liquid is heated to boiling, and on cooling the colour separates out in golden coloured scales.
>
> He claims as new: 1) the use of ordinary sulphuric acid; 2) the method of making the diazo-body, no description of how he converts an insoluble body into a diazo compound having previously been given; 3) the use of carbonate of soda instead of caustic soda; 4) the bringing together of the solid diazo body and the solid naphthol and not of solutions.
>
> The further hearing is fixed for Tuesday and we shall, I think, have no difficulty in meeting him. But it may be of importance for me to state what I saw at your works and I want you to telegraph me answers to a few questions.
>
> You told me you used ordinary acid, but I did not learn how you added the naphthylamine. Do you add it gradually or all at once and in what proportions? How long do you heat and to what temperature–I understand you to say about 100°C? Do you wash the crude acid and then dissolve in Na_2CO_3?.... I do not anticipate that it will be necessary to mention all these points but I want to be clear in case of need.[29]

The concentration of sulphuric acid specified in Caro's patent had indeed created problems because it was not suited to the sulphonation of naphthylamine. Ehrhardt explained in 1924 that it was not even the same concentration as had been used in the original experiment. An error had arisen because Caro did not bother to check the results obtained in his laboratory by a young assistant, who had confused 80 degrees Baumé (density) with 80 per cent strength.

> Caro's assistant–a promoted laboratory boy ... had not the education to distinguish between degree sign and percentage sign, so in his note book called this [sulphuric acid] 80 per cent. acid putting the percentage sign instead of the degree sign. This was copied into the draft specification and so gave occupation to the leaders at the

> Patent Bar and all the courts up to the House of Lords in this country. Caro told me that it was his intention to go into the box as a witness and explain this to the Court and not to rely on the sense of justice of the Judge not to upset the patent for the sake of a mistake like that, but he was prevented from giving evidence by illness. Another of the witnesses has boasted to me that he won that case by making Caro ill with a surfeit of champagne and so prevented his giving evidence.[30]

Henry Armstrong's verdict, however, was that Caro's specifications were adequate.[31] In 1937, the former Levinstein chemist Max Wyler had the final word on the fast red case:

> There is no time to go into technical details. The outcome of the case has been declared by disinterested, highly qualified persons not in the heat of the fight but 14 years later, as absurd and lamentable by law and policy, which opinion was shared by Dr. Caro, the opponent patentee, who told Ivan Levinstein that wild horses could not have dragged him to London to give evidence in his own case.[32]

Unsurprisingly, Ivan Levinstein was well aware of the fact that many new processes afforded isomers (compounds with the same formula but different structures). In 1883 he drew attention to the variety of compounds discovered in the product mixtures available from the alizarin processes, which in his view could have been used to show that the original patents were invalid.[33] Isomerism certainly remained a central issue when the Court of Appeal considered Levinstein's attempt to have the High Court ruling on fast red AV overturned. At the Hearing of the Appeal in 1885, Lord Justice Baggallay, who found in favour of BASF, pointed out that "The subject of isomerism is one comparatively new in the science of chemistry, and it is very recondite; it is at present by no means fully developed and was less understood seven years ago, at the date of the patent."[34] Though Caro was considered to be the original discoverer of the process,[35] Lord Justices Bowen and Frey disagreed with the outcome of the appeal, which must have strengthened Levinstein's resolve to continue, this time with an appeal before the House of Lords. Late in 1885, BASF's patent agent John Henry Johnson, and his partner George Beloe Ellis, made preparations in collaboration with Schaeppi for fighting the appeal, and in November, Caro was informed of progress.[36] Almost one year later, an optimistic Johnson advised Caro: "I am now expecting the Hearing of the Appeal in the House of Lords to come on shortly. We are all pretty confident of success." He also added: "P.S. In writing the above I have just had a letter from Dewar in which he says 'The more I study the evidence the more I am convinced in our case.'"[37]

In 1887, at the Hearing of the Appeal in the House of Lords, the BASF invention was declared novel, useful, and sufficiently described in the patent specification.[38] Levinstein's response was to transfer manufacture to the Netherlands, which, in common with Switzerland, had no patent law for chemical inventions.[39]

At BASF, the protection of patents, whether for fighting speculative patentees, or foreign or German adversaries, or in order to bring about strategic alliances, was considered so important that, as seen in chapter 8, it consumed much of the research effort during 1888-89. The problem, as the activities of Ewer & Pick had exposed, was that advances in chemical knowledge meant that patents for improved processes opened the way for invasion of the markets for existing products.

Heinrich Caro was the key person in the endeavours of BASF to protect its patent position. At the end of 1887 he had handed over research at the central research laboratory to Bernthsen in order to concentrate his efforts on the activities of the associated patent laboratory and the demands of the courtroom. In this endeavour, Caro continued to work closely with Henry Armstrong, a foremost specialist in naphthalene derivatives, and whose advice was greatly valued. In October 1888, Caro received Armstrong's opinion on how to tackle a case involving sulphonic acids of α-naphthol, a process of A. Leonhardt & Co., then in Mulheim, patented in London during 1887 (no. 11,318) by H. H. Lake:

> I am most anxiously awaiting the receipt of your account of your investigation of the α-naphtholsulphonic acids.
>
> Johnsons have sent me the draft declaration of Watson Smith, Levinstein and Liebermann. They are all very well in their way, but far too "wordy." The Comptroller does not understand a single technical chemical term and his "expert" advisers are incapable of dealing with such questions as are likely to arise in the case.
>
> Our only chance is to be very clear and simple and fortunately this is possible. Lake claims nothing but ... a method of producing a uniform disulphonic acid and we cannot prevent him getting his patent unless we show that he does not and cannot obtain such an acid.

Armstrong, apparently, had earlier failed to convince Caro that it would have been worth publishing his laboratory findings:

> I wish months ago you had taken my advice; we could then have pointed to published proof. However, I can say if I have the particulars of your investigation before me: that I am conversant with the particulars and details of a most searching investigation of the action of sulphuric acid on α-naphthol, and of the products of

> such action, and know from my own experiments that a uniform disulphonic acid cannot be prepared in the manner prescribed and in fact is not procurable. This is the case, is it not?
>
> In any case, let me see the account of all your work and let me have a good quantity of pure α-naphthol, so that I may go over all the work and be prepared to act at any moment. It may be possible later on, after Lake's answer is filed, to say something more.
>
> The more I see of these cases the more I am satisfied that with our law it is all important to be prepared at every point; we can never foresee what may be required and in the event of an action taking place I want to fortify my position by publishing something about α-naphthol-sulphonic acids.[40]

Though the outcome of this particular case is not recorded, considerable information on the litigation over naphthol yellow survives, no doubt because of its great commercial importance.

Naphthol yellow

Ivan Levinstein manufactured another of Caro's inventions without recourse to a licensing arrangement, namely naphthol yellow (a "sulpho acid of dinitronaphthol"), patented in December 1879.[41] Levinstein's chemists undertook a number of improvements in the process, as they had done with fast red AV, and these were patented in England and the United States towards the end of 1882. Two years later, BASF made preparations for a fight with Levinstein over patent infringement.

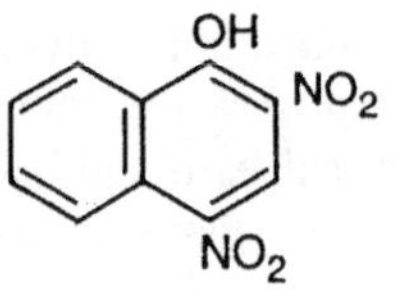

Martius yellow (Manchester yellow)
2,4-dinitro-1-naphthol
Martius, 1864

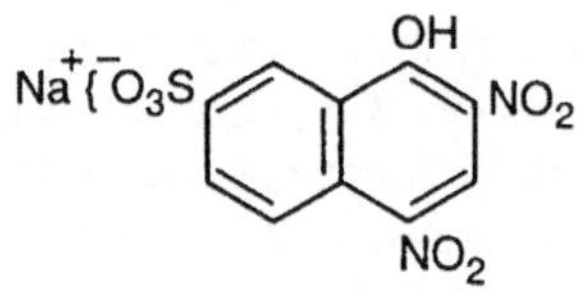

Naphthol yellow S
2,4-dinitro-1-naphthol-7-sulphonic acid sodium salt
Caro, 1879

Both sides were aware of the risks, and of the potential gains, to be had from litigation. Moreover, patent litigation did not necessarily bring about a total monopoly for one party and a total loss for the other. Quite the contrary, adversaries together in the courtroom were often the best partners for the creation of cartels, as Caro and the BASF management were well aware. This was the case where both sides in a dispute recognised competence, technical as well as business, in one other. A cartel arrangement was an ideal means for warding off competition, thereby avoiding litigation and maintaining profits, and was looked upon favourably in Germany, where in 1888 cartels were officially endorsed.

In March 1886, at a time when there was still considerable uncertainty over the outcome of the fast red AV case, and Levinstein was enlarging his works, Heinrich Caro presented to the management of BASF his statement concerning policies for purchasing patents from rival companies and embarking on patent litigation. It was not an easy time for BASF. Not long before, in 1884, the BASF patent monopoly on alizarin in the United States had been lost following expensive and lengthy litigation with Bayer's American agent, and in 1885 the European Alizarine Convention had collapsed.[42] Caro recommended that BASF should engage in litigation only in those cases where a great deal of business was at stake, but not where uncertainties might lead to prolonged litigation. Ewer & Pick dominated the first part of the document, followed with notes about other rivals and their products, including Levinstein's red and his sales of naphthol yellow in the United States.[43] According to August Bernthsen, BASF claimed infringement of its United States naphthol yellow patent by Levinstein during 1886-88.[44] On the other side of the Atlantic, the Blackley-made naphthol yellow of Levinstein, and sales in England of naphthol yellow produced by A. Leonhardt, were considered serious threats to BASF.

The position became so critical that Otto N. Witt, from the end of 1885 an academic chemist in Berlin, agreed early in 1886, in deference to the wishes of Caro and in accord with his consultancy contract with BASF, not to publish the results of his work on naphthol yellow. The aim was to prevent their having any influence on the negotiations, over both patents and business, in the United States and England.[45] The BASF tactic enabled it to bring about an agreement with Ivan Levinstein in 1888 for mutual sharing of the British and United States markets.

The creation of a close business alliance seemed to be the best strategy for protecting the joint British interests of Levinstein and BASF in those areas where they had achieved similar levels of success. From Ehrhardt, who spent about two weeks with Caro in London during May 1889, we learn that after BASF had reached an agreement with Levinstein over naphthol yellow, it almost immediately, on 13 May, commenced an action against the firm of Dan Dawson Brothers of Milnsbridge, near Huddersfield. Dawson manufactured naphthol yellow, and was backed by Read Holliday & Sons, also of Huddersfield.[46] The negotiations, as recorded in considerable detail by Ehrhardt, involved several firms, the BASF scientific expert Dewar, BASF witnesses Caro and Ehrhardt, and legal counsel. They were urgent, complex, and full of recriminations and provide a fascinating example of the legal machinations over control of chemical processes and products:

> Caro arrived at [the De Keyser's Royal Hotel] at noon on May 19th, and in the noon had a private interview with Mr. Levinstein with reference to that gentleman's attitude in the present case, and in other matters. This interview was on the whole satisfactory.... In the evening Mr. Ellis [Johnson's partner] called and up till midnight Caro was engaged in consultation with him, and Mr. Levinstein and Dr. Ehrhardt were present at this interview. The chemistry of the Patent and more particularly the course of the procedure at the trial were discussed. With reference to the latter point the desirability of calling Mr. Dan Dawson as our own witness was considered.

Neither Dan Dawson nor Hugo Müller, who occasionally assisted Caro in bringing about agreements with English firms, was chosen as BASF witnesses. The defendant, Dawson, appears to have been compromised by Holliday, at least according to its chemist Robert Hirsch.

> Mr. Ellis was also asked whether it was necessary to call Dr. [Hugo] Müller, and expressed an opinion that it was not, considering the evidence that Dr. Caro would be prepared to give with reference to the process of manufacture in the factory; it was however determined to refer the point to Counsel. The morning up till 12 o'clock was occupied in general discussion on the case with Mr. Levinstein. A letter and telegram arrived from Dr. [Robert] Hirsch saying that he would call on Dr. Caro at about 12 o'clock and asking for an interview then. At 12 o'clock he appeared and Dr. Caro had a private interview with him lasting 1 hour.
>
> [Hirsch] stated in the interview that his object in seeing Dr. Caro was to clear himself in Dr. Caro's opinion. He had not been the cause of the lawsuit but blamed Prof. Dewar for this. He alleged that Prof. Dewar had admitted Dawson's moral right to manufacture naphthol yellow but had for reasons of his own changed his mind before his visit to Dan Dawson a fortnight later. He wished to declare these reasons to Dr. Caro in strict confidence but Dr. Caro declined absolutely to have any confidential communication with him whatever. He stated that Dawson was now in possession of complete proofs of the Prior User, and he considers it perfectly hopeless that Dawson would give in.
>
> He [Hirsch] admitted having seen Mr. Leonhardt and Dr. Martius (and Dr. Weiler) and having spoken to them with reference to this case. He admitted that Hollidays were our chief opponents in this case, and that the objections to our patent

were suggested by them.

He complained of Prof. Dewar's and Dr. Caro's treatment of him at interviews stating that they had snubbed him; he admitted [as stated "in the interview between him and Mr. Dawson on the one hand and Dr. Caro and Dr. Schaeppi on the other at Ludwigshafen"] that the process they [Dawson] used before the date of the Patent did not yield pure naphthol yellow but a mixture of it with varying quantities of dinitronaphthol.

[Hirsch] admitted that Dawson would gain no commercial advantage from upsetting the patent as that would throw it open to all the world, but a verdict in our favour would make the patent very valuable. [Hirsch] asked whether he might propose a compromise with Hollidays for us on the basis of a license, the cost of the action incurred up to now to be borne by each party, but Dr. Caro told him that he could not make any overtures whatever, but if Hollidays had proposals to make they would if made at once be considered.

He [Hirsch] stated that the references in "Friedländer" referred only to our German patent [DRP no. 10,785, 28 December 1879] [and that this] differed essentially from our English one.

He made an appointment [for] another interview this evening, but has since telegraphed to Caro not to expect him today. [followed by a note in Caro's handwriting: "This telegram came from King's Cross Station, and it may be inferred that he [travelled] to Huddersfield to consult personally with Messrs. Dawson and Holliday."] He also inadvertently let out that he was not to be called as witness.

This interview is of great importance as it gives us an insight into the attack that we may expect.... This afternoon Dr. Caro had an interview with Prof. Dewar, at which, also, Mr. Levinstein and Dr. Ehrhardt were present and Prof. Dewar was told of the attack to be made upon him. The whole party proceeded thence to [BASF's defence attorney] Mr. [Frederick] Aston's Chambers and held an interview there with Mr. Aston, Mr. Lawson and Mr. Ellis. Mr. Aston questioned Mr. Levinstein on his [process] ... which the latter admitted infringed both the first and second claims of our Patent. Mr. Levinstein stated that it was only just before he applied for a License that he discovered th[is and] this led him to make his application.

The question as to whether Mr. Levinstein should be called was discussed but not settled.

This interview was succeeded by one in which the same question, the calling of Mr. Levinstein, again was the principal topic. It has been arranged that Dr. Caro shall give a lecture on the chemistry of naphthol yellow to our experts and Counsel.[47]

A few days later, Caro declined an invitation to spend an evening with Professor and Mrs. Meldola, "being engaged on that very day in an exciting legal contest."[48] The outcome of the contest was to the satisfaction of BASF, namely the upholding of its patent, followed by the granting of a license to Dawson. That this was considered good business practice was endorsed by Frederick Aston, who advised Caro on 26 May 1889, shortly before the end of the case:

> Although the Judge who has been trying the action of the Badische Comy v. Dawson has reserved his judgement I think we are justified in expecting a judgement in the Plts [plaintiffs] favour, upholding the validity of the patent for the sulpho acids of dinitronaphthol.
>
> Having agreed to the allegation made on behalf of the defense, that Messrs. Dawson, before the date of the patent, made sulpho acids of dinitronaphthol and sold them in the form of dyestuffs, I think you have acted very wisely in not refusing to listen to the defts [defendant's] overtures, made with a view of avoiding protracted litigation. One can never tell what witnesses may swear to as having been done by them 9 or 10 years ago before the time of giving their evidence–again when, without making too great a sacrifice, long litigation can be avoided, it is always prudent to accept the offer of peace.
>
> On the whole, therefore, I congratulate you upon the course you have taken, for which I have had, and still should have, complete confidence in our case. I feel sure it is better to grant a license than to fight out the case to the end. Let me add that it has been a great pleasure to me to study your very interesting case, and receive from you personally so much valuable instruction so clearly imparted.[49]

Levinstein, the ally of BASF in the naphthol yellow business, also applauded the agreement. On June 7 he sent a short but telling telegram from Manchester to Caro, then still at De Keyser's Royal Hotel in London: "My hearty congratulations on the happy ending of the legal case. Levinstein."[50] The "happy ending" provided Levinstein with an opportunity to draw the British manufacturers of naphthol yellow, that is, Dawson, Holliday, and his own firm, and the Manchester agent of BASF (Schott, Segner & Co.) into a cartel arrangement. Levinstein's report to Caro on the outcome of one meeting of the members reveals that a remarkably warm friendship had developed between the two men as they sat together in the London courtrooms during patent litigation.

> I shall not easily forget the days that I passed in your pleasant company. I became really fond of you and am proud in the thought that someone who is superior to me in so many ways may be considered as a friend. For I feel that you too have an extremely friendly attitude towards me and that it will be my endeavour to retain this throughout our lives. Yesterday I wrote to your company that I had brought about a meeting between Schott, Segner, Holliday, Dawson, and myself in order to decide whether the price of naphthol yellow can be increased without reducing the demand for it by dyers, and which measures have to be taken in order to stabilise the increased price. I informed your company that these people were unanimous in their opinion that the price could be fixed at 2/3d [2 shillings and 3 pence] per lb without any reduction in consumption provided that we cease to supply the merchants. At first we had difficulties to make Holliday agree to this last proposal, but in the end he gave in, delaying a definite decision until after he had seen his partners. In truth I think that he wishes, as a cautious Yorkshireman, to make us wait for the judgement

[of the court]. I hope that he will not keep us waiting for long.[51]

This friendship with Levinstein was certainly greater than anything Caro had experienced with his colleagues in Ludwigshafen, where the relationship with Carl Glaser and Heinrich Brunck, his associates on the management board from 1884, was highly strained. Caro was tolerated because of his central role in defending the firm's patents. Nevertheless, he had become so depressed with his position that in the spring of 1889 he decided to leave BASF. He did not, however, advise his colleagues on the management board. When Glaser and Brunck found out in October, they were extremely angry.

Caro's last year at BASF continued to be dominated by his involvement in patent matters, especially those related to the interests of BASF in England. The outcome of the fast red and naphthol yellow cases in London set the scene for the next stage in the collaborations between Levinstein and BASF. This time, however, their plans for a further merging of interests would not begin with a struggle over dyes they were both producing, but with an exchange of information relating to the benzidine–or benzopurpurine–dyes.

Benzidine dyes

The use of the compound benzidine in the preparation of what were later known as azo dyes had been observed by Caro and Griess during their collaboration in Manchester in the mid-1860s, and was included in one of Caro's patent applications (1866). Caro's dye known as Palatine orange, discovered in 1869, was also based on benzidine. More relevant here is the fact that in 1882 Peter Griess advised Caro that a benzidine-derived azo dye had the property of attachment to cotton without the aid of a mordant, but Caro showed no special interest. Henry Theodor Böttinger of Bayer in Elberfeld was told about this new compound when he visited Griess in 1883. A little later, Peter Seidler of Bayer travelled to England to purchase rights to the process from Griess. However, commercial manufacture turned out to be highly problematic, and production was discontinued.[52]

During subsequent research, Paul Böttiger of Bayer coupled 1-naphthionic acid (a sulphonated α-naphthylamine, 1-naphthylamine-4-sulphonic acid) with doubly diazotized benzidine and obtained a brilliant red dye for cotton that acted without the application of a mordant. Böttiger left Bayer in 1884, and filed a patent for the red dye while working for a dyer in Lodz. He then attempted to sell rights to Bayer, BASF, and Hoechst, but they showed little interest, probably because of inadequate fastness. Finally, the AGFA company decided to purchase rights to Böttiger's dye, and it was manufactured and sold as Congo red. This was the first commercially viable substantive dye, and rapidly achieved great popularity in Europe, and later in the decade in India and the Far East.

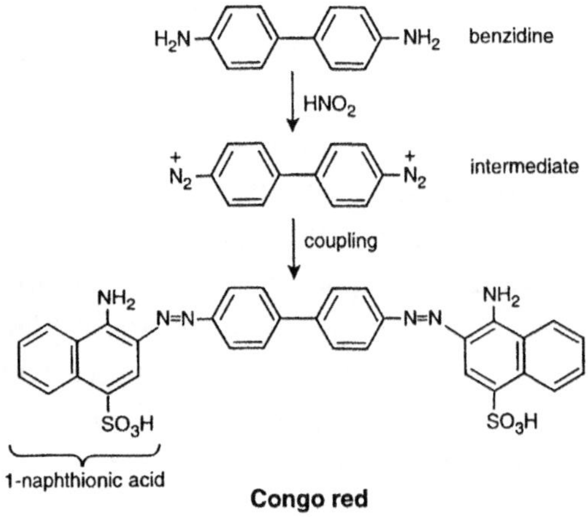

Congo red

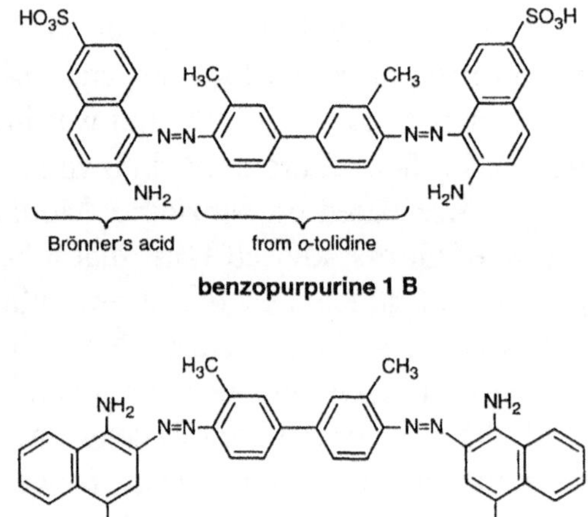

benzopurpurine 1 B

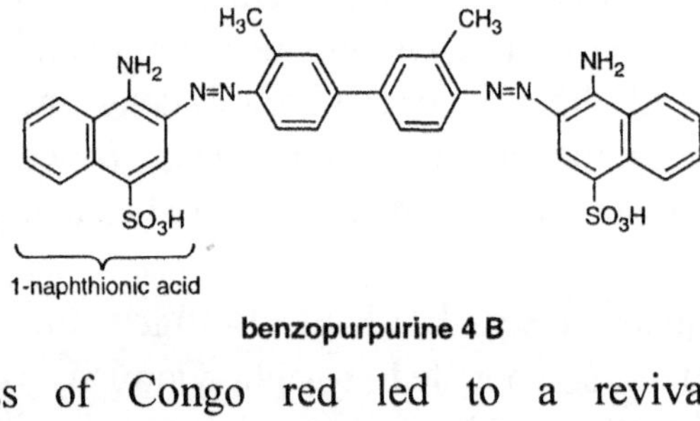

benzopurpurine 4 B

The success of Congo red led to a revival of interest in benzidine-based azo dyes at Bayer, where in 1884 Eugen Frank discovered Chrysamin G. Similar coupling reactions were investigated by

Carl Duisberg of Bayer, but the products turned out to be much too light sensitive. Duisberg then decided to try another naphthylamine sulphonic acid, the compound known as Brönner's acid (2-naphthylamine-6-sulphonic acid, a β-naphthylaminesulphonic acid), the patent for which was owned by AGFA. This was coupled with diazotized *o*-tolidine, a methylated congener of benzidine. The product offered more potential as a commercial dye, and Duisberg's process, which specified a novel preparative route to Brönner's acid, was filed in Germany on 17 March 1885. The dye, known as benzopurpurine (later benzopurpurine 1B), was on sale from the autumn of that year. Benzopurpurine, however, was less useful than Congo red, and Bayer chemists experimented with alternative coupling agents. One product turned out to be an even better dye than Congo red. It was made by coupling 1-naphthionic acid with the diazotized tolidine and sold as benzopurpurine 4B; the improved property as a dye arose from the fact that it was less sensitive to acid (due to the two methyl groups in tolidine).

AGFA, however, considered that the benzopurpurines were infringing the Congo red patent and began litigation against Bayer, attacking the patent application for benzopurpurine 4B. The court decided in favour of AGFA, but the Bayer management, instead of appealing, met with AGFA to consider a combination of interests. The outcome was that Bayer's benzopurpurine 4B patent became an addition to AGFA's Congo red patent, and the two firms agreed on a cross-licensing arrangement and formed a cartel, soon known as the benzopurpurine convention, to protect their mutual interests. Further research followed in Berlin and Elberfeld. Thus in 1886 Bayer introduced a range of blue dyes, the first of which was benzoazurine G, made by coupling Nevile acid (1-naphthol-4-sulphonic acid) with diazotized *o*-tolidine, and which competed with natural indigo. By this time the approach to inventing benzopurpurine dyes was dominated by the synthesis of new coupling components. Benzopurpurine patent applications included a growing number of novel components that were the outcomes of creative laboratory syntheses. Moreover, in an attempt by inventors to preempt the field, blanket patents were filed, in many cases covering coupling components that had not yet been prepared. This practice was adopted by AGFA and Bayer as well as by the speculative patentees, such as Ewer & Pick, which also began the manufacture of benzopurpurines. The benzopurpurine convention claimed infringement by Ewer & Pick, and the first judgement ruled in favour of the convention. Ewer & Pick appealed, claiming that the original Congo red patent was invalid. The appeal court rejected the claim of Ewer & Pick, which filed a second appeal. In 1889, the dispute again reached the highest German court, the Reichsgericht, in Leipzig.[53] Johannes Wislicenus and Adolf Baeyer appeared as witnesses for the plaintiff.[54]

Caro and the new technical effect

Heinrich Caro was then called in as an independent expert witness by the court. His lengthy presentation was not a defence of one side or the other but his own, ostensibly neutral, assessment. Caro considered that Congo red was indeed novel insofar as it offered a new technical effect, that of acting without the aid of a mordant. He stressed the point that though the relevant patent specified eleven couplings, only one afforded Congo red, and it was this coupling process that was patentable.[55] In this way, Caro argued for the validity of a patent that did not give blanket coverage.[56] His interpretation, put simply, was that the discovery of the technical effect–not a new concept but one that he used to great effect here–and the particular chemical process for the product that was first observed to give this effect were patentable.[57] This would provide scope for genuine inventors, and suppress the activities of those who filed "paper" patents. Caro had, in 1886, in his correspondence with Meldola, already predicted the very situation that he was now called upon to address, namely the problem of speculative patentees.

The Bayer company's Carl Duisberg recorded, in his obituary of Caro, that he gave Caro the credit for introducing the concept of this new technical effect, as distinct from the process or product, in the relevant patent.[58] However, in his later memoirs, Duisberg gave an account of a meeting with Caro during the recess held after Caro gave evidence. Duisberg claimed that he warned Caro of the negative impact of the latter's statement, which favoured a severe restriction on the variety of coupling components that were patentable. Duisberg was anxious to cover an entire range of possible isomers and homologues, as was usual in patenting organic chemical inventions. He considered this justified by the technical effect exhibited by certain of these azo compounds, such as Congo red. According to Duisberg, the properties of one product allowed patent protection of a host of broadly specified, even though not yet synthesized, products. Caro, as he demonstrated in the methylene blue case and by his work for the Imperial Commission, wanted product protection, but only for substances that could be produced, in accord with his proposed sample regulation. This became the cause of a clash between Duisberg and Caro.

If Caro's opinion was accepted by the court, Duisberg advised Caro, it would mean the "death-blow for the whole field of azo dyes."[59] More to the point, however, was the fact that if Caro's recommendation was to be implemented through a court judgement, it would bring about the collapse of the benzopurpurine convention. Caro considered that a patent for Congo red alone was valid, since this colorant showed the new technical effect. The analogues and homologues that had not been synthesized and those not individually claimed in related patents should not be allowed to receive protection. This, Caro realised but kept to himself, would open the door for competing firms, including BASF, to enter the field of benzopurpurines.

Carl Duisberg was now forced to rethink the issue. This he did by introducing a new twist to the story, one that accommodated Caro's evidence to Bayer's interests. Duisberg argued before the court for the validity of the patent specification for the product that exhibited the new technical effect, as suggested by Caro, but also for protection for all combinations of isomers and homologues of naphthalene sulphonic acids claimed in the various specifications for the benzopurpurine processes. Thus, on the basis of the technical properties of a single product, he argued for cover of a host of closely related but-not-yet synthesized substances whose technical properties were also unknown. His argument was accepted and the patents of the benzopurpurine convention were upheld on 20 March 1889.[60] As reported by *Die Chemische Industrie*, the judgement specified that "When a chemist, by applying a method to a situation to which it was not applied before, opens up new possibilities, then, from the point of view of patent law, he has invented a novel process."[61] The court had no doubt taken into account the fact that both Bayer and AGFA had been successfully manufacturing and selling benzopurpurine dyes for over five years, which was clear evidence of their inventive abilities. Accordingly, Ewer & Pick was denied access to Congo red and the other benzopurpurine dyes, as were all other competitors, real or potential, of the convention in Germany.

Caro's concept of the new technical effect for chemical patents was that "the inventive spark was not in the preparation of these [benzopurpurine] dyes, but in the discovery of their new and unexpected property of dyeing cotton without a mordant." It had a tremendous impact on court decisions and on the meaning and scope of chemical patents. The new patent law of 1891, which came into effect on 1 October of that year, also cleared up the confusion over processes and products with an unambiguous ruling that extended a patent for a chemical process to the products of that process. This was in response to the lobbying work of Caro as chairman of the patent committee of the Verein zur Wahrung der Interessen der chemischen Industrie Deutschlands, particularly his testimony as an expert before the Imperial Commission, and to BASF's patent litigation, especially over Caro's methylene blue.[62]

Caro and Levinstein

It is evident that Caro had not acted totally impartially during the benzopurpurine trial. The management at Ludwigshafen had an interest in securing for itself some of the benzopurpurine market. The evidence derives from two surviving letters written by Ivan Levinstein during July 1889. These letters show that Levinstein was working closely with BASF in an attempt to forge an alliance for the supply of benzopurpurines to the British market. They perhaps also provide an answer to the question of why outstanding differences over naphthol yellow had been brought to an end so amicably. This has long puzzled admirers of Levinstein's technical achievements, who considered that he had actually improved on BASF processes with the aid of German chemists, including some previously employed at Hoechst and Kalle.

For the collaboration between BASF and Levinstein, the latter's close friend Heinrich Caro was once again the key figure. Levinstein was a guest at Caro's home in Mannheim during the second half of June 1889, immediately after the conclusion of the British naphthol yellow case, and at which time, one of the letters reveals, they exchanged information about the Bayer and AGFA benzopurpurine patents. Levinstein, following his return to Manchester, wrote to Caro on 5 July, outlining his proposals for a possible working arrangement with German firms over benzopurpurine dyes.

> First, I thank you for your great hospitality while I was a guest in your home. I am only very sorry that I caused you so much trouble and took up so much of your

valuable time. With reference to the business affair, instead of taking as a basis for an eventual arrangement one or two definite patents I would like to propose a licensing agreement covering the manufacture and sale in England, as well as the rights for sale in America, for such English patents that have as the subject of invention the preparation of red benzidine and tolidine dyes for dyeing unmordanted cotton.... At this moment I do not know all the corresponding numbers which refer to these patents and therefore I mention only German ones, and, as far as it is possible for me to ascertain, the corresponding English ones. It is correct that patents 43125 and 42021 cannot be dealt with yet. But most probably these will be changed in the corresponding English specifications. It would be entirely worthless for me to obtain a license for one red colouring substance that might already be outmoded or have disappeared from the market as a result of subsequent improvements.

The following German patents I believe are the same as those of the red [benzidine and tolidine] dyes that are given above and as far as I can at present do so I also give the corresponding English patents:

German patents		Corresponding English patents
28753/84 [Congo red, Böttiger]		4415/84
35615/85	additional	3803/85
39096/85 [Congo corinth]	patents	2213/86 equivalent to 15296/85
41095/87 [Brilliant Congo G]	ditto	6687/87
43125/87	ditto	?
42021/86		? [63]

How is this letter concerning the Bayer and AGFA patents to be interpreted? The clear implication is that Levinstein was advising Caro of a proposed arrangement between AGFA, Bayer, and Levinstein over the English and United States markets, and, surprisingly, in association with BASF. Certainly, there is no question that this was not a private arrangement between Levinstein and a highly discontented (at BASF) Caro. The BASF involvement is confirmed by the fact that three days later Caro passed Levinstein's letter on to the BASF management, where its receipt was duly recorded.

Levinstein's second letter on the subject, dated 28 July, reveals, however, that approaches to AGFA concerning what Levinstein claimed to be errors in the benzopurpurine patent specifications had been rejected. Levinstein must have hoped that by revealing weaknesses in the patents, according to his interpretation, he could compromise the convention into an arrangement that would suit himself and BASF. The letter clearly relates to an alternative arrangement with BASF alone, based on assistance from Caro in discrediting the convention's English patents. Levinstein reported experiments by his chemists, and communications with his patent agent, John Fletcher Moulton, as to how the results might be used to oppose the Bayer and AGFA patents:

> Concerning the business matters discussed in your letter of 23rd. inst, I received yesterday the Berlin [Brönner's] acid and will immediately commence experiments and inform you of the results. I have sent my statement of objection to Moulton for revision and hardly believe that the Berlin people [AGFA] will be very happy about it when they receive it. I have found several other small points which put these patents in an even more unfavourable light and I shall allow myself to send you copies of the declaration as soon as I receive them. I regret, concerning the affair, that the Berlin people [AGFA] were short-sighted enough first to want to know about my arguments against theirs, for, as I have already told you, I am afraid that the comptroller will not let this pass easily.
>
> Meanwhile, on the advice of Moulton, I have started the manufacture of two dyestuffs, namely Chrysamin and Benzopurpurine 4B last week, and I shall bring them in a very short time to the market. In my opinion there is not the least doubt that the patents themselves with all their amendments are absolutely bad and I must confess that the last mentioned [the amendments] are also rather badly formulated, and that a direct contradiction exists with one part of the specification and also with the claim. At present I am busy with writing up the declaration against the Brönner's [acid] and Congo red patents. The last date for submitting this is 9 August.[64]

Levinstein planned to oppose the British patents of Bayer and AGFA, fully aware that the Congo red case was fought in German courts according to a law which in many ways was different from the situation in England. The extent to which Levinstein pursued this case suggests sophisticated levels of laboratory work in both improvements to the processes and the preparation of coupling components. He must then have held considerable trust in the English patent system, with its emphasis on the accurate reporting of details of a chemical process. For organic chemicals, certain precedents had been established by the outcome of the aniline red patent case in 1865, although since that time the problems related to homologues and isomers had created difficulties in interpretation, as observed during the fast red case.[65] Nevertheless, the English legal system, Levinstein must have conjectured, would be less impressed than the German system with the novel technical effects of a chemical discovery. Perhaps encouraged by Levinstein, BASF, filed a patent in London on 27 August 1889 for benzopurpurine dyes based on tolidine with *o*- and *m*- methyl groups.[66]

The union of Levinstein with AGFA and Bayer

As it turned out, Levinstein's attempt to discredit the AGFA and Bayer patents did not succeed. His position became precarious, since he no longer controlled a number of key products, particularly Blackley red and naphthol yellow. Without access to benzopurpurine dyes in England, Levinstein was of limited use to BASF. The cost of litigation during the 1880s was also crippling, as was his investment in the Wrexham Lager Beer Brewery. The latter provided the first taste of lager to British workmen, but much to their disapproval. During the final months of 1889, through the newly formed Chemical and Allied Trades Section of the Manchester Chamber of Commerce, Levinstein had attempted to improve his situation with an attack on English patent law as it applied to chemical inventions and particularly to azo dyes.[67] The chemical section's report, distributed to Members of Parliament of Manchester and district, drew on Levinstein's experiences while working closely with Heinrich Caro and against the benzopurpurine convention. In particular, Levinstein's main argument must have been inspired by Caro's statements at the Congo red case, as he drew attention to the fact that the "speculative faculties of some patentees have of late years been so marvellously extended, that it now frequently happens that a patentee specifies, and claims as part of his invention, chemical products or substances which he has never even seen, much less made or produced."[68] Again echoing Caro, Levinstein called for samples of products, as well as of novel intermediates and dyed samples, to be deposited with patent applications. However, all this was too soon for British legislators.

Levinstein's firm survived because Bayer and AGFA recognised the ability of their British rival to produce important intermediates, particularly those required in the manufacture of benzopurpurines. This was demonstrated clearly by Caro in his 1891 history of the dyestuff industry, where he showed concern about the future of coal-tar intermediate manufacture in Germany, especially since most of the existing patents would expire in the 1890s, and few new processes had been invented: "Crucial from now on are optimal economic conditions for manufacture and marketing, particularly the development of the heavy-chemicals industry and the transport situation. We cannot avoid the impression, that also abroad, especially in England, more progress will be made and that this would be to the disadvantage of the German [coal-tar] intermediates industry."[69] Caro was acutely aware that not only did England consume most synthetic dyes, but it was also a major producer of intermediates, and this could turn out to be problematic for Germany, particularly if English firms improved their dye-making capabilities.

Plaintiff	Defendant	Dispute over	Dates	Outcome
BASF	Levinstein	fast red AV (roccelline, Blackley red)	1881-87	Judgement in favour of BASF
BASF	Levinstein	naphthol yellow (acid yellow)	1888-89	Settled. Agreement between BASF and Levinstein
BASF	Dawson	naphthol yellow (acid yellow)	1889	Settled. Cartel between BASF, Levinstein, Dawson, Holliday
Levinstein (supported by Caro)	AGFA/Bayer	benzopurpurines	1889	Formation in 1890 of Levinstein Ltd. (Levinstein / AGFA / Bayer)

Highlights of litigation involving BASF and Ivan Levinstein in England, 1881 -1898

It was with such considerations in mind that Bayer and AGFA offered Levinstein a compromise that would save his firm and serve their interests, namely an alliance in which a jointly owned limited liability company would be set up, with each of AGFA, Bayer, and Levinstein holding one-third of the shares.[70] Ivan Levinstein's only declared hint of disappointment was voiced in a lecture given in December 1889 in which he called, as he had done earlier, for reform to the British patent system.[71] He had no choice other than to accept; the first meeting of the directors of the new company, I. Levinstein & Co. Ltd, was held in January 1890. Levinstein's naphthalene-derived intermediates were shipped to the factories of his German partners. The products included the Blackley red precursor α-naphthylamine, and β-naphthol and its derivatives, many of which were important for the manufacture of benzopurpurines.[72] By this time, incidentally, Lancashire's consumption of direct dyes, important in dyeing cotton for the Indian market, had fallen off considerably, since the Germans were supplying these colorants directly to Indian cotton dyers.

Caro's response

Caro's relationship with Levinstein did not suffer from the exclusion of BASF from the benzopurpurine market. On the contrary, their friendship lost none of its earlier intensity, especially after Caro left BASF on 1 January 1890. He could now, in private at least, permit himself to approve fully of Levinstein's new partnership with the rivals of BASF. On 16 January 1890, Caro advised Levinstein:

> I thank you very much for your friendly information about your business union with the Berlin and Elberfeld firms. The union was known to me already, and did not surprise me at all, being the logical outcome of your well-considered steps ... as well as of your partners. Either us or the competitors! An alternative was not thinkable. I remember that this question was answered with sufficient clarity several times when we discussed it in London and Mannheim. You could not have acted differently, and for us [BASF] the correct time for action had not come. In consequence, everything had to turn out the way that it did.
>
> Congratulations on your renewed triumph! With self-evident interest I am now looking forward to the forthcoming success of this union of the English and German colour industries. Time will tell. In the meantime you will also have been informed of my leaving the board of directors (Vorstand).... One of the most pleasant memories of my business life will forever be my having met you, and I ask you heartily to continue the friendship.[73]

Levinstein, deeply moved by Caro's endorsement of his actions, supported Caro's decision to give up his leading role at BASF that had stretched back over two decades and witnessed some of the greatest chemical inventions of that period. On 29 January 1890, Levinstein, whose unwell wife was seeking treatment at various spas on mainland Europe, wrote:

> Thank you for your letter of 16 January. I value that letter not only as a remembrance of an important episode in my life but also of a man whose friendship I shall hold in esteem for ever. My dear wife was also pleased with your letter which I sent to her in Miram. Though she is satisfied with the arrangement with the German factories [Bayer and AGFA] she said at that time in Miram that one thing alone did not please her, and that was the thought that you as a faithful friend who had stood by my side should feel hurt by my actions.
>
> Therefore it was a special pleasure for me to read that this was not the case.
>
> That you left the board of the Badische Anilin- und Soda-Fabrik naturally did not

> surprise me, and I think that this step is the best for the wellbeing of your health and of your mental powers, if you will allow me to express my opinion on that.[74]

Levinstein had been under the impression that Caro wished to return to academic work in Heidelberg. However, Caro had been obliged by BASF to become an independent consultant: "By the way, I am not going into pure teaching, but, for the moment, into highly intensive laboratory work in Mannheim."[75]

This was far from the end of Caro's involvement in patent litigation over direct dyes. Not long after leaving BASF, he acted as expert witness for Bayer, whose Chrysamin G came under attack from Oehler's Kresotingelb. Bayer also brought to the witness stand A. W. von Hofmann, whose death in 1892, however, caused Kekulé to take his place. The case was an interesting show of scientific strength, and of new alliances of expert witnesses, since Caro and Hofmann previously represented opposing commercial interests, in both England and Germany. Even more remarkable was the fact that Oehler was represented by Caro's former collaborator Adolf von Baeyer, whose professed ignorance of patent law, according to one account, helped Bayer win the case! However, Baeyer did give an opinion, namely that isomers and homologues should be protected only if they were specified in the patent description, which he considered to be the case for Oehler's patent. No doubt it was Caro's mastery of patent law that contributed to Bayer's success in 1893, and the attractive fees that overcame any concern among the witnesses over whose opinion they were opposing.[76]

Levinstein's partnership with Bayer and AGFA survived five years. Among the German directors were two of Caro's former colleagues at Roberts, Dale & Co., C. A. von Martius (AGFA) and Ludwig Schad (Bayer). The Germans probably considered the partnership a foothold by which they could adapt to anticipated changes in English patent law, particularly if compulsory working was mandated. When the changes were not forthcoming, they parted company with Levinstein in 1895, though the link was not completely severed until 1897. By that time the first direct dye patents were about to expire.

Patent reform in Britain

In the early 1880s the Society of Chemical Industry's Patent Laws Committee expressed considerable dissatisfaction with the limited provisions of the compulsory working clause in English patent law. The situation became critical once British manufacturers discovered their weaknesses when confronted by German firms armed with sophisticated scientific arguments in British courts. This happened after the mid-1880s, particularly following the impressive showing by BASF that relied on Caro and his patent laboratory, as well as on British lawyers and patent agents acting for BASF.

Once freed of his German partners, Ivan Levinstein returned to his lobbying for reform of the British patent system. The official body he had to deal with was the Board of Trade, created in 1862 from an earlier Privy Council committee that handled commercial matters, and that was responsible for compiling trade statistics. In 1883, under the presidency of Joseph Chamberlain, the board saw through Parliament the passage of the Patents, Design and Trade Mark Act. By 1890, manufacturers generally considered that it contained a number of deficiencies, particularly regarding the non-working of patents, a deficiency that did not exist in France and Germany. It was in the area of dye patents that the impact was greatest.

Following parliamentary questions concerning patent reform early in 1897, and Levinstein's success in an 1898 test case against Hoechst concerning the granting of a manufacturing license, the Board of Trade set up a Departmental Committee under Sir Edward Fry. Its brief was to investigate a number of questions related to patent law, in particular the matter of whether compulsory working should be made obligatory. The committee was the closest British equivalent of the 1886 German Imperial Commission, apart from the complete absence of chemists and technologists. Its cautious recommendation, in 1901, was against changes, much to the disappointment of Levinstein and other British manufacturers. Levinstein, however, stepped up his lobbying, including a lecture to the Society of Chemistry and Industry on "Education and Legislation."[77] This lecture received full and immediate coverage in the *Manchester Guardian* of 10 July 1902, and Levinstein sent a copy to Heinrich Caro.

Only in 1907 was the law changed to include a clause that required compulsory working of foreign patents.[78] For the British dye industry, this meant mainly German patents. As it turned out, the 1907 Act was not fully comprehensive, although it did cause German dye firms to open factories in England.

In 1917, Alfred Rée, President of the Society of Dyers and Colourists, and whose firm, Claus & Rée, had purchased Brooke, Simpson & Spiller in 1906, reviewed the recent history of Ivan Levinstein's involvement in patent reform, and accused, without naming them, the British lawyers and patent agents who had represented German firms for delaying the reform. Despite the less-than-mysterious anonymity, the accused must have included Lord John Fletcher Moulton, who had won an important rhodamine case for BASF in 1898, and John Henry Johnson's firm. Though written at a time of extreme anti-German sentiment, Rée's account certainly sheds much light on the sort of opposition that Levinstein and other British manufacturers had encountered:

> Between 1883 and 1906 Mr. Levinstein, through the Manchester Chamber of Commerce, frequently called attention to the injury inflicted on British industry owing to our unsatisfactory patent laws; but nothing was done until 1897 when [Members of Parliament] Captain Phillpotts, Sir Charles Swann, and Sir Frederick Cawley repeatedly called attention to this matter in the House of Commons. Mr. Ritchie, then President of the Board of Trade, appointed a Departmental Committee.... Unfortunately ... consisting mainly of officials, lawyers, and patent agents; manufacturers acquainted with the working of patents and the bearing thereof on our trade and industry were almost unrepresented.
>
> *The First Mistake*
> This was all the more strange considering that the opposition to the introduction of compulsory working clauses in our Patent Act came principally from lawyers and patent agents, many of them identified with the interests of the largest German colour manufacturers holding British patents. That the whole question was essentially an economic one was definitely ignored by the Board of Trade as well as by the Departmental Committee.... It is of some interest to recall at the present time that one of the members of the Departmental Committee was a patent agent to one of the largest German aniline colour manufacturers; three were lawyers, of whom two had very close and friendly relations with other large German aniline colour manufacturers, and these lawyers could hardly fail to be strongly influenced by the point of view which their foreign clients had impressed upon them for years. One of the witnesses called to give evidence against the desirability of introducing compulsory working was Mr. Weinberg, one of the four partners of the well-known and powerful firm of Cassella and Co.–another large German aniline colour manufacturer! It is hardly surprising that no practical results were obtained from this inquiry.
>
> However, the Association of Chambers of Commerce did not relinquish their agitation, and year by year the subject was brought up. Finally, in 1906, another deputation of the Associated Chambers waited upon the President of the Board of Trade.

> *Mr. Lloyd George*
> Fortunately, this time the occupant of that office was Mr. Lloyd George. The principal object of the deputation was to urge upon the Government the necessity of so amending the Patent Law as to enforce a forfeiture of all British patents worked without, but not within, the United Kingdom after the lapse of three years from date of application unless the patentee could justify his inaction to the satisfaction of the Board of Trade. In spite of the usual deputation from London patent agents opposing these proposals, Mr. Lloyd George embodied them in their entirety in the 1907 Patent Act.... The new Act became operative in August, 1908, and for a brief period of a little over a year the compulsory working clauses remained effective and had a beneficial influence upon the introduction of new industries into this country. Then, in 1909, owing to the careless drafting of certain parts of section 27 of the 1907 Act, Lord Parker was able to give a ruling that ... practically annulled the great benefit that had been brought about for British industry by the compulsory working clauses of the 1907 Act, and this in the face of Mr. Lloyd George's specific declaration to the deputation in 1906 that "the onus of proof should be cast on the patentee."

In 1914, the "Associated Chambers" of commerce appealed to the then President of the Board of Trade, Mr. John Burns, to amend the patent law

> in such terms as will place the burden of proof on the patentee. Unfortunately, prior to receiving the deputation Mr. John Burns had seen the usual deputation from London patent agents, who had presented views diametrically opposed to those of British manufacturers. Mr. Burns showed clearly that he was not sympathetic to the views of the deputation of the Associated Chambers. It should be mentioned that certain patent agents and patent lawers had been working very hard for a year or two prior to this to defeat the objects of the manufacturers, and the writer is in possession of interesting material which shows how far these vested professional interests were willing to go in helping foreign industrial interests on whose behalf they were working. Not that these people would have admitted that such was their real object.[79]

There was of course considerable truth in Rée's statements, though they can be interpreted quite differently. After all, not only had British representatives of German companies participated in the Board of Trade's Departmental Committee, but John Henry Johnson and others had earlier been called upon by Caro to assist in the review of German patent law, while John Fletcher Moulton defended both British and German dye manufacturers, particularly Levinstein and BASF. The British barristers and patent agents who represented Germans were, therefore, among the people best qualified to sit on such a committee, since they understood the workings of the British and German systems. And, maybe, their principal interest was in nothing more sinister than bringing about some sort of harmonisation between British and German patent laws.[80] That is something Ivan Levinstein had lobbied for since the early 1880s.

Summary

Caro's correspondence and reports relating to patents highlight the intensive and frequently complicated negotiations that took place in the dynamic world of innovative competition that characterized dye-making in the 1880s.[81] During this time, the definition of chemical invention was constantly evolving, partly as a result of litigation, and partly as a result of new chemical knowledge. Though patents set the ground rules for how competition occurred, there was the problem that the science of dye invention advanced faster than the legal issues that it raised. The fast red AV case was followed by negotiations between Levinstein and BASF over licensing and sales agreements concerning naphthol yellow, and complex but ultimately unsuccessful manoeuvring to gain some of the market in dyes that attached to cotton directly, the benzopurpurines. These dyes played major roles in the making of Anglo-German alliances based on Ivan Levinstein's commercial and technical prowess. Through the involvement of the leading protagonists in patent litigation, Heinrich Caro and Ivan Levinstein, they also contributed directly and indirectly to amendments in the German and British patent laws in 1891 and 1907, respectively. These laws held fast for several decades. In 1939, in both Germany and England, "the products themselves cannot be formally claimed, though the claims for the process are in practice held to cover the product." In France, the emphasis remained on the product, and in the "U.SA. new compounds are patentable as such apart from their method of manufacture," though, and echoing the German and English disputes over dyes in the 1880s, "the attitude of the examiners on chemical facts is sometimes based on incorrect theoretical reasoning rather than on solid fact."[82] Finally in 1950, English patent law was amended to permit patents for chemical products.

10
"Ambitious and Glory Hunting ... Impractical and Fantastic"

Caro could not delegate to others, and was really interested only in his own brilliant discoveries, except when, as with Adolph von Baeyer, he was the sole line between the B.A.S.F. and the University.

Herbert Levinstein, 1949.[1]

What made Heinrich Caro such a successful and prolific inventor? This is the principal question that we tried to answer as we followed his career, especially during the 1870s and early 1880s. Because of Caro's artistic inclinations, we might with considerable justification describe this as his second most fertile period, when, as development chemist and then research director at BASF, he became the most important inventor of synthetic dyestuffs in the 19th century. Despite the surviving personal journals, diaries, and correspondence, and even self-congratulatory accounts, this is, however, one part of Caro's life for which source material is thin, at least from his own perspective. Accordingly, other approaches to verisimilitude must be sought out. There is, fortunately, an important insight into Caro's working style at that time. This derives from a retrospective and somewhat one-sided account written by his main professional rival at BASF, Carl Andreas Glaser, who joined the firm in 1869.

Glaser's account is a rich and revealing source of tensions, capturing the emotions that accompanied the growth of a corporation that almost from the start was to rely on its inventiveness. Certainly, and as exposed uncompromisingly by Glaser, it was a time of turbulent relationships among the members of the managing board at BASF, and Glaser did not hide his contempt for the ways in which the company was run. As for Caro, it was Glaser's opinion that he lacked thoroughness, order, and self discipline, attributes traditionally associated with the German character. The fact that Caro's reputation rested on his fame as the leading inventor at BASF serves to increase scrutiny of Glaser's account. In particular, Glaser claimed that Caro's creativity could only be stimulated by the clever coaxing and manipulation of the head of BASF, Friedrich Engelhorn. This prompts the question of whether the near hero worship of Caro by many German and British chemists and industrialists made him appear to have possessed more power than he really had?

Certainly, when it came to invention, Heinrich Caro was innovative and creative, a man skilled in a number of important techniques derived from his education in chemistry, his apprenticeship as a calico printer, his employment at Roberts, Dale & Co., and his mastery of the synthesis of artificial alizarin during 1869-70, not long after he joined BASF. Moreover, through his work in Manchester, and arrangements with dye industry founder William Perkin over alizarin patents, Caro brought about the transfer of coal-tar dye-making technology from England to Germany. Could the same have been achieved by more academically qualified chemists with less extensive prior industrial experience? Could others have made such remarkable progress with alizarin, eosin, azo dyes, alizarin orange, naphthol yellow, fast red AV, and indigo, even if the outcomes were not always commercially successful?

Such questions make Glaser's reminiscences all the more valuable, since they also provide context for Caro's almost whimsical descriptions of his childhood and adolescence. This is particularly true of Caro's interest in adventure stories and music and his wont to dream. Certainly, Caro remembered his youth fondly. His experiences in late-1840s Berlin played important roles in his development, moulded as it was by a particular historical period. Further, on special occasions, such as in the courtroom, he wore a talisman, "a peculiar diamond pin, in the centre of which there was a pear-shaped diamond mounted as a pendant,"[2] which of course was in keeping with the character of a chemist driven by the real, the symbolic, and the imaginary, and perhaps even a little superstition.

Carl Glaser's independent evaluation of Caro's working style, a record of incompetence set against intense bickering among the management at BASF, appears in an unpublished manuscript in the archives of BASF, Ludwigshafen. There are perhaps good reasons why the Caro Nachlass does not also reside at Ludwigshafen. Caro's sojourn at BASF was, especially in the years leading up to 1889, when he left the firm, far from happy, as is made clear from his correspondence with the Manchester dye-maker Ivan Levinstein (see chapter 9). This is resonant with Glaser's astringent, sardonic portrayal of life at BASF.

Glaser, who worked closely with Caro for a decade after 1869, was a former assistant of Kekulé, but originally educated in engineering, which may in part explain his contempt for Caro's approach to laboratory work and, especially, to industrial scale-up. Glaser's terse and often caustic and incisive comments–and invectives reserved mainly for Caro–while representing the distorted testimony of a prejudiced contemporary, certainly excite attention.[3] His evaluation of Caro began, appropriately, with a reference to his displays of musical and singing abilities on those occasions when Engelhorn brought a few friends and colleagues from the BASF factory, including Heinrich Brunck, together for a social evening. Caro played the piano or led the singing, "and I vividly remember a merry evening when he put a chair on a table, sat down on it, and sang 'Den Fürst von Thoren' with the people around as chorus."[4]

Carl Glaser at age 75 at his home in Heidelberg. Here he probably wrote his "Erlebnisse und Erinnerungen" (1921). At left is a bust of Kekulé. (BASF Archives.)

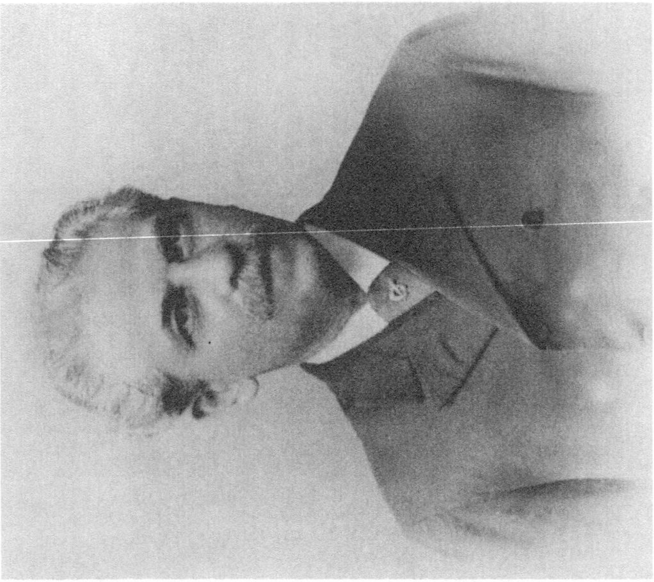

Heinrich Caro. Note that he is wearing his pear-shaped diamond talisman. (BASF Archives.)

Heinrich Brunck (1847-1911) as a young man. Brunck joined BASF in 1869, and was appointed director and member of the board in 1884. He was managing director of BASF until he left the board in 1906. (BASF Archives.)

During his first two years at BASF, Glaser worked with Caro on the alizarin synthesis, and after that "I was connected together with Caro in the firm for another 18 years. In as much as one can understand such a complicated personality I think that I can describe the man."[5] After acknowledging the "specialness of this great chemist," Glaser remarked that to make a description of Caro "true to life it is necessary to cast a few strong shadows; I consider it my task not to suppress the darker side of this character."[6]

Thus, continued Glaser, Caro "was wanting in self discipline. It was fortunate for him to have met a person like Engelhorn who with intensity and unending patience forced this overactive spirit again and again to his daily tasks." Engelhorn charmed Caro "with flattery and sweet words" but was resolute in his demands, and "knew how to keep this man, who was imbued with the best and worst qualities of an artist, on the right track." Caro tended to be "carried away by optimism and unbridled fantasy" and became very bitter when Engelhorn made it clear that some project was a waste of time.[7] Calm returned with Engelhorn's sensitive handling of the situation.

Glaser compared Engelhorn's control, encouragement, and flattery of Caro with that of the "prince behind his gold maker in the time of the alchemist.... But, contrary to the time of the alchemist, the endeavours were successful and the aniline factory reaped the benefit of this sowing of seed in fertile soil; Caro's inventions enhanced the image of the factory and added essentially to its position as first in the line."[8] Despite all this, Caro lacked "inner strength" and needed the "powerful personality" of Engelhorn during fifteen years of fruitful collaboration between 1868 and 1883, when Caro "established his fame through a series of important discoveries and outstanding works in the whole field of dyes.... There was probably nobody else in our industry [apart from Engelhorn] capable of inflaming the mind of this ambitious and glory-hunting soul of an artist."[9] These discoveries were also the reason why Caro was appointed research director at BASF in the mid-1870s, which made him an even greater threat to Glaser.

Engelhorn's appreciation of Caro was based on the seemingly sure knowledge that profitable products would appear from their uneasy alliance, aided from the end of 1873 by Caro's close working relationship with the academic chemist Adolf Baeyer. "I am deeply convinced," wrote

Glaser, "that if Caro had had to depend upon himself he would not have achieved half of what he succeeded in achieving while spurred on by Engelhorn."[10] It was only in 1884, when the management was reorganised and Engelhorn retired, that "the business constraints which had brought them [Caro and Engelhorn] together came to end."[11]

Time and again Glaser reiterated Caro's perceived personal failings, emphasising how he was held under the spell of Engelhorn, and "looked up to this strong and forceful man with a kind of shy admiration."[12] According to Glaser, Engelhorn boasted of his power over Caro to Glaser and fellow director August Clemm with jokes about Caro's weaknesses, and his need for flattery. This habit of talking about colleagues behind their backs, however, disgusted Glaser, who realised that he was also a pawn in the game whereby the senior management maintained control through encouragement of distrust.

Though Glaser readily acknowledged Caro's substantial contribution to the elevation of BASF to first place among German dye-makers, he presented a picture of an ill-disciplined, slapdash worker whose talent showed itself in fits and starts and whose inventiveness may have been well-suited to the laboratory bench but was hopelessly out of place when applied on a manufacturing scale. Caro, according to Glaser, was a dreamer and artist wrapped up in a world of his own, and whose inventiveness could only be exploited by the untiring efforts and charms of Friedrich Engelhorn.

> [T]hrough his years spent in calico printing and through his natural ability Caro was superb at working on a test-tube scale, especially in the art of establishing the nature of the smallest quantity of materials.[13]

Things were very different, according to Glaser, when the time came to transform laboratory experiments into large-scale processes. Then, Caro

> was impractical and fantastic. It is astonishing how little he brought from the great school of life that was the chemical industry of England. Despite his prior training in the field of machines and familiarity with many types of process equipment, his inability astounded me. I soon came to accept with great reservations his advice concerning technical installations.[14]

August Clemm had even less regard for Caro's abilities when it came to the development of large-scale equipment. Here, no doubt, Glaser was referring to delays in the scale-up of the alizarin process at Ludwigshafen.

What comes through from Glaser's description is the image of Caro as a brilliant bench worker who consistently demonstrated considerable personal and professional shortcomings. Thus, for Caro's "undisciplined personality every rule and pressure were anathema."[15] He did not maintain regular working hours, "was not punctual and the division of the day as accepted by normal people did not exist for him. In the same way, commercial pressures were burdensome to him."[16]

Nevertheless, Caro certainly knew his commercial worth. In the summer of 1869, just after Engelhorn had allotted 10,000 guilders to the development of alizarin and other processes, Caro began working at a reduced pace in order to make known to his employers that he felt entitled to better conditions, a matter that was soon resolved to his satisfaction.

In September 1869, Glaser's first assignment at the factory had been to establish the yields for reactions that Caro had developed in Manchester. "Now what I could do in twelve hours, Engelhorn could not get from Caro in half a year. Without special direction I could in half-kilo scale trials solve these problems and produce the results in tabular form for August Clemm ... who was highly satisfied with it and mentioned my work to Engelhorn." The latter, as Glaser pointed out, had got nothing from Caro after waiting six months.[17] "The solution of such tasks were much too uninteresting to the artist and were too distant from his way of thinking."[18]

Glaser wrote that he had never seen Caro "work with a balance and weights, or obtain results titrimetrically."[19] Caro would not accept the established methods for determining the fading characteristics of a dyed sample and became "very angry if somebody mentioned a smaller value of a dye's fastness which he [Caro] had estimated to be higher."[20]

According to Glaser, Caro was not a person to be entrusted with negotiations over business matters. Thus, while Engelhorn and August Clemm, when dealing with representatives of rival companies and agents, were discrete and learned much about other firms without revealing anything important about the activities of BASF, Caro was just the opposite. He was incapable of being

> secretive and loved to hear himself talking. It was not difficult to get information out of him that in the interests of the business should have been kept confidential. He was a poor keeper of business secrets, though this was not out of bad intentions. He simply could not keep his mouth shut.[21]

This dealing with others was made even more difficult because "[o]f the many chemists that were taken on ... by the aniline factory he was the only one who saw himself not bound to business hours; he was late in and left late. Very often he was kept at home feeling unwell."[22] Glaser recalled that during his first year at the BASF factory he would visit Caro at his home. Caro gave the appearance of being unwell and lethargic, at least "until you touched upon a subject that interested him. Immediately he was full of fire and flame and his illness disappeared." Otherwise getting business information out of Caro proved very difficult during the days when he was, apparently, not in high spirits:

> Information that others would have provided in ten minutes could not be got [from Caro] in less than two or three hours, and even then you were not sure that you had got what you wanted. I had to consider my time in order to complete my tasks. I was repeatedly treated in this way, and found it highly inconsiderate, to the extent that I eventually sent written questions [to Caro] by messenger.

Though Glaser "accorded respect to his older colleague and displayed a great deal of patience," this strategy also did not work.

Inevitably, there was a gradual deterioration in the communications between Caro and Glaser, and

> the lack of success of our working together deepened the oppositeness of our characters.... In the course of time the initial sympathy between the two of us had disappeared and a very strained situation resulted. The relationship became even more tense when Caro and Carl Clemm, brother of August Clemm, conspired against me and that intrigue was sustained by Engelhorn. By contrast, August Clemm, who hated Caro, incited me [Glaser] against him.... It is certainly not a beautiful picture of the personalities with which I had to deal and the unpleasant state of affairs which was prevalent when I entered the aniline factory.[23]

Glaser's account, which is somewhat at variance with the heroic image normally associated with Caro, raises questions about the quality of his judgement. Certainly Glaser was not alone in recording the difficulties of working with Caro. Another co-worker, but this time great admirer, of Caro was his assistant from early 1889, the Englishman Ernest F. Ehrhardt.

Despite his own reservations, Ehrhardt observed that "it is one of the attributes of genius that they are frequently difficult to get on with, and in this respect Dr. Caro was not altogether an exception."[24] Therefore Glaser's revealing, if not entirely objective, description of Caro's character might in hindsight deserve an alternative explanation, namely, that those very aspects of Caro that Glaser found most displeasing were expressions of creativity. If Caro flourished at BASF it was because Engelhorn understood and handled him superbly, and, within limits, provided freedom to explore whenever a profitable product or process seemed likely.

Glaser also informs us that Caro's record of collaborations with colleagues at BASF was not one of unmitigated success. How, therefore, was Caro so creative in such a seemingly uncomfortable environment? The answer, perhaps, must be sought in the period prior to 1870, and partly away from the laboratory and industry. Caro developed a distinctive style of working that owed as much to youthful experiences in Berlin, strongly influenced by drama and music, as it did to the calico-printing and dye-manufacturing industries of Germany and England. He had developed a wistful taste for dreamy, fantastic visions. These, no doubt, heightened his early creative senses and a love for epic drama. This was captured in his retrospective description of the turmoil of 1848, and in his history of the emergence of the synthetic dye industry.[25] If nothing else, Glaser's account, marked by a considerable measure of truth, helps us to understand Caro's creativity better by elaborating, even in a negative way, on features of Caro's personality.

It was Caro's individualism, blessed with an artistic perception, that set him apart from others. Caro was a free spirit, well-versed in chemistry and its application to printing and dyeing, and whose chemical intuition owed as much to his liberal upbringing and entrepreneurial streak as it did to science and technology. This interpretation of knowledge production in the laboratory was not Glaser's intention. But it is one way of using Glaser's memoirs, apart from the manner in which they describe a workplace dominated by jealous and scheming company leaders. Perhaps it was because Glaser remembered his colleagues with little fondness that he was moved to write such a provocative history of laboratory life at a crucial period in the development of BASF. Certainly it helps us to understand Caro's increasing unhappiness, especially after Engelhorn's departure.

Whatever else motivated Glaser, he unwittingly provided us with a rare firsthand account of the emergence of BASF as the leading German dye firm, and of the way in which this came about through the activities of its principal inventor, Heinrich Caro. Glaser's account contributes to the impression that Caro certainly did not have the power within the firm that his admirers have implied. He was controlled by senior management, at first in the person of Friedrich Engelhorn, and then during the years of research into indigo by Adolf Baeyer. None of this, however, detracts from Caro's remarkable accomplishments as the leading inventor of synthetic dyes at BASF.

The final word goes to Amalie Caro. To many people, she observed, Heinrich Caro appeared to make poor use of his time, though he was brilliant and productive. Caro's mind could never rest and "under the mask of wasted time new ideas grew." Sometimes he became depressed. Then, suddenly, perhaps after hearing happy news, he would become glad and joyful. This was the deceptive front that Caro showed to his close colleagues and friends. They saw in him the "eternally youthful man, with a wonderful sense of humour."[26]

The private Heinrich Caro

While Glaser and, to a lesser extent, Ehrhardt inform us on Caro's working style, and contribute towards an appreciation of his industrial life, which is the principal focus of this biography, there are few references in the Caro Nachlass to Caro's inner, and private, life. One obituarist pointed out that "[I]n private life he was of an amiable and winning disposition, ever ready to help his colleagues, especially those who were his junior in years."[27]

Certainly, and among other things, Caro was an accomplished draughtsman, a skill that he appears to have applied in occasional sketches. And his love of music remained unabated, as even Glaser noticed. According to Amalie Caro, her

> father enjoyed music very much. From early on he composed his own scores, and advanced so much in the course of time that it became a highly pleasurable experience to listen to his wonderful thoughtful fantasies at the piano and organ. This made up for many losses. In this, he always found great consolation and peace.

During his period of military service in Berlin, Caro's singing certainly enriched his social life, which was in sharp contrast to, and a welcome relief from, the relentless hard work he had to endure as an apprentice calico printer in Mülheim.

> As a young man he was considered a good baritone in the social circles of Berlin. Mrs. K[C]lara [Josephine] Schumann [wife of Robert] accompanied him at the grand piano in the concert hall and the venerable Emperor Wilhelm [from 1858-61 prince

regent] listened to him singing the role of the master in the Lied von der Glocke in the Domkirche. Every Sunday his voice could be heard in the choir. He was also a studious member of the well-known Stern'schen Gesangsverein singing society.[28]

Little is known about Heinrich Caro's family life, which was no doubt quiet and conventional, without any hint of scandals and disagreements, and certainly not to the extent that they permeated the factory, laboratory, and courtroom. Caro first met Edith Sarah Eaton, his future wife, in 1862. Born on 2 March 1842, she was a daughter of an employee engaged in the administration of the estates of Lord Manvers at Torsby Park in the Dukeries (north Midlands). They married in 1866, shortly before leaving England, though not before taking a honeymoon on the Isle of Wight. Following a short stay in Berlin the couple moved to Heidelberg. Caro had originally planned to go to Palermo to study with Stanislao Cannizzaro, but Philipp Pauli convinced him that Heidelberg's warm and pleasant climate would suit his health well.[29] The Caros' first daughter, Amalie Harriet, was born in Heidelberg in 1867.[30] It was Amalie who recorded her father's reminiscences and later organised his Nachlass.

Within a few years of joining BASF, Caro was well able to support his family and home, a three-storey building in Mannheim. He had earned a substantial salary at BASF, supplemented by various profit-sharing schemes that were his right as a director. He received 20,000 marks per annum after leaving BASF, which was considerably more than that of a leading professor. This was made up of 10,000 marks, in accord with his contract, plus an additional 10,000 marks for his consultancy services. Caro had demanded, as a condition for continuing his practical studies, a further sum towards the expense of his laboratory equipment and materials. However, though the management would not agree to this, Caro did continue with laboratory work at his home.

Like Glaser, Amalie described her father as possessed of an artistic and impractical nature. He was, she also suggested, a poor judge of character, admiring famous people ("the great") very much.[31] This snobbery, however, in one way turned out to be a valuable attribute. It encouraged Caro's strong, and sometimes leading, participation in various scientific and technical societies; his own reputation would have brought access to the scientific socialites of Prussia (see chapter 11).

Caro's deeply superstitious nature was also noted by Amalie. The number seven played an important role in his life, he preferred not to travel on Friday, and he was unhappy to have been born on the 13th (as he had been informed, though in fact it appears, according to Amalie, that he was actually born at 1 a.m. on the 14th). In court when engaged in patent litigation he always wore his inherited pear-shaped diamond. "When he saw its light he thought he could understand the language of the diamond."[32]

During Caro's years at Ludwigshafen, the interest in political events that existed at mid-century appears to have vanished, only to resurface half a century after the most formative event, the revolution of 1848, was recalled, and transcribed by Amalie. Between 1848 and 1866, when Caro returned to Germany from Manchester, he must have had similar feelings to those of Bismarck and many other Germans:

> It has perhaps, proved better for our future that we had to stray plodding through the wilderness of internal conflicts from 1848 to 1866, like the Jews before they entered the Promised Land.[33]

In Caro's case, the "wilderness of internal conflicts" brought about commitment to the struggles of apprenticeship between 1855 and 1859, and to untested science and technology in a foreign land from 1859 to 1866.

There is nothing in Caro's reminiscences about his religious beliefs, though that may be related to the complexities of his Jewish background and the obligation to become part of a Christian society. His choral contributions on Sundays suggest more love of singing than a strong church affiliation. Perhaps this void is a clue to his supposed superstitions, somewhat paradoxical in a scientist (though a number of notable scientists, particularly the English chemist William Crookes, did become obsessed with psychic activities and the paranormal). Perhaps, also, those superstitions were a convenient way of enveloping chemical inventiveness in mystique.

Caro's warm friendships with English chemists, particularly Ivan Levinstein, and his working relationship with Ehrhardt are worthy of note. Not only did the English pour great praise on Caro, and credit him with the international success of BASF, but they also reminded him of happy and less-inhibited days spent in Manchester. This must also have compensated for the strict Prussian aesthetic of the 1870s and provided much-needed solace during and after the turbulent years at BASF. Prussian-dominated Germany certainly offered a protective solidity, which–however acceptable to the utterly respectable and prosperous middle and ruling classes–did require conformity to a rigid cultural landscape. This is seen in Caro's retrospective description of the events of March 1848, in which enthusiasm for the revolution is juxtaposed with later and conventional sentiments for king and emperor. It is also perhaps resonant in his request that Ivan Levinstein not make known the circumstances of his leaving BASF.[34] Beyond this appeal for silence we can only speculate on the private Heinrich Caro.

11

A Chemical Celebrity

Dear Dr. Caro, no one knows better than you about the work of the early days of the Coal-Tar Colour Industry.... you have done so much for the enrichment of the industry itself and for its development.

Sir William Henry Perkin, 1906.[1]

The two decades that Caro spent in retirement provided little of interest in the way of new dyes and processes to BASF, despite his agreement to undertake research for the firm. He developed a novel process for the synthesis of rhodamine dyes, which, though patented, appears not to have been adopted. He also synthesized the only compound that carries his name, Caro's acid (persulphuric acid), through which he became known to generations of chemistry graduates, though probably few of them were aware of his industrial career. Nevertheless, Caro did make other contributions to the firm in the form of documentation, notes, and reports that were invaluable in patent litigation. Until 1898, he remained active on the consultative committee of the Verein zur Wahrung der Interessen der chemischen Industrie Deutschlands. As a pioneer in the development of synthetic dyes, he wrote the first comprehensive history of the industry, presented to the Deutsche Chemische Gesellschaft in 1891.[2]

Caro also attended or became involved in a number of commemorative events, often as a guest of honour. These events, including celebrations for 25 years of Kekulé's benzene ring (in 1890) and the 50th anniversary of Perkin's discovery of mauve (in 1906), provided occasions to renew old contacts and to review progress in both organic chemistry and the dye industry. Caro was a member of numerous industrial and scientific societies, and did much to enhance the standing of the Verein Deutscher Chemiker. His status in German society was such that he was often called upon to give speeches and lectures after 1890. He was especially sought out by British officials anxious to establish, for example, the threat that German synthetic indigo posed to the Indian plant-derived product, and any disadvantage that duty on industrial alcohol had on the English dye industry. On these and a number of other matters some correspondence survives. There are of course gaps, but what there is enables us to appreciate the earlier perceptions of Caro, particularly in England. While this does not go very far to explain the nature of Caro's peculiar talent, it does help to provide an insight into the significance of 19th- and early 20th-century industrial organic chemistry–its commercial and political impact–that owed much to Caro's mastery of chemistry and technology.

The departure from Ludwigshafen

The widely acknowledged importance of Caro to BASF led to considerable surprise when it became known that he had left the firm early in 1890. As with any important figure who takes a sudden and unexpected course of action, Caro's departure caused considerable speculation in the press, as correspondence with Ivan Levinstein revealed. Thus Levinstein, when asking for details of Caro's inventions and career, also drew his attention to rumours circulated by the press concerning the reasons for what appeared to be a quite newsworthy departure. Caro provided Levinstein with his response to certain press reports, displayed optimism for the future, and also made a rare admission of his own sense of failure at BASF. After advising Levinstein to refer to the catalogue of the 1885 International Inventions Exhibition, held at South Kensington, London, for information on his inventions, Caro continued:

> The main point for me however is what do you, my esteemed friend, need this information for? Not possibly the preparation of my obituary? In regard to this, we hope that there is not yet any hurry. By leaving my business position I have not left life. I hope that a new life with much work and a great deal of balance lies before me, and, God willing, many blank pages will be filled with the account of my future work. I certainly do not wish that my friends should show me the mirror of the past during my lifetime. Unfortunately I know only too well how much my activities and creativeness have not come up to my intentions! But it would be particularly disagreeable for me at the present time if the press, which has occupied itself with the facts and motives of my leaving the business, should unfortunately print mistaken information.[3]

Caro asked Levinstein not to make known his displeasure with former colleagues. "I am starting on a new way of life, because the former one had led me on to fruitless and desolate fields of work. So let us wait and see!" A few days later, Levinstein explained why he had requested so much personal information:

> Very far from my thoughts was the intention of writing a necrology for you. May I be spared this task for many, many more years! I simply intended to prepare a short

> notice about your leaving the Badische that would stop the press from reporting incorrect information.[4]

Caro continued to display remarkable frankness about his feelings towards the BASF management to the expatriate Ivan Levinstein, particularly in a letter dated 22 February 1890. At the same time, because of Levinstein's new and close business connection with AGFA and Bayer, Caro made it clear that their friendship should not be made public.

> Hearty thanks for your friendly letter of the 16th of this month. It is very kind of you that you show such close interest at the present point of change in my life. I shall never forget that.
>
> There are "friends" which now turn out to have been only "business friends." With you the opposite is the case. Nevertheless, I must avoid any indication in public of our warm friendship.
>
> My leaving the business has become a six-day wonder, and in view of the importance of the firm "naturally" has provoked various versions of events. Meanwhile the earth has gone on rotating and the world has got more important things to do than busying itself with me.
>
> However, in view of the present and future situations, I would very much appreciate it if you would bring to my notice the comments in the press mentioned in your letter which "are being eagerly discussed by my so-called friends." So far I have not seen anything of the kind. To an open critic I would like to reply openly. May I therefore ask you to inform me occasionally on what you have noticed.[5]

No subsequent correspondence dealing with the reports on Caro's departure from BASF survives. Caro made contact with Levinstein again in April 1891 with a request for statistics on coal-tar products, information required for his forthcoming lecture to the Deutsche Chemische Gesellschaft on the history of the dye industry. Levinstein was then in Wiesbaden, where his wife was receiving ongoing but not very successful medical treatment, and advised Caro that he "was heartily pleased to hear that you are happy with your present activities and at long last have found the quietness and satisfaction that you longed for."[6]

International recognition: Caro and industrial research

Heinrich Caro's indigo synthesis, though far from a commercial success, aroused considerable scientific interest, and samples of the intermediates and of his other inventions were among the products displayed at the 1885 London International Inventions Exhibition by BASF, the company "with which the name of Heinrich Caro will always be connected."[7] Caro's introduction to the display, which included all his major inventions, noted "[s]ome of the chemicals … have been discovered by our chemists, others were the result of scientific research."[8] English chemists were so impressed that several requested samples from the showcase. They included Caro's consultant and expert witness Henry E. Armstrong, then at the recently opened Central Institution, South Kensington (later associated with City & Guilds College, then Institute; it is now Imperial College of Science and Technology).[9] Another notable English scientist well-versed in coal-tar chemistry was Raphael Meldola, whose first contact with Caro, in 1885, may well have been to acquire BASF specimens for teaching purposes and for his 1886 lecture before the Society of Arts in London. Meldola advised Caro that in the lecture he intended to focus almost exclusively on Caro's products, and their roles in bringing about a convergence between science and technology:

> ... my object in writing to you is to beg a small favour for which I shall be very grateful if you will kindly accede to it. Some time ago my friend Dr. W. H. Perkin showed me a set of your products which you had presented to him.
>
> May I ask you to do the same for me here? The specimens which I am asking for are required for two purposes,–in the first place as lecture specimens for showing my students–in the next place for a special lecture which I am going to give this session before the Society of Arts and in which I am going to treat almost entirely of your discoveries and of those of your firm. The object of this lecture will be to illustrate by your products what science has done for technology and vice versa; so that your firm may also see that it will be to their advantage for me to be able to show their own preparations. I am more particularly going to dwell upon the Rosaniline group with special reference to your beautiful synthesis of these colours by condensation from tetramethyldiamidobenzophenone [Michler's ketone, used in the synthesis of crystal violet]. I should be very glad of a good specimen of the latter in order to show some of its reactions before the Society of Arts.

Meldola made known to Caro that he had recently left the dye industry to take up a post as professor of chemistry at the City & Guilds of London Institute, the Technical College, Finsbury (also known as the London Institution, and in 1885 renamed Central Technical College; chemistry was taught at a lower level than the South Kensington Central Institution, for which it was effectively a feeder).

> Pray excuse my troubling you in this matter but I know your readiness to help the cause of science and you may be sure that I shall always be willing to reciprocate your kind attention in any way that I can. I may add that I am no longer in the service of Brooke, Simpson & Spiller, so that there need be no fear of any specimens which you may send being used for trade purposes.[10]

Display cabinet for BASF dyes at the International Inventions Exhibition, South Kensington, London, 1885. (Deutsches Museum.)

BASF coat of arms, printed with methylene blue. According to Amalie Caro, it was printed in 1885 for display at the International Inventions Exhibition. (BASF Archives, from an original in the Caro Nachlass, Deutsches Museum.)

Caro must have been flattered at the great compliment paid to him and his firm. Meldola's lecture was also an opportunity for one of Britain's leading chemists to endorse the products of Ludwigshafen before an important public audience. On 21 November 1885, Caro informed Meldola:

> My colleagues as well as myself shall feel very glad to place a collection of our products into your able hands and thus to contribute towards the aims of your noble Institute. Within the course of the next month we expect back the specimens exhibited at Kensington and then we shall forthwith divide them amongst the numerous chemists, who have done us the honour of applying to us for the same. In case you should have already appointed a day for the intended lecture at the Society of Arts, please have the kindness of informing me at what latest date the specimens shall be required by you.
>
> I trust my Dear Professor Meldola that you will never hesitate to confide your chemical wishes to me![11]

Meldola's choice of BASF and Caro's inventions as a feature of his lecture was certainly deliberate, particularly since he announced, following extensive enquiries, that more than 80 per cent of coal-tar dyes used in Britain, the largest dye-using nation in Europe, were made in Germany. Moreover, in 1885 German production of synthetic dyes was some six times that of all the English firms. This must have shocked the audience. The revelation certainly shocked the Society of Dyers and Colourists, which extracted most of the lecture from the *Journal of the Society of Arts* of 28 May 1886 for its journal.[12]

Among the firms that Meldola had approached for his survey were Edward Ripley & Son, of Bradford, "perhaps the largest dyer of piece goods in the kingdom," who in 1885 used 86.5 per cent "of foreign coal-tar colours"; the yarn dyer Leckie & MacGregor, of Paisley, "who inform me that in the west of Scotland, including Glasgow and Paisley, they are certain that at least 90 per cent of the dyes used come from the Continent;" and the jute dyers James Stevenson, of Dundee, who used only 7.7 per cent of English dyestuffs, and Cox Bros., of Camperdown Jute Works, at Lochee, "who state that practically the whole of the 'aniline' colours used by them are of Continental manufacture." Other notable firms included the calico printers Z. Heys & Sons, of Barrhead, "who used over 10,000 lb. weight of colours (exclusive of alizarin), of which 700 lb. only were of English make," and James Black & Co., of Dunbarton, who "state that in their belief more than one-half of the colour

Firm	Place	Activity
Edward Ripley & Son	Bradford	dyer of piece goods
Walter Walker & Son	Dewsbury	wool dyer
John Newton	Macclesfield	wool dyer
G.W. Oldham	Netherton, near Huddersfield	silk dyer
James Templeton & Co.	Glasgow	yarn dyer
Alexander Harvey & Son	Glasgow	yarn dyer
Manson & Henry	Glasgow	yarn dyer
Leckie & MacGregor	Paisley	yarn dyer
James Stevenson	Dundee	jute dyer
Cox Bros., Camperdown Jute Works	Lochee	jute dyer
Z. Heys & Sons	Barrhead	calico printer
James Black & Co.	Bonhill, Dunbarton	calico printer
Walter Crum & Co.	Thornliebank, Glasgow	calico printer
John Orr Ewing & Co.	Dumbartonshire	Turkey red dyer
William Stirling & Sons	Glasgow	Turkey red dyer

British Consumers of German Synthetic Dyes from Raphael Meldola's 1886 Survey

used by calico printers is of foreign manufacture." The Turkey red dyer Walter Crum & Co., of Thornliebank, Glasgow, a large user of artificial alizarin, was "of the opinion that 'the great bulk of what is used in this country is manufactured in Germany.'"[13] Leckie & MacGregor, Heys, Black, and Crum were among the firms introduced to Heinrich Caro's products while he was working with Roberts, Dale & Co. in the early 1860s. Scottish firms that employed madder became some of the first users of BASF artificial alizarin, through the James Laing & Co. agency in Glasgow that had worked so closely with Caro before he left England.[14] The smooth transition to Caro's coal-tar dyes, whether made in Manchester or Ludwigshafen, set a precedent that encouraged British consumers to adopt, almost exclusively, German-made products by the 1880s.

Meldola concluded that the Germans had managed to corner the market because "[t]he strength of our competitors is in their laboratories, and not, as here, upon the [stock] exchanges."[15] It was a message that Meldola would repeat many times during the following three decades (and others ever since). And, drawing upon his interests in evolutionary biology and entomology, which included close contact with Charles Darwin, Meldola pushed home his point with a historical account of commercial dyes that

> reveals that fundamental law of the "survival of the fittest." Old products have been displaced by newer ones as fresh discoveries were made, or processes improved.... The moral conveyed to the manufacturer is sufficiently obvious. If we are to recover our former supremacy in this country, we must begin by dispelling conservative ideas–we must realise the fact that no existing process is final, and that no product at present sent into the market is destined to survive for an unlimited period.[16]

In 1885, William Perkin had also emphasised how laboratory work enabled the German companies to improve on processes, and that the "result of the application of this scientific labour to this industry is that Germany produces products of the highest class and at the lowest price."[17] Patent law had not prevented unlicensed imports into Britain (as Perkin had discovered in the 1870s when German-made alizarin from several firms arrived in England), with the result that the British "patentee had to compete against all other manufacturers with the exception of *his own countrymen*."[18] Furthermore there were no tariffs on dyes imported into England, though this was not the case elsewhere.

But the main distinguishing feature of the German dye industry, according to Perkin, was the attitude towards science.

> We find that in Germany the manufacturer understands the value of well-trained chemists, and sympathises with them; they also realise the value of theoretical chemistry–this is a condition of things we don't find in this country.... There is no chasm [in Germany], as we have already seen, between pure and applied chemistry, they do not even stand side by side, but are linked together, so that a technical chemist needs to be a thorough chemist, and unless we employ such men we must be at a great disadvantage in relation to foreign manufacturers.[19]

Perkin also drew attention to the economic importance of the dye industry, and the close link between technical and scientific chemistry. Benefits accrued to industry as an offspring of science and to science through the availability of new industrial products and topics for investigation. In 1886, Ivan Levinstein also proferred an opinion as to where Germany's advantages lay.[20] Though there were differences between the opinions of Meldola, Perkin, and Levinstein, they all acknowledged the importance of science-based research in German industry, as pioneered by Heinrich Caro.

Caro's fame as an inventor and originator of industrial research continued to spread far and wide after he left BASF, including across the Atlantic, where in 1898 the chemist Edward S. Johnson of Pennsylvania informed Caro that he was also preparing to lecture on coal-tar products. Caro reviewed Johnson's manuscript, and returned it with his comments. On 7 August 1899, Johnson responded:

> It is difficult for me to adequately express to you the mingled sense of pleasure and pride derived from your letter acknowledging the receipt of my review. Coming as it does from one whose scientific and technical achievements in the industries of the coal-tar colors have made him the most eminent figure in the general development of the greatest of chemical industries, and a main factor in the establishment and growth of the Badische Anilin- u. Sodafabrik, a simple word of acknowledgement would have been to me a matter of great pleasure and no little pride. To this you have graciously added, in most generous and encouraging terms, commendatory references to an effort to sketch a view of a vast field of chemical activity.[21]

The legacy of corporate invention

Caro's contribution to corporate invention went beyond products, processes, and the industrial research laboratory into the one area of commercial activity that from the late 1870s sustained and stimulated the enterprise of science-based industry. This was the domain of patents and patent protection, where the contrast between Germany and England was greatest, as described by Caro's last assistant in patent matters, Ernest F. Ehrhardt. Ehrhardt was unusual, in the eyes of the BASF management, because he was one of the few people who could manage to work with Caro. Perhaps this was in part because Ehrhardt was from England, where Caro had made some of his closest friendships. No doubt Ehrhardt felt it an honour to be working in the same laboratory as the greatest living inventor of synthetic dyes.[22]

The main features of the system of organised invention that became possible due to Caro's talents were delineated in Ehrhardt's paper presented in London to the Seventh International Congress of Applied Chemistry (1909). The emphasis in that paper was on the importance of large, strong, and well-organised corporations that could afford to invest in research and development programmes in which the risk was justified by the security of patent monopoly. This might seem somewhat at odds with the highly individualistic way in which Caro conducted his own business affairs, but it certainly was the logical outcome of the foundations he had laid at BASF. Ehrhardt's argument was based on the underlying and immediate differences between the German and British dye industries.

By way of example, Ehrhardt used the indigo synthesis, which though an industrial failure in Caro's time finally succeeded because of the exceptional situation in Germany that favoured long-term investment in research and development. The indigo programme consumed much of Caro's time in the early 1880s, and the collaboration with Baeyer led to a tremendous scientific achievement. This was the total structural elucidation of the natural product, a vital step towards the Heumann syntheses of 1890 that were immediately taken up by BASF and Hoechst. Ehrhardt's message was clear. Only a large profitable firm could afford to suffer the sustained and substantial losses that Caro's project generated and at the same time continue until the ultimate goal, the prescribed outcome of indigo research, was achieved. Implicit in the message was not only the need for substantial capital, particularly from reinvested profits, but also for the appropriate organisation, which included research and development laboratories. Ehrhardt's presentation must have appealed strongly to those who favoured trade protectionism and strong support for patents, both of which were fashionable around 1900. It was, moreover, a declaration on behalf of industrial capitalism and large-scale corporate invention: "In the chemical industry of to-day an inventor is helpless unless he is a capitalist or has one to support him, and when I speak of protection to the inventor it involves protection to the capitalist." Only a financially well-endowed firm could support Heinrich Caro's and Adolf Baeyer's venture into synthetic indigo, and–as Ehrhardt reflected–great hopes were raised by their scientific successes. However,

> although the invention was taken up by the two most powerful chemical firms of that day [BASF and Hoechst] who set chemists and engineers to work at it unstintingly, no commercial process for the production of indigo in bulk could ever be based on this synthesis. The time, and money, and labour, and [investment in] plant spent in endeavouring to base an industry upon these great chemical discoveries were to a great extent wasted.

While the scale and scope of industrial organic chemistry at the end of the 19th century was already far removed from the 1860s, there still remained many similarities in the ways in which scientists and inventors negotiated rights to processes. Thus Baeyer's arrangements with BASF and Hoechst in the 1880s were not altogether unlike those that Caro negotiated with Roberts, Dale & Co. over his mauve and other processes in the 1860s. Both inventors had to rely on their patents and the resources of established "capitalist firms" for transforming the new discoveries into industrial processes. The difference was that, with the increasing scientific content and complexity, the projects needed more time and money. The indigo programme lasted twenty years from the time it was first taken up by Caro and required considerable manpower, while his mauve process took no more than two years between discovery and the availability of a saleable product, and depended on a single inventor.

Typically, before 1870, chemists simply looked for a compound that showed the properties of a dye, and clues of where to search emerged from this highly empirical work. Between mauve and indigo in complexity was the industrial synthesis of alizarin, achieved by Caro and others in about three years from the time that Graebe and Liebermann established its chemical constitution. Increasingly there was a greater reliance on chemical theory, particularly structural knowledge, which is why the indigo synthesis could succeed only after Baeyer had established its structure. This, and the design of synthetic pathways, were the outcome of his collaboration with Caro. Nevertheless, and however much the work of Baeyer and Caro converged, there were sharp differences. Thus while Baeyer was an academic chemist, Caro was, as an employee

Title page of BASF price list for aniline dyes, 1896. The branches in Moscow (Russia) and Neuville-sur-Saône (France) are mentioned, as are medals awarded at international exhibitions for the firm's product. (BASF Archives.)

Heinrich Brunck, early 1900s. Brunck was the driving force behind the development of commercial indigo and important innovations in inorganic chemistry, most notably nitrogen fixation. (BASF Archives.)

of a chemical firm, a technologist, and Baeyer's overriding concern with structural elucidation was not something that Caro cared about very much.

To draw a comparison between Germany and the situation in England, Ehrhardt next turned to the risk taking, or "courage" as he called it, involved in protecting patents and undertaking research and development work. It was his opinion that despite recent revisions to English patent law (mainly due to the lobbying of Ivan Levinstein), the same courage could not be found in England because the weak patent system did not stimulate risky business ventures based on scientific discoveries.

> There are circumstances under which courage becomes foolhardiness, and I say that with the present uncertainty attending English patents, it would be foolhardy to invest in inventions in the chemical industry in the way it is done as a regular practice in Germany and in the United States.

Ehrhardt laid particular emphasis on the recently "defunct firm, which at last was known under the name of Brooke, Simpson & Spiller, Limited." This firm, of Hackney Wick, London, once employed Raphael Meldola (1877-85) and Arthur Green (1885-94), but their inventions were not properly exploited, in Ehrhardt's view, because of the failings of English patent law in providing protection for chemical inventions. Indeed, by ignoring the various mergers and acquisitions that had taken place, Ehrhardt argued that the problems had started much earlier, in 1865, when Thomas Holliday of Huddersfield successfully broke the patent monopoly over aniline red (magenta) held by the predecessor of Brooke, Simpson & Spiller, that is, Simpson, Maule & Nicholson.

> Shortly after the decision [of 1865] one of the partners left the business in disgust, withdrawing his capital. That is the sort of thing one might naturally expect, but the damage went much further. This firm [Brooke, Simpson & Spiller] subsequently had the good fortune, or as I prefer to put it, displayed the good management of engaging some of the most eminent coal tar chemists of this country on their scientific staff. Professor Green and Professor Meldola were both at the time chemists in the factory to which I am referring, and, as might be expected, they made inventions. What course did the firm take after their experience of British patents? They shirked the outlay for development, endeavoured to keep the inventions secret, and did not patent them. No chemical firm on earth when it has the good fortune to invent a colouring matter of the importance of [Green's] Primuline can afford to throw it away, but this invention and that of the ingrain colours and that of Meldola Blue were thrown away. With adequate patent protection the invention first mentioned

> alone might have brought in a princely income, and properly managed under favourable circumstances could have contributed largely towards placing the firm in the first rank of chemical manufacturers in the world.[23]

Though Arthur Green, by drawing attention to the self-interest and short-term aims of the partners, differed slightly in his opinion as to why Brooke, Simpson & Spiller failed, the end result was the same: "the business was weakened by the withdrawal of all the profits made.... Even the discovery of a number of important new reactions and new dyestuffs within the firm's laboratories did not avail to save them from decadence."[24] This was in sharp contrast to the situation at BASF, where until the early 1880s, Engelhorn had given every encouragement to his chief inventor, Heinrich Caro, who also played the most important role in securing monopolies for the firm's new discoveries through patent protection.

While Caro's work provided the basis for the development of science-based industrial capitalism, it also, somewhat ironically perhaps, provided considerable inspiration to the founders of another world order: Communism. This took place through the exposure of Carl Schorlemmer to Caro's work in Manchester, and in particular his own interest in the synthesis and manufacture of alizarin. From following and participating in these developments, both the practical and theoretical chemistry, Schorlemmer formulated philosophical views regarding the intimate relationships between theoretical ideas and their social and political contexts that were similar to those of Friedrich Engels and Karl Marx, with whom he came into close contact.[25] Schorlemmer published a widely acclaimed history of organic chemistry that in its last chapter emphasised the wider impact of coal-tar products, especially alizarin and the possibility of artificial indigo, and that was an early, and perhaps the earliest, combination of what later became known as internalist and externalist viewpoints. Carl Schorlemmer thus demonstrated that the history of scientific ideas (internal intellectual history) cannot be understood without reference to their external sociological contexts.[26]

Caro's history, 1891

The sense for history and self-celebration that German chemists revelled in at the end of the 19th century showed itself in numerous grand, and sometimes even spectacular, events such as the 25th anniversary of Kekulé's benzene [Benzol] theory in Berlin during March 1890. Caro, who was the first to advise Kekulé of the Benzolfest, had every intention of attending, and felt it proper that Carl Graebe, then professor of chemistry in Geneva, whose use of the benzene theory in his work on alizarin made him an early "structuralist," should also be present. In one letter, Caro did his utmost to convince Graebe to make the journey from Geneva, and at the same time revealed his own deep commitment to the scientific community of his time. Caro also demonstrated that he did not share some of the more nationalistic feelings that certain colleagues had shown through their own interpretations of history.

> Dear Friend,
>
> For a long time I have been intending to write to you, and also have looked forward to a written sign of life from your side. Influenza, work and all kinds of hindrances did not allow my good intentions to be realised. But I cannot procrastinate any longer. The real reason why I am writing, which also brings my greetings, concerns the forthcoming Kekulé celebrations, where you must be present!... The Benzol event represents a singularly important occasion in the history of all sciences. The present time is so poor in ideas that we must rejoice in the life of the redeemer [Kekulé] of the generation that made his ideas victorious. The 25-year-old existence of the theory is not just a German national celebration to be compared with the magnificent Schiller celebrations of 1859. The whole chemical world is taking part in it. And you to whom such great things are being credited certainly must be present. Even I have the courage to attend as a modest observer. But for you, most esteemed friend, it is your absolute duty to put in an appearance again among your German colleagues and take the place that you justly deserve. Hopefully, in the near future Germany will reclaim one of its best and noblest sons!

Caro closed with a note about his departure from BASF: "Another reason which should have put a pen in my hand some weeks ago was my leaving the Vorstand of BASF. This fact will be published officially at the end of April on the occasion of the next general meeting."[27]

The Benzolfest turned out to be as much a celebration of the achievements of the dye-makers over the previous quarter of a century as it was a salute to Kekulé's contribution to organic chemistry since 1865. Indeed, it was apparent from the speeches, toasts, and messages of congratulation, including Carl Glaser's address on behalf of the synthetic dye industry, that German chemical science and industry had benefited in equal measure from mastery of structural chemistry, as had the coffers and prestige of the Second Reich.[28]

Though Caro, in common with many of the participants at the Benzolfest, demonstrated strong feelings towards the fatherland, he was, as a result of his frequent travels, particularly to England, more fully aware of the international character of chemistry than many of his colleagues would have been prepared to admit. This is manifest in his own history of the dye industry. It was started in the late 1880s, partly building on earlier accounts, such as the story of azo dyes that Caro recalled in his obituary to Griess, though suitably doctored in assigning priority to Griess, Witt, and Caro. It must also have relied on the exhaustive literature reviews undertaken during the preparations for litigation. However, in these cases accurate historical detail was essential in supporting claims for priority. This is how Ivan Levinstein first became aware of the depth of Caro's historical studies:

August Wilhelm Hofmann, Heinrich Caro, and August Bernthsen, and their families, 18 October 1891, at Ludwigshafen. First row, left to right: Bertha von Hofmann (fourth wife of A. W. Hofmann), August Wilhelm von Hofmann, unknown, Amalie Caro, Heinrich Caro. Second row, left to right: P. W. Hofmann (nephew of A. W. Hofmann and partner in the Ludwigshafen-based company Hofmann & Schoetensack, producer of chlorinated organic intermediates), Mrs. P. W. Hofmann. August Bernthsen is second from left, back row. (Deutsches Museum.)

> I have a request to make of you. When we sat together in the law court in London some time ago, I quite by chance glanced at a declaration, which was, I think, an excerpt from one of your literary works which related particularly to the origin and development of the coal gas [lighting] industry. Would you be so kind as to send me a copy of this extract? Through the unusual ending of the court proceedings you were not deposed about your qualifications as a witness and complainant, otherwise I would not have bothered you with this request now.[29]

The completion of a comprehensive history was one of the first tasks that Caro set himself on leaving BASF. For any other author, it would have been long and perhaps almost overwhelming, and probably untidily brought together because of the range of personalities, companies, processes, products, and wide geographical spread. Caro's history turned out to be a masterpiece, the first complete technical account of the rise of the synthetic dye industry, in many ways extending the spirit of the Benzolfest celebrations, though of course entirely focused on the industrial applications of the benzene theory. It was presented to the Deutsche Chemische Gesellschaft in 1891 (and published in the *Berichte der Deutschen Chemischen Gesellschaft* during the following year), and was based mainly on Caro's own career and his voluminous correspondence with pioneers in Germany and other countries, which included the gathering of biographical information from participants.

In order to give coherence to this great rambling and highly complex subject, Caro created a fictitious German dyestuff manufacturer, one that merged all the elements of leading firms such as BASF, Hoechst, Bayer, and AGFA (with echoes of I. G. Farben). But there the fiction ended. His account was complete and correct in every detail. He had chosen a successful approach to making history accessible, one that has been used with equal effect in recent times by writers on history of science and technology and in drama documentaries.

Caro opened by taking his readers on a tour through an imaginary factory, equipped with all the buildings and departments of a modern dyestuff manufacturer. He played the role of a guide who explained to the audience the historical events through the structure of the firm, most particularly the technical departments for the production of inorganic chemicals, organic intermediates, dyestuffs, pharmaceuticals, perfumes, and explosives, etc. As he paused at each department he described its origins, formation, and development:

> A guide offers his services. He points at the tall chimney stacks of a huge factory. "There"–he says–"are the workshops of the 'Deutsche Theerproducten-Industrie.' I want to take you there. The factory unites all branches and workshops of this industry. It employs thousands of labourers and hundreds of chemists, engineers, and businessmen. Its services, achievements, and performance are the pinnacles of our time. Its market is the world."[30]

Caro went on to explain the success of the German dyestuff industry:

> The reasons for the success of industry, which is still developing, were, according to the guide, the penetration of science into the finest veins of manufacturing practice, the continuous contact with new inventions, the progress of theoretical and applied chemistry, its responsiveness to the changing needs of the market, a strict division of labour, and a planned and harmonious cooperation of all involved, from the first to the last, everybody at his place.[31]

The history and the information in the correspondence that this project entailed have been referred to many times in this biography. Since it originated in the years before Caro left BASF, various versions were sprung, invariably quite unexpectedly and at great length, upon his visitors. Ernest Ehrhardt described his first exposure to Caro's history thus:

> It was, and I suppose still is, a social custom over there for the new recruits on the staff to call on the older men, and these calls were paid between the hours of 11 and 1 on Sunday morning. I promptly paid my duty call on Dr. Caro. Instead of letting me go at the end of the regulation 10 minutes he kept me until he was fetched to dinner and insisted on taking me with him. He kept me the whole afternoon, we went for a walk and returned, he kept me for the evening meal, and for the whole of the evening until past midnight filled the time with practically a monologue on the history of the dye industry and his experiences in connexion with it. He made this most interesting to me and he thoroughly enjoyed talking in this way himself and pressed me to come again, and repeatedly my morning calls ended only at midnight.[32]

Another of the many visitors to the Caro household was Edmund Knecht, first head of the department of chemistry and dyeing at Bradford Technical College, and joint editor of the *Journal of the Society of Dyers and Colourists*, who

> remembered being at Dr. Caro's house in Mannheim on a Sunday, and he gave him the lecture he had delivered to the Berlin Chemical Society in great detail. It took six hours to do it. It was very interesting, but he was very tired when it was finished.[33]

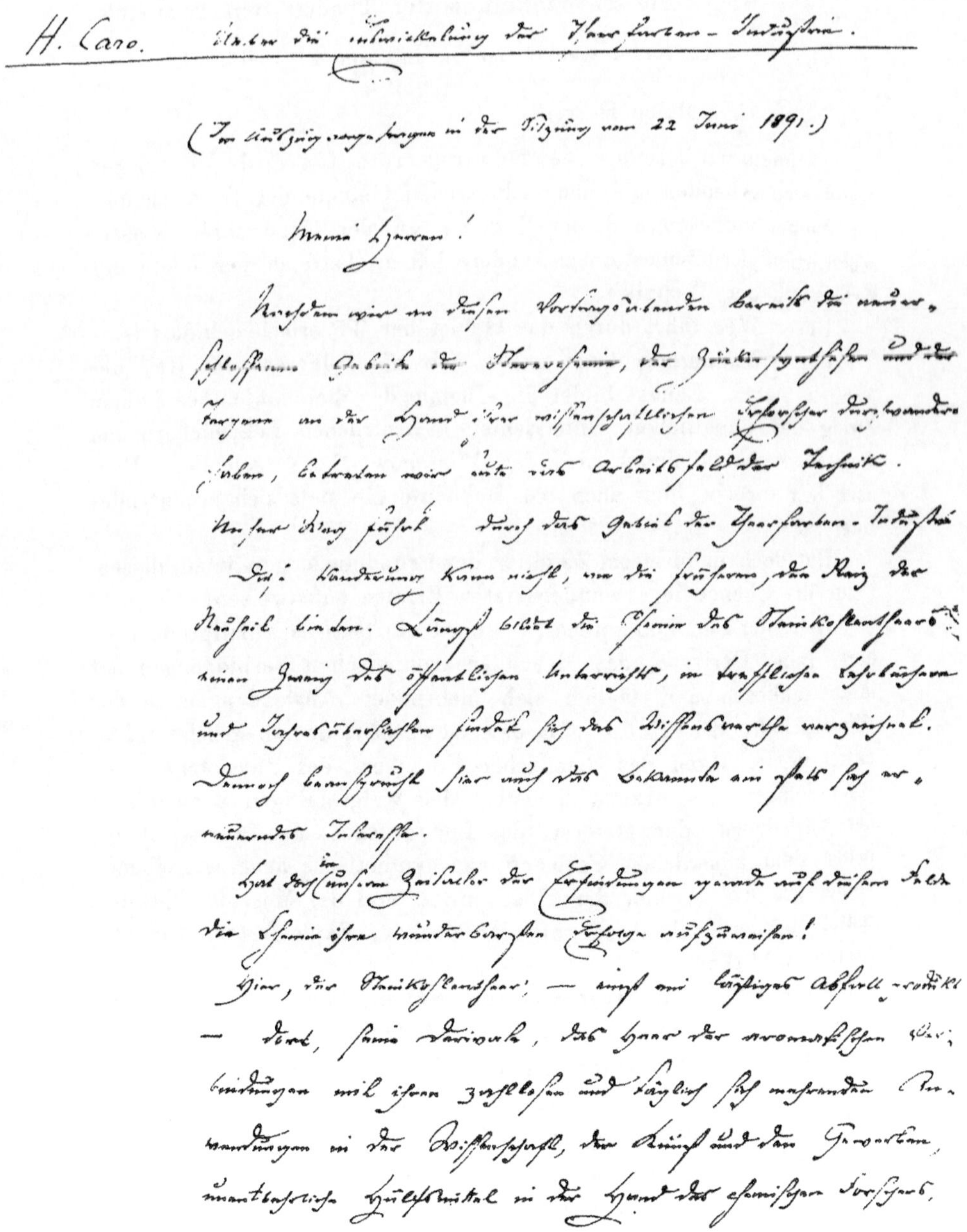
H. Caro. Ueber die Entwickelung der Theerfarben-Industrie.

(Im Auszuge vorgetragen in der Sitzung vom 22 Juni 1891.)

Meine Herren!

Nachdem wir in diesen Vortragsstunden bereits die neu-erschlossenen Gebiete der Stereochemie, der Zuckersynthesen und der Terpene an der Hand ihrer wissenschaftlichen Forscher durchwandert haben, betreten wir heute das Arbeitsfeld der Technik. Unser Weg führt durch das Gebiet der Theerfarben-Industrie.

Die Wanderung kann nicht, wie die früheren, den Reiz der Neuheit bieten. Zunächst bildet die Chemie des Steinkohlentheers einen Zweig des öffentlichen Unterrichts, in trefflichen Lehrbüchern und Jahresübersichten findet sich das Wissenswerthe verzeichnet. Dennoch beansprucht hier auch das Bekannte ein stets sich erneuerndes Interesse.

Hat doch in unserem Zeitalter der Erfindungen gerade auf diesem Felde die Chemie ihre wunderbarsten Erfolge aufzuweisen!

Hier, der Steinkohlentheer; — einst ein lästiges Abfall-Product — dort, seine Derivate, das Heer der aromatischen Verbindungen mit ihren zahllosen und täglich sich mehrenden Verwendungen in der Wissenschaft, der Kunst und den Gewerben, unentbehrliche Hülfsmittel in der Hand des chemischen Forschers,

Title page of the manuscript for Caro's lecture "Ueber die Entwickelung der Theerfarben-Industrie," presented to the Gesellschaft Deutscher Chemiker on 22 June 1891 in Berlin. The full lecture was published in 1892. It was as brilliant as it was demanding, and especially time-consuming, as those who heard versions at Caro's home recalled. (BASF Archives, from an original in the Caro Nachlass, Deutsches Museum.)

H. Caro: Ueber die Entwickelung der Theerfarben-Industrie.

(Im Auszuge vorgetragen in der Sitzung vom 22. Juni 1891.)

Meine Herren!

Nachdem wir bereits an den für »zusammenfassende Vorträge« bestimmten Abenden die neuerschlossenen Gebiete der Stereochemie, der Zuckersynthesen und der Terpene an der Hand ihrer wissenschaftlichen Erforscher durchwandert haben, betreten wir heute das Arbeitsfeld der Technik.

Unser Weg führt durch das Gebiet der Theerfarben-Industrie.

Diese Wanderung kann nicht, wie die früheren, den Reiz der Neuheit bieten. Längst bildet die Chemie des Steinkohlentheers einen Zweig des öffentlichen Unterrichts, in trefflichen Lehrbüchern und Jahresübersichten findet sich das Wissenswerthe verzeichnet. Dennoch beansprucht hier auch das Bekannte ein stets sich erneuerndes Interesse.

Hat doch in unserem Zeitalter der Erfindungen gerade auf diesem Felde die Chemie ihre wunderbarsten Erfolge aufzuweisen!

Hier, der Steinkohlentheer, — einst ein lästiges Abfallproduct — dort, seine Derivate, das Heer der aromatischen Verbindungen mit ihren zahllosen und täglich sich mehrenden Anwendungen in der Wissenschaft, der Kunst und den Gewerben, unentbehrliche Hülfsmittel in der Hand des chemischen Forschers, des Physiologen, des Bakteriologen, des Arztes, dienstbar den vielgestaltigen Bedürfnissen der Färbekunst, der Malerei, des Lichtdruckes, der Sprengtechnik; neben dem künstlichen Farbstoff das synthetische fiebervertreibende Heilmittel, das Aroma der Pflanzenwelt und des Moschus, Genussmittel, hundertemal süsser als der Zucker, Explosivstoffe von verheerender Wirkung.

Stets auf's Neue regt sich die Frage: Wie ist alles dies gekommen? Wie wird es sich weiter gestalten?

Der Entwickelungsgang der Theerfarben-Industrie giebt uns die Antwort. Auf dem Farbstoffgebiete hat die Bewegung ihren Ausgang genommen. Aus dem Vergangenen lernen wir die Gegenwart begreifen und das Kommende vorahnen.

Jews in the German Empire

Forty-one years after Caro's history was published, there was to be another part-fictitious, but now notorious, version of the history of the German dye industry. This time the name Heinrich Caro had been carefully erased, though no doubt the author had drawn upon Caro's history. Adolf Baeyer was also absent, and his indigo synthesis of 1878 was ascribed to the "chemische Institut der Universität München." In Karl Aloys Schenzinger's 1936 novel *Anilin*, the new heroes were Ferdinand Runge, who in the 1830s had observed colour-producing reactions from coal-tar products, Brunck, Duisberg, and other Germans untainted by Jewish ancestry. It might not have been worth mentioning here, but for the fact that over a million copies were printed by 1944, including a French edition. *Anilin* was hastily revised after the collapse of Nazi Germany, though Caro, Baeyer, and many others, including Carl Liebermann, remained absent from the pages of the denazified version, which remained in print until the 1970s.[34] Conspicuous by their absences from *Anilin*, German Jews were, however, prominent among the many chemists and individuals who created the European synthetic dye industry.

While Caro's reminiscences, a beguiling mix of youthful memories, accounts of colleagues in Manchester, and scientific observations, provide little hint of his Jewish background, several of his childhood friends were Jewish, as were a number of colleagues in science and industry, including Leonhardt, Levinstein, Liebermann, Victor Meyer, and Sonnenschein. Many of these individuals had abandoned their spiritual heritage, often undergoing baptism in order to gain openings in the civil service and universities.

In general, Caro's era was a period of Jewish emancipation, despite many difficulties arising from German prejudice, and also some resistance from Jewish religious leaders anxious to protect a sheltered society from assimilation. However, most Jews slowly but gladly entered into German society, and their ambitions and intellectual capabilities were to enable a successful and enriching participation in culture, science, and economy. In many cases acceptance by their non-Jewish contemporaries was conditional on relinquishment of their faith, and this applied above all to the academic professions, which were part of the civil service. Thus, of the thirty Jewish professors employed by German universities in 1875, twenty were baptised as Christians.[35]

In 1869 the newly created North-German Confederation, with Prussia as its leader, afforded equal rights to Jews. This legal emancipation facilitated economic success. The outcome was that whereas in the 1840s most Jewish inhabitants belonged to the lowest income groups, by the 1870s Jews were making major contributions to commerce, banking, and industry. However, though Jewish students entered German universities in increasing numbers, few subsequently gained full professorships. Most of those who remained in academia occupied the post of assistant or associate professor, without civil servant status. Since Germany at that time was in the process of industrialising, there were plenty of opportunities for Jewish chemists to become involved in start-up companies that served new industries, particularly textiles. Indeed, part of the incentive to start a new enterprise may well have been the fact that it offered a means to escape the barriers created by prejudices. To a lesser extent this was true also in England, where German Jewish immigrants such as Ivan Levinstein and Ludwig Mond opened chemical factories.

However, the situation in England was quite different, at least as far as self-identity was concerned. There were fewer pressures for abandoning culture and belief in order to gain academic posts, though there were certainly prejudices at leading institutions and difficulties with joining firms. But, as demonstrated by Raphael Meldola, grandson of the chief rabbi to London's Sephardic community, advancement was determined mainly by ability and determination. During 1871-73, Meldola had worked at Williams, Thomas & Dower, of Brentford, near London, where Otto N. Witt was employed from 1875. Meldola, like Caro, held no academic degree until relatively late in his career (in Meldola's case in 1910), though he made substantial contributions to chemistry and entomology and was highly regarded throughout the scientific world. In 1886, Meldola was elected Fellow of the Royal Society in recognition of his scientific work.

It is because of Meldola's interest in the achievements of Jews that we find a rare early reference to Caro's Jewish origins and to the general situation of Jews in the German academic community in a letter sent to him by Witt. Meldola had asked Witt for details of leading Jewish figures in Germany. Witt's response shows considerable disdain for those Jews who hid their origins, and even of some who had converted to

Christianity, mainly for "conventional" reasons, that is to gain employment, particularly in universities. Witt, incidentally, had no desire to employ Jewish assistants in his laboratory at the Berlin Polytechnic, though he did not consider himself an anti-Semite.[36]

My Dear Meldola,

I have just received your note of the 3rd and have much pleasure in naming some of our better men whom I know to be Jews. To give you a list of all of them would be very difficult because with us it is the reverse from what it is in England. There are so many Jews in all the professions, that a complete list of them would be a "Magnum Opus" indeed. I may add that many Jews have embraced the Christian faith, in nine cases out of ten merely for conventional reasons. This I consider very wrong; but of course these people do take great care to deny all connection with the race to which they belong. In the second or third generation it becomes almost impossible to find out, whether the Semitic cut of their features is merely accidental or inherited. Such was j.f. [jedenfalls - at all events] the case with our late minister of public instruction, Dr. von Gossler,[37] a very able man, whose grandfather was a Jewish convert.

In your list you name Baeyer; I may point out to you, that only his mother was a Jewess, while his father was an official in the Army, a fact precluding his being a Jew. On the other hand Victor Meyer to whose name you add ?? is a perfect specimen of the Semitic race; surely you have never seen him, or else you could not be in any doubt. He is one of those who cannot muster up sufficient pride to be what they are; so he had himself baptized in 1883 and calls himself a Protestant now. The same applies of course to his brother Richard M., whilst Lothar Meyer comes from a country where there never have been any Jews. Ladenburg ought to have a place on your list, although he too is a "Protestant" since a few years. The brothers Liebreich (the oculist [*sic*] in London and pharmacologist in Berlin) are Jews, although they married Christian ladies and bring up their children in our faith. Liebermann, Gabriel, Ehrlich, Brieger, Fraenkel (the bacteriologist), Rosenthal (the physiologist) are Jews. So is Lunge, Goldschmidt and Bamberger. Are you sure that the great Kirch[h]off was a Jew? I don't think so, he had not at all the features of a Jew. On the other hand you cannot forget A. W. Hofmann's most intimate friend, the great mathematician Prof. Kronecker, a wonderfully bright little fellow. Don't forget Caro and Magnus (the chemist and the botanist). Oppenheimer [Oppenheim?] was a Jew. Pic[c]ard (in Basle) denies being of Jewish descent, but both his name and his features are distinctly Jewish. Wallach is a Jew and a capital fellow he is, in every respect. Lieben and Benedikt (both in Vienna) are thoroughbred Jews, so is Hertz the great physicist in Bonn who demonstrated the wave length of the electric energy. Of course you know that all the Mendelssohns (the philosopher, the composer and the banker) were Jews and that the philosopher became a Christian from conviction [in actual fact, Felix the musician converted, but Moses the philosopher did not]. Lassalle the sociologist was a Jew. So was Schelling the philosopher, whose son is our present Justizminister.

I think, this list, which might be considerably extended, will suffice for the

> present. Here in Germany the relations between Jews and Arians [Aryans] are sometimes of an unpleasant nature and much has been said and done on both sides, that is not fair and just.[38]

The attitudes of German gentile chemists to their Jewish colleagues were certainly complex, ranging from Kolbe's rabid hatred, through Graebe's detached fascination with "primitive" ritual, to Hofmann's strong friendships.[39] But, apart from an oblique hint about Caro's "kinsmen" in the Pauli-Martius correspondence, there is no record of antagonism towards Caro because of his Jewish background. Heinrich Caro stood out as an example of how much Prussia, and the German Empire, had gained from emancipation of the Jews after the revolution of 1848.

German manufacturers and British commissions

By the turn of the century there were signs in Britain that its economic strength was on the wane, and that through neglect of the new chemical and electrical industries it had fallen far behind in industrial prowess. In the organic chemical industry, as Meldola and others had warned, there was even a sharp decline.[40] Now there was a further difficulty: Synthetic indigo, manufactured by BASF and Hoechst from 1897, threatened the British-dominated trade in the natural product, which included the Indian growers. When the British dye-makers were confronted with criticisms of their poor performances, they were not slow in declaring that a major cause was the duty on industrial alcohol, which placed an unfair burden on industry. Official bodies investigated the impacts of synthetic indigo, duty on alcohol, and patent law on the British dye industry. In the case of indigo and alcohol, Heinrich Caro's opinion was deemed essential.

The indigo business was of such tremendous importance for Britain's largest colony that the fate of the natural product was discussed extensively in Parliament and in the press. As for the German-made synthetic indigo, there were questions as to identity, price, and application to military uniforms, which in March 1900 led Wyndham R. Dunstan, director of the Scientific and Technical Department, Imperial Institute (of the United Kingdom, the Colonies, and India), in London, to make enquiries of Caro.

> Dear Dr. Caro,
>
> As we have had the pleasure of meeting on several occasions both here and abroad, I am writing to ask if you will be so good as to give me some information as to the present position of artificial Indigo.
>
> As director of the Scientific and Technical Department of the Imperial Institute I

> am constantly applied to for an opinion as to the value of the artificial product in comparison with natural Indigo, and I should like to have some definite information on the following points:
>
> 1. Is the artificial Indigo prepared by the Badische Company chemically identical with the blue colouring material of natural Indigo?
>
> 2. Is the colour produced by the artificial preparation as permanent, and in all other respects the same as that produced by the natural Indigo?
>
> 3. How does the present price of artificial Indigo compare with that of natural Indigo and about what quantity of the artificial substance is now annually produced?
>
> 4. Is it true that the German Government have ordered the blue cloth supplied for the German army and navy to be dyed with natural Indigo?[41]

Dunstan, probably believing that Caro still had considerable influence at the Ludwigshafen factory, requested information about the process, and asked whether it was patented. He also asked for a sample "of your artificial Indigo for exhibition here." Caro passed the questions and requests on to BASF, which, though unable or unwilling to provide all the answers, advised Dunstan that the synthetic and plant-derived indigo were identical, and that for military purposes the German authorities could order both forms. In Bavaria, "clear blue" uniforms were dyed with BASF indigo because of its purity and outstanding colour.[42] BASF was not prepared to provide information on the process, which was of course based on Heumann's original patented methods of 1890. As for the sample that Dunstan requested, this would depend on certain conditions that required clarification.

The alcohol question was less straightforward, and its investigation showed considerable ignorance on the part of those British manufacturers of dyestuffs who complained that it was the duty on industrial (ethyl) alcohol, employed both as solvent and reactant, which prevented them from competing with the Germans. (Methyl alcohol was in more general use for alkylation of the amino group of aromatic amines, to afford, for example, dimethylaniline.) In England from 1861 to 1891 the alcohol was free of duty if denatured with wood naphtha, and from 1891 to 1902 free of duty for industrial purposes also if denatured with mineral naphtha (petroleum). An Act of 1902 specified procedures for denaturing, and the Board of Inland Revenue gave permission for use of pure alcohol in certain circumstances. There was much confusion among users.

In 1904, the Chancellor of Exchequer appointed a committee to consider the duty on alcohol used in industry. This led to formation of the Industrial Alcohol Committee, which, among other things, set out to establish the extent to which duty on industrial alcohol had adversely affected the coal-tar dye industry in England. Information was gathered from the Association of Chambers of Commerce of the United Kingdom, and the Chambers of Commerce of London, Liverpool, Manchester and Birmingham. Perkin, Meldola, Green, and R. J. Friswell (also formerly employed at Brooke, Simpson & Spiller) were interviewed. The evidence was uncertain, especially where comparisons with Germany were made. British witnesses claimed that the Germans had an unfair advantage because of the heavy duty imposed on British industrial users of alcohol.[43]

In order to establish whether or not this was the case, a British sub-committee made a fact-finding tour of German dye and other alcohol-using and -processing factories. The sub-committee was made up of Professor Thomas Edward Thorpe, principal chemist of the Government Laboratory, Sir Henry William Primrose, chairman of the Treasury Committee (and also of the Board of Revenue), and the secretary, Mr. Cunningham.[44] Once more a request for assistance went out to Caro and other Germans. The sub-committee received considerable assistance from Privy Counsellors Koreuber and Dr. von Buchka (head of the chemical branch of the Imperial Treasury) "to whom, through our Ambassador, we have been referred by his Excellency the Secretary of the Imperial Treasury."[45] The party left London on 14 January 1905, arrived in Berlin on the next day, then travelled to Heidelberg and Darmstadt, and returned through Cologne, arriving back in England at the end of the month.

Thorpe wrote from his Berlin hotel to Caro in Mannheim, requesting Caro's help in gaining access to the Ludwigshafen works.[46] Despite Caro's intervention, the BASF factory gates remained closed to the British investigators.[47] However, the sub-committee was allowed to meet with Ehrhardt and Glaser in Mannheim, and were informed by Glaser that indigo and alizarin, which together represented about half the BASF output, did not require alcohol, while among azo dyes, which represented much of the rest, only a few required alcohol in their manufacture. However, the sub-committee was still anxious to receive Caro's own opinion on the matter. On 22 January 1905, Thorpe, then in Heidelberg, wrote to Caro.

> We desire to put before you certain statements which we have had in Evidence from

our witnesses in England, and which we have reason to believe are not wholly supported by the facts of the Case.... We quite understand that we are not to be permitted to see the works, and of course we do not press our request.

Indeed we fully appreciate the reason which has led the Director to decline to admit us, although at the same time we think there is some little misapprehension of the true objects of our visit to Germany. Certain statements have been made to us by interested persons in England which I know to be inaccurate, and it is with a view to bringing home the real facts of the case to the official mind that I have induced Sir Henry Primrose to come to Germany and make his own inquiries, and from persons who, like yourself, are able to speak with full knowledge and authority.[48]

One day after meeting Ehrhardt and Glaser, the sub-committee visited Caro,

who may be regarded as one of the principal founders of the industry in Germany. They all agreed that, as an historical fact, the question of alcohol had little or nothing to do with the matter. Dr. Caro pointed out that the movement [the manufacture of synthetic dyes] had begun, and had reached a point of considerable advancement, before the time at which the use of alcohol otherwise than as a solvent–a purpose for which methylated spirit is perfectly suitable–had been appreciably developed, and before the time at which reduction in the selling price of dyestuffs through competition had rendered economy of production of serious importance. Caro, Ehrhardt, and Glaser gave opinions on the great development of the coal-tar industry in Germany and its decline, or at any rate, its stagnation in Great Britain.

They also agreed that with the increasing use of alcohol as a reagent, "the price at which it can be procured, and of the facilities given for its employment–has become a matter of great, if not of cardinal importance."[49]

Though the sub-committee had been advised that in Germany "spirit could be used in manufacture duty-free and pure, with scarcely any restraint," its findings were that this "is very far from being the case."[50] In Germany, it was apparent, the price fluctuated, and the price was not much less than that in England, in contrast to what the English witnesses had said. The sub-committee established, on the basis of opinions and information made available in Germany, that at least 74 per cent of dyes then manufactured did not even require alcohol. So the duty on alcohol had not harmed the British dye industry. Nevertheless, the sub-committee did take into consideration the possibility of future changes: "the utilisation of waste products and the development of new methods may be hampered by a want of alcohol; while, for those dyestuffs for which alcohol is essential, its price and the conditions of use are matters of great moment."[51] The sub-committee also noted the greater importance of methyl alcohol over ethyl alcohol in the manufacture of aromatic intermediates for the dye industry. New measures were approved by the British Chancellor of Exchequer in 1906, and duty-free alcohol for industrial purposes became available in 1907-08.[52]

Caro and the Verein Deutscher Chemiker

Caro made a major contribution to the professional standing of chemists in his role as chairman from 1897 to 1901 of the Verein Deutscher Chemiker (VDC). The VDC was the successor of a society for analytical chemists and–partially during Caro's chairmanship–became the largest chemical society in Germany, mainly because of the many industrial chemists who were members. Between 1897 and 1901 the membership doubled from more than 1,100 to nearly 2,300. It was the most influential society representing the interests of chemists in industry, and owed much to Caro's management and enthusiasm.[53]

Caro was elected chairman on 10 June 1897 and was the immediate successor of the ailing Richard Curtius. It was a critical time for the society, which had changed its name to Verein Deutscher Chemiker only one year before. Guided by Carl Duisberg, the rising manager of Bayer and influential industrialist, the society strove for representation of all chemists and rejected particularism, both of purely scientific aspirations (as represented by the Deutsche Chemische Gesellschaft) and business interests (the Verein zur Wahrung der Interessen der chemischen Industrie Deutschlands, of which Caro was a prominent member). It was Duisberg who proposed the election of Caro, which was given by acclamation, and supported by the high status of Caro as "the distinguished representative" of technical chemistry.[54]

Earlier in June 1897, Duisberg had urged Caro to accept the chairmanship, after Caro already had declined the post. With an abundance of flattery, Duisberg exerted gentle pressure on his senior colleague, ingeniously drawing attention to the similarities between the VDC and the Verein Deutscher Ingenieure, which Caro had helped to create and whose chairman he had been in the early 1890s:

> [I] am convinced that you are the most suitable candidate from among all living German chemists for the chairmanship. The Verein has as its objective the unification of all chemists in theoretical [scientific] and in practical [industrial] positions, and the promotion and furthering of the interests of our professional status, and in this regard resembles the Verein Deutscher Ingenieure.... If I were in the same fortunate situation as yourself, being one's own master and independent of all

> business affairs, standing at the pinnacle of success in matters theoretical and technical, I would not hesitate for a moment to accept the chairmanship of the Verein Deutscher Chemiker.[55]

Caro was indeed flattered, but still resisted the offer. In his response, he pointed out that he would have liked to again play a more active role, but considered himself too old and not capable of best representing the interests of members. Moreover, he remembered the time when he was chairman of the Verein Deutscher Ingenieure as time-consuming and demanding:

> In the meantime, I had become an alien in my own beloved laboratory. After I returned to it again, I experienced moments of purest satisfaction in my work, and I do not want once more to exchange the test tube for the pen, to deal daily with correspondence, to write circulars, to control the editor and the manager, to preside over meetings and–the most horrible of all horrible things–to suffer with dignity banquets full of official toasts and boastful phrases.[56]

It was Jacob Volhard, member of the board of the VDC and a close friend of Caro, who finally managed to convince Caro to take the post, by arguing convincingly that the VDC should represent all chemists and not only the economic interests of the manufacturers. This appealed to Caro's strong feelings for social unity and identity among chemists.[57]

Caro proved himself to be a powerful chairman, both in his functions as manager and in his role as "elder statesman" of technical chemistry, supported by the fact that he was no longer identified with the interests of a single manufacturer. In his inaugural speech as chairman in Darmstadt, the birthplace of Justus von Liebig, he used the status of this most revered of German chemists to urge, in characteristic prose, that the members become unified and proud German chemists:

> Everyone is a pupil of Liebig! Everyone competes to imitate his master! As in days of old, when Correggio saw Raphael's painting, and exclaimed "Anch' Io sono pittore!"–"I am also a painter," everyone here strives so he can proclaim with manly awareness, "I am a German chemist, too!"[58]

Caro was not only a very able lecturer and, when the occasion demanded, an effective orator, but he showed that under the right circumstances he could also demonstrate outstanding managerial qualities. He reorganised the VDC by converting it into a not-for-profit limited company ("eingetragener Verein"), and appointed a full-time professional manager (Geschäftsführer). During his chairmanship the VDC set up an agency to assist members seeking employment. Moreover, he took care that the level of the membership was kept high, and–typical of the era–excluded non-academic applicants, and especially women, who normally could not have an academic education at this time.[59] This required a change in the statutes of the society after the Verein Deutscher Zucker-Industrieller (Society of German Sugar Industrialists) in 1900 proposed to give the title "chemist" to women after six weeks of training in laboratory work. Caro called this an abuse of the title of chemist.[60] This was a prelude to the society's strong opposition to the acceptance as members of non-academically educated chemists in 1906. The first female member of the VDC was the daughter of Emanuel A. Merck, the successor of Caro as chairman, in 1910.[61]

Group picture, at the annual meeting of the Verein Deutscher Chemiker, 24 May 1899. Left to right: Prof. Berthold Rassow, Dr. Friedrich Raschig, unknown, Heinrich Caro, Carl Goldschmidt, Mrs. Edith Caro, and Amalie Caro. (Deutsches Museum, DM NL93/10.)

Group picture, on the occasion of the Annual Meeting of the Verein Deutscher Chemiker, 24 May 1899, at Königshütte, close to the border with Russia. Left to right: Ferdinand Fischer, Freund, unknown, Heinrich Caro, Fritz Lüty, E. von Cochenhausen, W. Steffen, Carl Goldschmidt, and unknown. (Deutsches Museum, DM NL93/10.)

Especially noteworthy was Caro's role in bringing about the higher status of the society's journal, *Zeitschrift für Angewandte Chemie*. According to Merck, the success of the journal derived entirely from Caro's close involvement.[62] Following protracted and difficult negotiations, Caro acquired for the VDC a 50 per cent share in the journal and went on to improve the content. Moreover, profits from the journal after the change in ownership contributed considerably to the financial well-being of the society.[63] The journal came out weekly and–in addition to the already established scientific and technical articles–now included news on business and commerce. Caro was even editor for a short period. He declined re-election on the grounds of his ill health, but during 1901-02 served a one-year term as interim deputy chairman (stellvertretender Vorsitzender) to assist Merck. Caro handed over to his successor a far stronger and more unified society than he had taken on three years before. The only setback was the failure of the VDC, despite Duisberg's efforts, to establish a state examination for academic chemists. This met with considerable resistance from the professorial elite, represented by Adolf von Baeyer.[64]

A view on organised labour

There exists one document which shows that Caro was sympathetic to workers' organisations that collaborated with industry, but was highly critical of what was considered to be the growth of extremist elements among workers in the early 1900s. In August 1907, he wrote to Duisberg in connection with the annual report of the Verband von Arbeitgebern Elberfeld-Barmen (Association of Employers of Elberfeld-Barmen), expressing the hope that more moderate groups of workers would eventually displace those whose persuasiveness, based (often not unreasonably) on demands for better working conditions, had generated tremendous support in the early 1900s.

> The question of the workers is a villainous one! But it is a sign of our times. The idea of an esprit de corps [Corpsgeist] is flourishing everywhere, and causes even the most sensible people to become blind to the principles of reason and to be not free in their thoughts and deeds. They will awake at some time, but not until a new "Lassalle" [head of the Arbeiterverein, a predecessor of the German socialist party] appears, who calls the workers to fight against the despotism of their present leaders. Up to this time, the employers should reject without exception any interference in the "organisations" [of workers] bound by the harmony of industry. Otherwise, the women will also become "organised," that is stirred up, against their husbands, and the children against their parents.[65]

Caro's 70th birthday

Heinrich Caro's 70th birthday was celebrated on 12 February 1904 with much pomp and circumstance at the Park-Hotel in Mannheim, and organised by the Mannheimer Bezirksverein Deutscher Ingenieure and the Oberrheinische Bezirskverein Deutscher Chemiker, two societies in which Caro had been prominent throughout his life.[66] The ceremonies commenced with the presentation to Caro of the highest award the Grand Duke of Baden was able to confer, the Knights Cross 1st Class (Ritterkreuz 1. Klasse) Zähringer Löwen (Zähringer Lion, named in honour of the family of a grandduke of Baden). It was the second occasion on which Caro received a prestigious public award. The first was in 1890, when he had been elevated to the status of Grossherzoglich Badischer Hofrat (Court Councillor).

This was followed by the award of honorary doctorates from the University of Heidelberg, represented by Theodor Curtius, and Darmstadt Polytechnic, represented by Friedrich Dingeldey. Spokesmen from all major German chemical and engineering societies brought greetings to the guest of honour.[67] The participation of the Verein Deutscher Ingenieure (VDI) was an outcome of Caro's role in its formation during 1856, when as a member of the Hütte society at the Gewerbeinstitut in Berlin, he was present at a special meeting, held in Alexisbad (Harz). He also co-founded the Mannheimer Bezirksverein in 1869 and was its first chairman, and at the inaugural meeting gave a lecture on "artificial madder dyestuffs."[68] The Mannheimer Bezirksverein was the first section of the VDI in southern Germany. Despite the political unification of Germany at that time, the VDI was still under north German influence. Caro subsequently played an important role in its expansion to southern Germany. In 1890-92, he served as chairman of the national VDI, which became one of the largest societies of engineers in the world. (In 1910, the year of Caro's death, there were 23,000 members.) Also represented was the second society in which Caro played a leading role, the Verein Deutscher Chemiker.

The address of the Deutsche Chemische Gesellschaft served to underscore the scientific style of work that Caro used during his investigations at BASF and the resulting cooperation with academic chemists.[69] Likewise, the certificate accompanying the Ph.D. *honoris causa* from Darmstadt Polytechnic mentioned explicitly how Caro had enabled the development of the synthetic dyestuff industry through his application of strict scientific methods. In his response, Caro recognised that this scientific style of work was the very "nature, goal, and result of my whole professional life."[70] He also acknowledged the importance and inspiration of men such as Liebig, Hofmann, and Kekulé as well as the progressive thinking of German industrialists who early on employed academically trained chemists and engineers, and who founded scientific laboratories.

Caro was also co-founder of the Verein zur Wahrung der Interessen der chemischen Industrie Deutschlands in 1877, in which year he served as a member of the board, as well as acting as chairman of its patent committee from 1885-98. He belonged to several other chemical and technical societies.[71]

Among the various letters of congratulation was one from Carl Alexander Martius, to whom Caro responded by recalling earlier days in Lancashire:

> Your words brought me back to Manchester, more than four decades ago! We planned, thought, and worked together! I remember the Cornbrook Chemical Works. Old John Dale, the always kind, enthusiastic man, the knowledgeable, energetic, manufacturer, always full of ideas, who rushed with his impressive head and his John Bull figure into the laboratory, that he did not leave before he had made a mess, and then began the questioning: "Well Dr. Martius, well Caro, have you not got anything fresh to show me?"

Caro mentioned the meetings in the Thatched House with Carl Schorlemmer, Philipp Pauli, Theodor Reissig, Burkhardt, Davison, Kellner, the pharmacist Siebold, Frank, Ammon, and Seckendorff. These days were the "cradle of our later successes and with it a stage in the development of the dyestuff industry. Strange! There in our midst were 4 of the later German leaders: You, Pauli, Leonhardt and I!"[72]

Caro's home in Mannheim, ca. 1900. Crosses on windows at right mark the room where indigo was synthesized, 1879-80 (top), a private office (middle), and a laboratory, 1890-1910 (street level). (Deutsches Museum, DM NL93/10/2.)

In a letter to Graebe, Caro emphasised that his own success was mainly derived from close collaboration with Peter Griess, Adolf Baeyer, Victor Meyer, and Carl Graebe.[73] By contrast, the powerful influence that Caro exerted on his academic colleagues is seen in a letter from Emil Fischer, who looked back to the period of the structural elucidation of the triphenylmethane dyes:

> [I] can imagine that you received many kind reminders of your active life.... But you also gave a lot to the many men with whom you have been in contact, not only as a recipient yourself, but more often as donor.... Twenty-five years ago, when I came to you and asked for help, I was not only at the most receptive time of life, but I also stood at the beginning of my scientific career, and quick successes then influenced the goals of life. With your suggestion and your material assistance you supported my investigations in an important manner and I may say that we would not have solved the fuchsine question without your help. Moreover, I have learned from you the brilliant way of transferring the results of theoretical research to the living values of industry, and as a result I have become more attuned to the usefulness of scientific research.[74]

50th Anniversary of the foundation of the coal-tar dye industry, 1906

At the end of 1905, Caro's keen sense of historical occasion caused him to remind William Henry Perkin that 1906 marked the 50th anniversary of the discovery of mauve. In the meantime, Raphael Meldola, Arthur G. Green, and John Cannell Cain were engaged in the planning of a grand celebration of this golden jubilee in London. In May 1906, Perkin shared with Caro his response to the plans for the event:

> My Dear Caro,
>
> When I received your new year's card in the early part of this year, in which you so kindly reminded me that this year was the Golden Jubilee of the discovery of the mauve, I did not anticipate that I would hear anything more about the matter, but some time afterwards I was privately informed that a movement was in hand to celebrate this jubilee and that you and your countrymen were especially active in this matter, and I felt that it was very kind of you all to think of drawing attention to the early days when it fell to my lot to discover this colouring matter and when I had to struggle with the difficulties of its production, introduction, and to further take my part in the development of this wonderful industry it initiated, and which has grown to such enormous dimensions and has had such far-reaching influences. I think you will agree with me that all this has been chiefly due to the union of science and industry.... You also appreciated the great importance of research in connection with the coal tar colouring matters and especially initiated it at the Badische Anilin & Soda Fabrik, the example being followed by other works in your country, and [how] has the union of science and industry been prolific? How wonderfully chemical science has itself benefited. Think what organic chemistry ... was in 1856, and what

We English chemists desire to thank our foreign friends for making this ceremony an international one (hear, hear)–a scientific entente cordiale *among all nations. I see amongst our guests distinguished representatives of chemistry both pure and applied–some to whom has been given the task of wresting from Nature her secrets; some who apply these discoveries to the good of mankind–and among these I rejoice to see the face of my old friend Dr. Caro. (Cheers.)* – Sir Henry Roscoe, *Jubilee of the Discovery of Mauve and of the Foundation of the Coal-Tar Colour Industry by Sir W. H. Perkin, F.R.S., D.Sc., LL.D., Ph.D., Dr.Ing.*, eds. Raphael Meldola, Arthur G. Green, and John Cannell Cain (London: Perkin Memorial Committee, 1906), 42.

Here on English soil, where the gas and tar industry started, where benzene, naphthalene, and anthracene were first obtained in large quantities, is the cradle of this industry, here this industry began its existence. It did not, however, make its home solely on these shores, but, like a bird of passage, as soon as it could use its wings, peregrinated through France and Switzerland to finally settle on German ground. – Carl Duisberg, *Jubilee of the Discovery of Mauve and of the Foundation of the Coal-Tar Colour Industry by Sir W. H. Perkin, F.R.S., D.Sc., LL.D., Ph.D., Dr.Ing.*, eds. Raphael Meldola, Arthur G. Green, and John Cannell Cain (London: Perkin Memorial Committee, 1906), 50.

From the addresses to a "large and distinguished company," the participants, as shown here, at the banquet held on 26 July 1906 at the Hotel Métropole, London, in connection with the jubilee celebrations for the discovery of mauve by William Perkin. In the row nearest the camera are, second from right, Arthur G. Green (University of Leeds), and fourth from right, Ernest F. Ehrhardt (BASF). Immediately behind Green is Herbert Levinstein, son of Ivan Levinstein. At the top table, from left to right, are Right Honourable Lord Justice Fletcher Moulton, F.R.S. (who represented Ivan Levinstein and BASF in patent litigation), Dr. August Bernthsen (BASF), Sir Arthur Rücker, F.R.S. (Principal of the University of London), Right Honourable Lord Kelvin, O.M., G.C.V.O., Professor Paul Friedlaender (Austrian representative), Right Honourable The Earl of Halsbury, D.C.L., F.R.S. (Late Lord High Chancellor, D.C.L., F.R.S., Chairman of Council, City and Guilds of London Institute), Professor Emil Fischer (President, Deutsche Chemische Gesellschaft), and, standing, Sir William Henry Perkin, Ph.D., F.R.S., and Professor Raphael Meldola, F.R.S. (President, Chemical Society). Heinrich Caro is five places to the right of Meldola. Present also were Hugo Müller, F.R.S., Professor W. R. Dunstan, F.R.S. (Director, Imperial Institute), Professor Henry E. Armstrong, F.R.S., Professor Carl Liebermann, Sir Henry E. Roscoe, F.R.S., Carl Duisberg (Bayer), Sir William Ramsay, K.C.B., F.R.S., Sir James Dewar, F.R.S., and Professor Percy F. Frankland, F.R.S. The table-seating plan is shown in *Jubilee of the Discovery of Mauve and of the Foundation of the Coal-Tar Colour Industry by Sir W. H. Perkin, F.R.S., D.Sc., LL.D., Ph.D., Dr.Ing.*, eds. Raphael Meldola, Arthur G. Green, and John Cannell Cain (London: Perkin Memorial Committee, 1906), opposite 38. (Zeneca Archives.)

> it is today, and how greatly this is due to this union. But if I were to go on with this subject and speak of all its influences I don't know where I should leave off. But you know all about this just as well as I do, especially as you are one of the very few remaining chemists who have a practical and intelligent knowledge of the early days of this industry and this makes me appreciate your sympathy so much. I also feel very much the kindly feeling of your countrymen who have so much to be proud of in connection with this industry. I hear you are to be in London during the celebrations of this Jubilee and I look forward to having the pleasure of meeting you again especially as it is some years since we saw each other.[75]

Caro was in charge of arrangements for the German contingent. But because of rheumatism and concern over his attendance, he asked Carl Duisberg to prepare and deliver the main speech on behalf of German participants. Caro did manage to make the journey to England, and must have been pleased to spend time once again with his many English friends. On 26 July 1906, he participated in the formal proceedings at the Royal Institution, in London, chaired by Meldola and attended by representatives of science and industry from many countries. On behalf of the Verein zur Wahrung der Interessen der Chemischen Industrie Deutschlands, Caro presented an address of congratulation to Perkin, and scientific addresses were given by August Bernthsen and Carl Liebermann. In the evening there was a magnificent banquet held at the Hotel Métropole.[76] Caro was among the guests of honour, sitting at the top table, close to Perkin and Meldola. The following day, he attended a garden party at Perkin's home in Sudbury, not far from the Greenford Green factory that he had visited in 1869 to tie up the alizarin agreement for BASF, and again in 1870 to glean technical information of value to BASF.[77]

Heinrich Caro in old age. (Deutsches Museum.)

Death of Caro

Heinrich Caro often suffered from poor health, including bronchial catarrh (particularly in Manchester), as well as occasional bouts of influenza. Health reasons dictated his move to Heidelberg in 1867, and were responsible for his frequent absences from the BASF factory, and even, perhaps, from the fast red case in London. On one trip to England he became so ill that Peter Griess had to take care of him for some time. During his final years Caro was frequently very sickly, and in the winter months was not able to leave his home, though he maintained contact with his colleagues in the dye industry, including Bayer's Duisberg.[78]

In August 1910 he visited Berlin, the city of his youth and adolescence, and then went on to Dresden in Saxony to show his wife and Amalie the places he had often visited during holidays as a child. After a few days greatly enjoying music and the arts he became very ill. Heinrich Caro died on 11 September 1910, a Sunday, in the Hotel Bellevue, Dresden. He was 76 years old. He was buried five days later in Mannheim.

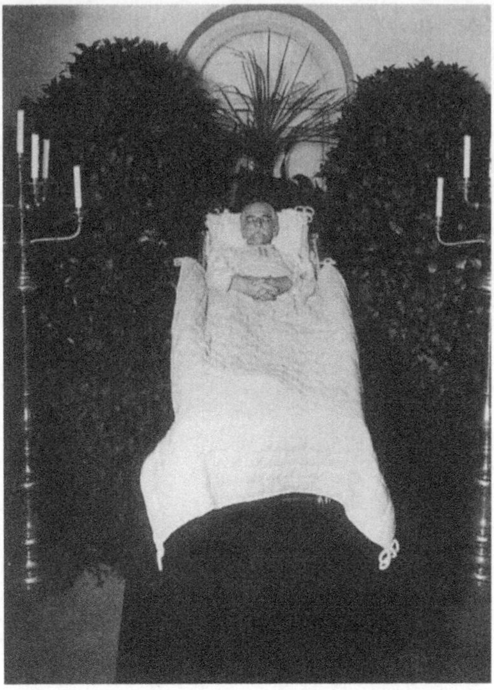

Caro in coffin, Mannheim, 1910. (Deutsches Museum, DN NL93/10.)

12

Heinrich Caro: Genius and Myth

> Of all the great chemists and lawyers that it has been my great fortune to meet, Dr. Caro is the one who seems to me to correspond most satisfactorily to the definition of a genius, and it is perhaps for this reason that he is becoming something of a fetish.
>
> *Ernest Ehrhardt, 1924.*[1]

Myth and history are sometimes almost inextricably bound together, especially when the myth has been created from actual events to draw lessons and provide examples. There is no doubt that during the early years of the 20th century, Heinrich Caro's career and achievements in relation to the overwhelming success of the German dye industry reached almost mythical proportions, particularly in England, where chemists and industrialists sought out reasons for the decline of the British synthetic dye industry. Responses ranged from Meldola's claim that England lost the dye industry when Caro returned to Germany to the collective belief that the genius of men like Caro had masterminded the rise of the German dye industry. British chemists turned the German model of dye-making to their own contemporary ends, which of course only served to magnify Caro's contribution. At a more mundane level, reasons for failure were sought in education, legislation, research, and the duty on industrial alcohol. Certainly there were elements of truth in these claims, apart from the duty on alcohol, all of which have been perpetuated to the present day. To understand the earlier perceptions, and indeed the randomness of these perceptions, and how they came about, we here review the versions of Caro's life–and of other German pioneers in the dye industry–that were presented between 1900 and the 1920s by British chemists and industrialists who rewrote histories of the dye industry to suit their changing times and needs.

Meldola and the British chemists

From the mid-1880s, Raphael Meldola, as professor at the progressive Central Technical College, held up the synthetic dye industry as the supreme example of the successful application of science to technology. That success, however, had been at the expense of England, and many answers were sought to the question of why the British dye industry had been all but lost to Germany. One suggestion put forward by Meldola, on the occasion of Caro's 70th birthday in 1904–but only published in 1924–was that the decline of the English coal-tar dye industry could be attributed to Caro's departure from Manchester: "*The worst thing that ever happened to the coal-tar colour industry of this country was the loss of Heinrich Caro!* Now we have nearly lost the industry altogether, and serve us right."[2]

Though dye invention was the central endeavour and achievement of Caro's life, and his record was unmatched, he offered, in response to Meldola, other reasons for the decline of the British dye industry: the retirement of the English pioneers, the return of Hofmann to Germany, and the development of chemistry in Germany:

> In your kindly worded letter, I have noted an expression, which coming from an authority like yours, has assumed the character of a verdict. You are alluding to my former participation in the rise of the ENGLISH COAL-TAR INDUSTRY, and then you go on saying that its deplorable decline may be partly traced back to my leaving your country in 1866. Now, my dear Professor, with all due respect, I beg to be allowed to differ from you in my views on that question. I think that many fatal circumstances have been working together to shift the leadership in the development of the COLOUR-INDUSTRY from ENGLAND into GERMANY. At about the same time the great and successful manufacturers PERKIN and NICHOLSON retired from business, HOFMANN, then the head of the scientific "GENERAL STAFF" left his glorious laboratory in the ROYAL INSTITUTION [actually the Royal School of Mines, which had taken over the Royal College of Chemistry] and created a new era of scientific programmes in GERMANY, [and] his ENGLISH SCHOOL was scattered into the winds. ADOLF BAEYER commenced his splendid career in BERLIN, KEKULE'S BENZOLIC THEORY remained comparatively speaking disregarded and fruitless in England, whilst in Germany the laboratories became too narrow [too small for the students]. The worst thing was that the ENGLISH MANUFACTURING CHEMIST, in consequence of his innate SELF-RELIANCE, rather trusted to his own energy and practical experience, than to the skill and knowledge of scientifically trained assistants, wishing to save wages spoiled himself his own trade, and when he belongst [became aware] of his folly, the reins had already slipped from his hands. If I had remained in ENGLAND I could not have stopped the fatal change. I now see no reason why the lessons of the PAST should not be rendered fruitful by the PRESENT GENERATION OF ENGLISH CHEMISTS, who, as your own noble example shows, are in–in respect of the high qualities of HEART and MIND–certainly not inferior to their GERMAN COLLEAGUES. Ever yours, Heinrich Caro.[3]

Caro's opinion, which has also been adopted by modern historians,[4] did not alter the verdict of Meldola, who, though now in retirement, continued to encourage improvements in chemical education, research, and industry in Britain, especially in the dye industry. Meldola's agenda was to bring about an improvement in the status of chemists, greater employment opportunities for his pupils (the lack of which was a principal cause of the failure of the Finsbury Technical College) and a role for chemists in company management. Even if Caro was not mentioned by name, he was certainly the type of person that Meldola had in mind as he continued to promote the development of a chemical industry based on the German example. This was intensified as Meldola became increasingly disappointed with the lack of impact of his own technical college and similar institutions. He drummed home his message as a representative of the "technical education movement" in *Nature* and other journals, at Oxford (1899), in presidential addresses before the Chemical Society (1907) and the Society of Chemical Industry (1909), and on other suitable occasions, though there was little response.[5]

Many leading chemists preached a similar message. Henry E. Roscoe, the chemist-turned-politician who between 1870 and 1885 had relied on Caro for information used in his lectures on synthetic dyes, noted in the columns of *Nature* that at a meeting held in London during February 1906, attended by the Lord Mayor and "many men of position and influence in the scientific world," and in connection with the Perkin Jubilee celebrations, he pointed out how

> at Owens College, I knew three talented young German chemists whose names have since become watchwords in Germany (Caro, Martius, and Pauli) who were then employed in chemical works in Manchester and the neighbourhood.... Had they been supported by men of financial light and leading in Lancashire the industry might have flourished in this country. Not, however, finding the necessary support here, they returned to Germany, where they became the leading members of the great colour works at Ludwigshafen, Höchst, and Berlin.

Roscoe considered that the industry had been lost from England through the "absence of appreciation by capitalists and others engaged in industry of the importance of scientific method."[6] This was despite his own successes at raising funds from industrialists for bringing about improvements at Owens College.[7] Ironically, it was the German chemists who most admired the new British and American developments in physical and inorganic chemistry, and expressed considerable concern that they might lose leadership in the chemical sciences. Though this was unrelated to aromatic organic chemistry and dye manufacture, in which Germany's lead was still uncontested, the perception contributed to the argumentation that encouraged the founding of new research institutes, notably by the Kaiser Wilhelm Society, whose first institute was for chemistry, and supported by the dye industry.[8]

It was the outbreak of war with Germany in August 1914 and the almost immediate crisis caused by the absence of dyestuffs–mostly made in Germany–in Britain that brought the lobbying for a British science-based organic chemical industry to the fore. This time the message could no longer be ignored. The public was informed of proposals for a British national dye industry under government control. In November 1914, Ivan Levinstein's former patent lawyer in matters related to benzopurpurines and other dyes, Lord (John Fletcher) Moulton (an accomplished scientist in his own right), and Professor Arthur Green of Leeds University began negotiations on behalf of the British government with Read Holliday, Claus & Co. of Manchester, and Levinstein Ltd, with the intention of outright purchase of one or more of these firms. Lord Moulton's "Important Statement," delivered in Manchester on 8 December 1914, and other addresses concerning dye manufacture received extensive coverage in the January 1915 issue of the *Journal of the Society of Dyers and Colourists.*[9] Shortly afterwards, however, Moulton became involved in munitions manufacture, and promotion of a British national dye industry was left to others.[10]

On 9 January 1915, Meldola was appointed to the Dyewares Supply Enquiry Committee of the Society of Dyers and Colourists.[11] Meldola and other chemists were upset by the fact that the new dyestuff concern was to be entrusted to business people with absolutely no knowledge of chemistry or chemical technology. The directors were a Scottish solicitor, James Falconer, as chairman; George Pepler Norton, a Huddersfield chartered accountant; Sir Gilbert Claughton, chairman of the London and North Western Railway; and Sir Frank Forbes Adam, India merchant and a banker. Falconer, Claughton and Adam, apart from knowing nothing about dye chemistry, were well beyond their prime. The chemist Sir William Ramsay had already pointed out in the 12 November 1914 issue of *Nature* that the management of German dye firms was of rather different composition: "First, the management consists, not in a board of well-meaning elderly gentlemen with a works manager in their employment, but in a board of specialists, whose business in life is to manage the factory financially, chemically, and as engineers, and who are very highly paid for their services."[12]

Members of the dyewares committee, increasingly critical of the lack of representation by chemists, had made their views known to the Board of Trade just a few days before Meldola was co-opted. Meldola, who was in complete agreement, decided to bring the matter to the attention of the widest possible audience through a letter to the *Times*:

> For over 30 years I have been trying to instil into the public mind the lesson conveyed by the development of the coal-tar colour industry in Germany. Their method has again been emphasised in your columns on January 14 wherein, quoting Professor Grossmann of Berlin, it is truly said that it would take us many years before we could raise the English chemical colour industry to such a pitch that it could meet all British requirements. They had only to remember how Germany had spent many years and large amounts of capital in research work before achieving results.
>
> That, Sir, is the spirit which, having been ignored here, has led to the development of this great industry in the factories of our competitors. And, now, when the opportunity is before us, it is hoped that this fatal error will not be perpetuated. If it is, all such schemes are foredoomed to failure.[13]

Meldola's letter triggered a number of responses in the *Times, Journal of the Society of Dyers and Colourists*, *Journal of the Society of Chemical Industry*, and elsewhere during the early months of 1915.[14] Meldola had certainly placed the dye industry at centre stage, and, however invidious and uncomfortable for the English, forced upon them comparisons with the superior position in Germany.

The proposals for a national, government-controlled dye industry also caused considerable controversy among dye users, some recognising advantages in a large home-based industry, and others fearing dependence upon a monopoly.[15] Leading chemists, in addition to Meldola, continued to voice their concern at the absence of scientifically trained men at the most senior level of what was to be known as British Dyes, Ltd. When the government-backed scheme–in itself remarkable for the level of state intervention–was discussed in the House of Commons during February and March 1915, the fact that not one chemist was among those at the helm received short shrift. Chemists conveyed their disapproval with renewed, though not entirely accurate, comparisons with

Germany, some that were embarrasingly odious. In the ensuing debate, Caro was mentioned occasionally, such as when, in the *Times* of 10 March 1915, he was placed foremost by William Ramsay among the Germans declared guilty of voraciously plundering British chemical technology. Martius was placed second, followed by Bernthsen and Brunck. Ramsay opined that the "reason for certain failure [of British Dyes] is this:- It is not under the management of chemists."[16]

Sir Henry E. Roscoe, in the following letter, expressed a similar view, and acknowledged the need to draw lessons from the enemy:

> The Germans acted upon … confidence in the researcher from the beginning, and gave him a voice in the management. They did not hesitate to pay men a thousand a year to make the experiments to produce a new and attractive colour. Ninety-nine experiments may fail, but the hundredth it is that rewards and repays the outlay on his salary over and over again. We British chemists have known it and preached the same doctrine for 30 years without much success. Are we still to continue upon the old lines? Are we too proud to take a leaf–a golden leaf–out of the enemy's book? If we fail to do so, success is improbable, if not impossible.

Henry E. Armstrong argued in similar vein.[17] The British dye industry, according to British chemists, really did need men like Heinrich Caro.

Meldola also voiced his and the dyewares committee's concern before chemists and industrialists, pointing out that the weakness of the British Dyes scheme was in the "subordination of science to business in an industry in which science should govern the directorate."[18] His presidential address to the Institute of Chemistry provided another useful platform for promoting the role of chemists in the boardroom:

> To suppose that we can retrieve our position after 40 years of neglect by starting a company the directorate of which is to consist solely of business people is simply ludicrous. It was against this principle that I ventured to raise my voice in *The Times* of January 20th, and I am extremely glad to find that not only the chemical and technical worlds, but the large and representative body of dye users and producers which form the Dyewares Supply Enquiry Committee of the Society of Dyers and Colourists fully endorse this view.[19]

On 25 March 1915, William H. Perkin Junior, son of the founder of the synthetic dye industry, added his voice to the protesters in his presidential address to the Chemical Society. He also reminded the audience that the duty on alcohol did not place the British dye industry at a disadvantage when compared with Germany, and acknowledged, as did many others, Meldola's bold letter in the *Times* of 20 January.[20] Later in the year,

Walter M. Gardner of Bradford Technical College, a prominent member of the Society of Dyers and Colourists, and its joint editor, brought together a number of influential papers dealing with the dye industry in his aptly titled volume, *The British Coal-Tar Industry: Its Origin, Development and Decline.*[21]

Dispelling the myth

These examples reveal the reasons why many leading British scientists came to view the rise of the German dye industry through the spectacularly successful accomplishments of men like Heinrich Caro. This was a result of the lobbying, mainly by Raphael Meldola, for greater awareness of the need for chemical education that was applicable to industry, and, particularly, for scientists among corporate leaders. Meldola's recognition of the uniqueness of Caro's contributions, both in England and Germany, led him to endow the former calico printer with an almost legendary status. However, there was a paradox, since, as Ehrhardt had pointed out, and others had long known, Caro was hardly the epitome of a good business leader. Carl Martius, one of Caro's contemporaries, and a successful scientist-entrepreneur who had also spent several years in England, would have been a much better role model for those English chemists clamouring for representation at board level. Martius, however, lacked Caro's celebrity status, especially among academic chemists, the close associations with major inventions, such as the synthesis of alizarin, and Caro's blend of theory and practice that appealed to Meldola and other British chemists. Moreover, Martius, unlike Caro, did not play a role in the critical stage of introducing British dye users to the advantages of synthetic dyes. In any case, BASF was a far more important concern than AGFA.

Caro embodied the success of the dye industry among British chemists precisely because his career profile as chemist-inventor was best suited to their interests as they argued the need for both technical and scientific representation on the board of British Dyes. Certainly British government officials were not among those easily convinced that good scientists made good business leaders. J. M. Robertson, Parliamentary Secretary to the Board of Trade, is on record as having responded to a question in Parliament about the directorate of British Dyes that he was "aware of cases where concerns have been brought to ruin in the hands of the most eminent chemists."[22]

The newly formed British Dyes Ltd. was built around Read Holliday & Sons Ltd. Though Meldola was chairman of the advisory council, British Dyes did not benefit from scientific leadership, even after Meldola's death in November 1915. The firm rapidly moved towards munitions production. While Walter Gardner became one of the principal critics of British Dyes Ltd, Ivan Levinstein did what the promoters of British Dyes had originally set out to do. He took over various smaller firms and, eventually, the sequestered Hoechst synthetic indigo factory at Ellesmere Port.[23]

The management of British Dyes Ltd remained problematic even after the war. In November 1918, the firm was merged with Levinstein Ltd to form the British Dyestuffs Corporation Ltd. Herbert Levinstein was appointed joint managing director, and from 1921 was sole managing director. However, ongoing friction with the Huddersfield division led to his removal from the board in 1922. One outcome was the revival of comparisons between the English and German dye industries, especially after it was revealed that British Dyestuffs and the German dye cartels were drawing up far-reaching trading agreements.[24] It was no doubt the ensuing debate during 1924 that caused Caro once more to become a talking point, and an extension of the public science debate, in England. In November of that year Herbert Levinstein addressed the West Riding section of the Society of Dyers and Colourists on the state of the British dye industry. While acknowledging the success of Germany he was quick to point out, through a blend of history and opinion given over to exaggeration and half-truths, that England had shown the Germans how to succeed:

> The famous Caro, afterwards of the B.A.S.F., whose great period came later, and Martius, afterwards one of the leading figures in the A.G.F.A., were both in Manchester with Roberts, Dale & Co.... The point I wish to make is that the people who subsequently founded and developed the big German dyeworks learned their business in England. They found that a lot of money could be made in the dyestuff industry when a knowledge of chemistry was combined with energetic salesmanship ... they developed the technical sales organisation, which is such a very important part of the colour works.... Purely commercial, very human and natural reasons took the few men of great talent such as Caro, Witt and others back to their native country.

Whatever else he had in mind, Herbert Levinstein was unwittingly acknowledging the progress that Caro had made during his most creative years.[25] Further, Levinstein's version of events was based on his own self-serving perceptions following his departure from the British Dyestuffs Corporation Ltd, and its subsequent negotiations with the German dye cartels.

It was perhaps in response to the false perception in England of Caro as a successful chemist-businessman that Ehrhardt drew attention to his failings in 1924, notwithstanding the fact that both Ehrhardt and Glaser acknowledged Caro's role as a brilliant chemical inventor. But while Glaser was more scathing than praiseworthy, and his thoughts remained locked in the BASF archives, Ehrhardt publicly explored the background to Caro's "becoming something of a fetish," in a paper before the Manchester Section of the Society of Chemical Industry.[26]

Thus though Caro had failures and setbacks, it was his personality that Ehrhardt saw as his one real problem. According to Ehrhardt, Caro "was a difficult man to get on with, and was constantly quarrelling with his colleagues."[27] As an example, Ehrhardt referred to his own early experience at BASF. Six months after joining the firm and a seemingly successful period of probation, Ehrhardt requested a salary increase as compensation for working abroad. Though an increment for this reason was rejected, Heinrich Brunck responded: "we will give you the extra [equivalent of] £30 per annum, not for living with us here but you have got to work under Caro, no one can get on with him, and we have noticed in the last six months that you have got on with him; we will give you the extra £30 per annum for that." Ehrhardt remarked: "When one managing director speaks like this of his colleague it is not exactly a recommendation that the latter should be given a free hand for running a factory." Certainly there was no hint of Caro as a business leader.

Superstition, chance, and the role of calico printing

Carl Glaser likened the relationship between Engelhorn and Caro to that of the "prince behind his gold maker in the time of the alchemist."[28] If alchemy was imbued with superstition, then Glaser had indeed captured the spirit that Caro sometimes wished to display of his inventive genius. This trait was also observed by Ehrhardt, who, when discussing indigo with Caro, suggested,

> ... that the supernatural powers who had favoured him in this way [with xanthate of soda as reducing agent] might have given him a hint of how to prepare indigo in bulk, for after all the manufacture and sale of the "propiolic" acid was more a matter

of prestige than of dividends, but he did not take the criticism of his spook kindly.

Serendipity, Ehrhardt admitted, inevitably played a more likely role: "Similarly Dr. Caro liked to emphasise the effect of chance on his inventions." Here there were several examples, particularly his alizarin process, which demonstrated how trusting to chance in the early dye industry ensured an adequate success rate. But chance favoured a mind that was properly prepared to realise how a product could be used, or sufficiently experienced to recognise the identity of a reaction product with a known commercial natural colorant. In other words, dye design was a matter of knowing where to look for suitable compounds, starting with the obvious targets: madder and indigo. However, once a discovery was made, Caro knew that trusting to chance in its exploitation was out of the question. That is where patenting activity came in, though experiences in Prussia from 1869 led him to prefer secrecy for almost a decade. This changed with Hofmann's publication of the constitutions of eosin and azo dyes, and passage of the German patent law in 1877. From then on, protection of patents encouraged new factors to enter the search for dyes: institutionalised R&D strategies and better technology. Despite Caro's claim in his 1891 history that azo dye discovery was "an endless combination game," chemists in industrial laboratories knew what they were looking for even if the research was a mix of serendipity, speculation, and laborious screening. Sooner or later a potentially useful intermediate or dye turned up. And while Bayer's Duisberg could talk of "no flash of genius" in dye research laboratories, variants of old ideas and working by analogy did provide results that could not have been foreseen, such as René Bohn's discovery of the first of the indanthrene, or vat, dyes, at BASF in 1901.

As far as Ehrhardt and others were concerned, Caro's genius was, apart from his mastery of technical chemistry, a matter of experience and training in a major dye-using industry. This applied also to other successful inventors in the dye industry. Thus, according to Edmund Knecht, Caro "attributed much of his success to his early training in calico printing, which always stood him in good stead in the works; and what Caro said in this respect was borne out also by Bohn's experience."[29]

Certainly Bohn's discovery of vat dyes had a tremendous impact on the 20th-century dye industry, though it bore no comparison with Caro's achievement. Caro was in at the start and remained with the industry for its first three decades. He had acquired his "wonderful genius for discovery" in Manchester during the 1860s, which is why Meldola was to some extent justified in making a connection between the loss of both Caro and the dye industry from England. Heinrich Caro oversaw a profound change in which dye invention and the practice of chemistry evolved from discovery to design. Through a combination of inventive technical and chemical skills and the capability of recognising a likely winner, he brought about the rapid emergence of the dye industry in a land that was better prepared and more receptive. This was in part because of the absence of heavy industry, at least on the English scale, and large colonial enterprises. Germany was ripe for technology transfer, and through his own acquired skills as chemist and calico printer, and arrangements over intellectual property rights with dye-industry founder William Perkin, Heinrich Caro brought it in abundance from England.

Medallion commemorating Heinrich Caro. (Deutsches Museum.)

Caro's dyes

Finally, a few words on the fates of the many intermediates and dyes discovered during the time that Heinrich Caro was the technical leader in the realm of science-based industry. Anthraquinone and its derivatives became the basis of vat dyes (indanthrenes), discovered in 1901 by René Bohn when he subjected an aminoanthraquinone to the conditions of the indigo synthesis. Vat and azo dyes were to become the main colorants of the 20th century, even displacing indigo, until the fashion for denim emerged in the 1960s, which brought about a major revival of the late-19th-century processes. Other important new dye classes were invariably based on derivatives of long-known azo and vat dyes. These included metallized dyes, dyes for synthetic fibres, and fibre-reactive dyes. (The latter, the first dyes to attach directly to cotton through chemical bonding, were developed at ICI Blackley in the 1950s.) The only exceptions were phthalocyanine dyes, discovered in Britain in the 1930s, and of a completely novel structural type. Numerous dye intermediates formed the bases of the modern pharmaceutical and explosives industries.

That a number of the 19th-century dyes were dropped by manufacturers in Europe and North America from the 1960s had nothing to do with the lack of demand or the availability of strong rivals. Among other things, it was the outcome of environmental difficulties faced by the industry, a situation going back to the early days of dye manufacture. Moreover, the factory floor in the coal-tar dye industry presented several hazards to health, including the inherent problems of strong acids and alkalis and toxic gases. Of considerable gravity, and unique to the dye industry, were cyanosis or "blue-lip," first observed among workers in nitrobenzene and aniline departments, and, from around 1900, bladder cancer that was investigated by physicians, particularly Ludwig Rehn. Though the exact causes of cancer were not known, the main culprits were intermediates used in the manufacture of azo dyes (later shown to be benzidine and β-naphthylamine), and contaminants in aniline.

The inevitable concern demanded a response from the management of dye factories. Caro's advice to Duisberg in October 1905 was perhaps typical, that is, the hygiene policy in the industry should be based on educating workers about the toxicity of the substances that they handled, but only in a very limited sense. If they knew too much, according to

Caro, they would become unnecessarily frightened, and imagine that dangers existed where there were none.[30] Caro believed that careful planning at management level to avoid accidents and mishaps was a better way of dealing with the situation. Half a century later, the benzidine and β-naphthylamine dyes, many of which Caro had pioneered, were phased out.[31]

Notes

Introduction

1. Arthur G. Green, in discussion following Ernest F. Ehrhardt, "Reminiscences of Dr. Caro," *Chemistry and Industry* 43 (1924): 561-65, on 564.
2. This is mentioned by Ehrhardt, in "Reminiscences of Dr. Caro," on 561, who is probably referring to a letter from Raphael Meldola published in the London *Times* on 20 January 1915. Though in 1904 Meldola drew a connection between Caro's departure from England and the decline of the British dye industry, Caro is not mentioned in Meldola's letter to the *Times*. See also Ehrhardt, "Reminiscences of Dr. Caro," 564-65.
3. For a review of the industrial impact of Haber's ammonia synthesis, see Anthony S. Travis, "High Pressure Industrial Chemistry: The First Steps, 1909-1913, and the Impact," in *Determinants in the Evolution of the European Chemical Industry, 1900-1939*, eds. Anthony S. Travis, Harm G. Schröter, Ernst Homburg, and Peter J. T. Morris (Dordrecht: Kluwer, 1998), 1-21.
4. Ehrhardt, "Reminiscences of Dr. Caro," 564. A useful study of Caro is Curt Schuster, "Heinrich Caro," in *Ludwigshafener Chemiker*, ed. Kurt Oberdorffer (Düsseldorf, 1960), vol. 2, 45-83. See also John J. Beer, *Dictionary of Scientific Biography*, s.v. Heinrich Caro; and Ernst Darmstaedter, "Heinrich Caro," in *Das Buch der grossen Chemiker*, ed. Günther Bugge (Berlin: Chemie Verlag,1929), vol. 2, 298-309. The most informative of the obituaries is August Bernthsen, "Heinrich Caro," *Berichte der Deutschen Chemischen Gesellschaft* 45 (1912): 1987-2042.
5. Green, in discussion following Ehrhardt, "Reminiscences of Dr. Caro," on 564.
6. For the dearth of archival material on the British dye industry before around 1880, see entries in Peter J. T. Morris and Colin A. Russell, *Archives of the British Chemical Industry 1750-1914: A Handlist*, British Society for the History of Science Monographs, no. 6 (Faringdon, Oxfordshire: British Society for the History of Science, 1988).
7. Sir William Ramsay, *Nature* 12 November 1914; quoted in W. A. Tilden, "The Supply of Chemicals to Britain and Her Dependencies," *Journal of the Society of Dyers and Colourists* 31 (1915): 19-20, and extracted from *Journal of the Society of Arts*, 27 November 1914, 26.
8. The relevant texts are: Travis, "Heinrich Caro, Chemist and Calico Printer, and the Changeover from Natural to Artificial Dyes," in *Natural Dyestuffs and Industrial Culture in Europe, 1750-1880*, eds. Robert Fox and Agustí Nieto-Galan (Canton, Mass.: Science History Publications, 1999), 285-307 (chapter 2); Travis, "Heinrich Caro at Roberts, Dale & Co.," *Ambix* 38 (1991): 113-34 (chapter 3); Carsten Reinhardt and Travis, "The Introduction of Aniline Dyes to Paper Printing and Queen Victoria's Postage Stamps," *Ambix* 44 (1997): 11-18 (chapter 4); Travis, "Theory from Practice: Portraying the Constitutions of Aniline Dyes in the 1860s," in *The Invisible*

Industrialist, eds. Ilana Löwy and Jean-Paul Gaudillière (Houndmills, Basingstoke: Macmillan, 1998), 122-42 (chapter 5); Reinhardt, "An Instrument of Corporate Strategy: The Central Research Laboratory at BASF, 1868-1890," in *The Chemical Industry in Europe, 1850-1914: Industrial Growth, Pollution, and Professionalization*, eds. Ernst Homburg, Anthony S. Travis, and Harm G. Schröter (Dordrecht: Kluwer, 1998), 239-59 (chapter 8); Travis, "'Ambitious and Glory Hunting ... Impractical and Fantastic': Heinrich Caro at BASF," *Technology and Culture* 39 (1998): 105-15 (chapter 9); and Travis "Heinrich Caro and Ivan Levinstein: Uniting the Colours of Ludwigshafen and Lancashire," in *The Chemical Industry in Europe, 1850-1914*, eds. Homburg, Travis, and Schröter, 261-80 (chapter 10).

9. Amalie Caro edited Heinrich Caro's lectures at meetings of engineers, delivered between 1890 and 1909, and speeches to gatherings of chemists between 1890 and 1908, published as *Gesammelte Reden und Vorträge von Heinrich Caro* (Leipzig: Otto Spamer, 1913).

Chapter 1

1. The sister of Caro's mother was married to a respected physician in Breslau, and their son was a professor of law in Strasbourg.
2. "Mein Curriculum Vitae für mein Abiturienten-Examen, Berlin, den 5. September 1852," (hereafter cited as "Curriculum Vitae"), bound with "Erinnerungen an Dr. Heinrich Caro," unpublished volumes of typescript and other documents, including transcriptions of reminiscences by Caro and others, DM NL93/10/1, 1-4. All quotations in this chapter are translations from the German.
3. Thomas Nipperdey, *Deutsche Geschichte 1800-1866. Bürgerwelt und starker Staat* (München: Beck, 5th ed., 1991), 248-51.
4. "Curriculum Vitae," 4.
5. "Erinnerungen an Dr. Heinrich Caro," (hereafter "Erinnerungen"), DM NL93/10/1, 1-2.
6. Caro's father had purchased estates in Angermünde near the Baltic Sea and leased them out. Political unrest and ill luck of the tenants caused the Caro family to suffer considerable misfortune and financial loss. Eventually, the lands were sold off.
7. "Curriculum Vitae," 6.
8. "Curriculum Vitae," 7.
9. "Curriculum Vitae," 9.
10. "Erinnerungen," 3.
11. According to Amalie, on one occasion Meyerbeer "turned up to see his friend [Simon Caro] and told him with enthusiasm and delight that he had just discovered a young woman singer with wonderful talent." Soon this young woman featured in one of Meyerbeer's works at the Berlin opera house. She was Jenny Lind, "the Swedish Nightingale," born Johanna Maria Lind (1820-87).
12. "Curriculum Vitae," 11.
13. "Erinnerungen," 3-4.
14. The meeting of the Unified Landtag, an assembly of the provincial parliaments in Prussia, had been initiated in order to raise taxes to pay for a Berlin-to-Königsberg railway. It was convened on 11 April 1847, and brought together East-Prussian

Junkers and the wealthy citizenry of the Rhineland. Disputes led to cancellation of the proposed tax, and stoppage of the construction work on the railway.

15. "Curriculum Vitae," 13-14.
16. "Beschreibung meiner Erinnerungen der 48er Märztage, miterlebt als Tertianer, aufgezeichnet 1908," (hereafter "48er Märztage"), bound with "Erinnerungen," 24-25.
17. Heinrich Wilhelm Krausnick (1797-1882) was mayor of Berlin from 1834 to 1848. As a result of the revolution he was forced to resign, but was re-elected in 1850 and remained in office until 1862.
18. "48er Märztage" 1-18.
19. "48er Märztage," 1-18.
20. "Curriculum Vitae," 14-15.
21. "Curriculum Vitae," 16-17.
22. Rüdiger Hachtmann, *Berlin 1848. Eine Politik- und Gesellschaftsgeschichte der Revolution* (Bonn: Dietz, 1997), 252-56.
23. "Curriculum Vitae," 19.

Appendix to Chapter 1

1. Rüdiger Hachtmann, *Berlin 1848. Eine Politik- und Gesellschaftsgeschichte der Revolution* (Bonn: Dietz, 1997), 107-08, 525.
2. Certain historical information that is not related to Caro's own experience in 1848 has been omitted. A valuable account of the events of March 1848 by a participant is Karl Ludwig von Prittwitz, *Berlin 1848. Das Erinnerungswerk des Generalleutnants Karl Ludwig von Prittwitz und andere Quellen zur Berliner Märzrevolution und zur Geschichte Preußens um die Mitte des 19 Jahrhunderts*, ed. Gerd Heinrich (Berlin: Walter de Gruyter, 1985). Von Prittwitz was commander of Prussian troops in Berlin from the afternoon of 18 March. The best impression from the other political side is the very detailed account by the deputy editor of the *Berliner Zeitungshalle*, Adolf Wolff, *Berliner Revolutionschronik. Darstellung der Berliner Bewegungen im Jahre 1848 nach politischen, sozialen und literarischen Beziehungen*, 3 vols. (Berlin, 1851-54; reprinted, Leipzig, 1979). The most authoritative history of the events in Berlin is Hachtmann, *Berlin 1848*.
3. "Beschreibung meiner Erinnerungen der 48er Märztage, miterlebt als Tertianer, aufgezeichnet 1908," (hereafter "48er Märztage"), bound with "Erinnerungen," 8.
4. Hachtmann, *Berlin 1848*, 137-39.
5. Theodor Körner (1791-1813), poet of the wars of liberation against Napoleonic France, wrote the tragedy *Zriny* in 1812. Niklas Zriny, a Hungarian count, opposed Turkish troops during a 1566 offensive, and was killed during the siege of his fortress.
6. "48er Märztage," 9.
7. "48er Märztage," 10.
8. For a description of the fighting, see Hachtmann, *Berlin 1848*, 152-67.
9. "48er Märztage," 10-14.
10. For an account of the events, see David E. Barclay, *Frederick William IV and the Prussian Monarchy*, 1840-1861 (Oxford: Oxford University Press, 1995), 138-45.

11. Hachtmann, *Berlin 1848*, 189-202.
12. "48er Märztage," 21.
13. "48er Märztage," 22-24.
14. This follows Thomas Nipperdey, *Deutsche Geschichte 1800-1866. Bürgerwelt und starker Staat* (München: Beck, 5th ed., 1991), 527-89.

Chapter 2

1. F. W. Nottebohm, *Chronik der Königlichen Gewerbe-Akademie zu Berlin. Festschrift zur Feier des Fünfzigjährigen Bestehens der Anstalt* (Berlin, 1871), 29.
2. See Caro to Lürmann, 4 March 1904, DM NL93/10/3. The mathematical ability was in the use of the Quetelet equation that Caro had just learned for his final examination at the Realgymnasium.
3. Rammelsberg and Magnus had joined the Gewerbeinstitut in 1850, but retained their links with the University of Berlin, where Magnus had been appointed a full professor in 1845, and Rammelsberg an associate professor in 1846. For the role of academic chemists in German polytechnics see Ernst Homburg, *Van beroep 'Chemiker:' De opkomst van de industriële chemicus en het polytechnische onderwijs in Duitsland (1790-1850)* ("'Chemiker' by Occupation: The Rise of the Industrial Chemist and Polytechnic Education in Germany (1790-1850)") (Delft: Delftse Universitaire Pers, 1993).
4. "Lehr- und Wanderjahre," bound with "Erinnerungen an Dr. Heinrich Caro" (hereafter cited as "Erinnerungen"), unpublished volumes of typescript and other documents, including transcriptions of reminiscences by Caro, DM NL93/10, 27.
5. "Erster kindlicher Versuch einer Patentanmeldung, Berlin 1854," bound with "Erinnerungen," 28-29.
6. Caro to Lürmann, 4 March 1904, DM NL93/10/3; August Bernthsen, "Heinrich Caro," *Berichte der Deutschen Chemischen Gesellschaft* 45 (1912): 1987-2042, on 1988, where Bernthsen recorded that a special state school devoted to dyeing and calico printing was proposed.
7. "Seine Leistungen in allen wissenschaftlichen Unterrichtsgegenständen waren ungewöhnlich gross, seine Arbeiten im Laboratorium, worin er sich teilweise schon mit selbständigen Untersuchungen beschäftigte, hatten einen umso besseren Erfolg, als er bereits vor seinem Eintritt in das Gewerbe-Institut sich mit chemischen Analysen beschäftigt hatte." Bound with "Erinnerungen," 30.
8. Ernst Homburg, "The Influence of Demand on the Emergence of the Dye Industry. The Roles of Chemists and Colourists," *Journal of the Society of Dyers and Colourists* 99 (1983): 325-33. See also Ernst Homburg, "From Colour Maker to Chemist: Episodes from the Rise of the Colourist, 1670-1800," *Natural Dyestuffs and Industrial Culture in Europe, 1750-1880*, eds. Robert Fox and Agustí Nieto-Galan (Canton, Mass.: Science History Publications, 1999), 219-57.
9. Charles O'Neill, *The Practice and Principles of Calico Printing, Bleaching, Dyeing, etc.*, 2 vols. (Manchester: Palmer & Howe, 1878), vol. 2, 108.
10. [H.] Edward Schunck, R. Angus Smith, and Henry E. Roscoe, "On the Recent Progress and Present Condition of Manufacturing Chemistry in the South Lancashire District," in *Report of the British Association for the Advancement of*

Science, Manchester, September 1861 (London: John Murray, 1862), 125.

11. August Wilhelm Hofmann, "Colouring Derivatives of Organic Matter, Recent and Fossilised," in *Reports of the Juries, International Exhibition, London, 1862*, Class II, Section A, "Chemical and Pharmaceutical Products and Processes," eds. J. S. Iselin and P. Le Neve Foster (London: Society for the Encouragement of Arts, Manufactures and Commerce, 1863), 114.
12. Edward Baines, Junior, *History of the Cotton Manufacture in Great Britain* (London: H. Fisher, R. Fisher & P. Jackson [1835]), 272.
13. Patterned effects were achieved by printing a resist, or reserve, paste onto the bleached fabric. The cloth was then dyed, the resist paste removed, and other colours added to the white areas with hand blocks or by painting. Bleaching agents were used to remove (discharge) the madder colour from areas of dyed cloth. Other colours could then be applied to the bleached areas. See Anthony S. Travis, "Between Broken Root and Artificial Alizarin: The Textile Arts and Manufactures of Madder," *History and Technology* 11 (1994): 1-21, esp. 6-7, and Anthony S. Travis, *From Turkey Red to Tyrian Purple: Textile Colours for the Industrial Revolution* (Jerusalem: Jewish National and University Library, 1993).
14. William Crookes, *A Practical Handbook of Dyeing and Calico-Printing*, 2 vols. (London: Longmans, Green & Co., 1874), vol. 2, 273.
15. Girardin also recommended colorimetry, in which the colour of a carefully made up solution of madder with alum was compared with a standard solution made up with pure madder.
16. Bernthsen, "Heinrich Caro," 1988.
17. "Geschäftsvertrag," bound with "Erinnerungen," 33-35, on 33.
18. "Geschäftsvertrag," bound with "Erinnerungen," 33.
19. One Thaler was equivalent to about 1 2/3 florin or gulden.
20. "Geschäftsvertrag," bound with "Erinnerungen," 34. See also Annemarie Diem and Otto P. Krätz, "Vom Alchimistenherd zur BASF. Die Lehrjahre Heinrich Caros," *Die BASF* 24 (1974): 3-10.
21. In 1839, Prussian colourists received between 800 and 1600 Thaler per annum. This was often considerably higher than the pay of a well-established chemistry professor. Thus in 1849, Bunsen at Marburg received 1,200 Thaler. The salary differentials between colourists and academic chemists are discussed in Ernst Homburg, "The Influence of Demand on the Emergence of the Dye Industry," 328.
22. Also, the proprietors had the right to dismiss Caro at any time if he broke this agreement, or if he broke any laws. Clause twelve noted that any period of absence from the factory made necessary by military service would be added to the three years specified in the contract. The proprietors agreed to allow Caro fourteen days for vacation each year. He was also required to bring written approval of the conditions of employment from his father, Simon Caro. "Geschäftsvertrag," bound with "Erinnerungen," 34-35.
23. Schunck, Smith and Roscoe, "On the Recent Progress and Present Condition of Manufacturing Chemistry," 120.
24. "Erinnerungen," 36.
25. "... mit der sicheren Erwartung, dass er sich in allen Teilen der industriellen

chemischen Praxis leicht orientieren und allen Anforderungen Genüge leisten werde, welche man an einen gründlich gebildeten technischen Chemiker stellt." "Auszug aus dem Abgangszeugniss vom Gewerbe-Institut," bound with "Erinnerungen," 31.

26. "Erinnerungen," 32.
27. Bernthsen, "Heinrich Caro," 1989.
28. Bernthsen, "Heinrich Caro," 1988.
29. Hand block printing had earlier been improved through the application of blocks in large presses, but the cloth had to be hand fed. Though the perrotine was fully mechanised, its vertical action restricted the design repeat. The block was pressed against a sieve, fed with mordant or dye, which was then moved aside, and then pressed against the cloth, after which the printed cloth was moved forward and the process repeated. Printing from up to six blocks at the same time enabled several colours to be applied in a single step. Perrotines were popular in France, Germany, Holland, Italy, and Belgium. They were also used to a lesser extent elsewhere, including in England, where ten were employed at the Deeply Vale Printing Co. near Bury during the 1840s. However, this was quite exceptional for England. See A. V. Sandiford and T. E. Ashworth, *The Forgotten Valley* (Bury: Bury and District Local History Society, 1981), 32-33; and Geert Verbong, "The Dutch Calico Printing Industry between 1870 and 1875," in *Natural Dyestuffs and Industrial Culture in Europe, 1750-1880*, 193-218.
30. "Fabrik der L[o]uisenthaler Aktien-Gesellschaft für Spinnerei, Weberei & Druckerei, Nr. II, 1858-1859," DM, item 37927, 74-98. See also Otto P. Krätz and Annemarie Diem, "Heinrich Caro: Die Louisenthaler Actiengesellschaft in Mülheim an der Ruhr–eine kombinierte Naturfarbstoff-Fabrik und Färberei zur Zeit der ersten Anilinfarben," *Chemie, Experiment & Didaktik* 2 (1976): 179-86.
31. "Fabrik der Louisenthaler Actiengesellschaft, 1856-1857," DM, item 37926.
32. Resin soap was made by reacting resin-containing (colophony) acids with alkalis, and used almost exclusively in the textile industry for madder-related processes and after calico printing. For a description of the bleaching of cloth that was subsequently to be printed, see Edmund Knecht, Christopher Rawson, and Richard Lowenthal, *A Manual of Dyeing: For the Use of Practical Dyers, Manufacturers, Students, and All Interested in the Art of Dyeing*, 2 vols. (London: Charles Griffin, 7th. ed., 1922), vol. 1, 93-94.
33. Caro's notebook, DM item no. 37925 (1858 or 1859), 104-21 (singeing) and 128-93 (bleaching). For bleaching, see also notebook no. 37927, 61-206. The resin soap was the critical part of this so-called original madder bleach process because it ensured that the cloth was cleared of stains in unmordanted parts after printing.
34. Travis, "Between Broken Root."
35. "Collectaneen, Heinrich Caro, 1857," DM, item no. 37924. Despite the 1857 date, this notebook contains references to articles for the period 1856-59. See also printed samples in DM, item no. 37926, 127-67.
36. DM, item no. 37925, 1-8, where tables for dye consumption for 1856, 1857, and 1858 are drawn up. The Prussian pound was fixed at 0.4677 kg after the post-Napoleonic reform. It was also supposed to be two Cologne Marks, which was

actually slightly lighter in weight.

37. DM, item no. 37925, 28.
38. DM, item no. 37925, 29.
39. DM, item no. 37925, 29-31.
40. DM, item no. 37925, 28.
41. DM, item no. 37925, 32-60. See also Krätz and Diem, "Heinrich Caro."
42. "Collectaneen, Heinrich Caro, 1857," 110-15. For murexide, see Anthony S. Travis, "Artificial Dyes in John Lightfoot's Broad Oak Laboratory," *Ambix* 42 (1995): 10-27.
43. Almost certainly A. Kellermann, who on 28 July 1858 took out a patent in London for obtaining extracts of flowers and leaves of the elm tree for use as dyes. From instructions of Max Troost to Heinrich Caro, "Für meine erste Reise nach Manchester, März 1857," on notepaper of "Die Louisenthaler Actien-Gesellschaft für Druckerei, Weberei & Spinnerei," bound with "Erinnerungen."
44. "Chemische Arbeiten, H. Caro, 1855," DM, item no. 37917. This notebook, which appears to be written up in French and German by several hands, contains an enormous number of recipes for using dyes (mainly for textiles, but including other applications, such as coloration of feathers).
45. Anthony S. Travis, "Artificial Dyes in John Lightfoot's Broad Oak Laboratory."
46. Bernthsen, "Heinrich Caro," 1990, who suggests that Caro also visited Meyer's factory laboratory.
47. For August Leonhardt (1827-99), see *Die Chemische Industrie* 22 (1899): 341-42.
48. DM, item no. 37927, 12-25. See also Krätz and Diem, "Heinrich Caro."

Chapter 3

1. Ernst Homburg, "The Influence of Demand on the Emergence of the Dye Industry. The Roles of Chemists and Colourists," *Journal of the Society of Dyers and Colourists* 99 (1983): 325-33.
2. Maurice R. Fox, *Dye-Makers of Great Britain, 1856-1976: A History of Chemists, Companies, Products and Changes* (Manchester: ICI, 1987). For Perkin & Sons, see Anthony S. Travis, "Perkin's Mauve: Ancestor of the Organic Chemical Industry," *Technology and Culture* 31 (1990): 51-82, and references therein.
3. "John Dale" (obituary), *Journal of the Chemical Society* 57 (1890): 446-48; *Journal of the Society of Chemical Industry* 8 (1889): 528-30; and "John Gallemore Dale" (obituary), *Journal of the Chemical Society* 39 (1872): 344. An account of a number of innovations at Roberts, Dale & Co. appears in Heinrich Caro, "Peter Griess" (obituary), *Berichte der Deutschen Chemischen Gesellschaft* 24 (1891): i-xxxviii, especially iv-viii.
4. Anthony S. Travis, *The Rainbow Makers. The Origins of the Synthetic Dyestuffs Industry in Western Europe* (Bethlehem, Pa.: Lehigh University Press, 1993), chapter 5.
5. Meyer to Caro, 14 November 1859, DM HS 1524.
6. For Roberts, Dale & Co.'s oxalic acid process, see August Wilhelm Hofmann, "Colouring Derivatives of Organic Matter, Recent and Fossilised," in *Reports of the Juries, International Exhibition, London, 1862*, Class II, Section A, "Chemical and

Pharmaceutical Products and Processes," eds. J. S. Iselin and P. Le Neve Foster (London: Society for the Encouragement of Arts, Manufactures and Commerce, 1863), 109-10. For the manufacture of caustic soda at Roberts, Dale & Co. see Robert F. Bud and Gerrylynn K. Roberts, *Science versus Practice: Chemistry in Victorian Britain* (Manchester: Manchester University Press, 1984), 114; and "Patent Caustic Detergent Prepared by Roberts, Dale & Co., Manchester," publicity leaflet, probably late 1861, DM NL93.

7. "Erinnerungen an Dr. Heinrich Caro" (hereafter "Erinnerungen"), unpublished volumes of typescript and other documents, including transcriptions of reminiscences by Caro and others, DM NL93, 36. Koepp's factory was located at Oestricha am Rhein.
8. Lunge's salary of one pound per week was "two shillings more than a labourer but less than a skilled process man." D. W. Broad, *Centennial History of the Liverpool Section, Society of Chemical Industry, 1881-1981* (London: Society of Chemical Industry, 1981), 8. Bernthsen stated that Caro received one pound and fifty pence per week.
9. Raphael Meldola, "The Position and Prospects of Chemical Research in Great Britain," *Journal of the Chemical Society* 53 (1907): 626-58, on 630.
10. See Caro's notes in "Commercial Scribbling Diary, No. 8, 1862," DM HS 2355.
11. (H.) Edward Schunck, R. Angus Smith, and Henry E. Roscoe, "On the Recent Progress and Present Condition of Manufacturing Chemistry in the South Lancashire District," in *Report of the Thirty-First Meeting of the British Association for the Advancement of Science (Manchester, 1861)* (London: John Murray, 1862), 124.
12. Anthony S. Travis, "Heinrich Caro at Roberts, Dale & Co.," *Ambix* 38 (1991): 113-34. For scientific and industrial life in 19th-century Manchester, see Robert H. Kargon, *Science in Victorian Manchester: Enterprise and Expertise* (Baltimore: Johns Hopkins University Press, 1977).
13. John Dale and Caro, Great Britain patent no. 1,307, 26 May 1860.
14. Schunck, Smith, and Roscoe, "On the Recent Progress and Present Condition of Manufacturing Chemistry," 127.
15. Draft indenture, dated 1862, of partnership between Heinrich Caro, John Dale, and Thomas Roberts for working the aniline purple process, DM HS 37943.
16. Another supplier named Higgins is indicated by Caro. This was probably James Higgins, an inventor and supplier of chemicals to the dye trade, who may have been the agent for a French brand of aniline purple.
17. "Our present price for aniline is 11/- per lb. Dis[count] of 2½%–cash 14 days–In large quantity and for continuous supply we might do it a little lower." Simpson, Maule & Nicholson to Roberts, Dale & Co., 4 December 1860, DM NL93.
18. Pillmer to Roberts, Dale & Co., 21 November 1861, DM NL93.
19. Heinrich Caro's laboratory notebook, 1862/1863. This opens with experiments made on aniline in August 1862. A further supplier, Luxer & Co. appears on 26. DM item no. 37930.
20. The dye, tannin, and thickener (generally gum Senegal) could be applied directly, then steamed and treated with "tartarized antimony" (alternatively, the tannin and

thickener could be applied together as the first step, followed by steaming, passage through antimony solution, and, finally, dyeing).

21. Printed patterns with mauve paste at Schwabe, 1862, DM NL93.
22. Meyer to Roberts, Dale & Co., 16 June 1861, DM HS 1527. Meyer submitted samples of prints prepared by the direct application of mauve and the tungsten (wolfram) compound to bleached unmordanted cloth, by dyeing tungsten-mordanted material, and by printing with albumen on bleached cloth. The colours were fixed by steaming and rinsing, or by steaming, rinsing, and boiling in a soap bath. The use of tungsten was probably due to the fact that tungsten is chemically related to chromium, an element that had become extremely important in the production of "chrome," or chrome-mordanted, colours.
23. Meyer to Roberts, Dale & Co., 7 August 1861, DM HS 1529.
24. Meyer to Roberts, Dale & Co., 21 August 1861, DM HS 1530. At the same time Meyer was anxious to promote his new process for tanning shoe leather in England, and provided Caro with details. On 30 April 1861, Meyer registered Great Britain patent no. 1,079, on behalf of Sonnenschein, for a tanning process suited to skins and hides using tungsten or molybdenum oxides or salts.
25. Anthony S. Travis, "From Manchester to Massachusetts via Mulhouse: The Transatlantic Voyage of Aniline Black," *Technology and Culture* 35 (1994): 70-99. For Johann J. Müller-Pack (1825-99), see Alfred Bürgin, *Geschichte des Geigy-Unternehmens von 1758 bis 1939. Ein Beitrag zur Basler Unternehmer- und Wirtschaftsgeschichte. Veröffentlichung zum 200jährigen Bestehen des Geigy-Unternehmens 1958* (Basel: Birkhäuser, 1958), 108 ff.
26. John Lightfoot, *The Chemical History and Progress of Aniline Black* (Burnley, 1871).
27. August Bernthsen, "Heinrich Caro," *Berichte der Deutschen Chemischen Gesellschaft* 45 (1912): 1987-2042, on 1992.
28. J. Dale, from Basel, to Roberts, 12 March 1863, DM HS 1977/32/62A/8. Another partner in the agreement is named as "Shaw."
29. See Anthony S. Travis, "Poisoned Groundwater and Contaminated Soil: The Tribulations and Trial of the First Major Manufacturer of Aniline Dyes in Basel," *Environmental History* 2 (1997): 343-65.
30. Schlumberger, from the Paris office of J. J. Müller & Cie, to Caro, 9 September 1865, DM/NL93.
31. "Versuche mit Anilin-Schwarz," note signed by Carl Schorlemmer, Owens College, 1 April 1863, DM NL93. Carl Schorlemmer (1834-92) studied under Heinrich Will and Hermann Kopp in Giessen. In 1859, he replaced Wilhelm Dittmar as private assistant of Henry Roscoe, and in March 1861 again replaced Dittmar, this time as assistant in the Owens College laboratory. In 1873, Schorlemmer was appointed lecturer, and one year later professor of organic chemistry.
32. Caro's notebook, 8 April 1863, 37 ff., DM, item no. 37930.
33. James Laing, of James Laing & Co., to Caro, 27 July 1864, DM HS 1977/32/181/1. Laing requested a sample of aniline black, and enclosed swatches of aniline colours from Lomer Schourburg & Co., noting that the colours were "quite equal to Simpsons and much cheaper."

34. Draft agreement between Heinrich Caro, representing Leonhardt, and John Dale, April 1860, DM NL93.
35. Caro to Martius, March 1904 DM NL93.
36. Travis, "From Manchester to Massachusetts via Mulhouse," 70-99.
37. Schunck, Smith, and Roscoe, "On the Recent Progress and Present Condition of Manufacturing Chemistry," 127. ("The product of this reaction is a bronze-like brittle mass, which contains aniline-red, always accompanied by purple colours. Boiling water extracts the red colouring-matters and separates them from the purple dyes, which after some purification constitute valuable substitutes for the mauve colour.")
38. Caro's laboratory notebook, DM, item no. 37930, shows that on 23 February 1863 he was treating aniline with water-free arsenic acid. This may have been experimental work in support of Wilson & Fletcher, who claimed that Medlock's patent was invalid since "dry" arsenic acid was stipulated.
39. Farbwerke Hoechst, *Dokumente aus Hoechster Archiven,* Heft 3, *Neunzig Jahre Fuchsin in Hoechst* (Frankfurt: Hoechst, 1965), 9-29.
40. "Remarks on the Manufacture of Magenta," a report, signed Gans & Leonhardt, May 1876, accompanying a letter from Leonhardt to Caro, 12 August 1878, DM HS 1977/32/187/5.
41. J. Dale to Caro, 24 October 1862, DM HS 1977/32/62A/7.
42. J. Dale to Caro, in Berlin, 2 October 1862, DM HS 1977/32/62A/5.
43. According to the *Neue Badische Landeszeitung* and a newspaper clipping attached to correspondence in the Caro Nachlass, "Prof. Dr. August Eisenlohr" was born on 6 October 1832 in Mannheim, and died on 24 February 1902. He studied at Heidelberg and Göttingen, where he obtained his Ph.D. in 1866 in science. In 1869 he completed a habilitation in Egyptology at the University of Heidelberg, and in 1885 was appointed honorary professor at Heidelberg. In 1877, he authored a mathematical handbook of the ancient Egyptians. Newspaper clipping dated 25 February 1902, DM HS 1977/32/87.
44. The patent application for Eisenlohr's process was filed in London on 10 December 1862, and covered the production of blue from organic salts of aniline and magenta.
45. Eisenlohr to Caro, 22 December 1862, DM HS 1977/32/87/2.
46. Eisenlohr to Caro, 29 January 1863, DM HS 1977/32/87/3.
47. Wanklyn, Heidelberg, to J. Dale, 2 February 1863, DM NL93. The blue was available in violet and green shades, and Wanklyn explained: "In the wool districts of Yorkshire there is a large demand for the more violet shade of which the second 5 lbs was a very good sample, and the greenish shade is taken largely by the silk dyers." Eisenlohr's terms were: "On his part he undertakes: –to make you his sole agent for England and not to sell this patent nor to grant licences for it. On your part he requires: –That you will not make blues nor buy them from any body else and that you will take at least 100 lbs of his blue weekly (on average). The agreement is to be terminated at three months notice from either party. The price at which Eisenlohr will furnish the blue dye is at present £7.15. 0s per lb. for the violet shade and for the ordinary green shade. The lb. is 500 grammes. A very fine greenish shade which he hopes to be able to furnish by and by will be dearer, but at present it

is impossible to fix the price of it. Any adjustments of price are to be made on the principle of giving you 2/5 of the entire profits and Eisenlohr 3/5. I ought to tell you that we have just got to know of a substitute for benzoic acid, so that the policy of manufacturing benzoic acid on a large scale becomes doubtful."

48. Wanklyn to Caro, 19 February 1863, DM NL93. Wanklyn ended: "I have at last been definitely appointed to the London Institution." Eight days later Eisenlohr filed a patent for his second blue process, which stipulated the sodium salts of benzoic or acetic acid.
49. Schorlemmer to Caro, 24 March 1863, Caro DM NL93.
50. Undated notes, DM HS1977/32/62A/3.
51. The remainder of Roberts's letter reveals interest in new products from the Continent, a close working relationship with Wilson & Fletcher, and the wish to provide reagents for overseas manufacturers: "Have included small bit of new green–and shall tonight meet two gentlemen about a new red that I am sure is destined to <u>cut out Coch[inea]l altogether</u>–the process will I expect be under offer to me and Wilson.... I am glad I came down here ... make Hyposulphide of lime. Muller wants it in connection with his new [aldehyde] green." Roberts to John Dale, 12 March 1863, DM HS 1977/32/62A/8.
52. Notes for contract, 20 March 1863, DM HS 1977/32/62A/9. It continues from DM HS 1977/32/62A/4, which provides the following information:
"The price of the colour furnished to Roberts, Dale & Co. delivered in Heidelberg (By Dr. Aug. Eisenlohr) shall be as follows:
<u>For silk</u>
1st Shade (weak)
Ten pounds per lb (English)
<u>For silk and wool</u>
2nd Shade (strong)
Eight pounds per lb (English weight)
3rd Shade (strong)
More violet
Six pounds per lb–Eng.
<u>For wool</u>
4th Shade (weak)
Four pounds ten shillings per lb English.

Roberts, Dale & Co. shall until the expiration of three months from the present date sell exclusively the Blue Analine [*sic*] Colour of Dr. A. Eisenlohr in such quantity as they are able, and for such sales shall themselves incur all the responsibility and this agreement provides that the sales shall be effected openly on the principle that such Blue Colours are neither directly nor indirectly infringement of others rights. That the amounts of blue colour including all shades shall be delivered to Roberts, Dale & Co. by Aug. Eisenlohr in quantity no less than Fifty pounds per week and this is the quantity that Roberts, Dale & Co. shall be compelled to receive from Dr. Eisenlohr." [£5,000, added later.] The agreement stipulated that after three months Roberts, Dale & Co. would make an offer to Eisenlohr for purchase of his process.

53. Eisenlohr to Caro, 26 April 1863, DM HS 1977/32/87/4; trans. from the German. Hydrochlorate was the term then in use for the present hydrochloride.
54. Eisenlohr to Caro, 13 September 1863, DM HS 1977/32/87/5.
55. J. Dale to Caro, 7 February 1864, DM HS 1977/32/62A/10. Dale added: "I have some good information on the manufacture of the green which will please you and perhaps lead to our making it thru' the acrolein process." Dale expressed satisfaction with progress on the phenylene brown, and the situation over mauve: "and when we get out our cheap mauve–I think we shall make some way with it."
56. F. Smith to Caro, 29 March 1864, DM NL93. Smith continued: "Your mauve crystals as compared with Perkin's crystals is a bluer shade and find them to produce a deeper colour. Your crystals are not as readily soluble as Perkin's and require repeated boilings before solution is affected."
57. Anthony S. Travis, "Science's Powerful Companion: A. W. Hofmann's Investigation of Aniline Red and Its Derivatives," *British Journal for the History of Science* 25 (1992): 27-44; and Travis, *Rainbow Makers*, chapter 3.
58. Anthony S. Travis, "Science and Technology for an Empire: A. W. Hofmann and Heinrich Caro in England," in *Die Allianz von Wissenschaft und Industrie: August Wilhelm Hofmann (1818-1892): Zeit, Werk, Wirkung,* eds. Christoph. Meinel and Hartmut Scholz (Weinheim: VCH, 1992), 119-32.
59. Frederick Crace(-)Calvert (1819-73) for a short time in 1841 worked at the factory of Robiquet and Pellicti in Paris. *Chemical News* 31 (1875): 56-57.
60. Charles Lowe had been associated with Frederick Crace Calvert and Samuel Clift. He founded Charles Lowe & Company at the Phoenix Works, Newton Heath, and a second works was later opened at Reddish.
61. Travis, "Science's Powerful Companion," 27-44; and Frank A. J. L. James, ed., *Chemistry and Theology in Mid-Victorian London: The Diary of Herbert McLeod, 1860-1870* (London: Mansell, 1987).
62. Caro's notebook, DM item no. 37930, samples dyed with aniline blue of Renard frères (Girard's process), sent from C. A. Martius in London, 26 March 1863, 20. Preparations of aniline blue, following Girard's recipe, using sample of acetate salt of rosaniline made by Simpson, Maule & Nicholson, and sulphate and hydrochlorate [ide] salts of rosaniline, all from the laboratory of Hofmann in London, and sent by Martius, 24 March 1863, 28. Experiments on aniline blue supplied by Martius at the beginning of April 1863 are noted on 30.
63. A. Poirrier and C. Chappat, Great Britain patent no. 1,036, 25 April 1863.
64. Martius to Caro, 20 April 1863, DM NL93; trans. from the German.
65. Martius to Caro, 21 May 1863, DM NL93; trans. from the German. "From rosaniline with ammonium benzoylate you obtain blue dyestuff. Benzamide seems to give the same results. It is a pity that I cannot send you the promised chloracetyl because the supplier has not delivered it yet. Tomorrow there is a lecture by Roscoe at the Royal Institution."
66. Martius to Caro, undated, DM NL93; trans. from the German.
67. Martius to Caro, 8 July 1863. DM NL93; trans. from the German.
68. Martius to Caro, 8 July 1863, DM NL93; trans. from the German. The letter closed with a further item of chemical interest: "P.S. I would like to suggest that in your

patent for brown you include the following substances: quinone and its brominated and chlorinated substitution products, and chloranilic acid and its salts, and dichlorophenylated acid."

69. Martius to Caro, 12 July 1863, DM NL93; trans. from the German.
70. Martius to Caro, 23 July 1863, on Royal College of Chemistry notepaper, DM NL93; trans. from the German.
71. Caro's notebook, 62-63 (undated), and 28 August 1863, 69, DM item no. 37930.
72. William Henry Perkin, "Proceedings of the Fourth Annual General Meeting. The President's Address," *Journal of the Society of Chemical Industry* 4 (1885): 427-38, on 435.
73. The reaction was reinvestigated by Otto N. Witt during 1875-76.
74. Antonio Gallenga, *Episodes of My Second Life* (London, 1884), quoted by Wilfred Vernon Farrar, in "Edward Schunck, F.R.S.: A Pioneer of Natural Product Chemistry," *Notes and Records of the Royal Society of London* 31 (1977): 273-96, on 274.
75. Philipp Pauli (1836-1920) was later associated with Meister, Lucius & Brüning (the Hoechst Dyeworks). H. Reissenegger, "Zu Dr. Paulis achtzigstem Geburtstage," *Chemiker Zeitung* 40 (1916): 173.
76. "Aus folgenden Briefauszügen und Notizen erfahren wir die Bekanntschaften mit Ludwig Mond, Martius, Reissig, [Ivan] Levinstein und Lunge," two pages of reminiscences of Oscar Behrens, 11 December 1909, bound with "Erinnerungen," 44-45. For Mond, see Peter J. T. Morris, "The Legacy of Ludwig Mond." *Endeavour* 13 (1989): 34-40.
77. J. M. Cohen, *The Life of Ludwig Mond* (London: Methuen, 1956), 71-73.
78. Martius to Caro, 8 February 1864, DM NL93; trans. from the German.
79. Martius, from Mersey Bank Works, to Caro, 12 [January or June] 1864, DM NL93; trans. from the German.
80. Martius to Caro, 8 February 1864, DM NL93; trans. from the German.
81. Martius to Caro, 25 May 1864, DM NL93; trans. from the German.
82. Martius to Caro, 3 June 1864, DM NL93; trans. from the German.
83. For Leigh, see Kargon, *Science in Victorian Manchester*, 66-74.
84. John Leigh to John Dale, 4 April 1863, DM NL93.
85. Peter Griess and Heinrich Caro, British patent no. 1,956, 28 July 1866, for chromium salts of "azo compounds." "The precipitate obtained is very explosive and must be dried carefully at a low temperature.... Certain of these azo bodies are used in the preparation of dye-stuffs, and explosives."
86. Paraf to Caro, 27 November 1866, DM NL93; Keisser to Caro, 18 October 1866 DM HS 1977/32/156/1; and Lucien Picard to Caro, 17 November 1866, DM NL93. Picard had earlier been in touch with Caro at Roberts, Dale & Co. regarding blue and violet aniline dyes. Lucien Picard & Co. to Caro, 8 September 1866, DM NL93.
87. W. Kellner to Caro, 11 May 1866, DM HS 1977/32/158. Frederick Abel to Caro, 6 June 1866, DM HS 1977/32/1.

Chapter 4

1. See, for example, the correspondence of Ludwig Mond described in Peter J. T. Morris, "The Legacy of Ludwig Mond," *Endeavour* 13 (1989): 34-40.
2. H. Reissenegger, "Zu Dr. Paulis achtzigstem Geburtstage," *Chemiker Zeitung* 23 (1916): 173.
3. Martius to Pauli, 17 March 1864, DM NL93; trans. from the German.
4. From 1869, Koenig was with the Hoechst Dyeworks. See Carsten Reinhardt. *Forschung in der chemischen Industrie. Die Entwicklung synthetischer Farbstoffe bei BASF und Hoechst. 1863-1914* (Freiberg: Technische Universität Bergakademie Freiberg, 1997), 246-47.
5. Martius to Pauli, 15 April 1864, DM HS 1978/9/19/3; trans. from the German.
6. Martius to Pauli, 24 May (1864), DM HS 1978/9/19/4; trans. from the German.
7. Martius to Pauli, 9 June (1864), DM HS 1978/9/19/5; trans. from the German.
8. Martius to Pauli, 22 August 1864, DM HS1978/9/19/6; trans. from the German. Theodor Reissig later joined BASF.
9. Martius to Pauli, DM HS 1978/9/19/8; trans. from the German.
10. Martius to Pauli, 10 April 1865, DM NL93.
11. Other consumers included Littlewood, Wilson & Co. (Foxhillbank works); R. Kay, at the Adelphi Dyeworks; Foxcroft; R. Walker; John Crossley & Son of Halifax; H. and G. Ainsworth; Thomas Hoyle & Son; Knowles; John Wilkinson; Bright & Co. (the preceding five of Rochdale); and Grafton & Co. of Accrington. Most mauve was sold in the form of a paste; the rest at this time was supplied as liquor. In Manchester, mauve and other Roberts, Dale & Co. products could also be obtained from Mottershead & Co. of Market Street. Sales sheets in notebook for period January to April 1862, DM NL93.
12. In April 1862, Maison Hannart of Lille, and in October 1862, Gaydet, pére et fils, of Roubaix, were customers introduced by Pauli. Pauli to Caro, 2 October 1862, DM NL93.
13. Caro's laboratory notebook shows that in March 1863 he was reacting mauve with acrolein to obtain new shades such as "Blue Mauve." DM, item no. 37930.
14. T. P. Miller to Caro, 8 April 1864, DM NL93.
15. Müller to Caro, letters dated 1862 and 1863, DM NL93.
16. By 1867 papermakers were large users of aniline colours. August Wilhelm Hofmann, Charles Girard, and Georges de Laire, "Report on the Coal-tar Colours Shown at the [1867] French Exhibition," Appendix to Max Reimann, *On Aniline and Its Derivatives: A Treatise upon the Manufacture of Aniline and Aniline Colours*, trans. from the German, rev. and ed. by William Crookes (New York: John Wiley & Son, 1868), 153-54.
17. Carsten Reinhardt and Anthony S. Travis, "The Introduction of Aniline Dyes to Paper Printing and Queen Victoria's Postage Stamps," *Ambix* 44 (1997): 11-18.
18. "Obituary Notice. Hugo Müller," *Journal of the Chemical Society* 61 (1915): 572-88.
19. Gustav Schultz, "Bericht ueber die Feier zu Ehren August Kekulé's," *Berichte der Deutschen Chemischen Gesellschaft* 23 (1890): 1265-1312, on 1306.
20. Müller to Caro, 22 July 1862, DM NL93; trans. from the German.

21. August Wilhelm Hofmann, "Colouring Derivatives of Organic Matter, Recent and Fossilised," in *Reports of the Juries, International Exhibition, London, 1862*, Class II, Section A, "Chemical and Pharmaceutical Products and Processes," eds. J. S. Iselin and P. Le Neve Foster (London: Society for the Encouragement of Arts, Manufactures and Commerce, 1863), 133.
22. Müller to Caro, 10 January 1863, DM NL93; trans. from the German.
23. Müller to Caro, 10 April 1863, DM NL93.
24. Müller to Caro, 13 April 1863, DM NL93; trans. from the German.
25. Müller to Caro, 17 July 1863, DM NL93; trans. from the German.
26. Müller to Caro, 21 December 1863, DM NL93; trans. from the German.
27. Müller to Caro, 19 January 1864, DM NL93; trans. from the German.
28. Müller to Caro, 1 February 1864, DM NL93; trans. from the German.
29. Müller to Caro, 20 March 1864, DM NL93; trans. from the German.
30. Müller to Caro, 16 April 1866, DM NL93; trans. from the German.
31. Müller to Caro, 24 April 1866, DM NL93; trans. from the German.
32. Müller to Caro, 6 May 1866, DM NL93; trans. from the German.
33. Müller to Caro, 8 June 1866, DM NL93; trans. from the German.
34. Müller to Caro, 8 August 1866, DM NL93; trans. from the German.
35. Müller to Caro, 15 August 1866, DM NL93; trans. from the German.
36. Müller to Caro, 22 October 1879, DM NL93. The successes of the mechanical and chemical improvements that Müller introduced into the De La Rue factory were rewarded with a partnership in the firm. He was also associated with Warren De la Rue's studies in astronomy, celestial photography, a silver chloride battery, and experiments on the discharge of electricity in gases.
37. Roberts to Caro, 5 August 1864, DM NL93.
38. Edward Crossley to Caro, 3 June 1864, DM HS 1977/32/60/1.
39. Crossley to Caro, 23 February 1865, DM HS 1977/32/60/2.
40. See, for example, Crossley to Caro, 26 October 1869, DM HS 1977/32/60/3; James Laing & Co. to Caro, 28 (October) 1869, DM HS 1977/32/181/2; and Campbell (for Laing) to Caro, 1869, DM HS 1977/32/47.
41. Adshead to Caro, 15 February 1865, DM HS 1977/32/2/1.
42. J. Caldeswood, Rochdale, to Caro, 2 August 1864, DM HS1977/32/44.
43. Caldewood to Caro, 6 January 1865, DM HS 1977/32/46A/3. New developments in natural colorants were also carried out at Roberts, Dale & Co. The letter continues: "I have not got the new lot of Archill paste tried yet and cannot now find a beck or two as we stop work last night and do not recommence until Tuesday next."
44. Peter Adshead to Caro, 14 August 14, 1865, DM HS1977/32/2/2.
45. Colin Campbell to Caro, 27 February 1865, DM NL93.
46. Charles Schubert to Caro, 17 October 1865, DM NL93.
47. C. H. Greville Williams to Caro, 11 August 1865, DM NL93.
48. Charles Hanson Greville Williams (1829-1910) in 1868 co-founded the dye manufacturing firm of William, Thomas & Dower, at Brentford, Middlesex.
49. "Before Mr. Justice Blackburn and Special Juries. Cotton Goods and Africa. Castellain and another v. Greenhalgh," newspaper cutting, dated December 1864 (source unknown), accompanying a hand written document, "On the cause of the

different degree of rotteness in the Whites and the Blues," and attachment "Tove Janeway & Tagarit, 38 Bedford Row, Middlesex, Agents for Grundry and Davies of Manchester in the County of Lancaster, Attorneys for the Plaintiffs. 3rd December 1864," DM NL93. See also *The Daily Courier* (Liverpool), 22 December 1864, "Nisi. Prius Court – Yesterday (before Mr. Justice Blackburn) Important Calico Case."

50. Heinrich Caro and William Dancer, "An Instance of the Injurious Action of Alkalies on Cotton Fibre," *Proceedings of the Literary and Philosophical Society of Manchester* 4 (1864-65): 149-52, quoting from 151.
51. Wanklyn to Caro, 23 July 1865, DM NL93.
52. Wanklyn to Caro, undated, DM NL93.
53. Wanklyn to Caro, 20 December 1865, DM NL93.
54. Wanklyn to Caro, 28 December 1865, DM NL93. Wanklyn ended: "When you get tomorrow's Chemical News you will see that I have been delivered of a very great chemical baby [a ketone, from the reaction between carbon monoxide and ethyl sodium]: $CO + 2NaC_2H_5 = Na_2 + CO(C_2H_5)_2$."
55. "I am informed that this formation of ether as a by-product in the manufacture of ethylated rosaniline has also been noticed by Continental manufacturers." J. Alfred Wanklyn, "On a Curious Example of Etherification," in "Notices and Abstracts of Miscellaneous Communications to the Sections. Chemistry," *Report of the Thirty-Fourth Meeting of the British Association for the Advancement of Science (Bath, 1864)* (London: John Murray, 1865), 44-45.
56. Anthony S. Travis, "Heinrich Caro at Roberts, Dale & Co.," *Ambix* 38 (1991): 113-34.
57. These were, however, investigated at Roberts, Dale & Co., after Caro's departure. See entries in 1868 laboratory notebook of John Dale, Junior, The Museum of Science and Industry in Manchester, item no. 0420, and Anthony S. Travis, "Surrogate Instruments: Industrial Chemical Reactors," in ed. Christoph Meinel, *Instrument–Experiment: Historische Studien* (Berlin: Diepholz, 2000), 201-16.
58. Adshead to Caro, 24 October 1866, DM HS 1977/32/2/3.
59. Ernest F. Ehrhardt, "Reminiscences of Dr. Caro," *Chemistry and Industry* 43 (1924): 561-65, on 564.
60. R. S. Dale to Caro, 27 February 1867, DM HS 1977/32/62B/1.
61. (Mo. Morry) to Caro, 27 February 1867, DM NL93. Caro was advised that "the Brown does not either work well now, but I think it is owing to the careless way it is now made. [We] must have a change with it or every body will cease to use it and we should not like it to be thrown out all at once with a large stock on hand." John Dale followed with a personal request: "Our solicitor considers that for the successful conduct of our case, it is absolutely necessary that we have you over here, and as the state of your health will not permit you now to come we intend to apply for a postponement of the trial. In order to obtain this, we must prove that we have used our best endeavours to get you here. We would put your last letter as evidence but that it contains remarks that would not do [if] put into court. Would you kindly send to me a letter stating your inability to attend at present." Dale to Caro, 13 March 1867, DM HS 1977/32/62B/2.

Chapter 5

1. Müller to Caro, 10 January 1863, DM NL93.
2. Müller to Caro, 10 April 1863, DM NL93; trans. from the German.
3. Müller to Caro, 17 July 1863, DM NL93; trans. from the German.
4. Müller to Caro, 19 January 1864, DM NL93; trans. from the German.
5. Müller to Caro, 20 March 1864, DM NL93; trans. from the German.
6. Hugo Müller, "On Rosolic Acid," *Journal of the Chemical Society* 11 (1859): 1-5.
7. Hermann Kolbe and Rudolf Wilhelm Schmitt, "Rother Farbstoff aus dem Kreosot," *Annalen* 119 (1861): 169-72. See also Alan J. Rocke, *The Quiet Revolution. Hermann Kolbe and the Science of Organic Chemistry* (Berkeley: University of California Press, 1993), 431-32. Jules Persoz in Paris almost certainly adapted Kolbe and Schmitt's work to the development of a commercially useful process for rosolic acid, also known as yellow coralline. Persoz and his son were credited with devising processes that afforded rosolic acid and two of its derivatives that were commercial dyes. Rights to these were sold to Guinon, Marnas & Bonnet. With ammonia, rosolic acid gave a dye called red coralline (Turkey red lake) or péonine (Figure 3). The presence of nitrogen in péonine was said to be responsible for its being a better dye than rosolic acid. Treatment of péonine with aniline gave the blue dye azuline, also known as bleu d'acide phénique. Marnas noted that on a trip to Paris in July 1860 he had received from Jules Persoz a sample of the blue. Credit for the discovery of azuline was ascribed to Persoz's son, and the industrial process became available as a result of the work of an M. Richoud at Marnas's firm. Other names for rosolic acid included aurin(e). The slight difference in the constitutions of rosolic acid and aurin was not always recognised. Aurin was sometimes described as a yellow-brown paste of uncertain composition, but considered to consist of rosolic acid and aurin.
8. In 1866, Caro acknowledged that the pure phenol used in his research at that time was supplied by Charles Lowe.
9. Heinrich Caro, "Ueber die Entwickelung der Theerfarben-Industrie," *Berichte der Deutschen Chemischen Gesellschaft* 25 (1892): 955-1105, on 1033-34 Caro gives the British patents as no 2130, filed by Guinon, Marnas & Bonnet, and no. 2,132, filed by W. Spence, both on 28 July 1862.
10. Inventory, drawn up on 9 March 1943 by the director of the Deutsches Museum, Jonathan Zenneck, and supplied to Otto Ambros of I. G. Farben, Caro Nachlass, DM NL93. These include: 39273, attempted first rosolic acid, Richard Dale; 39274, aurin; 31238, jaune phénique (picric acid?); 31465, Aurin-Ammonverbindung (red coralline?); 31737, Acetylrosolsäure; 33152, Corallin-lake (Turkey Red lake); and 33464, Roberts, Dale (& Co.) aurin.
11. Frederick Crace Calvert, *Lectures on Coal-Tar Colours, and on Recent Improvements in Dyeing and Calico Printing* (Manchester: Palmer & Howe [1863]), 33, 39.
12. James Alfred Wanklyn, "On the Rational Formula of Rosaniline," in "Notices and Abstracts of Miscellaneous Communications to the Sections. Chemistry," *Report of*

the Thirty-Fourth Meeting of the British Association for the Advancement of Science (Bath, 1864) (London: John Murray, 1865), 42-44. See also *Chemical News* 10 (1864): 157.

13. James Alfred Wanklyn, "On the Probable Constitution of Kolbe and Schmitt's Colouring Matter Obtained by Acting Upon Carbolic Acid with Oxalic and Sulphuric Acids," in "Notices and Abstracts of Miscellaneous Communications to the Sections. Chemistry," *Report of the Thirty-Fourth Meeting of the British Association for the Advancement of Science (Bath, 1864)*, 44-45. See also *Chemical News* 10 (1864): 171.
14. Kolbe's interest in coal-tar dyes was confined to rosolic acid, and was soon lost when others profited from his publication of the reaction conditions.
15. Possibly the reaction sequence: naphthylamine → diazotise → naphthol → dinitronaphthol (dinitronaphthylalcohol, or Martius yellow, discovered in 1864). See also Peter Griess and Heinrich Caro, British patent no. 1,956, 28 July 1866, for chromium salts of "azo compounds," from, for example, aniline hydrochloride.
16. Caro, "Ueber die Entwickelung," 1054.
17. Wanklyn to Caro, undated letter, DM NL93.
18. Heinrich Caro and J. Alfred Wanklyn, "On the Relation of Rosaniline to Rosolic Acid," *Proceedings of the Royal Society of London* 15 (1866): 210-13. See also *Chemical News* 14 (1866): 37-39.
19. Heinrich Caro, "On the Formation of Rosolic Acid and Rosaniline," *Philosophical Magazine* 32 (1866): 126-32, on 131.
20. This was apart from an interest in naphthol (naphthyl alcohol), used in the preparation of Martius's dinitronaphthylalcohol (Martius yellow). See Müller to Caro, 24 April 1866, and 16 May 1866, DM NL93.
21. Müller to Caro, 18 October 1866, DM NL93; trans. from the German.
22. William H. Brock, *Dictionary of Scientific Biography*, s.v. James Alfred Wanklyn.
23. From 1867, Wanklyn's rather odd personality caused him to become engaged in highly spirited vendettas with his academic colleagues. This damaged his academic credibility considerably, and did little to encourage further use of his ethylene type. At the end of the 1860s, Wanklyn was ejected from the Chemical Society (and in 1878, also under unpleasant circumstances, from the Society of Public Analysts, which he had helped to found in 1874).
24. Heinrich Caro and Peter Griess, "Vorläufige Notiz über das Phenylenbraun," *Zeitschrift für Chemie* 3 (1867): 278-80.

Chapter 6

1. Herbert Levinstein, "Proceedings of the Society. The First George Douglas Lecture: George Douglas, His Times, and Some Thoughts on the Future," *Journal of the Society of Dyers and Colourists* 65 (1949): 269-75, on 273. Denmark was defeated, and not Schleswig-Holstein. Martius left Manchester late in 1864, or early in 1865.
2. John J. Beer, *The Emergence of the German Dye Industry* (Urbana: University of Illinois Press, 1959; reprinted New York: Arno, 1981).
3. Beer, *The Emergence*, 29, 45 and 65.
4. Beer, *The Emergence*, 66-69.

5. Georg Meyer-Thurow, "The Industrialization of Invention. A Case Study From the German Chemical Industry," *Isis* 73 (1982): 363-81; Ernst Homburg, "The Emergence of Research Laboratories in the Dyestuffs Industry," *British Journal for the History of Science* 25 (1992): 91-111; Peter Borscheid, *Naturwissenschaft, Staat und Industrie in Baden. 1848-1914* (Stuttgart: Klett, 1976); Walter Wetzel, *Naturwissenschaften und chemische Industrie in Deutschland. Voraussetzungen und Mechanismen ihres Aufstiegs im 19. Jahrhundert* (Stuttgart: Steiner, 1991); Henk van den Belt and Arie Rip, "The Nelson-Winter-Dosi Model and Synthetic Dye Chemistry," in *The Social Construction of Technological Systems*, eds. Wiebe E. Bijker, Thomas P. Hughes, and Trevor Pinch (Cambridge, Mass.: MIT Press, 1987), 135-58.
6. Thomas Nipperdey, *Deutsche Geschichte 1800-1866. Bürgerwelt und starker Staat* (Munich: Beck, 5th ed., 1991), 198, 200. These figures are for the German territories later unified under the German empire.
7. The exact figures are: 51.5 per cent, 25.7 per cent, and 21.4 per cent. Nipperdey, *Deutsche Geschichte 1866-1918*, 269.
8. Anthony S. Travis, *The Rainbow Makers. The Origins of the Synthetic Dyestuffs Industry in Western Europe* (Bethlehem, Pa.: Lehigh University Press, 1993), 147. Between 1858 and the mid 1860s some 23 companies were founded in Germany. See Heinrich Voelcker, *75 Jahre Kalle. Ein Beitrag zur Nassauischen Industriegeschichte. 1863-1938* (Wiesbaden-Biebrich: Kalle & Co., 1938), 50-51.
9. Wetzel, *Naturwissenschaften und chemische Industrie in Deutschland*, 52; Hoechst AG, ed., *Dokumente aus Hoechster Archiven*, vol. 26, *Dr. Sells Teerdestillation in Offenbach* (Höchst am Main: Hoechst, 1967).
10. See for the Rhine area Hans Pohl, Ralf Schaumann, and Frauke Schönert-Röhlk, *Die chemische Industrie in den Rheinlanden während der industriellen Revolution.* Vol. 1 *Die Farbenindustrie* (Wiesbaden: Steiner, 1983), 50-51, 55, 79-83, 86-87, 97-98, 112-14, 210-21.
11. Wolfgang Metternich, "Historische Vorbemerkung," preface to Anna Elisabeth Schreier and Manuela Wex, *Chronik der Hoechst AG. 1863-1988* (Frankfurt am Main: Hoechst, 1990), iv-xiv; Ernst Bäumler, *Ein Jahrhundert Chemie* (Düsseldorf: Econ, 1963); Hermann Pinnow, *75 Jahre Werksgeschichte Hoechst. Zur Erinnerung an die 75. Wiederkehr des Gründungstages der Farbwerke vorm. Meister Lucius & Brüning* (Munich: Bruckmann, 1938).
12. Erik Verg, Gottfried Plumpe, and Heinz Schultheis, *Meilensteine. 125 Jahre Bayer, 1863-1988* (Leverkusen: Bayer, 1988); Hermann Pinnow, *Werksgeschichte der Gefolgschaft der Werke Leverkusen, Elberfeld und Dormagen zur Erinnerung an die 75. Wiederkehr des Gründungstages der Farbenfabriken vorm. Friedr. Bayer & Co.* (Munich: Bruckmann, 1938).
13. Voelcker, *75 Jahre Kalle*, 29-35.
14. Founded by Carl Alexander Martius and Paul Mendelssohn-Bartholdy, and from 1873 known as Aktiengesellschaft für Anilinfabrikation (AGFA). Richard Willstätter, "Zur Geschichte der AGFA," *Berichte der Deutschen Chemischen Gesellschaft* 64 (1931): 140-49.
15. From 1894 known as Leopold Cassella & Co., see Wetzel, *Naturwissenschaften und*

chemische Industrie, 55-56; and L.F. Haber, *The Chemical Industry During the Nineteenth Century. A Study of the Economic Aspect of Applied Chemistry in Europe and North America* (Oxford: Clarendon, 1958), 131.

16. From 1896 known as Chemische Fabriken vorm. Weiler-ter Meer. Wetzel, *Naturwissenschaften und chemische Industrie*, 60; Haber, *Chemical Industry During the Nineteenth Century*, 133-34; Wolfgang Scheinert, "Joseph Wilhelm Weiler, Julius Weiler und das Anilin. Zur Entwicklungsgeschichte der deutschen Teerfarbenindustrie und der chemischen Technik vor dem Ersten Weltkrieg," *Zeitschrift für Unternehmensgeschichte* 33 (1988): 217-31.
17. Pauli to Caro, 5 January 1867, DM NL93/7.
18. Following his return from France to Germany in 1865, Pauli joined a saltpetre factory in Ziegelhausen, and later took over this enterprise. In 1871 he co-founded Chemische Fabrik Rheinau of Mannheim, and in 1880 set up the sulphuric acid plant of Farbwerke Hoechst. H. Reisenegger, "Zu Dr. Paulis achtzigstem Geburtstag," *Chemiker-Zeitung* 40 (1916): 173.
19. Borscheid, *Naturwissenschaft, Staat und Industrie in Baden. 1848-1914*.
20. Though in later years Heidelberg would be reduced to little more than a degree factory, and lose its innovative status among the German universities. See Jeffrey A. Johnson, "Academic Self-Regulation and the Chemical Profession in Imperial Germany," *Minerva* 23 (1985): 241-71, on 243.
21. Rita Meyer, "Emil Erlenmeyer (1825-1909) als Chemietheoretiker und sein Beitrag zur Entwicklung der Strukturchemie" (Ph.D. diss., University of Munich, 1984).
22. Anthony S. Travis, "Heinrich Caro at Roberts, Dale & Co.," *Ambix* 38 (1991): 113-34, on 129-31.
23. The Manchester firm of Tudor Mabley handled Caro's patent applications in England, and Caro's account was settled by his relative, Jacob Behrens. DM NL93.
24. Kershaw & Bullock to Caro, 21 and 26 March 1867, DM NL93.
25. Lowe to Caro, 13 January 1868, DM HS 1977/32/201/4.
26. Frederick Crace(-)Calvert to Caro, 17 December 186(?), DM HS 1977/32/46.
27. Lowe to Caro, 6 March 1867, DM HS 1977/32/201/2.
28. Lowe to Caro, 1 April 1867, DM HS 1977/32/201/1.
29. Lowe to Caro, 1 April 1867, DM HS 1977/32/201/1.
30. Lowe to Caro, 13 January 1868, DM HS 1977/32/201/4.
31. Carl Glaser, "Erlebnisse und Erinnerungen nach meinem Eintritt in die Badische Anilin- & Soda-Fabrik im Jahre 1869," unpublished typescript, 1921, BASF Archives, W1 Glaser; Hans Schröter, *Friedrich Engelhorn. Ein Unternehmer-Portrait des 19. Jahrhunderts* (Landau: Pfälzische Verlagsanstalt, 1991); Gustaf Jacob, *Friedrich Engelhorn. Der Gründer der Badischen Anilin- & Soda-Fabrik* (Mannheim: Gesellschaft der Freunde Mannheims, 1959); Alfred von Nagel, *Fuchsin, Alizarin, Indigo. Der Beginn eines Weltunternehmens* (Ludwigshafen: BASF, 1968); Curt Schuster, *Vom Farbenhandel zur Farbenindustrie. Die erste Fusion der BASF* (Ludwigshafen: BASF, 1973); Gerhart Wolf, *BASF. Development of a World-Wide Enterprise* (Ludwigshafen: BASF, 1970); Lothar Meinzer, Karl Dettke, Jutta Kissener, and Klaus-Jürgen Matz, *125 Jahre BASF. Stationen ihrer Geschichte. Katalog zur Ausstellung im Rathaus-Center*

Ludwigshafen, 28. April bis 29. Juni 1990 (Ludwigshafen: BASF, 1990).

32. Wolfgang Zorn, "Clemm, Carl," in *Neue Deutsche Biographie*, ed. Historische Kommission bei der Bayerischen Akademie der Wissenschaften, 18 vols. (1954-97), vol. 3 (1957): 286-87.
33. Wolfgang Zorn, "Clemm, August," in *Neue Deutsche Biographie*, vol. 3 (1957), 285-86; Schröter, *Engelhorn*, 101.
34. Arne Andersen, *Historische Technikfolgenabschätzung am Beispiel des Metallhüttenwesens und der Chemieindustrie. 1850-1933* (Stuttgart: Steiner, 1996), 240-53.
35. Andersen, *Historische Technikfolgenabschätzung*, 245. Andersen here quotes from Emil Nesseler, "Vom Festungswerk zur modernen Industrie- und Handelsstadt," in *125 Jahre Rheinhafen Ludwigshafen* (Ludwigshafen, 1950), 29.
36. Wolfgang Pieper, "Seligmann Ladenburg als Finanzier der BASF," *Tradition* 12 (1967): 553-75; Jacob, *Engelhorn*, 44. A list of the first shareholders can be found in Schröter, *Engelhorn*, 110, 119.
37. Schreier and Wex, *Chronik der Hoechst AG*, 356; Homburg, "The Emergence of Research Laboratories in the Dyestuffs Industry," 105, table 2.
38. "Freud- und gewinnlose Nachahmungsindustrie." Heinrich Caro, "Über die Entwicklung der chemischen Industrie in Mannheim-Ludwigshafen," *Zeitschrift für Angewandte Chemie* 17 (1904): 1343-62, on 1351.
39. Anthony S. Travis, "Science's Powerful Companion. A. W. Hofmann's Investigation of Aniline Red and Its Derivatives," *British Journal for the History of Science* 25 (1992): 27-44, on 32, note 14. See Glaser, "Erinnerungen," 13.
40. Schröter, *Engelhorn*, 120; Nagel, *Fuchsin*, 14-18.
41. "Vertrag zwischen der BASF einerseits und Heinrich Keßler und der Firma Wirth & Co. in Frankfurt andererseits vom 21. März 1867." See related correspondence, all in BASF Archives, A/13.
42. Protocol of the 27th session of the administration council of BASF, Mannheim 27 March 1867, transcript in BASF Archives, C 11.
43. Contract between BASF and Jean Théodore Coupier, 8 January 1869, BASF Archives, A/13. See Travis, *Rainbow Makers*, 96-97.
44. Paul A. Zimmermann, *Über die Grenzen hinaus. Notizen zur industriellen Entwicklung im 19. Jahrhundert* (Ludwigshafen: BASF, 1971), 53.
45. Protocol of the 35th session of the administration council of BASF, Mannheim, 4 October 1868, BASF Archives, C 11. See also Anthony S. Travis, "Poisoned Groundwater and Contaminated Soil: The Tribulations and Trial of the First Major Manufacturer of Aniline Dyes in Basel," *Environmental History* 2 (1997): 343-65.
46. Glaser, "Erinnerungen," 19. On 1 November 1869, Félix Duprey signed a ten-year contract with BASF. He received a share of profits, and a special increment for improvements to existing manufacturing processes. Contract between Duprey and BASF, and Duprey to BASF, 20 February 1871, BASF Archives C 627/11. In 1882, Duprey was employed at the French branch of BASF in Neuville. He appears to have left BASF on 1 January 1883: Gustav Siegle to Glaser, 25 November 1882, and Glaser to management in Ludwigshafen, 1 December 1882, BASF Archives, I 1101/7, Alizarin.

47. An exception was the development of a new reduction method (zinc dust in alkaline solution) by August Clemm in 1868. Heinrich Caro, "Ueber die Entwickelung der Theerfarben-Industrie," *Berichte der Deutschen Chemischen Gesellschaft* 25 (1892): 955-1105, on 993, note 3.
48. Caro to management of BASF, 17 June 1867, BASF Archives, C 627/1.
49. Contract between Heinrich Caro and BASF, 14 October 1868, "Erinnerungen an Heinrich Caro," vol. 2, DM NL93/10. Transcribed in Evelyn Wiedenmann, "Die Konstruktion der richtigen Formel. Strukturaufklärung und Synthese des Indigblau, dargestellt an Hand des Briefwechsels Baeyer-Caro," 2 vols. (Ph.D. diss., Technical University of Munich, 1978), vol. 2, 292-93; see also contracts of August and Carl Clemm with BASF, 15 April 1865, BASF Archives, C 627/1.
50. "Herr H. Caro übernimmt vorzugsweise die Arbeiten im Laboratorium, welche sowohl in theoretischer als praktischer Beziehung nöthig sind—er verpflichtet sich aber auch zur Leitung einzelner Fabrikationszweige (besonders der Anilinbranche) soweit dies durch Reise- Todes- Krankheits- oder anderer störender Zwischenfälle zeitweise als geboten erscheint." Contract between Heinrich Caro and BASF, 14 October 1868, § 3, "Erinnerungen an Heinrich Caro," vol. 2, DM NL93/10. Transcribed in Wiedenmann, "Die Konstruktion der richtigen Formel," vol. 2, 292-93.
51. Glaser, "Erinnerungen," 34-35; Gustav Schultz and Paul Julius, *Tabellarische Übersicht über die künstlichen organischen Farbstoffe* (Berlin: R. Gaertner's Verlagsbuchhandlung, 1888), 4-5.
52. Caro, "Ueber die Entwickelung der Theerfarben-Industrie," 972-73; Ernest Ehrhardt, "Reminiscences of Dr. Caro," *Chemistry and Industry* 43 (1924): 561-65, on 563-64. For rejection of the Prussian patent application, see Caro to the Königlich [Preußisches] Ministerium für Handel, Gewerbe und öffentliche Arbeiten, 27 April 1869; and response from the Ministerium, 24 May 1869, BASF Archives, document volume, no. 35.
53. Supplement to the contracts of Carl Clemm, Caro, August Clemm, and Giese, approved at the session of the supervisory board of BASF on 4 July 1869, BASF Archives, C 627/1; Protocol of the session of the supervisory board of BASF, 4 July 1869, BASF Archives, C 11.
54. Heinrich Caro, laboratory notebook, "1870, London," BASF Archives, W1 Caro.
55. Just before joining BASF, Caro offered the results of his own investigations into the constitutions of rosaniline and rosolic acid to Rudolf Schmitt, who in collaboration with Hermann Kolbe had discovered the synthesis of rosolic acid from phenol, oxalic acid and sulphuric acid. Schmitt to Caro, 28 September 1868, DM NL93/7.
56. Elisabeth Vaupel, "Carl Graebe (1841-1927) – Leben, Werk und Wirken im Spiegel seines brieflichen Nachlasses" 2 vols. (Ph.D. diss., University of Munich, 1987), vol. 1, 204-17.
57. On 1 January 1873, Caro probably acquired shares to the nominal value of 40,000 marks. Undated note, DM NL93/2.
58. "Die Grundlage der vollkommenen Lösung der Aufgabe besteht für den Alizarinfabrikanten in zwei Punkten: 1.) möglichst vollkommene Producte 2.) möglichst billige Herstellung derselben. Was den ersten Punkt betrifft, so müssen

alle bei der Fabrikation von künstlichem Alizarin auftretenden Farbstoffe so rein als möglich dargestellt werden.... Mehr als 100 Chemiker (und nicht der schlechtesten Sorte) suchen sich den Rang abzulaufen und die ganze Entwicklung dieser Industrie steht geradezu ohne Beispiel da in den Leistungen, durch welche sie mit Hülfe der subtilsten chemischen Prozesse zum Ziele treibt." Engelhorn and A. Clemm to Pickhardt & Kuttroff, New York, 26 April 1876, BASF Archives, I 1101/7/4.

59. "Engelhorn gab mir immer die Lehre, wenn eine neue Einrichtung geschaffen wurde, stets daran zu denken, wie man das zwanzigfache Quantum bewältigen könnte, und stets im Auge zu behalten, das (sic) Alizarin ein Massenkonsumartikel sei, der waggonweise zum Versand käme. Nicht auf das reinste Produkt käme es dabei an, sondern auf das verhältnismäßig billigste; unser Bestreben müsse sein durch Produktion ungeheurer Mengen den Konsum an uns zu reissen...." Glaser, "Erinnerungen," 44.

60. See for example, Henry Roscoe's requests to Caro for technical and scientific information on alizarin during 1870-71. This was used by Roscoe for lecture purposes and in publication. Roscoe to Caro, correspondence dated 1870 and 1871, DM NL93.

61. Travis, *Rainbow Makers*, 174-86; Vaupel, "Graebe," vol. 1, 147-81.

62. Alan J. Rocke, "Hypothesis and Experiment in the Early Development of Kekulé's Benzene Theory," *Annals of Science* 42 (1985): 355-81; Rocke, "Kekulé's Benzene Theory and the Appraisal of Scientific Theories," in *Scrutinizing Science. Empirical Studies of Scientific Change,* eds. Arthur Donovan, Larry Laudan, and Rachel Laudan (Dordrecht: Kluwer, 1988), 145-61; John H. Wotiz, ed., *The Kekulé Riddle. A Challenge for Chemists and Psychologists* (Clearwater, Fla.: Cache River Press, 1993); Hans-Werner Schütt, "Der Wandel des Begriffes 'aromatisch' in der Chemie," in *Begriffswandel und Erkenntnisfortschritt in den Erfahrungswissenschaften,* eds. Friedrich Rapp and Hans-Werner Schütt (Berlin: Technical University of Berlin, 1987), 255-72, on 255.

63. Rocke, "Kekulé's Benzene Theory," 145.

64. Until 1888, the term "aromatic" was used only for compounds that included one benzene ring or fused benzene rings. In that year, Victor Meyer proposed use of the term for all compounds with typical aromatic properties, including compounds containing elements other than carbon in the aromatic ring.

65. , Rocke, "Hypothesis and Experiment"; Wotiz, *The Kekulé Riddle*; Aaron Ihde, *The Development of Modern Chemistry* (New York: Harper and Row, 1964; reprinted Dover, 1970), 310-17; James Riddick Partington, *A History of Chemistry*, 4 vols. (London: Macmillan, 1964), vol. 4, 802-05; Colin Archibald Russell, *The History of Valency* (Leicester: Leicester University Press, 1971), 242-57.

66. Anthony S. Travis, "Artificial Dyes in John Lightfoot's Broad Oak Laboratory," *Ambix* 42 (1995): 10-27.

67. F. W. Nottebohm, *Chronik der Königlichen Gewerbe-Akademie zu Berlin. Festschrift zur Feier des 50 jährigen Bestehens der Anstalt* (Berlin, 1871); Walter Ruske, "Zur Geschichte der technischen Chemie in Berlin," in *Wissenschaft und Gesellschaft. Beiträge zur Geschichte der Technischen Universität Berlin, 1879-1979*, ed. Reinhard Rürup, 2 vols. (Berlin: Springer, 1979), vol. 2, 153-76, on

164.

68. Vaupel, "Graebe," vol. 1, 127-28.
69. Meyer, "Emil Erlenmeyer".
70. Travis, *Rainbow Makers,* 166; Julius Wolff and Adolph Strecker, "Ueber die rothen Farbstoffe des Krapps," *Annalen der Chemie und Pharmacie* 75 (1850): 1-27; Adolph Strecker, "On the Red Colouring Matters of Madder," *Quarterly Journal of the Chemical Society* 3 (1850): 243-56.
71. Vaupel, "Graebe," vol. 1, 95-109.
72. Contract between BASF, Carl Graebe, and Carl Liebermann, Mannheim, 29 May 1869. BASF Archives, document volume, no. 1, fol. 38. Transcribed in Vaupel, "Graebe," vol. 1, 642-44.
73. Vaupel, "Graebe," vol. 1, 144-47.
74. August Bernthsen, "Heinrich Caro," *Berichte der Deutschen Chemischen Gesellschaft* 45 (1912): 1987-2042, on 2003; Adolphe Wurtz, "Transformation des Carbures Aromatiques en Phénols," *Comptes Rendus de l'Académie des Sciences* 64 (1867): 749-51; August Kekulé, "Sur quelques dérivés de la benzine," *Comptes Rendue des Académie des Sciences* 64 (1867): 752-55; Lucien Dusart, "Note pour servir à l'histoire des phénols," *Comptes Rendue des Académie des Sciences* 64 (1867): 859-61.
75. Liebermann to Caro, 19 November 1869, DM HS 2082, in Vaupel. "Graebe," vol. 2, 756-57.
76. Ehrhardt, "Reminiscences," 563.
77. Vaupel, "Graebe," vol. 1, 152-54.
78. BASF, Great Britain patent no. 1,936, 25 June 1869; William Perkin, Great Britain patent no. 1,948, 26 June 1869.
79. See Liebermann to Caro, 6 October 1869, DM HS 2079, and, undated, DM HS 2083; Liebermann to Engelhorn, 1 November 1869, DM HS 2080; Engelhorn and Caro to Liebermann, 5 November 1869, DM HS 2124. All transcribed in Vaupel, "Graebe," vol. 2, 747-53.
80. For contractual information, see Vaupel 1, 155-57, contract between Graebe, Liebermann, and BASF, 29 May 1869, supplement dated 19 September 1872, and contract between Graebe, Liebermann, and BASF, 20 February 1872, in Vaupel, "Graebe," 642-46. Vaupel cites correspondence stating that BASF was allowed to sell alizarin in Great Britain
81. Ehrhardt, "Reminiscences," 563; Bernthsen, "Heinrich Caro," 2003.
82. See Liebermann to Caro, 19 November 1869, DM HS 2082, in Vaupel. "Graebe," vol. 2, 756-57. Graebe and Liebermann claimed that they together with Caro achieved direct sulphonation of anthraquinone. This was based on their summary of the English patent of Caro, Graebe, and Liebermann, in Carl Graebe and Carl Liebermann, "Ueber Anthracenderivate," *Annalen der Chemie und Pharmacie* 160 (1871): 121-45, on 130. See also Heinrich Caro, Carl Graebe, and Carl Liebermann, "Ueber Fabrikation von künstlichem Alizarin (Englisches Patent datirt den 25. Juni 1869)," *Berichte der Deutschen Chemischen Gesellschaft* 3 (1870): 359-60.
83. Graebe to Liebermann, 30 July 1869, DM HS 1933/81/1/6, in Vaupel, "Graebe," vol. 2, 175.

84. A comprehensive account of this pathway to alizarin is given in Vaupel, "Graebe," vol. 1, 134-41.
85. Protocol of session of the administration council (Verwaltungsrat) of BASF, Mannheim, 4 July or 4 June 1869, transcript in BASF Archives, C 11.
86. Glaser, "Erinnerungen," 52.
87. Willem J. Hornix, "From Process to Plant. Innovation in the Early Artificial Dye Industry," *British Journal for the History of Science* 25 (1992): 65-90, on 78-84.
88. Glaser, "Erinnerungen," 40-41.
89. The following account is based on Glaser, "Erinnerungen." See also Hornix, "From Process to Plant," 86, note 56.
90. Thomas & Henry Metcalf, Miles Platting Chemical Works, Manchester, to Caro, 31 October 1869, DM NL93.
91. Travis, *Rainbow Makers*, 183, 187.
92. Glaser, "Erinnerungen," 42, and Hornix, "From Process to Plant," 84.
93. Travis, *Rainbow Makers*, 194, 199 f.
94. For a description of this process see BASF laboratory report, probably 1872, copy dated 15 August 1918, BASF Archives, D 02.3/5, no. 1a, pp. 6-12.
95. Hornix, "From Process to Plant," 78-80; Vaupel, "Graebe," vol. 1, 161-65, 169-71; Glaser, "Erinnerungen," 38-39, 50-52.
96. Travis, *Rainbow Makers*, 199-200.
97. Glaser, "Erinnerungen," 92-94.
98. BASF; Hoechst; Bayer; Neuhaus; Burt, Boulton & Haywood; Gauhe & Co.; Dr. C. Leverkus & Söhne; and J. Broenners Fabrik. Later Arzberger, Schöpff & Co. and Franz Rabeneck of Moscow joined the Alizarine Convention. Travis, *Rainbow Makers*, 209, and Harald Hückstädt, "100 Jahre synthetisches Alizarin," *Unser Werk* 12 (1969): 20-25, on 24; Carl Glaser, "Heinrich von Brunck," *Berichte der Deutschen Chemischen Gesellschaft* 46 (1913): 352-89, on 370.
99. Glaser, "Erinnerungen," 110 ff.
100. Glaser, "Erinnerungen," 89.
101. This section relies extensively on Vaupel, "Graebe."
102. " ... doch werden die Herren Graebe und Liebermann die Badische Anilin- & Soda-Fabrik gerne weiter mit ihrem Rath und Auskunft unterstützen." In "Uebereinkommen zwischen der Badischen Anilin- & Soda-Fabrik Ludwigshafen a.Rh. und den Herren Professor Dr. Liebermann in Berlin und Professor Dr. Graebe in Königsberg, Ludwigshafen Rh, Berlin und Königsberg am 26ten October 1876, § 4." In Vaupel, "Graebe," vol. 1, 647.
103. Vaupel, "Graebe," vol. 1, 358-74.
104. Vaupel, "Graebe," vol. 1, 233-46.
105. Carl Riedel, "Zur Kenntnis der Carbonsäuren des Chinolins und des Pyridins," *Berichte der Deutschen Chemischen Gesellschaft* 16 (1883): 1609-16.
106. Vaupel, "Graebe," vol. 1, 245, quoting a letter from Caro to Graebe dated 29 July 1883.
107. Vaupel, "Graebe," vol. 1, 222-32.
108. Carl Graebe, "Ueber Carbazol," *Annalen der Chemie und Pharmacie* 202 (1880): 19-31.

109. W. A. van Dorp, "Ueber eine neue Synthese des Anthracens," *Berichte der Deutschen Chemischen Gesellschaft* 5 (1872): 1070-72; A. Kekulé and A. Franchimont, "Ueber das Benzophenonchlorid und die Bildung von Antrachinon bei der Darstellung von Benzophenon," *Berichte der Deutschen Chemischen Gesellschaft* 5 (1872): 908-10.
110. Carl Graebe, "Ueber einen neuen dem Anthracen isomeren Kohlenwasserstoff," *Berichte der Deutschen Chemischen Gesellschaft* 5 (1872): 861-63; E. Ostermayer and Rudolph Fittig, "Ueber einen neuen Kohlenwasserstoff aus dem Steinkohlentheer," *Berichte der Deutschen Chemischen Gesellschaft* 5 (1872): 933-37; Rudolph Fittig, "Ueber Phenanthren und Anthracen," *Berichte der Deutschen Chemischen Gesellschaft* 6 (1873): 167-69. See also Vaupel, "Graebe," vol. 1, 246-54.
111. Arno Behr and W.A. van Dorp, "Überführung von β-Benzoylbenzoësäure in Anthrachinon," *Berichte der Deutschen Chemischen Gesellschaft* 7 (1874): 578.
112. Richard Meyer, "Die Phtaleine," *Die Naturwissenschaften* 3 (1915): 576-82.
113. Baeyer and Caro, "Synthese von Anthrachinonabkömmlingen aus Benzolderivaten und Phtalsäure," *Berichte der Deutschen Chemischen Gesellschaft* 7 (1874): 968, and *Berichte der Deutschen Chemischen Gesellschaft* 8 (1875): 152. In Adolf Baeyer, *Adolf von Baeyer's Gesammelte Werke*, 2 vols. (Braunschweig: Vieweg, 1905), vol. 1, 613-20, and 627-28.
114. Baeyer to Caro, 18 January, 5 February, 13 February, 8 March and 12 June 1874, DM HS 1570, 1571, 1572, 1575 and 1580, respectively, in Wiedenmann, "Die Konstruktion der richtigen Formel," vol. 2, 1-3, 7-9, 13-14.
115. Travis, *Rainbow Makers*, 253-54.
116. See for example Baeyer to Caro, 29 November 1874, DM HS 1588, in Wiedenmann, "Die Konstruktion der richtigen Formel," vol. 2, 24-25.
117. "Mit Alizarin sind wir noch immer nicht auf dem gewünschten Standpunkte, es wird aber fleißig daran gearbeitet u. wie mir Caro sagt, muß das Resultat der Laboratoriumsarbeiten sich günstig auf die Fabrikation auswirken, u. will ich mir den Tag doppelt roth im Kalender anstreichen, wenn wir sagen können, besser wie wir kann niemand Alizarin machen." Engelhorn to Gustav Siegle, 5 October 1875, BASF Archives, A 15/1.
118. Copy (28 June 1918) of report dated 2 August 1875, "Untersuchung von anthrachinosulfos. Natronsalzen," BASF Archives, D 02.3/5, no. 1c.
119. Copy (12 September 1918) of report dated 2 August 1875, "Flavopurpurin: Alizarin S aus Anthrachinonbisulfonsäure," BASF Archives, D 02.3/5, no. 1f.
120. Copy (13 September 1918) of report dated 1 December 1875, "Anthraflavinsäure," BASF Archives, D 02.3/5, no.1g. See Edward Schunck, *Chemical News* 23 (1871): 157.
121. Copy (26 June 1918) of report dated 4 November 1875, "Mononitroanthrachinon," BASF Archives, D 02.3/5, no. 1e.
122. Copy (13 August 1918) of report dated 15 March 1876, "Alizarinschwefelsäure," BASF Archives, D 02.3/5, no. 1n.
123. Robert Holdmann, copy (8 August 1918) of report dated 1 October 1876, "Alizarin aus Anthracensulfosäuren durch Oxydation," BASF Archives, D 02.3/5, no. 1u.

124. Holdmann, copy (12 September 1918) of report dated 1 December 1876, "Purpurin. Darstellung aus Alizarin u. Arsensäure," BASF Achives, D 02.3/5, no.1x.
125. August Burghard, copy (13 August 1918) of report dated 10 May 1876, "Trockenes Alizarin mit Färbefähigkeit," BASF Archives, D 02.3/5, no. 1 r.
126. Theodor Reissig, copy (5 August 1918) of untitled report dated 15 October 1876, BASF Archives, D 02.3/5, no. 1v.
127. See summary of session of the British Chemical Society, held on 4 June 1875 in *Berichte der Deutschen Chemischen Gesellschaft* 8 (1875): 780.
128. Daniel-Auguste Rosenstiehl, "L'alizarin nitrée," *Annales de chimie et de physique* (5th Ser.) 12 (1877): 519-29.
129. *Pli Cacheté* deposited with the Société Industrielle de Mulhouse, 22 March 1876, copy, dated 15 August 1918, held in BASF Archives, D 02.3/5, item no. 10; Caro, Great Britain patent no. 1,229, 22 March 1876; John H. Johnson, for Caro, United States patent no. 186,032, 1877.
130. The three assistants were August Burghard, Robert Holdmann, and Ernst Mylius. See research reports nos. 1 h, i, m, o, q, in BASF Archives, D 02.3/5.
131. Letter from Rosenstiehl to Caro, Mulhouse, 2 May 1877, DM NL93/7.
132. Carl Glaser, undated copy of report dated July 1878, "Bericht über die Darstellungen von künstlichem Alizarin nach den im Patent No. 4321 (datirt 4. April 1871) von Chs Graebe und Chs Liebermann beschriebenen Verfahren oder Methoden," BASF Archives, D 02.3/5, no. 1z.
133. Glaser, "Erinnerungen," 84-85.
134. Heinrich Caro, "Zur Erinnerung an Peter Griess," *Berichte der Deutschen Chemischen Gesellschaft* 24, Referate, Patente, Nekrologe (1891): i-xxxviii, on xxxiii.
135. August Wilhelm Hofmann, Emil Fischer, and Heinrich Caro, "Zur Erinnerung an Peter Griess," *Berichte der Deutschen Chemischen Gesellschaft* 24, Referate, Patente, Nekrologe (1891): 1007-78 and i-xxxviii (after 1078); H. Grossmann, "Peter Griess," in *Das Buch der großen Chemiker*, ed. Günther Bugge, 2 vols. (Berlin: Verlag Chemie, 1929, reprinted 1965), vol. 2, 217-28.
136. August Kekulé, "Beziehung zwischen den Diazoverbindungen und den Azoverbindungen, und Umwandlung des Diazoamidobenzols in Amido-azobenzol," *Zeitschrift für Chemie* N.F. 2 (1866): 689-93, reprinted in Richard Anschütz, *August Kekulé*, 2 vols. (Berlin: Verlag Chemie, 1929), vol. 2, 462-66, on 465: "Man kann in einer Diazo-amidoverbindung den einen oder den anderen Bestandtheil nach Willkür wechseln und dann durch Einwirkung eines entsprechenden Amidoderivates eine dem Amidoazobenzol ähnliche Verbindung darstellen."
137. August Kekulé and Coleman Hidegh, "Beiträge zur Kenntniß der Azoverbindungen," *Berichte der Deutschen Chemischen Gesellschaft* 3 (1870): 233-34, in Anschütz, *Kekulé*, vol. 2, 547-49.
138. "Mit der Bildung der Azoderivate aus Diazokörpern und Phenolen habe ich mich infolge unseres neulichen Gespräches auch beschäftigt. Man kann dieselben außerordentlich leicht durch Zusatz des Phenols zu salpetersaurem Diazobenzol und Neutralisiren mit Kali ganz rein erhalten. Ich habe so auch den Resorcinkörper als prachtvoll zinnoberrothe Nadeln bekommen. Wie steht es mit der weiteren Verfolgung

dieses umfangreichen Gebietes? Ich hatte vor, einen Praktikanten daran zu stellen, da Sie jetzt aber selber damit arbeiten, möchte ich Sie vorher über Ihre Wünsche in dieser Beziehung befragen." Baeyer to Caro, 17 November 1874, DM HS 1587. In Wiedenmann, "Die Konstruktion der richtigen Formel," vol. 2, 22-24, on 23.

139. Baeyer and C. Jaeger, "Ueber die Amide des Diazobenzols," *Berichte der Deutschen Chemischen Gesellschaft* 8 (1875): 148-51; in Baeyer, *Gesammelte Werke*, vol. 2, 1056-59. See Baeyer to Caro, 10 February 1875, in Wiedenmann, "Die Konstruktion der richtigen Formel," vol. 2, 43-44.

140. Otto N. Witt, "Das Chrysoidin und seine Umsetzungen," *Berichte* 10 (1877): 654-62, on 654-55.

141. Otto N. Witt, "Zur Kenntniss des Baues und der Bildung färbender Kohlenstoff-verbindungen," *Berichte der Deutschen Chemische Gesellschaft* 9 (1876): 522-27. For O. N. Witt (1853-1915), see E. Beckmann, *Berichte der Deutschen Chemischen Gesellschaft* 48 (1915): 736-39; and E. Noelting, *Berichte der Deutschen Chemischen Gesellschaft* 49 (1916): 1751-824.

142. Witt to Caro, 8 May 1876, DM NL93/8.

143. "Die Induline zwangen mich zur Darstellung von Diazoamido- und Amido-azokörpern–da lag das Chrysoidine nahe. Die weitere Ausarbeitung der unter gewöhnlichen Umständen nicht gerade glatten Reaction, die völlige Reindarstellung und Erkenntniss der rein gelben Nuance führten zur technischen Verwerthung." Witt to Caro, 7 June 1876, DM NL93/8.

144. Bernthsen, "Caro," 2012 ff.

145. A. W. Hofmann, "Zur Kenntniss des Chrysoidins," *Berichte der Deutschen Chemischen Gesellschaft* 10 (1877): 213-18, and A. W. Hofmann, "Noch ein Wort über das Chrysoidin," *Berichte der Deutschen Chemischen Gesellschaft* 10 (1877), 388-91. See also Willem J. Hornix, "August Wilhelm Hofmann and the Dyestuffs Industry," in *Die Allianz von Wissenschaft und Industrie. August Wilhelm Hofmann (1818-1892). Zeit, Werk, Wirkung*, eds. Christoph Meinel and Hartmut Scholz (Weinheim: VCH, 1992), 151-65, on 161-63.

146. "2476a. Chrysoidine, a new basic orange dye for silk, wool, cotton, leather, &c. Manufactured by the exhibitors. Williams, Thomas, and Dower. Chrysoidine, is, according to quality, the sulphate or hydrochloride [sulphonate or hydrochloride salt] of a new bi-acid base, belonging to the benzene series. It is a valuable orange-yellow, and owing to the readiness with which it crystallises, can be obtained in a state of perfect purity. Except phosphine [by-product of magenta manufacture], it is the only basic yellow dye known, and as it is the result of a direct process (not a secondary product) it can be obtained at a much lower price than phosphine, which it equals, and in some of its applications surpasses in strength and beauty of shade. It dyes in neutral or slightly basic baths, and has a great affinity for silk, wool and even unmordanted cotton. Mordanted cotton is dyed a yellow or orange shade according to the mordant employed. It combines readily with magenta and other red colours, giving rise to clear and beautiful scarlets. The chrysoidine was discovered quite recently in our laboratory by Dr. Otto N. Witt." From *Catalogue of the Special Loan Collection of Scientific Apparatus at the South Kensington Museum ,1876* (London: Eyre & Spottiswoode, for HMSO, 3rd. ed., 1877), 655.

147. "Die Zeit der Arcanisten ist vorüber. Wer in dem letzten Viertel des neunzehnten Jahrhunderts seinen Fachgenossen ein chemisches Räthsel aufgeben will, der muss sich schon darauf gefasst machen, dass dieses Räthsel früher oder später gerathen wird." August Wilhelm Hofmann, "Zur Kenntniss des Chrysoïdins," *Berichte der Deutschen Chemischen Gesellschaft* 10 (1877): 213-18.
148. Peter Griess, "Neue Untersuchungen über Diazoverbindungen, III. Mitteilung: Ueber Phenoldiazobenzol und diesem analoge Verbindungen," *Berichte der Deutschen Chemischen Gesellschaft* 9 (1876): 627-30.
149. Bernthsen, "Caro," 2014-16.
150. "Die Producte von Roussin waren dagegen Farbstoffsäuren von bahnbrechend 'neuem technischen Effect'. Sofort gaben sie sich als erfolgreiche Gegner der natürlichen Farbstoffe zu erkennen." Caro, "Ueber die Entwickelung der Theerfarben-Industrie," 1088.
151. Caro, "Ueber die Entwickelung der Theerfarbenindustrie," 1095.
152. Willem J. Hornix, "Azo-Dye Research 1877-1887: Patents, Products, Chemists, Companies," abstract in "XVIIIth International Congress of History of Science, 1-9 August 1989," eds. Fritz Krafft and Christoph J. Scriba (Hamburg/ Munich, 1989), no. H2/4.
153. A. W. Hofmann, "Ueber einen neuen Farbstoff," *Berichte der Deutschen Chemischen Gesellschaft* 10 (1877): 1378-81.
154. Schraube to Caro, 24 and 30 June 1877, DM NL93/7.
155. BASF, DRP no. 5,411, 12 March 1878, "Verfahren zur Darstellung rother und brauner Naphtalinfarbstoffe," in Friedlaender, *Fortschritte der Theerfarben-fabrikation*, vol. 1, 358-61, see also p. 344; Bernthsen, "Caro," 2017, note 6.
156. Victor Meyer to Caro, 13 July 1879, DM HS 1476.
157. "Es sind dies Vorgänge, welche die Statik des Moleküls nur angehen, und man könnte sich vielleicht (entre nous!) ein Bild oder eine Vorstellung hiervon machen, wenn man bedenkt, daß mit der Veränderung der im Innern des Moleküls gegen einander gravitierenden Atome auch der intra-atomistische [solle heissen inter-atomare] Abstand in der den Ausschlag gebenden Bindegruppe–die Gitteröffnung–sich verringern oder vergrößern muß. Und das ist wohlbekannt, wie man mit demselben Gewicht eine Öffnung, einen Spalt einmal schließen, das andere Mal öffnen kann, je nach der Construction dieser Öffnung, und je nach der Richtung in welcher die Kraft wirkt." Caro to Victor Meyer, 16 July 1879, Duisberg Papers, Bayer Archives.
158. See unpublished typescript "Ueber Phenolbidiazobenzol" in DM NL93/3. A summary is published in Carl Liebermann, "Correspondenzen. Die Chemie auf der Naturforscherversammlung in Munich, 1877," *Berichte der Deutschen Chemischen Gesellschaft* 10 (1877): 2230-31.
159. Caro, "Ueber die Entwickelung der Theerfarben-Industrie," 1093-95.
160. Paul A. Zimmermann, *Patentwesen in der Chemie. Ursprünge, Anfänge, Entwicklung* (Ludwigshafen: BASF, 1965), 44 ff.; Caro, "Ueber die Entwickelung der Theerfarbenindustrie," 1097-98.
161. Paul Böttiger, DRP, no. 28,753, 27 February 1884, "Verfahren zur Darstellung von Azofarbstoffen durch Combination von Tetrazodiphenylsalzen mit α- und

β-Naphtylamin oder deren Mono- und Disulfosäuren," in Friedlaender, *Fortschritte der Theerfarbenfabrikation*, vol. 1, 470-72.

162. Levinstein, "Proceedings of the Society. The First George Douglas Lecture," 270.
163. BASF, DRP no. 2,096, 16 December 1877, "Verfahren zur Darstellung der Sulfosäuren des Rosanilins," in Friedlaender, *Fortschritte der Theerfarbenfabrikation*, vol. 1, 108-10, 105-07.
164. Caro, "Ueber die Entwickelung der Theerfarben-Industrie," 1090-91.
165. BASF, DRP no. 10,785, 28 December 1879. BASF, DRP no. 10,785, 28 December 1879, "Verfahren zur Darstellung der Nitrosulfosäuren des Alphanaphtols und insbesondere zur Darstellung der Binitronaphtolsulfosäure," in Friedlaender, *Fortschritte der Theerfarbenfabrikation*, vol. 1, 327-30.
166. BASF, DRP no. 14,612, 22 February 1880, "Verfahren zur Umwandlung der Naphtole in ihre entsprechenden primären, secundären und tertiären Monamine," in Friedlaender, *Fortschritte der Theerfarbenfabrikation*, vol. 1, 411-13. Liebermann and Fr. Scheiding, "Ueber das isomere β-Naphtylamin," *Berichte der Deutschen Chemischen Gesellschaft* 8 (1875): 1108-10.
167. "Die Methode selbst aber verdankt ... ihren Ursprung einem jener gewagten Analogieschlüsse, welche den Empiriker meistens zu seinen überraschenden Entdeckungen führen." Caro, "Ueber die Entwickelung der Theerfarben-Industrie," 995.
168. Caro, "Griess," xxxi-xxxii.
169. Holdmann to Caro, 8 January 1887, BASF Archives, W1 Holdmann.
170. See Baeyer to Caro, 5 July, 12 July, and 14 July 1880, and copy of a letter from Baeyer to K. Oehler, 13 July 1880, DM HS 1704-06, in Wiedenmann, "Die Konstruktion der richtigen Formel," vol. 2, 180-84.
171. Carl Graebe, "Über die Reaktionsfähigkeit der Naphtole," *Berichte der Deutschen Chemischen Gesellschaft* 13 (1880): 1849-51.
172. Graebe to Caro, 8 October 1880, DM HS 2032, in Vaupel, "Graebe," vol. 2, 93-95, on 94. Caro did not object to Holdmann's name appearing in print.

Chapter 7

1. "Wie Vieles war von mir erfleht, aber nicht erreicht, wie Vieles von mir erlangt, mir aber wieder entrißen worden! Vor allem zeigte sich wieder die alte Frage: Warum mußte der damals so schöne und förderliche persönliche Verkehr mit Ihnen ein vorzeitiges Ende nehmen? Welche rauhe Hand hat das zarte Band zwischen Wissenschaft und Technik zu zerreißen vermocht?" Caro to Baeyer, 10 November 1902, DM HS 1802, quoted from Evelyn Wiedenmann, "Die Konstruktion der richtigen Formel. Strukturaufklärung und Synthese des Indigblau, dargestellt an Hand des Briefwechsels Baeyer-Caro," 2 vols. (Ph.D. diss., Technical University of Munich, 1978), vol. 2, 287-88, on 288.
2. Carsten Reinhardt, *Forschung in der chemischen Industrie. Die Entwicklung synthetischer Farbstoffe bei BASF und Hoechst. 1863-1914* (Freiberg: Technische Universität Bergakademie Freiberg, 1997), 330-34.
3. Elisabeth Vaupel, "Carl Graebe (1841-1927) – Leben, Werk und Wirken im Spiegel seines brieflichen Nachlasses," 2 vols. (Ph.D. diss., University of Munich, 1987).

vol. 1.

4. William H. Brock, *Justus von Liebig. The Chemical Gatekeeper* (Cambridge: Cambridge University Press, 1997).
5. Alan J. Rocke, *The Quiet Revolution. Hermann Kolbe and the Science of Organic Chemistry* (Berkeley: University of California Press, 1993).
6. Christoph Meinel and Hartmut Scholz, eds., *Die Allianz von Wissenschaft und Industrie. August Wilhelm Hofmann. 1818-1892. Zeit, Werk, Wirkung* (Weinheim: VCH, 1992).
7. For academic-industrial relationships that include BASF, see Peter Borscheid, *Naturwissenschaft, Staat und Industrie in Baden. 1848-1914* (Stuttgart: Klett, 1976), 111-57. The academic network connected to the pharmaceutical interests of Bayer, Hoechst, and Schering is described in Wolfgang Wimmer, "*Wir haben fast immer was Neues." Gesundheitswesen und Innovationen der Pharma-Industrie in Deutschland, 1880-1935* (Berlin: Duncker & Humblot, 1994). An excellent study of cooperation between the pharmacist and chemist Eugen Baumann and the Bayer company at the end of the 19th century is supplied by Beatrix Bäumer, *Von der physiologischen Chemie zur frühen biochemischen Arzneimittelforschung. Der Apotheker und Biochemiker Eugen Baumann (1846-1896) an den Universitäten Straßburg, Berlin, Freiburg und in der pharmazeutischen Industrie* (Stuttgart: Deutscher Apotheker Verlag, 1996). For academic-industrial collaboration in the United States pharmaceutical industry see John P. Swann, *Academic Scientists and the Pharmaceutical Industry. Cooperative Research in Twentieth-Century America* (Baltimore: Johns Hopkins University Press, 1988).
8. The best survey of Caro's relationships with academic chemists can be found in Curt Schuster, *Wissenschaft und Technik. Ihre Begegnung in der BASF während der ersten Jahrzehnte der Unternehmensgeschichte* (Ludwigshafen: BASF, 1976).
9. See Joseph S. Fruton, *Contrasts in Scientific Style. Research Groups in the Chemical and Biochemical Sciences.* (Philadelphia: American Philosophical Society, 1990), 118-62; Ruth Anne Gienapp, *Dictionary of Scientific Biography*, s.v. Adolf von Baeyer; Karl Schmorl, *Adolf von Baeyer* (Stuttgart: Wissenschaftliche Verlagsgesellschaft, 1952); and Richard Willstätter, *Aus meinem Leben. Von Arbeit, Muße und Freunden* (Weinheim: Verlag Chemie, 1949), 103-46.
10. For the University of Strasbourg see John E. Craig, *Scholarship and Nationbuilding. The Universities of Strasbourg and Alsatian Society 1870-1939* (Chicago: University of Chicago Press, 1984).
11. Caro, "Aus dem Briefwechsel mit Adolf v. Baeyer," undated manuscript, DM HS 1569.
12. See August Clemm to Caro, 30 April 1869, DM HS 1969, and Adolf Baeyer, "Über die Basen der Picolinreihe," *Berichte der Deutschen Chemischen Gesellschaft* 2 (1869): 398-400.
13. Adolf Baeyer, "Über die Verbindungen der Phtalsäure mit den Phenolen. Erste Abhandlung," *Annalen der Chemie* 183 (1876): 1 ff., reprinted in Adolf Baeyer, *Adolf von Baeyer*'s *Gesammelte Werke*, 2 vols. (Braunschweig: Vieweg, 1905), vol. 1, 637-86, on 638.

14. Heinrich Caro, "Ueber die Entwickelung der Theerfarben-Industrie," *Berichte der Deutschen Chemischen Gesellschaft* 25 (1892): 955-1105, on 1009 and Carl Glaser, "Erlebnisse und Erinnerungen nach meinem Eintritt in die Badische Anilin- & Soda-Fabrik im Jahre 1869," unpublished typescript, 1921, BASF Archives, W1 Glaser, 78.
15. Baeyer to Caro, 3 January 1875, DM HS 1590, in Wiedenmann, "Die Konstruktion der richtigen Formel," vol. 2, 26-27.
16. Caro, "Ueber die Entwickelung," 1049.
17. Adolf Baeyer, "Zur Geschichte des Eosins," *Berichte der Deutschen Chemischen Gesellschaft* 8 (1875): 146, in Baeyer, *Gesammelte Werke*, vol. 1, 626-27; E. Fischer, "Über Fluorescein und das Phtalein des Orcins," *Berichte der Deutschen Chemischen Gesellschaft* 7 (1874): 1211, in Baeyer, *Gesammelte Werke*, vol. 1, 621-25; A. W. Hofmann, "Ueber das Eosin," *Berichte der Deutschen Chemischen Gesellschaft* 8 (1875): 62-66. Robert Gnehm assumed that eosin belonged to the phthaleins: R. Gnehm, "Correspondenzen. Sitzungen der Chemischen Gesellschaft Zürich vom 2., 16. und 30. November 1874," *Berichte der Deutschen Chemischen Gesellschaft* 7 (1874): 1741-49, on 1743, note 1.
18. Adolf Baeyer, "Über die Verbindungen der Phtalsäure mit den Phenolen. Zweite Abhandlung, " *Annalen der Chemie* 202 (1880): 36 ff., in Baeyer, *Gesammelte Werke*, vol. 1, 712-83, on 712-20.
19. Reinhardt, *Forschung in der chemischen Industrie*, 340, 358-59.
20. Adolf Baeyer, "Über die Bildung von Nitrosokörpern," *Berichte der Deutschen Chemischen Gesellschaft* 2 (1869): 682, in Baeyer, *Gesammelte Werke*, vol. 2, 581-83.
21. "Ich habe diesen Gegenstand wegen Überhäufung mit anderen Arbeiten aber nicht weiter verfolgt, bis ich im Jahre 1874 durch H. Caro wieder darauf gebracht wurde, der mir ein Präparat von salzsaurem Nitrosodimethylanilin übergab, das er durch Einwirkung von Amylnitrit auf eine salzsaure Lösung von Dimethylanilin erhalten hatte." Baeyer, "Meine wissenschaftlichen Arbeiten in den Jahren 1865 bis 1905," in Baeyer, *Gesammelte Werke*, vol. 1, xxxiv.
22. Adolf Baeyer and Heinrich Caro, "Über die Einwirkung der salpetrigen Säure auf Dimethylanilin," *Berichte der Deutschen Chemischen Gesellschaft* 7 (1874): 809 ff., in Baeyer, *Gesammelte Werke*, vol. 2, 583-85; Baeyer to Caro, 30 May 1874, DM HS 1579, in Wiedenmann, "Die Konstruktion der richtigen Formel," vol. 2, 11-12.
23. "Überhaupt schwindelt mir manchmal der Kopf, wenn ich an das unübersehbare Gebiet denke, welches vor uns liegt." Baeyer to Caro, 17 November 1874, DM HS 1587, in Wiedenmann, "Die Konstruktion der richtigen Formel," vol. 2, 22-24, on 24.
24. Adolf Baeyer, et al., "Untersuchungen über die aromatischen Nitrososubstitutionsprodukte," *Berichte der Deutschen Chemischen Gesellschaft* 8 (1875): 614 ff., in Baeyer, *Gesammelte Werke*, vol. 2, 593-627.
25. "Einige Zeit nach Beginn meiner wissenschaftlichen Laufbahn bin ich auch in Berührung mit der Technik gekommen. Die ersten Techniker, die ich gesehen habe, waren die Herren Engelhorn, Clemm und Caro, die nach Berlin kamen, um mit

Gräbe und Liebermann über das Alizarin zu verhandeln. Ich staunte sie an, denn ich hatte in meinem Leben noch nie einen Techniker gesehen. In Straßburg war es dann Freund Caro, mit dem ich in intimen Verkehr kam, und mit dem zusammen ich eine große Anzahl von Arbeiten ausgeführt habe. Durch den Indigo wurde meine Freundschaft mit den Technikern noch inniger." "Vorfeier des 70. Geburtstages von Adolf von Baeyer," *Zeitschrift für Angewandte Chemie* 18 (1905): 1617-22, on 1620.

26. Baeyer to Caro, 2 February 1875, DM HS 1597, in Wiedenmann, "Die Konstruktion der richtigen Formel," vol. 2, 43.
27. Baeyer to Caro, 16 March 1877, DM HS 1631, in Wiedenmann, "Die Konstruktion der richtigen Formel," vol. 2, 89.
28. At the end of 1876, Caro and Baeyer worked on erythrosine, nitro-, amino- and oxyphthalic acid, coerulein and chrysaniline. Baeyer to Caro, 7 November 1876, DM HS 1625; and Baeyer to Caro, 4 December 1876, DM HS 1627, in Wiedenmann, "Die Konstruktion der richtigen Formel," vol. 2, 78-82.
29. Baeyer to Caro, 29 April 1874, DM HS 1578, in Wiedenmann, "Die Konstruktion der richtigen Formel," vol. 2, 11.
30. "Ich beabsichtige in dieser Woche die Resultate unserer Arbeiten zusammenzustellen und werde Ihnen das Manuskript baldmöglichst schicken ... und möchte Sie bitten, mir zu sagen, was ich über die Isomerie der Alizarine angeben kann oder ob ich diesen Punkt ganz weglassen soll." Baeyer to Caro, 12 June 1874, DM HS 1580, in Wiedenmann, "Die Konstruktion der richtigen Formel," vol. 2, 13-14, on 14.
31. See, for example, letter of 22 February 1877, DM HS 1629, in Wiedenmann, "Die Konstruktion der richtigen Formel," vol. 2, 84-87.
32. Baeyer to BASF, 13 May, 28 July and 23 October 1875, BASF Archives, W2 Baeyer. See also the correspondence of Baeyer with Caro, 25 May 1875, 11 July 1875, 28 July 1875, 13 October 1875, 3 and 24 November 1875, 11 December 1875, 9, 10 and 16 January 1876, 25 February 1876, 10 and 16 March 1876, 16 April 1876, DM HS 1602-1615, in Wiedenmann, "Die Konstruktion der richtigen Formel," vol. 2, 47-65.
33. "... alle von mir gemachten Beobachtungen, welche mir technisch verwerthbar erscheinen, der BASF zuerst mitzutheilen, diese (Vor) Mittheilung kann mit oder ohne Vorbehalt meinerseits geschehen. Erfolgt sie ohne Vorbehalt so geht sie in den Besitz der Fabrik über ... Im anderen Falle tritt die Fabrik nur dann in den Besitz der Erfindung, wenn eine Einigung betreffs der Nutzbetheiligung, der Entnahme von Patenten u. der Ertheilung von Licenzen erzielt worden ist." Baeyer to BASF (August Clemm), 13 May 1875, BASF Archives, W2 Baeyer.
34. "In Bezug auf die wissenschaftliche Publikation, würde ich in allen Fällen, wo entweder ein stillschweigendes od. bestimmt formulirtes Uebereinkommen stattgefunden nur im Einvernehmen mit der Fabrik vorgehen." Baeyer to BASF (August Clemm), 13 May 1875, BASF Archives, W2 Baeyer.
35. "Dies ist der Punkt, an dem ich Anstoß nehme und ich möchte Sie bitten in Erwägung ziehen zu wollen, ob es eine Form giebt, nach welcher mir in dem Falle einer unabhängig von der Fabrik gemachten Entdeckung die Möglichkeit gesichert

bleibt bei der Festsetzung der Bedingungen mitreden zu können. Indem ich schließlich den lebhaften Wunsch ausspreche, daß mein Verhältnis zu der Fabrik, welches für mich bisher ebenso angenehm als fördernd gewesen ist, durch diese Verhandlungen noch an Fruchtbarkeit für beide Theile gewinnen möge ..." Baeyer to BASF (Engelhorn), 28 July 1875, BASF Archives, W2 Baeyer.

36. Baeyer to BASF (Engelhorn and A. Clemm), 23 October 1875, BASF Archives, W2 Baeyer; BASF (Engelhorn and A. Clemm) to Baeyer, 4 November 1875, Private Archives of Alexander von Baeyer. The contract expired in 1878: Baeyer to Caro, 12 March 1880, DM HS 1683, in Wiedenmann, "Die Konstruktion der richtigen Formel," vol. 2, 151. See also Borscheid, *Naturwissenschaft, Staat und Industrie in Baden*, 148, and Curt Schuster, *Wissenschaft und Technik*, 55.
37. Reinhardt, *Forschung in der chemischen Industrie*, 196-212.
38. See Carsten Reinhardt, "Die Farbe Blau: Indigo," in *Ein blaues Wunder. Blaudruck in Europa und Japan*, ed. Hartmut Walravens (Berlin: Akademie Verlag, 1993), 14-24, on 17-18.
39. The name aniline was first given by Carl Julius Fritzsche. See James Riddick Partington, *A History of Chemistry*, 4 vols. (London: Macmillan, 1961-70), vol. 4, 183-84; Emil Ploss, "Indigo. Die merkwürdige Geschichte eines Namens," *Die BASF* 10 (1960): 85-91.
40. Partington, *A History of Chemistry*, vol. 4, 389, 397.
41. Baeyer, "Über die Reduktion aromatischer Verbindungen mittels Zinkstaub," *Annalen der Chemie* 140 (1866): 295, in Baeyer, *Gesammelte Werke*, vol. 1, 206-07.
42. "Wenn man das Indol auf synthetischem Wege darstellen will, so muß man nach obiger Formel in das Benzol eine zweigliederige Kohlenstoffkette und ein Stickstoffatom einführen und dann beide miteinander verbinden." Baeyer and A. Emmerling, "Synthese des Indols," *Berichte der Deutschen Chemischen Gesellschaft* 2 (1869): 679, in Baeyer, *Gesammelte Werke*, vol. 1, 209-11, on 209.
43. Laboratory notebook of Heinrich Caro, 1876-77, entry dated 8 March 1877, 31, BASF Archives, W1 Caro.
44. Baeyer to Caro, 16 March 1877, DM HS 1631, in Wiedenmann, "Die Konstruktion der richtigen Formel," vol. 2, 89.
45. Baeyer and Caro, "Indol aus Äthylanilin," *Berichte der Deutschen Chemischen Gesellschaft* 10 (1877): 692, in Baeyer, *Gesammelte Werke*, vol. 1, 217-18; "Über die Synthese des Indols aus Abkömmlingen des Anilins", *Berichte der Deutschen Chemischen Gesellschaft* 10 (1877): 1262 ff., in Baeyer, *Gesammelte Werke*, vol. 1, 218-20.
46. "An die Patentirung habe ich gar nicht gedacht, da der Preis des Indigblaus so niedrig ist ... Ich habe aber die Isatindarstellung gleich nach der Entdeckung in der Freude meines Herzens in der Akademie vorgetragen und habe auch kurz darauf das Manuscript nach Berlin geschickt. Es stand bei mir während der Arbeit fast wie ein Dogma, das kann nicht technisch verwerthbar werden.... Darüber wollen wir uns nicht ärgern, sondern lieber etwas Neues machen." Baeyer to Caro, 24 June 1878, DM HS 1662, in Wiedenmann, "Die Konstruktion der richtigen Formel," vol. 2, 121-23, on 122.

47. "Seit Weihnachten geht die Fabrik von neuen Sachen wieder besser und es ist besonders die Indigofrage in ein neues Stadium getreten. Sie brauchen zwar nicht zu erschrecken, der technische Indigo ist noch nicht da, aber wenigstens eine Methode, welche sich gewöhnlicher Hilfsmittel bedient. Ich bin nun noch im Zweifel, ob ich dieses schlank weg publiciren soll, oder ob ich ein Patent nehmen soll." Baeyer to Caro, 22 January 1880, DM HS 1679, in Wiedenmann, "Die Konstruktion der richtigen Formel," vol. 2, 145-46, on 145. See also "Zum 70. Geburtstage von Adolf von Baeyer," *Zeitschrift für Angewandte Chemie* 18 (1905): 1729-32, on 1731.
48. Contract between Baeyer and BASF, 16 March 1880, BASF Archives, I 1101/8, vol. 2.
49. Copy of letter from BASF management to Baeyer, 7 May 1880, BASF Archives, C 10, correspondence between Caro and the management of BASF.
50. BASF management to Caro, 7 May 1880, BASF Archives, C 10, correspondence between Caro and management of BASF.
51. See Anna Elisabeth Schreier and Manuela Wex, *Chronik der Hoechst Aktiengesellschaft, 1863-1988* (Frankfurt am Main: Hoechst, 1990), 26.
52. Baeyer to Caro, 30 June 1880, DM HS 1703, in Wiedenmann, "Die Konstruktion der richtigen Formel," vol. 2, 179-80; Baeyer to Caro, 17 August 1880, DM HS 1710, in Wiedenmann, "Die Konstruktion der richtigen Formel," vol. 2, 186-87.
53. See summary of indigo contracts drawn up by the BASF patent lawyer Max Hecht, 1890, BASF Archives, I 1101/10, vol. 2.
54. See summary in Paul Friedlaender, *Fortschritte der Theerfarbenfabrikation und verwandter Industriezweige*, 11 vols. (Berlin: Springer, 1888-1915), vol. 1, 124-26 and German patents of BASF: DRP no. 11,857, 19 March 1880, "Darstellung der Orthonitrozimmtsäure," in Friedlaender, *Fortschritte der Theerfarbenfabrikation*, vol. 1, 127-30; and no. 15,516, 6 February 1881, "Neuerungen im Verfahren zur Darstellung des künstlichen Indigos," in Friedlaender, vol. 1, 133-34; Caro's laboratory report for the period from 24 May to 24 July 1880, DM NL93/10/5; and Baeyer, "Über die Beziehungen der Zimtsäure zu der Indigogruppe," *Berichte der Deutschen Chemischen Gesellschaft* 13 (1880): 2254 ff., in Baeyer, *Gesammelte Werke*, vol. 1, 248-56.
55. BASF, DRP no. 17,467, 14 August 1880, "Neuerungen in dem Verfahren zur Darstellung von Zimmtsäure," in Friedlaender, *Fortschritte der Theerfarbenfabrikation*, vol. 1, 26-27. See also Caro to Schorlemmer, 22 February 1887, Geißler transcript, fol. 283-86.
56. Baeyer to Caro, 30 June 1880, DM HS 1703, in Wiedenmann, "Die Konstruktion der richtigen Formel," vol. 2, 179-80.
57. "Was meine Versuche und Arbeiten betrifft, so muß übrigens jetzt eine Änderung eintreten. Bei dem ewigen Herumprobiren geht so viel kostbare Zeit verloren und es ist besser, daß ich mit den zahlreichen mir zu Gebote stehenden Kräften jetzt an eine systematische Durcharbeitung gehe. Anfangs werden wir dadurch natürlich etwas langsamer vorrücken, haben aber den Vortheil uns auf bekanntem und gesicherten Boden zu bewegen." Baeyer to Caro, 11 November 1880, DM HS 1724, in Wiedenmann, "Die Konstruktion der richtigen Formel," vol. 2, 200-03, on 201.
58. Ernest F. Ehrhardt, "Reminiscences of Dr. Caro," *Chemistry and Industry* 43

(1924): 561-65, on 563.

59. H. E. Armstrong to Caro, 12 January 1881, DM HS 1977/32/5/1.
60. For Roscoe's letters to Caro, 12 January 1881 to 7 June 1882, concerning artificial indigo, see DM NL93. Roscoe, who was prominent in the founding of the Society of Chemical Industry in 1881, and was appointed its first president, in 1885 became a British Member of Parliament, representing the Liberal party. He continued to lecture on progress in the coal-tar dye industry, including in 1886 at the Royal Institution, London, for which Caro's assistance was once again requested. See Roscoe to Caro, 21 February 1886. DM NL93. For the founding of the Society of Chemical Industry see Anthony S. Travis, "The Meeting of Practical Men," *Chemistry and Industry*, 19 July 1990, 451-56.
61. Caro to Roscoe, 11 May 1881, Royal Society of Chemistry, Roscoe Papers.
62. Roscoe to Caro, 11 May 1881, DM NL93.
63. Roscoe to Caro, 16 May 1881, DM NL93.
64. Roscoe to Caro, 4 June 1881, DM NL93.
65. Caro to Roscoe, 12 June 1881, Royal Society of Chemistry, Roscoe Papers.
66. Caro to Roscoe, 10 December 1881, Royal Society of Chemistry, Roscoe Papers.
67. Adolf Baeyer and Viggo Drewsen, "Darstellung von Indigblau aus Orthonitrobenzaldehyd," *Berichte der Deutschen Chemischen Gesellschaft* 15 (1882): 2856 ff., in Baeyer, *Gesammelte Werke,* vol. 1, 305-12; Baeyer to Caro, 20 and 23 February 1882, DM HS 1765 and 1766, in Wiedenmann, "Die Konstruktion der richtigen Formel," vol. 2, 244-48.
68. Heinrich Brunck, "Die Entwickelungsgeschichte der Indigo-Fabrication," *Berichte der Deutschen Chemischen Gesellschaft* 33, III (1900): lxxi-lxxxvii, on lxxv.
69. Baeyer to Caro, 23 December 1905, DM NL93/10.
70. BASF, DRP no. 15,743, 20 February 1881, in Friedlaender, *Fortschritte der Theerfarbenfabrikation*, vol. 1, 60. See ibid., 52 f.
71. Baeyer to Caro, 6, 10, 13 and 14 January 1881, DM HS 1738, 1740, 1741 and 1742, in Wiedenmann, "Die Konstruktion der richtigen Formel," vol. 2, 213-19.
72. Baeyer to Caro, 29 May 1881, DM HS 1746, in Wiedenmann, "Die Konstruktion der richtigen Formel," vol. 2, 222-23, on 222. The publication Baeyer referred to is probably his "Über die Verbindungen der Indigogruppe. Erste Abhandlung," *Berichte der Deutschen Chemischen Gesellschaft* 14 (1881): 1741 ff., in Baeyer *Gesammelte Werke*, vol. 1, 257-62.
73. Baeyer to Caro, 3 August 1883, DM HS 1779, in Wiedenmann, "Die Konstruktion der richtigen Formel," vol. 2, 264; Adolf Baeyer, "Über die Verbindungen der Indigogruppe. Vierte Abhandlung," *Berichte der Deutschen Chemischen Gesellschaft* 16 (1883): 2188 ff., in Baeyer, *Gesammelte Werke*, vol. 1, 319-35.
74. Brock, *Justus von Liebig. The Chemical Gatekeeper*, 329.
75. Heinrich Brunck, "Die Entwickelungsgeschichte der Indigo-Fabrication," lxxii.
76. Ernest F. Ehrhardt, "The Influence of Patent Law on Chemical Industry," paper presented at the Seventh International Congress of Applied Chemistry, London, May 1909. Copy in BASF Archives, W1 Ehrhardt.
77. Vaupel, "Graebe," 204-17.
78. Vaupel, "Graebe," 209.

79. Baeyer to Caro, 2 April 1874, in Wiedenmann, "Die Konstruktion der richtigen Formel," vol. 2, 9-10.
80. Baeyer to Caro, 22 February 1878, in Wiedenmann, "Die Konstruktion der richtigen Formel," vol. 2, 84-85.
81. Graebe and Caro, "Ueber Rosolsäure," *Annalen der Chemie* 179 (1875): 184-203.
82. Vaupel, "Graebe," 197-203.
83. Eduard Farber, *Dictionary of Scientific Biography*, s.v. Emil Fischer; and Horst Remane, *Emil Fischer* (Leipzig: Teubner, 1984).
84. Obituary by Max Bodenstein in *Berichte der Deutschen Chemischen Gesellschaft* 65 A (1932): 78.
85. Emil Fischer to Caro, 3 May 1876, DM HS 1816. See also Vaupel, "Graebe," vol. 1, 212-13.
86. "Heute hat Fischer eine Entdeckung ersten Ranges gemacht, der Kohlenwasserstoff aus dem Rosanilin giebt beim Nitriren und Reduciren Leukanilin, durch Erhitzen in Rosanilin überführbar.... Die Tragweite dieser Entdeckung in technischer Beziehung ist wohl noch nicht zu übersehen, da man noch nicht weiß, ob und zu welchem Preise der Kohlenwasserstoff direkt darstellbar ist. Da man indessen heutzutage über eine so große Anzahl ausgezeichneter synthetischer Methoden gebietet, wäre die Lösung dieses Problems in technischer Beziehung immerhin denkbar und ich möchte Sie bitten mir Ihre Meinung darüber mitzutheilen.... Bitte theilen Sie diese für die Geschichte des Fuchsins so wichtige Entdeckung Herrn Engelhorn und Clemm zugleich mit meinen besten Empfehlungen mit, sonst wird es aber wohl gut sein die Sache vorläufig geheim zu halten." Baeyer to Caro, 19 December 1877, DM HS 1649, in Wiedenmann, "Die Konstruktion der richtigen Formel," vol. 2, 107-08. See also Schuster, *Wissenschaft und Technik*, 96.
87. Emil Fischer to Caro, 15 January 1878, DM HS 1814. See also Vaupel, "Graebe," vol. 1, 215.
88. "Ihre Versuche über diese Substanz sind weit mehr geeignet, jeden Zweifel über die Natur des Aurins zu beseitigen, als die von uns angestellten theoretischen Betrachtungen und die eben nicht ganz glatt verlaufene Umwandlung in den Kohlenwasserstoff ... Denn so drückend es auch für uns ist, Ihren Antheil an unseren Arbeiten verschweigen zu müssen, so wissen wir doch die Gründe, welche Sie dazu bestimmen, zu respectiren, und werden auch fernerhin in den Publikationen Alles sorgfältig vermeiden, was irgend Bezug auf Ihre Untersuchungen und überhaupt auf technische Zwecke hat. Unsere Arbeit verfolgt, wie ich Ihnen dies auch im vorigen Herbst versprach, ausschließlich reine wissenschaftliche Zwecke und mir würde nichts angenehmer sein, als wenn wir dieselbe mit einem beweisenden Experiment bezüglich der Rosanilinconstitution zum Abschluß bringen könnten. Eine weitere, erschöpfende Untersuchung der Rosanilinderivate würde meine Zeit und Arbeitskraft bei weitem übersteigen und ich kann zudem Ihrer Ansicht aus voller Überzeugung beipflichten, das solches von Anderen schon geschehen wird." Emil Fischer to Caro, 14 March 1878, DM HS 1816.
89. Caro and Graebe, "Ueber Rosolsäure und Rosanilin," *Berichte der Deutschen Chemischen Gesellschaft* 11 (1878): 1116-23.
90. Caro and Graebe, "Zur Kenntniss der Rosolsäuren," *Berichte der Deutschen*

Chemischen Gesellschaft 11 (1878): 1348-51.

91. Alfred Kern (1850-93) studied chemistry at Zurich Polytechnic and was employed at the Chemische Fabrik Karl Oehler in Offenbach from 1872 to 1878. From then until 1884 he was works manager of the aniline dye department at Bindschedler & Busch of Basle. After he left, patent rights for his discoveries remained the property of Bindschedler & Busch. In 1886, Kern and Edouard Sandoz founded Kern & Sandoz, later Sandoz AG. A biography of Kern and a description of his collaboration with Caro is to be found in Renate Riedl-Ehrenberg, *Alfred Kern (1850-1893), Edouard Sandoz (1853-1928). Gründer der Sandoz AG, Basel* (Basel/Zürich: Verein für wirtschaftshistorische Studien, 1986).

92. Contract between Bindschedler & Busch and BASF, Karlsruhe 11 May 1883, CIBA-Geigy AG, Archives, B&B, Pr 4.00.3.

93. Caro to Kern, 29 July 1885, Geißler transcript, fol. 138-152, quotation fol. 149.

94. Caro to Perkin, 10 April 1884, Geißler transcript, fol. 51-52.

95. BASF, DRP no. 29,060, 11 March 1884, "Verfahren zur Darstellung gelber, orangerother und brauner Farbstoffe, genannt Auramine," in Friedlaender, *Fortschritte der Theerfarbenfabrikation*, vol. 1, 99-101.

96. Caro to Knecht, 16 January 1886, Geißler transcript, fol. 195-97. See also Caro to Gnehm, undated (between 4 and 10 April 1884), Geißler transcript, fol. 49-50.

97. See Schuster, *Wissenschaft und Technik*; Reinhardt, *Forschung in der chemischen Industrie*, 101-38, 146-52.

98. Vaupel, "Graebe," vol. 1.

99. Carl Engler (1842-1925) was appointed professor of technical chemistry at Karlsruhe Polytechnic in 1876. His contacts with Caro were mainly in the field of methylene blue (Engler investigated a homologue of this important BASF dye, and its relationship to Caro's product, which was relevant to patent matters), and indigo (Engler in 1870 had synthesized traces of indigo, an observation that was not reproducable for a long time. He asked Caro for support with intermediates to prove the validity of his experiment.) Engler was an important consultant in patent affairs and the greater part of the correspondence deals with his reports. In 1903, Engler joined the supervisory board of BASF. In this position his influence was very valuable to BASF. He negotiated the contracts of the company with Fritz Haber and this collaboration brought about the famous ammonia synthesis. Engler's research interests were dye and petroleum chemistry, and in his later career he did research on pyridine derivatives and autooxidation. The correspondence between Caro and Engler is stored in DM HS 1977/32/90 and covers the years 1879-1907. See Schuster, *Wissenschaft und Technik*, 108-27; Fritz Haber, "Zum 80. Geburtstage von Carl Engler," *Chemiker-Zeitung* 46 (1922): 2-3; Karl Pfeiffer, "Carl Engler," in *Die Technische Hochschule Fridericiana Karlsruhe. Festschrift zur 125-Jahrfeier* (Karlsruhe, 1950), 40-45.

100. See chapter 6, and Schuster, *Wissenschaft und Technik*, 75-94.

101. Emilio Noelting (1851-1922) studied chemistry in Paris and Zurich, and received his doctorate in 1875. He worked in the silk-dyeing works of Renard, Viller & Bunaud in Lyon, and the dye works of Monnet & Co. in La Plaine near Geneva, where he concentrated on eosin and related dyestuffs, and discovered erythrosin, an iodine derivative of fluorescein (eosin is a bromine derivative). In 1880, Noelting became

director of the Ecole municipale de chimie industrielle in Mulhouse. His contact with Caro was of a more informal character, though he provided Caro with information on the application of eosin in France and the probable composition of the orange azo dyes of Poirrier, for which see Noelting to Caro, 14 August 1876, 22 March 1877, 28 April 1877, 21 June 1878, and 16 October 1878, DM NL93/6.

102. Skraup is known through a quinoline synthesis named after him, a reaction of great technical importance because quinoline is part of the quinine molecule. Skraup's synthesis was also important for the production of Thallin, an antipyretic, the only pharmaceutical that BASF produced in the 19th century. Carsten Reinhardt, "Vom Alizarinblau zum Thallin, Pharmazeutisch-chemische Forschung der BASF in den achtziger Jahren des 19. Jahrhunderts," in *Brückenschläge. 25 Jahre Lehrstuhl für Geschichte der exakten Wissenschaften und der Technik an der Technischen Universität Berlin. 1969-1994*, eds. Hans-Werner Schütt and Burghard Weiss (Berlin: Engel, 1995), 253-76.

103. Victor Meyer (1848-97) studied chemistry in Berlin and Heidelberg, and from 1868 to 1871 was with Adolf Baeyer at the Gewerbeakademie in Berlin. In 1871 Meyer became professor of organic chemistry at Stuttgart Polytechnic but after one year accepted a position as professor of chemistry at Zurich Polytechnic. In 1885 he moved to the University of Göttingen, and in 1888 became Robert Bunsen's successor at the University of Heidelberg. Meyer's research interests covered the whole field of organic chemistry. He became famous as a result of his work on the measurement of vapour densities and thus of molecular weights. Richard Meyer, *Victor Meyer. Leben und Wirken eines deutschen Chemikers und Naturforschers. 1848-1897* (Leipzig: Akademische Verlagsgesellschaft, 1917).

104. V. Meyer to Caro, 13 July 1879, DM HS 1476; R. Meyer, *Victor Meyer*, 116-17.

105. V. Meyer to Caro, 10 December 1880, DM HS 1478. This reaction was originally discovered by Hugo Schiff, and was used by Caro for the characterization of aldehydes. Meyer asked Caro for permission to cite the reaction in a publication. See R. Meyer, *Victor Meyer*, 129-30.

106. V. Meyer wrote to Baeyer on 27 July 1883: "Caro hat mir über 2000 kg Toluol auf Methylthiophen verarbeitet, so daß ich reichlich Arbeitsmaterial habe." Quoted in R. Meyer, *Victor Meyer*, 154.

107. V. Meyer to Caro, 22 and 29 November 1883, DM HS 1496 and 1497; R. Meyer, *V. Meyer*, 149-50.

108. V. Meyer to Caro, 24 July 1883, DM HS 1490. See also V. Meyer and M. T. Lecco, "Darstellung des Phenylhydrazins," *Berichte der Deutschen Chemischen Gesellschaft* 16 (1883): 2976.

109. R. Spagl, "Bernthsen, August," in *Neue Deutsche Biographie*, ed. Historische Kommission bei der Bayerischen Akademie der Wissenschaften (1954-97), 18 vols., vol. 2 (1954), 143; Ruth Anne Gienapp, *Dictionary of Scientific Biography*, s.v. Heinrich August Bernthsen; Karl Holdermann, "August Bernthsen zum Gedächtnis," *Zeitschrift für Angewandte Chemie* 45 (1932): 141-43; Paul Julius, "Zu August Bernthsens 70. Geburtstag," *Zeitschrift für Angewandte Chemie* 38 (1925): 737-39; August Bernthsen, *50 Jahre Tätigkeit in chemischer Wissenschaft und Industrie. Einige Lebenserinnerungen* (Heidelberg, 1925).

110. Bernthsen, *50 Jahre*, 29. As early as 1881, Bernthsen had a close connection to Caro through his investigations of *para*-coumaric acid. See Bernthsen to Caro, 15 May 1881, DM NL93/3.
111. Bernthsen to Caro, 13 November 1882, DM NL93/3.
112. August Bernthsen, "Studien in der Methylenblaugruppe," *Annalen der Chemie* 230 (1885): 73-211.
113. "Ich habe daher, sobald ich meiner Sache genügend sicher geworden war, mir die Frage der Patentirung überlegt, und, jedenfalls in Uebereinstimmung mit Ihnen, mir meinen Fund durch Patentanmeldung zu sichern gesucht. Unserer Verabredung gemäß werde ich denselben Ihrer geschätzten Fabrik nicht vorenthalten." Bernthsen to Caro, 30 May 1883, DM NL93/3. Bernthsen's patent was transferred to BASF. (DRP no. 25,150, 29 May 1883, "Verfahren zur Darstellung schwefelhaltiger Farbstoffe," in Friedlaender, *Fortschritte der Theerfarbenfabrikation*, vol. 1, 252-54.)
114. "Eine wissenschaftliche Untersuchung der auf Nitrosodimethylanilin bezüglichen neueren Patente habe ich bis jetzt nicht oder nur nebenbei in Angriff genommen ... Im Ganzen habe ich die Empfindung, daß die wissenschaftliche Ausbeute bei den betr. Untersuchungen im Vergleich zur Arbeit, welche sie verursachen, in keinem rechten Verhältnis steht ... In ähnlicher Weise lege ich für meine Person wenig Werth darauf, die Frage nach der Ueberführbarkeit des Lauth'schen Violett in Methylenblau weiter zu bearbeiten, zumal ich nicht weiß, ob sie publicationsfähig ist." Bernthsen to Caro, 19 July 1884, DM NL93/3.
115. "Ich erwähne bei dieser Gelegenheit, daß ich viel Wert darauf lege, Ihre bewährte Mitarbeit in der Zukunft durch fortlaufende, Sie gleichzeitig interessierende und nicht zu sehr von Ihren wissenschaftlichen Zielen ablenkende, Zwischenfragen zu einem für Sie und uns ersprießlichen Verkehr zu gestalten!" Caro to Bernthsen, 8 December 1884, Geißler transcript, fol. 77.
116. Bernthsen to Caro, 5 July 1885, DM NL93/3.
117. See for example Bernthsen to Caro, 24 April 1884, and enclosure accompanying Bernthsen to Caro, 19 July 1884, DM NL93/3.
118. Bernthsen to Caro, 19 July 1884, DM NL93/3; Caro to Bernthsen, 22 July 1884, Geißler transcript, fol. 59.
119. Bernthsen to Caro, 20 December 1885, DM NL93/3, and Caro to Bernthsen, 28 December 1885, Geißler transcript, fol. 189.
120. Caro recommended Paul Julius, who later joined BASF. See Caro to Julius, 12 February 1886, Geißler transcript, fol. 198-199; Bernthsen to Caro, 20 December 1885, DM NL93/3.
121. Paul A. Zimmermann, *Patentwesen in der Chemie. Ursprünge, Anfänge, Entwicklung* (Ludwigshafen: BASF, 1965), 39-43; and Arndt Fleischer, *Patentgesetzgebung und chemisch-pharmazeutische Industrie im deutschen Kaiserreich. 1871-1918* (Stuttgart: Deutscher Apotheker Verlag, 1984), 137-40.
122. See the Witt-Caro correspondence in DM NL93/8.
123. Swann, *Academic Scientists and the Pharmaceutical Industry*.
124. See note 7 above, Wetzel, *Naturwissenschaften und chemische Industrie*, 147-76; and Reinhardt, *Forschung in der chemischen Industrie*, 101-39, 268-84, 330-34.
125. See Reinhardt, *Forschung in der chemischen Industrie*, 268-84.

Chapter 8

1. Raphael Meldola, "The Scientific Development of the Coal-Tar Colour Industry," under "Abstracts from English and Foreign Journals. V. Coal-Tar Colours," *Journal of the Society of Dyers and Colourists* 2 (1886): 95-101, on 97.
2. Meldola, "The Scientific Development," 96.
3. John J. Beer, "Coal Tar Dye Manufacture and the Origins of the Modern Industrial Research Laboratory," *Isis* 49 (1958): 123-31; Georg Meyer-Thurow, "The Industrialization of Invention: A Case Study from the German Chemical Industry," *Isis* 73 (1982): 363-81; Ernst Homburg, "The Emergence of Research Laboratories in the Dyestuffs Industry, 1870-1900," *British Journal for the History of Science* 25 (1992): 91-111; Ulrich Marsch, "Strategies for Success: Research Organizations in German Chemical Companies and I.G. Farben Until 1936," *History and Technology* 12 (1995): 23-77; and Carsten Reinhardt, "Basic Research in Industry: Two Case Studies at I. G. Farbenindustrie AG in the 1920s and 1930s," in *Determinants in the Evolution of the European Chemical Industry. 1900-1939. New Technologies, Political Frameworks, Markets and Companies*, eds. Anthony S. Travis, Harm G. Schröter, Ernst Homburg, and Peter J. T. Morris (Dordrecht: Kluwer, 1998), 67-88. Note that Marsch and Reinhardt extend the story up to the era of I. G. Farben.
4. "Technische Erläuterungen," in "Beschreibung der geplanten Anlage für die Anilin- und Teerfarbenfabrikation," 27 June 1866, BASF Archives, document vol. 28.
5. Curt Schuster, *Vom Farbenhandel zur Farbenindustrie. Die erste Fusion der BASF.* (Ludwigshafen: BASF, 1973), 52-70.
6. Carsten Reinhardt, *Forschung in der chemischen Industrie. Die Entwicklung synthetischer Farbstoffe bei BASF und Hoechst. 1863 bis 1914* (Freiberg: Technische Universität Bergakademie Freiberg, 1997), 61-62, and references therein.
7. Contract between BASF (Rudolph Knosp, as president of the supervisory board) and Caro, 21 May 1874, bound with "Erinnerungen an Heinrich Caro," (hereafter "Erinnerungen"), vol. 2, DM NL 93/10, transcribed in Evelyn Wiedenmann, "Die Konstruktion der richtigen Formel. Strukturaufklärung und Synthese des Indigblau, dargestellt an Hand des Briefwechsels Baeyer-Caro," 2 vols. (Ph.D. diss., Technical University of Munich, 1978), vol. 2, 294.
8. Graebe to Liebermann, 2 April 1874, DM HS 1933/81/6/4, in Elisabeth Vaupel, "Carl Graebe (1841-1927) – Leben, Werk und Wirken im Spiegel seines brieflichen Nachlasses," 2 vols. (Ph.D. diss., University of Munich, 1987), vol. 2, 218-20.
9. Supplement to the contract of 21 May 1874 between BASF and Caro, 12 October 1874, "Erinnerungen," vol. 2, DM NL93/10, in Wiedenmann, "Die Konstruktion der richtigen Formel," vol. 2, 295.
10. Victor Meyer to Caro, 21 and 28 December 1875, DM HS 1469 and 1470; 5 and 10 February 1876, DM HS 1471/2 and 1471/3; Hugo Müller to Caro, 21 January 1876 DM HS 1471/1; and Wilhelm Weith to Caro, 3 March 1877, DM NL93/08.
11. August Bernthsen, "Heinrich Caro," *Berichte der Deutschen Chemischen Gesellschaft* 45 (1912): 1987-2042, on 2018, note 4.
12. Nickels to Caro, 22 September 1879, and 4 November 1879 (with attachments),

DM NL93. See also Anthony S. Travis, "Colour Makers and Consumers: Heinrich Caro's British Network," *Journal of the Society of Dyers and Colourists* 108 (1992): 311-16, on 315.

13. "Die Interpretation Ihrer Pflichten, welche Sie gegen das Geschäft der B. Anilin Sodafabrik zu erfüllen haben bleibt diejenige des bisherigen Vertrags und Nachtrags vom 12. October 1874. Alle Erfindungen, welche Sie während der Vertragsdauer machen und alle dafür genommenen Patente gehen sofort in den Besitz des Geschäfts über und sind von Ihnen zu diesem Zwecke [?] an dasselbe zu cediren. Zur Präcisierung Ihrer Stellung bemerke ich folgendes: Sie haben das Recht von allen geschäfthlichen Verhältnissen der B. Anilin Sodafabrik Einsicht zu nehmen; Sie haben die Pflicht, den rein chemischen Theil bis in die Details zu verfolgen und besonders in dieser Richtung zum Gedeihen des Geschäftes das Ihrige beizutragen." Supplement to contract between the supervisory board of BASF and Heinrich Caro (signed by Rudolph Knosp and Heinrich Caro), 6 February 1878, BASF Archives, C 627/1.
14. However, there is no indication that this happenend at the end of 1877, as Ernst Homburg suggests in his "The Emergence of Research Laboratories," 99. See also Griess to Caro, 18 November 1877, DM HS 1894; and Curt Schuster, *Wissenschaft und Technik. Ihre Begegnung in der BASF während der ersten Jahrzehnte der Unternehmensgeschichte* (Ludwigshafen: BASF, 1976), 85-87.
15. Salary lists (Salairkonto), 1873 to 1899, BASF Archives, C 652/1.
16. "Notes relating to Brooke, Simpson and Spiller's 1876 Price List," by H.W. Wilkinson, Zeneca Archives, DH 1732. Wilkinson was chief dyer at the firm from 1903 to 1905.
17. For the number of workers, see the statistical summary compiled in 1915, BASF Archives; for the chemists at BASF see statistical summary compiled in 1964, BASF Archives, C 623/3; for the number of chemists at the central research laboratory see salary lists, BASF Archives, C 652/1. Included in the latter are those chemists who were employed at the end of each year, the head of the laboratory, and the two non-academic members of the laboratory, Holdmann and Feez.
18. Homburg, "The Emergence of Research Laboratories," 93-94, 99.
19. See notebook "Chemiker der BASF", no. 11; and notebook of Eugen Mentha (hereafter "Mentha"), no. 9, both BASF Archives, C 623, and salary lists, BASF Archives, C 652/1. The notebook "Chemiker der BASF" gives autumn 1873 as the beginning of Wienand's employment, and spring 1874 as the end. Because the salary lists were continuously updated, and were related to a book-keeping function, we regard their information as reliable.
20. "Chemiker der BASF," no. 14.
21. Contract of Köhler with BASF, 18 April 1878, BASF Archives, C 627/2.
22. Reinhardt, *Forschung in der chemischen Industrie*, 95.
23. "Chemiker der BASF," no. 20, "Mentha," no. 19, and salary lists. See also contracts of Burghard with BASF, 1 January 1878, 18 May 1883, and biographical notes in BASF Archives, W1 Burghard.
24. "Chemiker der BASF," no. 24; "Mentha," no. 5; salary lists; Manuela Wex, "Edmund ter Meer," in *Neue Deutsche Biographie*, ed. Historische Kommission bei

der Bayerischen Akademie der Wissenschaften (1954-97), 18 vols., vol. 16 (1990), 605-06.

25. "Wie ich sehe, brauchen Sie einen jungen Chemiker, der gut, zuverlässig und sauber organisch arbeitet und dabei fügsam und gerne bereit ist, unter Ihrer Leitung und auf Ihre Anweisung zu arbeiten." Victor Meyer to Caro, 13 March 1875, DM HS 1466.
26. Biographical note, dated December 1958; Statement regarding the discovery of the conversion of naphthols into amino-derivatives, 8 January 1887, both BASF Archives, W1 Holdmann; laboratory notebooks of Holdmann, BASF Archives.
27. "Waaren-, Betriebs- und Fabrikationskonto," BASF Archives, T 01. There is no indication of the purposes to which these sums were put.
28. This approximation is based on several dyestuff production lists and research reports held in BASF Archives, I 01/2, I 005/2, I 12/A3; Gustav Schultz, *Farbstofftabellen* (Leipzig: Akademische Verlagsgesellschaft, 7th. ed., 1931) 2 vols.; and Paul Friedlaender, *Fortschritte der Theerfarbenfabrikation und verwandter Industriezweige* (Berlin: Springer, 1888).
29. Sources are "Chemiker der BASF" and "Mentha," both BASF Archives C 623; salary list BASF Archives, C 652/1. Paul Friedlaender and Albert Hehner were assistants of Adolf Baeyer in Ludwigshafen, and Hehner was later employed by BASF. For general biographical information see Reinhardt, *Forschung in der chemischen Industrie.*
30. Reinhardt, *Forschung in der chemischen Industrie*, 91-92, 228-36, 359, passim.
31. Reinhardt, *Forschung in der chemischen Industrie*, 282-84, 343-44, passim.
32. "Ich habe mein eigenes kleines, aber nettes Laboratorium und mit dem Fabrikbetrieb sonst nichts zu thun, vielmehr soll ich hier dasselbe Amt bekleiden, welches Sie in Ludwigshafen haben; das eines Erfinders!" Nietzki to Caro, 24 January 1879, DM NL93/6.
33. This approximation is based on several dyestuff production lists and research reports held in BASF Archives, I 01/2, I 005/2, I 12/A3; Schultz, *Farbstofftabellen*; and Friedlaender, *Fortschritte der Theerfarbenfabrikation.*
34. Organisational statutes of BASF, 31 December 1883, § 12, BASF Archives, C 10.
35. Carsten Reinhardt, "Vom Alizarinblau zum Thallin, Pharmazeutisch-chemische Forschung der BASF in den achtziger Jahren des 19. Jahrhunderts," in *Brückenschläge. 25 Jahre Lehrstuhl für Geschichte der exakten Wissenschaften und der Technik an der Technischen Universität Berlin. 1969-1994*, eds. Hans-Werner Schütt and Burghard Weiss (Berlin: Engel, 1995), 253-76.
36. "Von Ihrem liebenswürdigen Anerbieten vom vergangenen Sommer, mir beim Eintritt in die Technik behülflich sein zu wollen, Gebrauch machend, theile ich Ihnen mit, dass ich mich jetzt entschlossen habe, zu versuchen, ob ich in der Technik zu brauchen bin. Sie wissen, so gut wie ich, dass jetzt allmählich die Alkaloidfrage technisch zu werden beginnt und darin hoffe ich unter Umständen etwas leisten zu können. Wenigstens kenne ich das Gebiet gut." Eduard von Gerichten to Caro, 4 December 1882, DM HS 1977/32/115/1.
37. Siegle to Caro, 25 December 1882, DM NL93/8.
38. Eduard von Gerichten to Caro, 5. January 1883, DM HS 1977/32/115/2. See also Reinhardt, *Forschung in der chemischen Industrie*, 262-68.

39. Hermann Ost (1852-1931) studied chemistry at Göttingen and Leipzig, and received his Ph.D. in 1875. He received the *venia legendi* in 1879, and in 1884 became professor of organic and analytical chemistry at Hanover Polytechnic, where in 1887 he accepted the chair of technical chemistry.
40. Ost to Caro, 6 January [1884] and 13 January 1884, DM NL93/6.
41. Ost to Caro, 10 December 1884, DM NL93/6.
42. Caro to Ost, 11 December 1884, DM HS 6786.
43. Ost to Caro, 18 February 1885, DM NL93/6.
44. Emil Fischer to Caro, 28 May 1883, in Schuster, *Wissenschaft und Technik*, 99-103 (a facsimile of the letter is shown on 100-03); Emil Fischer, *Aus meinem Leben* (Berlin: Springer, 1922, reprinted 1987), 98-99; Siegle to Caro, Stuttgart 27 May 1883, DM NL93/8.
45. Fischer, *Aus meinem Leben*, 98-99.
46. Fischer, *Aus meinem Leben*, 98-99; Victor Meyer to Baeyer, 5 September and 30 October 1883, partially transcribed in Schuster, *Wissenschaft und Technik*, 98-106. See also Victor Meyer to Caro, 28 October 1883, DM HS 1494.
47. Caro to Engler, 4 December 1884, Geißler transcript, fol. 76; Brunck and Hanser to Caro, 23 January 1885, BASF Archives, C 10, correspondence between management of BASF and Caro.
48. Schuster, *Wissenschaft und Technik*, 93-94.
49. Memorandum from Glaser and Hanser to Caro, 1 September 1884; Richard Meyer to Caro, 6 September and 9 October 1884, DM NL93/6. For Richard Meyer's later work as a consultant for Hoechst see Reinhardt, *Forschung in der chemischen Industrie*, 270-72.
50. "Zu meinem größten Bedauern vernahm ich heute Ihre definitive Ablehnung der Ihnen angetragenen Stellung in unserem Geschäft. Ich hatte gehofft, an Ihnen einen treuen Collegen und Mitarbeiter zu gewinnen, und mit Ihnen gemeinsam die großen und schönen Aufgaben der Farbenpraxis zur Lösung zu führen. Natürlich kann ich jetzt nichts mehr an Ihren Entschlüßen ändern, und fürchte ich, daß Sie die Schwierigkeiten und Schattenseiten des praktischen Berufes mehr in das Auge gefaßt haben, als seine hohe Bedeutung und seine unvergleichlichen Vorzüge vor dem Lehrfach." Caro to O. Fischer, 4 February 1884, Geißler transcript, fol. 38-39.
51. Richard Anschütz and Carl Müller, "Zu Carl Glasers 85. Geburtstag," *Zeitschrift für Angewandte Chemie* 40 (1927): 273-81, on 280.
52. Caro to Knosp, 27 October 1884, Geißler transcript, fol. 67-68. See contract between BASF and Caro, 23 May 1885 and Knosp to Caro, 23 May 1885, DM NL93/10/2, also in Wiedenmann, " Die Konstruktion der richtigen Formel," vol. 2, 296 f., and summary of negotiations over 1885 contract with Caro, BASF Archives, C 627/1.
53. Caro to BASF management, 24 November 1885, Geißler transcript, fol. 182-85.
54. Caro to BASF management, 24 November 1885, Geißler transcript, fol. 182-85, on fol. 183.
55. Reinhardt, *Forschung in der chemischen Industrie*, 357.
56. Contract between BASF and A. Bernthsen, 21 July 1887, BASF Archives, W1 Bernthsen. See R. Spagl, "Heinrich August Bernthsen," *Neue Deutsche Biographie*

(1954), vol. 2, 143; Ruth Anne Gienapp, *Dictionary of Scientific Biography*, s.v. Heinrich August Bernthsen; Karl Holdermann, "August Bernthsen zum Gedächtnis," *Zeitschrift für Angewandte Chemie* 45 (1932), 141-43; Paul Julius, "Zu August Bernthsens 70. Geburtstag," *Zeitschrift für Angewandte Chemie* 38 (1925), 737-39; August Bernthsen, *50 Jahre Tätigkeit in chemischer Wissenschaft und Industrie. Einige Lebenserinnerungen* (Heidelberg, 1925).

57. Caro to BASF management, 6 July 1887, Geißler transcript, fol. 325.
58. Bernthsen, *50 Jahre*, 35-36.
59. Bernthsen, *50 Jahre*, 37.
60. Bernthsen, *50 Jahre*, 39.
61. See Caro to BASF management, June 1885, Geißler transcript, fol. 114.
62. Paul Julius, "Zu August Bernthsens 70. Geburtstag," 738.
63. "Ich würde also der Leiter der wissenschaftlich-chemischen Abtheilung des Hauptlaboratoriums werden und meine Instructionen von der Direction empfangen. Ich würde die von letzterer mir überwiesenen Themata, welche sich auf die Schaffung neuer oder auf die Verbesserung bestehender Fabrikationszweige beziehen, durcharbeiten zu lassen haben, die wissenschaftlichen Untersuchungen der Betriebslaboratorien auf Verlangen mit Rath und That zu fördern, die Arbeiten der Abtheilung für Patentwesen nach Maßgabe der Direction durch gutachtliche Äußerungen zu unterstützen, und mich aus eigener Initiative mit der Ermittelung neuer Fabrikationszweige und -methoden auf Grund der wissenschaftlichen und technischen Literatur zu befassen haben." Bernthsen to BASF management, 14 July 1887, BASF Archives, W1 Bernthsen.
64. Arthur G. Green, "The Reinstatement of the Dyestuff Industry in England," in "Science and Industry. The Organic Chemical Industry in England," supplement to *Manchester Guardian*, 30 June 1917, 16.
65. For biographical details see Reinhardt, *Forschung in der chemischen Industrie*, 337, 343.
66. Karl Holdermann, "Die Patentabteilung der BASF," unpublished typescript, BASF Archives; Karl Holdermann, "Der Bau C 13 im Wandel der Zeiten," *BASF Nachrichten* 6 (1955): 14.
67. Bernthsen, *50 Jahre*, 37.
68. An example is the naphthol yellow patent. See Caro to Otto N. Witt, 20 February 1886, Geißler transcript, fol. 203-06.
69. BASF, DRP no. 1,886, 15 December 1877, "Verfahren zur Darstellung blauer Farbstoffe aus Dimethylanilin und anderen tertiären aromatischen Monaminen," in Paul Friedlaender, *Fortschritte der Theerfarbenfabrikation und verwandter Industriezweige*, 11 vols. (Berlin: Springer, 1888-1915), vol. 1, 247-49, see also 243-46.
70. Bernthsen, "Caro," 2011.
71. Caro to Meldola, 8 June 1886, Newham, bound volume of correspondence, 33. See also Geißler transcript, fol. 86a.
72. Caro to Bösler, 9 February 1884, Geißler transcript, fol. 43-44. See also K. Oehler, DRP no. 24,125, 4 February 1882, "Verfahren zur Darstellung blauer schwefelhaltiger Farbstoffe," in Friedlaender, *Fortschritte der Theerfarbenfabrikation*, vol. 1, 249-50.

73. Karl Saftien, "Kekulé als Gutachter," *Die BASF* 15 (1965): 190-98, on 191-92.
74. Hoechst received 27 per cent, and Zimmer 18 per cent. The reasons for Zimmer's involvement are not known. Contract between BASF, Hoechst, and Georg Carl Zimmer (Mannheim), 1 August 1888, Hoechst Archives, "Auswärtige Mitarbeiter," C/1/2/a. For Zimmer see Caro, "Über die Entwicklung der chemischen Industrie in Mannheim-Ludwigshafen a. Rh.," *Zeitschrift für Angewandte Chemie* 17 (1904): 1343-62, on 1347.
75. Bernthsen, "Caro," 2035-36, note 3.
76. Caro to BASF management, 29 March 1886, BASF Archives, C 10, correspondence between management of BASF and Caro.
77. Caro to BASF management, 29 March 1886, BASF Archives, C 10, correspondence between management of BASF and Caro.
78. Caro to Witt, 20 February 1886, Geißler transcript, fol. 203-06.
79. Paul A. Zimmermann, *Patentwesen in der Chemie. Ursprünge, Anfänge, Entwicklung* (Ludwigshafen: BASF, 1965), 44-47; Arndt Fleischer, *Patentgesetzgebung und chemisch-pharmazeutische Industrie im deutschen Kaiserreich. 1871-1918* (Stuttgart: Deutscher Apotheker Verlag, 1984), 142-47.
80. According to the German patent law, the first person to register a patent was the holder. See the arguments of Caro in BASF memorandum of 17 April 1879, published in *Die Chemische Industrie* 2 (1879): 146-50, on 148.
81. Unpatented knowledge was, in all cases, kept secret, and the chemists involved were bound by strict contractual conditions concerning disclosure that extended beyond the end of their periods of engagement. This, however, was often a handicap when it came to cooperation with academic chemists, whose new knowledge was expected to be made public. Generally, academic chemists who collaborated with industry were willing to delay publication, but in some cases this discrepancy between the industrial and academic worlds gave rise to tensions.
82. Brunck and Glaser to Rudolph Knosp (president of the supervisory board of BASF), 14 October 1889, BASF Archives, "Direkte Korrespondenz der Direktion," fol. 3-6.
83. "... welche durch die ihnen obliegende Thätigkeit in unserem Geschäfte von den Patentfragen näher berührt werden." BASF management circular, 2 January 1890, BASF Archives, E 01/2.15; facsimile in appendix of Zimmermann, *Patentwesen in der Chemie.*
84. Brunck and Glaser to Knosp, 15 October 1889, BASF Archives, "Direkte Korrespondenz der Direktion," fol. 7-8.
85. Brunck and Glaser to Knosp, 4 January 1890, BASF Archives, "Direkte Korrespondenz der Direktion," fol. 23-26.
86. Knosp to Caro, 25 November 1889, in Wiedenmann, "Die Konstruktion der richtigen Formel," vol. 2, 298-99. See Brunck to Knosp, 11 November 1889, BASF Archives, "Direkte Korrespondenz der Direktion," fol. 9-12. Caro thought that the sum of 20,000 marks was insufficient as compensation for the requested work. In any case, he had the right to receive 10,000 marks per year during his "Karenzzeit" (the period when he was not allowed to join a rival company). See Knosp to Caro, 23 May 1885, DM NL93/10/2, also in Wiedenmann, "Die Konstruktion der richtigen Formel," vol. 2, 297. For a further 10,000 marks, Caro would be obliged to

establish a laboratory, to write reports, etc. However, though he complained that this sum would not cover the costs, he did undertake the work. See Brunck and Glaser to Knosp, 4 January 1890, BASF Archives, "Direkte Korrespondenz der Direktion," fol. 23-26.

87. BASF, DRP no. 81,042, 12 May 1894, "Verfahren zur Darstellung der Rhodaminfarbstoffe mittels Chloralhydrat," in Friedlaender, *Fortschritte der Theerfarbenfabrikation*, vol. 4, 177-79.
88. BASF, DRP no. 105,857, 2 June 1898 (not in Friedlaender); BASF, DRP no. 110,575, 2 June 1898, "Verfahren zur Darstellung von Nitroso- und Nitroverbindungen," in Friedlaender, *Fortschritte der Theerfarbenfabrikation*, vol. 5, 45-47. See also Bernthsen, "Caro," 2038.
89. Bernthsen to Kekulé, 3 January 1890, TH Darmstadt, Kekulé-papers.
90. "...die wissenschaftliche Seite des Geschäfts." Bernthsen to Kekulé, 30 October 1889, TH Darmstadt, Kekulé-papers.
91. Bernthsen to Kekulé, 30 October 1889, TH Darmstadt, Kekulé-papers.
92. "…meine Person wird insofern mit hinzugezogen, als die meisten Patentsachen vor der Ablieferung an Herrn Dr. Glaser von mir durchgesehen und geprüft werden sollen. Das bedeutet hoffentlich einen lebhafteren Antheil am Pulsschlag des Geschäfts." Bernthsen to Kekulé, 3 January 1890, TH Darmstadt, Kekulé-papers.
93. Paul Julius, "Zu August Bernthsens 70. Geburtstag," *Zeitschrift für Angewandte Chemie* 38 (1925): 737-39, on 738.
94. Bernthsen, *50 Jahre*, 41-42, 45.
95. Bernthsen, *50 Jahre*, 47, 51.
96. Arthur G. Green, *Manchester Chemistry and Chemists in the Nineties. The Second Ivan Levinstein Memorial Lecture. Manchester Chemical Club, 22 November 1938* (Manchester: Manchester Chemical Club, 1938), 3.
97. Green, *Manchester Chemistry and Chemists*, 3. For Clayton Aniline see E. N. Abrahart, *The Clayton Aniline Company Limited, 1876-1976.* (Manchester: Clayton Aniline Company Ltd, 1976.)

Chapter 9

1. Otto N. Witt, quoted by Ivan Levinstein, "Indigo and the Patent Laws," *Journal of the Society of Dyers and Colourists* 17 (1901): 28.
2. Herbert Levinstein, "Chemical Inventions with Special Reference to Chemical Patents," *Journal of the Society of Chemical Industry* 49 (1929): 980-87, on 986.
3. Walter M. Gardner, ed., *The British Coal Tar Industry: Its Origin, Development and Decline* (London: Williams & Norgate, 1915; reprinted New York: Arno, 1981). For recent studies on Britain's so-called decline, see David Edgerton, *Science, Technology and British Industrial "Decline," 1870-1970* (Cambridge: Cambridge University Press, 1996); Sidney Pollard, *Britain's Prime and Britain's Decline. The British Economy, 1870-1914* (London: Arnold, 1989); W. D. Rubinstein, *Capitalism, Culture, and Decline in Britain, 1750-1990* (London: Routledge, 1993); and M. J. Wiener, *English Culture and the Decline of the Industrial Spirit, 1850-1980* (Cambridge: Cambridge University Press, 1981). Wiener's thesis, which is based on attitudes at Oxford and Cambridge, has been

criticised by Michael Sanderson in his "The English Universities and the 'Industrial Spirit,' 1870-1914," *Historical Research* 61 (1988): 90-104. Sanderson demonstrates the strong links between English civic universities and industry in the 19th century, focusing on Henry Roscoe at Owens College (Victoria University), and Liverpool and Birmingham. For the dye industry, see Harm G. Schröter and Anthony S. Travis, "An Issue of Different Mentalities: National Approaches to the Development of the Chemical Industry in Britain and Germany before 1914," in *The Chemical Industry in Europe, 1850-1914: Industrial Growth, Pollution, and Professionalization*, eds. Ernst Homburg, Anthony S. Travis, and Harm G. Schröter (Dordrecht: Kluwer, 1998), 95-118; and Peter J. T. Morris and Anthony S. Travis, "The Chemical Society of London and the Dye Industry in the 1860s," *Ambix* 39 (1992): 117-26.

4. John J. Beer, *The Emergence of the German Dye Industry* (Urbana: University of Illinois Press, 1959; reprinted New York, 1981); Georg Meyer-Thurow, "The Industrialization of Invention: A Case Study from the German Chemical Industry," *Isis* 73 (1982): 363-81.
5. Caro to Meldola, 8 June 1886, Newham, Meldola correspondence volume, 33. Geißler fol. 232 (the complete letter is fol. 229-32), transcript on 86a.
6. Meldola to Caro, 19 June 1886, DM NL93.
7. Arndt Fleischer, *Patentgesetzgebung und chemisch-pharmazeutische Industrie im deutschen Kaiserreich. 1871-1918* (Stuttgart: Deutscher Apotheker Verlag, 1984), 99-101; "Protokoll der außerordentlichen Hauptversammlung des Vereins zur Wahrung der Interessen der chemischen Industrie, Berlin 19.20. April 1879," *Die Chemische Industrie* 2 (1879): 145-50; "Protokoll der IV. Hauptversammlung," *Die Chemische Industrie* 2 (1879): 305-09, on 308. See also Gustav Siegle to Caro, 1 February 1879, DM NL93/8.
8. "Zur Auslegung des deutschen Patentgesetzes," *Die Chemische Industrie* 9 (1886), 269-70.
9. Caro to Johnson, 8 November 1886, DM NL93.
10. "I have therefore translated some questions which I thought you should like to pass your opinion about at the proper quarter–and I shall feel happy to receive your replies and to communicate them to the Commission as emanating from a very high authority on all questions connected with the Patent-Law." Caro to Johnson, 8 November 1886, DM NL93. Johnson acknowledged receipt of Caro's letter on 11 November. Caro's list included Frederick Aston, Q.C.; John Henry Johnson, Sir Richard Webster, A.G.; Tudor Mabley (Caro's Manchester patent agent in the 1860s); and George B. Ellis.
11. See "Vereins-Angelegenheiten," *Die Chemische Industrie* 10 (1887): 377-415, on 385-91.
12. For Witt's criticisms of Caro's proposal, see *Die Chemische Industrie* 12 (1889): 391.
13. Review of Otto N. Witt, *Chemische Homologie und Isomerie in ihrem Einflusse auf Erfindungen aus dem Gebiete der organischen Chemie. Eine patentrechtliche Studie vom Standpunkte des Chemikers* (Berlin, 1889), in *Die Chemische Industrie* 12 (1889): 391-92.

14. Fleischer, *Patentgesetzgebung*, 138-40; see also Paul A. Zimmermann, *Patentwesen in der Chemie: Ursprünge, Anfänge, Entwicklung* (Ludwigshafen: BASF, 1965), 42-43.
15. "What interest the BASF had in Caro's last piece of work for them is hard to see." Thus commented Herbert Levinstein, who had taken over the Manchester-based dye-making business of his father, Ivan Levinstein, during World War I, in his 1949 Douglas Lecture before the Society of Dyers and Colourists. Herbert Levinstein, "Proceedings of the Society. The First George Douglas Lecture: George Douglas, His Times, and Some Thoughts on the Future," *Journal of the Society of Dyers and Colourists* 65 (1949): 272.
16. It also answers the question posed by the historian of Imperial Chemical Industries (ICI), W. J. Reader, as to "What lay behind this curious in-and-out episode?" W. J. Reader, *Imperial Chemical Industries: A History*, Vol. 1, *The Forerunners 1870-1926* (London: Oxford University Press, 1970), 262.
17. Fritz Stern, *Gold and Iron: Bismarck, Bleichröder, and the Building of the German Empire* (Harmondsworth: Peregrine/Penguin, 1987), note on 17-18.
18. Maurice R. Fox, *Dye-Makers of Great Britain, 1856-1976: A History of Chemists, Companies, Products and Changes* (Manchester: ICI, 1987), chapters I and II.
19. Anthony S. Travis, *The Rainbow Makers: The Origins of the Synthetic Dyestuffs Industry in Western Europe* (Bethlehem, Pa.: Lehigh University Press, 1993), 131-34.
20. "Laborjournal Heinrich Caro 1876-77." This includes, in page order, experiments on indigo carmin, salicaldehyde, dyes from Nencki, Dimethylanilin-Phthaleine from Dr. Fischer, Amido-Dimethylanilin (the 4-amino compound of *N,N*-dimethylaniline that was converted into methylene blue), Bayer & Co. dyes (commencing 26 February 1877), then Meister, Lucius & Brüning (Hoechst) products, Indigopurpur, Luticiene of A. Poirrier, corralline, methylene blue, blue dye of azonaphthalene of Petersen, several azo dye experiments connected with Griess, Bromgallein, Bromocoerulein, and eosin of oxyphthalic acid from Baeyer (connected with letters of 3 and 12 May 1877), Phenaline, and other products, including azo dyes, methylene blue, and [Roussin's] Orange II.
21. Heinrich Caro, Great Britain patent no. 786 of February 1878, and BASF DRP no. 5,411 of 12 March 1878. For a comprehensive early history of azo dyes, see Heinrich Caro, "Ueber die Entwickelung der Theerfarben-Industrie," *Berichte der Deutschen Chemischen Gesellschaft* 25 (1892): 955-1105.
22. John Cutler, ed., *Reports of Patent Cases Decided by Courts of Law in the United Kingdom* (London: The Patent Office), 2 (1886): 73-118, on 98-101. Trial dates covered in this volume are 19, 20, 22, 24-27, and 29 November 1884, 1 and 8 December 1884, 18 and 21 March 1885, and 3 July 1885 (Court of Appeal, before Lords Justices Baggallay, Bowen and Frey).
23. Cutler, ed., *Reports of Patent Cases*, 98-101.
24. Cutler, ed., *Reports of Patent Cases*, 112.
25. Herbert Levinstein, "Proceedings of the Society. The First George Douglas Lecture," 272.
26. Green, in discussion following Ernest F. Ehrhardt, "Reminiscences of Dr. Caro,"

Chemistry and Industry 43 (1924): 561-65, on 564.

27. Ehrhardt, "Reminiscences of Dr. Caro," 562.
28. Ehrhardt, "Reminiscences of Dr. Caro," 562.
29. Armstrong to Caro, 9 June (1883 or 1884), DM HS 1977/32/6/12. On notepaper of London Institution, Finsbury, which Armstrong left in 1885.
30. Ehrhardt, "Reminiscences of Dr. Caro," 562-63.
31. "From my experiments on a small scale I had no practical doubt that even the 80% acid could without difficulty be used in working on the large scale, but I am glad to hear that you have been so successful. I am afraid that the facts you mention cannot now be made public; and even if they were the Court would would take no note of them. It might even be treated as contempt of court if we were to say anything publicly until Judgement is delivered." Armstrong to Caro, 6 April ?, DM HS 1977/32/6/11. Probably 1883 or 1884. On notepaper of London Institution, Finsbury. On another occasion, and while on a visit to mainland Europe, including to the Caro household, Armstrong advised Caro: "I was detained longer than I expected so did not venture to come again to your works. As I have said if you think it will be of any service to you, I shall be glad to examine the sulpho-acids formed by Process I and to point out as soon as occasion offers that not only the 80% acid but even the 100%, can be used on the large scale without danger to life and with advantage. You will no doubt afford me the necessary material at the proper time. It has given me great pleasure again to visit Mannheim and I shall look forward to the next occasion of seeing you whether here or elsewhere. Thanking you and Mrs. Caro for your great kindness." Armstrong to Caro, undated, DM HS 1977/32/6/14.
32. Max Wyler, "Ivan Levinstein: What I Know of Him," The First Ivan Levinstein Memorial Lecture, The Manchester Chemical Club, 5 October 1937, 8-9, and reproduced in *Journal of the Society of Dyers and Colourists* 55 (1939): 142-46. Wyler's account is probably confused by his impression of the Vidal Black case fought by Henri Raymond Vidal against Levinstein and Read Holliday during 1910-12. See Fox, *Dye-Makers of Great Britain*, 38-39. Wyler, who studied under Heumann in Zurich, worked at Bindschedler & Busch, and Cassella before joining Levinstein in 1907.
33. Ivan Levinstein, "The Development and Present State of the Alizarin Industry," *Journal of the Society of Chemical Industry* 2 (1883): 213-27, on 214.
34. Fox, *Dye-Makers of Great Britain*, 18-20; See Zimmermann, *Patentwesen in der Chemie*, 74-77.
35. Fox, *Dye-Makers of Great Britain*, 8-20, 23.
36. Johnson to Caro, 25 November 1885, DM NL93.
37. Johnson to Caro, 11 November 1886, DM NL93.
38. John Cutler, ed., *Reports of Patent, Design and Trade Mark Cases Decided by Courts of Law in the United Kingdom*, 4 (1888): 449-71. Trial dates 31 January, 1, 3, 4, 7, 8, 10, 11, and 14 February, 26 July (in the House of Lords, before the Lord Chancellor, Lord Herschel, and Lord Macnaughten), and 1 November 1887 (High Court of Justice, Chancery Division, before Mr. Justice Chitty). See also Zimmermann, *Patentwesen in der Chemie*, 74-76.
39. Fox, *Dye-Makers of Great Britain*, 20

40. Armstrong to Caro, 27 October 1888, DM HS 1977/32/6/4.
41. BASF, DRP no. 10,785 of 28 December 1879.
42. Zimmermann, *Patentwesen in der Chemie*, 114-15.
43. Leonhardt was mentioned in connection with naphthol yellow, and Geigy of Basle in connection with methylene blue and auramine.
44. Levinstein's patents for nitroso-α-naphthol mono- and disulphonic acids, Great Britain no. 5,692 of 30 November 1882, United States no. 289,543 of 4 December 1883.
45. This is an excellent example of the tension between private and public knowledge, especially at critical moments in the history of a company.
46. Cutler, ed., *Reports of Patent, Design and Trade Mark Cases*, vol. 6 (1890): 387-96. Trial dates 27, 28, and 29 May, and 27 June 1889 (High Court of Justice, Queen's Bench Division, before Mr. Justice Charles). The action was commenced against four Dawson brothers, but proceedings were discontinued against all except John. The defendant did not bring forward witnesses.
47. Ernest F. Ehrhardt, "Badische v. Dawson," statement of the case dated 20 May 1889. Management correspondence, BASF-Heinrich Caro, 1878-1908, BASF Archives, C10.
48. Caro, Royal Hotel Blackfriars, to Mrs. Meldola, 24 May 1889, Newham, Meldola correspondence volume, on 33.
49. Theodore Aston & Co., Lincoln's Inn, London, from Royal Courts of Justice, to Caro, 26 May 1889, DM NL93.
50. Levinstein to Caro, 17 June 1889, DM HS 1977/32/191/3; trans. from the German.
51. Levinstein to Caro, 1889, DM HS 1977/32/191/5; trans. from the German.
52. Erik Verg, Gottfried Plumpe, and Heinz Schultheis, *Milestones: The Bayer Story, 1863-1988* (Leverkusen: Bayer, 1988), 74-79.
53. Henk van den Belt and Arie Rip, "The Nelson-Winter-Dosi Model and Synthetic Dye Chemistry," in *The Social Construction of Technological Systems*, eds. Wiebe E. Bijker, Thomas P. Hughes, and Trevor Pinch (Cambridge, Mass.: MIT Press, 1987), 135-58.
54. Verg, et al., *Milestones*, 118-20.
55. "Gutachten von Herrn Dr. Caro i.S. [in Sachen] Congoroth [n.d., 1888-89]." Copy in BASF Archives, W1 Caro.
56. Witt, *Chemische Homologie und Isomerie.*
57. This was in keeping with Caro's considerable admiration for the United States patent system, which gave the product precedence over the process.
58. Zimmermann, *Patentwesen in der Chemie*, 45, based on August Bernthsen, "Heinrich Caro," *Berichte der Deutschen Chemischen Gesellschaft* 45 (1912): 1987-2042, on 2037. See also Carl Duisberg, "Heinrich Caro," *Zeitschrift für Angewandte Chemie* 23 (1911): 1057-58.
59. Carl Duisberg, *Meine Lebenserinnerungen* (Leipzig, 1933), 44.
60. Fleischer, *Patentgesetzgebung*, 142-47.
61. *Die Chemische Industrie* 12 (1889): 235-36.
62. Many questions related to patents in Germany and England remained unresolved. Witt supported the concept of "equivalence," that is, one process from which may

be obtained many products. This was strongly debated in both countries, particularly during the 1890s. On 3 January 1892, George Beloe Ellis sent Caro a copy of his paper on the subject of equivalence that he had read before the Patent Institute. Ellis to Caro, 3 January 1892, DM NL93. On 8 March, Ellis advised Caro: "You probably gathered that the paper on Equivalents was written to promote a discussion; and it is very good of you to have written me such a long letter on the subject. The Secretary of our Patent Institute finds difficulty in obtaining papers on Patent matters and I try to help him out of his difficulty." Ellis to Caro, 8 March 1892, DM NL93.

63. Levinstein to Caro, 5 July 1889, DM HS 1977/32/191/2; trans. from the German. These are the patents listed in Friedlaender, vol. 1, 460, covering red dyes from benzidine and tolidine in combination with the sulphonic acids of naphthylamine. Only one patent is missing, DRP no. 41,362. Nearly all are addition patents (Zusatzpatente) to the original Congo red patent, and, except for 42,021, which was filed by Bayer, are AGFA patents.
64. Levinstein to Caro, 28 July 1889, DM HS1977/32/191/4; trans. from the German.
65. Travis, *Rainbow Makers*, chapter 5.
66. The same as DRP no. 54,599 of 22 March 1889. The inventor was Georg Körner, a works chemist, formerly in Conrad Schraube's aniline laboratory, and in Caro's laboratory. BASF became considerably involved in the direct azo dye business after Caro left the firm, especially following the discovery of J-acid by Paul Julius in 1892. See Carsten Reinhardt, *Forschung in der chemischen Industrie. Die Entwicklung synthetischer Farbstoffe bei BASF und Hoechst. 1863-1914* (Freiberg: Technische Universität Bergakademie Freiberg, 1997), 230, 350, 168-74.
67. Fox, *Dye-Makers of Great Britain*, 31. Ivan Levinstein, "Sectional Committees of Chambers of Commerce," *Journal of the Society of Chemical Industry* 8 (1889): 962-65.
68. "The Law of Patents: Suggested Amendments," *Journal of the Society of Chemical Industry* 8 (1890): 676-77, on 676. See also "Manchester Section," *Journal of the Society of Chemical Industry* 9 (1890): 1100-01.
69. "In Frage treten die besten natürlichen Bedingungen für Production und Absatz. In erster Linie entscheidet die Entwickelung der chemischen Grossindustrie und der Verkehrsverhältnisse. Man kann sich nicht dem Eindruck verschliessen, dass auch im Ausland, und namentlich in England, ein weiterer Fortschritt in dieser Richtung sich zu Ungunsten der deutschen Zwischenproducten-Industrie vollziehen wird." Caro, "Ueber die Entwickelung," 1016.
70. Fox, *Dye-Makers of Great Britain,* 20.
71. "Sectional Committees of the Chambers of Commerce, December 1889," *Journal of the Society of Chemical Industry* 7 (1889): 962-65, esp. 963-64.
72. Arthur G. Green, *Manchester Chemistry and Chemists in the Nineties. The Second Ivan Levinstein Memorial Lecture, The Manchester Chemical Club, 22 November 1938* (Manchester: Manchester Chemical Club, 1938), 7.
73. Caro to Levinstein, 16 January 1890, Geißler transcript, 150; trans. from the German.
74. Levinstein to Caro, 29 January 1890, DM HS 1977/32/191/6; trans. from the

German.

75. Caro to Levinstein, 4 February 1890. Geißler transcript, 151; trans. from the German.

76. Karl Saftien, "Kekulé als Gutacher," *Die BASF* 15 (1965): 190-98, on 192 and 196. See also Caro's report, DM HS 2362, and Baeyer's report, 23 April 1893, DM HS 2255.

77. Ivan Levinstein, "President's Address: Education and Legislation: The Influence of Trade and Industry," *Journal of the Society of Chemical Industry* 21 (1902): 893-99.

78. In April 1897, Levinstein was a member of a deputation to the Board of Trade that called for an amendment to the compulsory working clause of the patent law. That not every British expert in patent matters considered this to be a genuine impediment is indicated by F. W. Golby, "The Patent Law," *Times*, 18 September 1897, 12. Golby, who observed that a British inventor could also take advantage of this clause, was responding to "The Patent Law (From a Correspondent)," *Times*, 10 September 1897, 9, where, incidentally, it was stated "By the German law an inventor is bound within three years to put an invention to practical use within the realm, and to grant licences on reasonable terms to other persons who may desire to work it." Levinstein, in fact, wanted the English patent law to be changed such that the compulsory working clause was similar to that in German law.

79. Alfred Rée, "Patent Law Reform," in "Science and Industry. The Organic Chemical Industry in England," supplement to *Manchester Guardian*, 30 June 1917, 20.

80. Such harmonisation would also have been welcomed by German firms, whose battles in London courts were not fought only against British manufacturers. Thus in 1897, judgement went against BASF, represented by Moulton, in a case in which Bindschedler of Basle shipped a yellow colorant, identical with a BASF product patented in England, via the post to a British agent. (Postal carriage was not considered infringement.) Harmonisation was discussed by Edgar de Laire, in his "Nécessité d'un brevet international remplaçant les brevets Nationaux dans les contestations entre étrangers," *Seventh International Congress of Applied Chemistry, London, May 27th to June 2nd 1909. Section XI. Law, Political Economy, and Legislation Affecting Chemical Industry*, eds. Sir William Ramsay and William Macnab, assisted by R. Moritz (London: Partridge & Cooper, 1910), 68-73.

81. There were 42 cartels, or syndicates, in Germany during 1887, and the number had grown to 77 at the end of 1889.

82. Percy May, "Patents and the Chemist," *Chemistry and Industry*, 20 May 1939, 485-88, on 487.

Chapter 10

1. Herbert Levinstein, "Proceedings of the Society. The First George Douglas Lecture: George Douglas, His Times, and Some Thoughts on the Future," *Journal of the Society of Dyers and Colourists* 65 (1949): 271.

2. Ernest F. Ehrhardt, "Reminiscences of Dr. Caro," *Chemistry and Industry* 43 (1924): 561-65, on 563.

3. Carl Glaser, "Erlebnisse und Erinnerungen nach meinem Eintritt in die Badische Anilin- & Soda-Fabrik im Jahre1869," unpublished typescript, Heidelberg, 1921, held at BASF Archives, W1 Glaser (hereafter cited as "Glaser"). All quotations are translations from the German, and are taken from 29-34.
4. "Glaser," 30.
5. "Glaser," 30.
6. "Glaser," 30.
7. "Glaser," 30.
8. "Glaser," 31. Ernst Homburg in his "The Emergence of Research Laboratories in the Dyestuffs Industry, 1870-1900," *British Journal for the History of Science* 25 (1992): 91-111, has suggested that the relationship accorded with Engelhorn's view of "science more as a lucrative gamble than a necessary element in company management" (on 99). Glaser, moreover, pointed out that Engelhorn's single passion was for making money; see "Glaser," 29.
9. "Glaser," 31.
10. "Glaser," 31.
11. "Glaser," 31.
12. "Glaser," 31.
13. "Glaser," 32.
14. "Glaser," 32.
15. "Glaser," 32.
16. "Glaser," 32.
17. "Glaser," 32.
18. "Glaser," 32-33.
19. "Glaser," 33.
20. "Glaser," 33.
21. "Glaser," 33.
22. "Glaser," 33.
23. "Glaser," 34.
24. Ehrhardt, "Reminiscences of Dr. Caro," 561.
25. Heinrich Caro, "Ueber die Entwickelung der Theerfarben-Industrie," *Berichte der Deutschen Chemischen Gesellschaft* 25 (1892): 955-1105.
26. Amalie Caro, "Erinnerungen an Dr. Heinrich Caro," (hereafter "Erinnerungen), vol. 1, 158-60. DM NL93/10/1.
27. See obituary of Caro in *Journal of the Society of Dyers and Colourists* 29 (1910): 246.
28. "Erinnerungen," vol. 1, 3, DM NL93/10/1.
29. "Erinnerungen," vol. 1, 50-51, DM NL93/10/1.
30. They had six more children, daughters Edith, Louise, and Fanny, born in 1869, 1871, and 1875, respectively; and sons Heinrich, Alfred, and Victor Adolf, born in 1870, 1873, and 1880. Edith married Joseph Rheinboldt, and their son Heinrich became a chemist and professor at the University of Bonn. He emigrated to Brazil shortly after the Nazis came to power, where he joined the University of Saõ Paulo. Other members of the Caro family moved to Australia. For this family information we thank Chava Agmon, of Tel Aviv. We can assume that no expense was spared in

the education of the children, since Fanny went to a finishing school at Morges, Lake Geneva, as recommended to Caro by Hofmann. See Caro to H. E. Armstrong, 29 April 1893, letter no. 102, Imperial College Archives, London. Through Carl Duisberg's intervention, Caro's youngest son Victor Adolf joined Bayer's legal department on 2 January 1909, though Duisberg stated that he would be critical, and judge him impartially. Adolf worked under the supervision of the lawyer Doermer. Caro to Duisberg, 30 December 1908, and Duisberg to Caro, 20 January 1909, Duisberg Papers, Bayer Archives. Nikodemus Caro (1871-1935), who was engaged in nitrogen fixation studies early in the 1900s, was a distant family relative. Sources of information on the Caro family will be found in David S. Zubatsky and Irwin M. Bernet, *Sourcebook for Jewish Genealogies and Family Histories* (Teaneck, N.J.: Avotaynu, Inc., 1996), 67.

31. "Erinnerungen," vol. 1, 158-60, DM NL93/10/1.
32. "Erinnerungen," vol. 1, 158-60, DM NL93/10/1.
33. Otto von Bismarck, in his memoirs, trans. and quoted by Fritz Stern, *Gold and Iron: Bismarck, Bleichröder, and the Building of the German Empire* (Peregrine/Penguin: Harmondsworth, 1987), 14.
34. Caro to Ivan Levinstein, 4 February 1890, DM HS 3671, and 22 February 1890, DM NL93.

Chapter 11

1. Sir William Henry Perkin, in *Jubilee of the Discovery of Mauve and of the Foundation of the Coal-Tar Colour Industry by Sir W. H. Perkin, F.R.S., D.Sc., LL.D., Ph.D., Dr.Ing.*, eds. Raphael Meldola, Arthur G. Green, and John Cannell Cain (London: Perkin Memorial Committee, 1906), 18.
2. Perkin and Meldola had also written competent, but much shorter, historical surveys, and Caro had earlier delineated the history of azo dyes in his obituary of Griess, which was of course adapted to suit the priority claims of Witt, Griess, and Caro. See William Henry Perkin, "Proceedings of the Fourth Annual General Meeting. The President's Address," *Journal of the Society of Chemical Industry* 4 (1885): 427-38; and Raphael Meldola, "The Scientific Development of the Coal-Tar Colour Industry," under "Abstracts from English and Foreign Journals. V. Coal-Tar Colours," *Journal of the Society of Dyers and Colourists* 2 (June 1886): 95-101, both reprinted in Walter M. Gardner, ed., *The British Coal Tar Industry: Its Origin, Development and Decline* (London: Williams & Norgate, 1915; reprinted New York: Arno, 1981).
3. Caro to Levinstein, 4 February 1890, DM HS 3671; trans. from the German.
4. Levinstein to Caro, 16 February 1890, DM HS 1977/32/191/7; trans. from the German.
5. Caro to Levinstein, 22 February 1890, DM NL93; trans. from the German.
6. Levinstein to Caro, 7 May 1891, DM HS 1977/32/191/8; trans. from the German.
7. Watson Smith, "International Inventions Exhibition London. Report on the Exhibits Relating to the Chemical Industries," *Journal of the Society of Chemical Industry* 4 (1885): 469-83, on 479. Information about the BASF products, including patents and publications, appear in tabulated form on 480-83. The exhibition was organised

by a committee under the 1851 Royal Commission, and held in the old Horticultural Society Halls.

8. Smith, "International Inventions Exhibition London," 479.
9. "You were good enough to say when here in the summer that you would be able to give me specimens illustrating your various manufactures and I now venture therefore to remind you ... As we are a new Institution, anything and everything will be of value. Of course, I am particularly anxious to get together a collection illustrating the applications of organic chemistry." Armstrong to Caro, 21 December 1885, DM HS 1977/32/6/3.
10. Meldola to Caro, 6 November 1885, DM NL93.
11. Caro to Meldola, 21 November 1885, Newham.
12. Meldola, "The Scientific Development of the Coal-Tar Colour Industry," 95-101.
13. Meldola, "The Scientific Development of the Coal-Tar Colour Industry," 99-100.
14. Anthony S. Travis, "Colour Makers and Consumers: Heinrich Caro's British Network," *Journal of the Society of Dyers and Colourists* 108 (1992): 311-16.
15. Meldola, "The Scientific Development of the Coal-Tar Colour Industry," 100.
16. Meldola, "The Scientific Development of the Coal-Tar Colour Industry," 97.
17. Perkin, "Proceedings of the Fourth Annual General Meeting. The President's Address," 436.
18. Perkin, "Proceedings of the Fourth Annual General Meeting."
19. Perkin, "Proceedings of the Fourth Annual General Meeting," 437.
20. Ivan Levinstein, "Observations and Suggestions on the Present Position of the British Chemical Industries with Special Reference to Coal-Tar Derivatives," *Journal of the Society of Chemical Industry* 5 (1886): 351-59.
21. Edward S. Johnson, chemist, 773 Orchard Street, Avalon, Pennsylvania, to Caro, 23 October 1898, and 7 August 1899, DM NL93. Johnson discussed the possible publication of his lectures in book form and a forthcoming lecture on synthetic indigo. He had studied chemistry in Heidelberg, and later met Bernthsen "in Prof. Witt's laboratory in Berlin."
22. Ernest F. Ehrhardt, "Reminiscences of Dr. Caro," *Journal of the Society of Chemical Industry* 43 (1924): 561-65, and "Society of Chemical Industry. Manchester Section," *Journal of the Society of Chemical Industry* 43 (1924): 142-43.
23. Ernest F. Ehrhardt, "The Influence of Patent Law on Chemical Industry," paper presented at the Seventh International Congress of Applied Chemistry, London, May 1909, 7-9, on 9.
24. Arthur G. Green, "The Reinstatement of the Dyestuff Industry in England," in "Science & Industry: The Organic Chemical Industry in England," supplement to *The Manchester Guardian*, 30 June 1917, 16.
25. See, in particular, Friedrich Engels, *Ludwig Feuerbach und der Ausgang der klassischen deutschen Philosophie* (Stuttgart: Dietz, 1888). For Schorlemmer see Theodor O. Benfey and Anthony S. Travis, "Carl Schorlemmer: The Red Chemist," *Chemistry and Industry*, 15 June 1992, 441-44.
26. Carl A. Schorlemmer, *The Rise and Development of Organic Chemistry*, rev. ed., ed. Arthur Smithells (Macmillan: London, 1894), 240-51.

27. Caro to Graebe, 25 February 1890, DM HS 3881; trans. from the German. Germany did eventually reclaim Graebe from Switzerland, but not until 1906, when he moved to Frankfurt.
28. For the speeches, see Gustav Schultz, "Bericht ueber die Feier zu Ehren August Kekulé's," *Berichte der Deutschen Chemischen Gesellschaft* 23 (1890): 1265-1312.
29. Levinstein to Caro, 29 January 1890. DM HS 1977/32/191/6; trans. from the German.
30. "Ein Führer bietet sich uns an. Er zeigt auf die ragenden Essen einer weithin ausgedehnten Fabrik. 'Dort'–sagt er–'sind die Werkstätten der 'Deutschen Theerproducten-Industrie.' Dorthin will ich Sie geleiten. Die Fabrik vereinigt in sich alle Zweige und Hülfsbetriebe dieser Industrie. Sie beschäftigt viele Tausende von Arbeitern und Hunderte von Chemikern, Ingenieuren und Kaufleuten. Ihre Einrichtungen und Leistungen stehen auf der Höhe der Zeit. Ihr Absatzgebiet ist der Weltmarkt." Caro, "Ueber die Entwickelung," 957-58.
31. "Die Quelle des andauernden Erfolges sei bei dieser, noch in unaufhörlicher Entwickelung begriffenen Industrie: eine bis in die letzten Adern der Fabrikation sich verzweigende, wissenschaftliche Durchdringung der Praxis, unablässige Fühlung mit der Bewegung auf dem Erfindungsgebiete, den Fortschritten der theoretischen und angewandten Chemie und den wechselnden Bedürfnissen des Marktes, streng durchgeführte Teilung der Arbeit und ein planmässig geleitetes, harmonisches Zusammenwirken aller Kräfte, von dem Ersten bis zu dem Letzten, Jeder an dem ihm gebührenden Platz." Caro, "Ueber die Entwickelung," 960.
32. Ehrhardt, "Reminiscences of Dr. Caro," 561-62.
33. Ehrhardt, "Reminiscences of Dr. Caro," 565. Knecht had studied for his doctorate under Victor Meyer at Zurich Polytechnic, and in 1890 became chief lecturer in chemistry and dyeing at the Manchester School of Technology. Later he became professor of technological chemistry at the University of Manchester, and head of the chemistry department of the Municipal School of Technology. Maurice Tordoff, *The Servant of Colour: A History of the Society of Dyers and Colourists, 1884-1984* (Bradford: The Society of Dyers and Colourists, 1984), 38-39.
34. Karl Aloys Schenzinger, *Anilin* (Berlin: Zeitgeschichte-Verlag, 1936). See also Michael N. Keas, "Karl Aloys Schenzinger's Novel, *Anilin*; Chemistry and Chemical Technology in Nazi *Literaturpolitik*," *Ambix* 39 (1992): 127-40.
35. Ute Deichmann, "Chemie–Innenansicht einer Wissenschaft, 1933-1945. Chemie und Biochemie an deutschen Universitäten und Kaiser Wilhelm-Instituten; Entlassung und Exil jüdischer Chemiker und Biochemiker." (Habilitationsschrift, Mathematisch-Naturwissenschaftliche Fakultät der Universität Köln, 1998).
36. Elisabeth Vaupel, "Carl Graebe (1841-1927) – Leben, Werk und Wirken im Spiegel seines brieflichen Nachlasses," 2 vols. (Ph.D. diss., University of Munich, 1987), vol. 1, 281, vol. 2, 528, quoting a letter from Witt to Graebe, 13 July 1904.
37. Gustav Konrad Heinrich von Goßler (1838-1902), Prussian minister of education/instruction, 1881-91. His grandfather was Conrad von Goßler, who was ennobled in 1813.
38. O. N. Witt, Westend-Charlottenburg, to Meldola, 5 October 1892, Newham.
    The Jewish chemists identified in Witt's letter to Meldola included, in addition to

Baeyer, Eugen Bamberger, Adolf Benedikt, Caro, Paul Ehrlich, Siegmund Gabriel, Guido Goldschmidt, Albert Ladenburg (nephew of Seligmann Ladenburg, co-founder of BASF), Adolf Lieben, Carl Liebermann, Georg Lunge, Victor and Richard Meyer, Alphons Oppenheim [Oppenheimer], Jules Piccard, and Otto Wallach. Jewish intellectuals include the physicians Ludwig Brieger (1849-1919) and Albert Fraenkel (1848-1916), the physicist Heinrich Hertz, the mathematician Leopold Kronecker (1823-91), Ferdinand Lassalle (1825-64) (theoretician and organiser of the German labour movement), the pharmacologist Oskar Liebreich (1839-1908; in 1869 he discovered the sedative properties of chloral hydrate), the occulist Richard Liebreich (1830-1917), the botanist Paul Magnus (1844-1914), the philosopher Moses Mendelssohn (1729-86), the banker Joseph Mendelssohn (1770-1848), the composer Felix Mendelssohn-Bartholdy (1809-47), and the physiologist Isidor Rosenthal. Gustav Kirchhoff was not Jewish, neither was Schelling.

39. Alan J. Rocke, *The Quiet Revolution. Hermann Kolbe and the Science of Organic Chemistry* (Berkeley: University of California Press, 1993), 357-63; and Vaupel, "Graebe," vol. 1, 281-84.
40. Harm G. Schröter and Anthony S. Travis. "An Issue of Different Mentalities: National Approaches to the Development of the Chemical Industry in Britain and Germany before 1914," in *The Chemical Industry in Europe, 1850-1914: Industrial Growth, Pollution, and Professionalization*, eds. Ernst Homburg, Anthony S. Travis, and Harm G. Schröter (Dordrecht: Kluwer, 1998), 95-118.
41. Wyndham R. Dunstan to Caro, 23 March 1900, DM HS 1977/32/81.
42. BASF to Caro, 27 March 1900, DM NL93.
43. "Industrial Alcohol. Report of the Departmental Committee on Industrial Alcohol to the Chancellor of the Exchequer. Presented to Parliament, 11 April 1905, Issued 15th April 1905," *Journal of the Society of Chemical Industry* 24 (1905): 397-426.
44. Edward Thorpe (1845-1925), had studied at Owens College (under Roscoe), Heidelberg and Bonn; worked at Owens College, and the Andersonian Institution, Glasgow; and from 1874 was at Yorkshire College of Science, Leeds, from where on 17 March 1879 he asked Caro to recommend possible applicants for an "Instructorship in Dyeing." In 1885, Thorpe succeeded Edward Frankland at the Royal College of Science, South Kensington; in 1894 he was appointed director of the Government Laboratory; and from 1910-13 was again at the Royal College of Science. P. W. Hammond and Harold Egan, *Weighed in the Balance: A History of the Laboratory of the Government Chemist* (London: HMSO, 1992), chapter 4, esp. 123-24.
45. "Industrial Alcohol," 402.
46. "My dear Dr. Caro,

    Some little time since our Chancellor of the Exchequer appointed a commission to enquire and report whether it was not possible to grant increased facilities for the use of alcohol in our industries without payment of duty and he named, amongst others, the Chairman of the Board of Revenue, Sir Henry Primrose, and myself as members of this Commission–We are now in Berlin seeing Geheimrath Prof. Dr. von Buchka and other officials respecting the conditions under [which] spirit is allowed to be used in German industries without payment of duty, and we hope to have the opportunity of visiting a few works in which alcohol is employed industrially and learn what denaturing substances are used, and generally speaking what control is exercised by the revenue authorities.

Some time since I wrote to Dr. Glaser whom I knew when at Bonn to know whether it would be possible for me to bring Sir Henry Primrose with our secretary Mr. Cunningham to see the works of the Badische Anilin & Soda Fabrik at Ludwigshafen, but since I have been in Berlin I have learnt through Dr. Witt, that Dr. Glaser has recently suffered a great bereavement through the loss of his son, and it is possible therefore that he has not been able to attend to my letter which was addressed to him at Ludwigshafen and not to his house at Heidelberg.

Under the circumstances may I inquire of you whether it would be possible for Sir Henry Primrose and myself, with the Secretary of the Commission Mr. Cunningham, to visit Ludwigshafen for the purpose I have indicated.

Our intention is to leave Berlin on Saturday next, if possible, for Heidelberg and should you be able to obtain permission for us, to visit the works on Monday next. A line in reply would greatly oblige."

Thorpe, Conrad Uhl's Hotel Bristol, Berlin, to Caro, 15 January 1905, DM NL93.

47. See BASF to Caro, 18 January 1905, III No. 633, DM. Two days later, Thorpe followed up with a second letter:

"My dear Dr. Caro,

Almost immediately after I had written to you I received a letter from Dr. Glaser saying that he was no longer one of the Directors of the Badische Anilin- & Soda Fabrik, but that he had forwarded my request to his successor. Subsequently I received a letter from Ludwigshafen, saying that the Company were unable to grant us permission to see their works. My object in proferring the request was to afford Sir Henry Primrose, the Chairman of our Treasury Committee, the opportunity of seeing a typical and well ordered modern German Chemical Works. Sir Henry is a man pretty high up in the Government service, a near connection of Lord Roseberry's, of great intelligence and grasp, but in no sense a man of science. We have had so much said to us in the course of our inquiry which I know is not accurate that I persuaded Sir Henry to induce the Chancellor to let us come out to Germany and so afford us an opportunity of conferring with leaders of chemical technology with a view of arriving at a knowledge of the truth. Our object was not so much to see the works in Germany as to see and talk with the men who direct them and who have made them what they are. Thanks to the kind action of Freiberr von Stengel we have had every facility from the official people, and have learnt much that is important to us to know.

We have also seen a number of places using denatured spirit in the neighbourhood of Berlin and have had the opportunity of witnessing the methods of Spirit Control in a variety of works. Mr. Merck, at Darmstadt, has been so good as to allow us to visit his works for the same object and we propose to visit him sometime next week.

If the time permits we may go on to Heidelberg, if for nothing more than to have a day or two's rest, when possibly I may hope to have the pleasure of seeing you and Dr. Glaser, as well as other of my friends in and about that neighbourhood." Thorpe to Caro, 20 January 1905, DM NL93.

48. Thorpe, Hotel de l'Europe, Heidelberg, to Caro, 22 January 1905, DM 23/1 No. 648.
49. "Industrial Alcohol. Report of the Departmental Committee," 404.
50. "Industrial Alcohol. Report of the Departmental Committee," 402.
51. "Industrial Alcohol. Report of the Departmental Committee," 399.
52. The standard mineralised methylated spirit was ethyl alcohol denatured with 10 per cent methyl alcohol (wood spirit) and one per cent petroleum spirit, while industrial methylated spirit, as required in a number of manufacturing processes, was denatured with 5 per cent of methyl alcohol. "Official Notice: Duty-free alcohol," *Journal of the Society of Chemical Industry* 33 (1914):1119.
53. For the history of the Verein Deutscher Chemiker see Jeffrey A. Johnson, "Academic, Proletarian, Professional? Shaping Professionalization for German Industrial Chemists, 1887-1920," in *German Professions 1800-1950*, eds. Geoffrey Cocks and Konrad H. Jarausch (New York: Oxford University Press, 1990), 123-42; Walter Ruske, *100 Jahre Deutsche Chemische Gesellschaft* (Weinheim: Verlag Chemie, 1967), 39-42; and Berthold Rassow, *Geschichte des Vereins Deutscher Chemiker in den ersten 25 Jahren seines Bestehens* (Leipzig: Spamer 1912).
54. Carl Duisberg, *Zeitschrift für Angwandte Chemie* 10 (1897): 510.
55. Duisberg to Caro, 1 June 1897, Duisberg Papers, Bayer Archives; trans. from the German.
56. Caro to Duisberg, 2/3 June 1897, Duisberg Papers, Bayer Archives; trans. from the German.
57. Caro to Duisberg, 2/3 June 1897, Duisberg Papers, Bayer Archives.
58. "Jeder sei Liebig's Schüler! Jeder wetteifere dem Meister nach! Jeder strebe dahin, dass er bei dem Anblicke seines Bildes–wie einst Correggio ausrief vor dem Bilde Rafaels: Anch' Io sono pittore!–Auch ich bin ein Maler!–mit frohem Mannesbewusstsein ausrufen darf: Auch ich bin ein deutscher Chemiker!" From Caro's inaugural speech at the annual meeting of the society in Darmstadt, 2 June 1898, in *Zeitschrift für Angewandte Chemie* 11 (1898), 817.
59. The first woman in Germany to complete a doctorate in chemistry was Fritz Haber's first wife, Clara Immerwahr (1900).
60. Protocol of the meeting of the board in Hanover, 6 June 1900, *Zeitschrift für Angewandte Chemie* 13 (1900), 870-75.
61. Jeffrey A. Johnson, "German Women in Chemistry 1895-1925," Part I, *N.T.M.* 6 (1998), 1-21, on 4-7 (preprint page numbers).
62. Emanuel A. Merck to Caro, 31 December 1901, DM NL93/10/2. The journal was very different from its modern successor.
63. The contract with the publisher, Julius Springer of Berlin, was signed on 29 September 1898. See the stipulations mentioned in the protocol of the meeting of the board of the society, 1 June 1898, in Darmstadt, *Zeitschrift für Angewandte Chemie* 11 (1898), 795 f. and 803-06 and board meeting, 24 May 1899, in Königshütte (Upper-Silesia), *Zeitschrift für Angewandte Chemie* 12 (1899), 924.

64. For a discussion of this controversy and the introduction of the so-called Verbandsexamen, an examination regulated by the professors and not the state, see Jeffrey A. Johnson, "Academic Self-Regulation and the Chemical Profession in Imperial Germany," *Minerva* 23 (1985), 241-71.
65. Caro to Duisberg, 6 August 1907, Duisberg Papers, Bayer Archives; trans. from the German.
66. Invitation, January 1904, DM NL93/10/3.
67. These include Hans Bunte (Polytechnic of Karlsruhe), Carl von Linde (Verein Deutscher Ingenieure), Emanuel A. Merck (Verein Deutscher Chemiker), Carl Duisberg (Verein zur Wahrung der Interessen der chemischen Industrie Deutschlands), Theodor Curtius (Deutsche Chemische Gesellschaft), Emil Knoevenagel (Chemische Gesellschaft zu Heidelberg), Cantzler (Freie Vereinigung Deutscher Nahrungsmittel-Chemiker), Carl Theodor Petersen (Frankfurter Physikalischer Verein, Frankfurter Chemische Gesellschaft), Bluemcke (Mannheimer Bezirksverein Deutscher Ingenieure), the Verein ehemaliger Garde-Füsiliere, and, for BASF, August Bernthsen. "Erinnerungen," 85-86, DM NL93/10/1.
68. "Festschrift zum 40jährigen Stiftungsfeste des Mannheimer Bezirksvereins Deutscher Ingenieure, 1909." DM NL93/10/4.
69. Letter from Deutsche Chemische Gesellschaft (E. Buchner), February 1904, DM NL93/10/3.
70. Caro to Polytechnic Karlsruhe, 15 March 1904, DM NL93/10/3.
71. Caro was a member of the Society of Chemical Industry from 1882; of the Deutsche Chemische Gesellschaft (out-of-town member of the board in 1880 and 1891-1902); and the Chemische Gesellschaft zu Heidelberg (co-founder 1890; deputy chairman in 1891; chairman in 1892). He had received an honorary Ph.D. degree from the University of Munich (2. Sektion der Philosophischen Fakultät) on 10 November 1877. In a letter dated November 1877, Adolf Baeyer wrote that Caro's "[i]deal and selfless interest for the sciences" were the reason for this honorary degree. (Baeyer to Caro, 12 November 1877, DM NL93/10/V.) In 1906, on the occasion of the Perkin's mauve 50th-anniversary celebration, Caro was awarded an honorary doctorate from the University of Leeds (4 August 1906) at a meeting of the British Association for the Advancement of Science at York. According to "Erinnerungen an Dr. Heinrich Caro," DM NL93/10/1, vol. 1, 192, he received in 1878 (actually in 1875) an offer of a post from Zurich Polytechnic, and in 1894 from the Imperial Patent Office in Berlin.
72. "Ihre Worte führten mich zurück nach Manchester–über 4 Jahrzehnte liegen dazwischen! Wir planten, dachten, arbeiteten zusammen! Da stiegen die Cornbrook Chemical Works vor meiner Erinnerung auf. Old John Dale, der immer gutherzige, enthusiastische Mann, der kenntnisreiche, energische, ideenreiche Fabrikant stürmte mit seinem ausdrucksvollen Kopf–mit seiner John Bull Gestalt in das Laboratorium hinein, das er nicht eher verliess, before he had made a mess, und nun ging das Fragen los: 'Well Dr. Martius, Well Caro, have you not got anything fresh to show me?' Gedenken wir jener Tage ... denn sie waren die Wiege unserer späteren Erfolge und damit auch eine Etappe in der Entwickelung der Teerfarben-Industrie. Wie sonderbar! Dort in unserem Kreis weilten 4 der späteren deutschen Leiter: Sie,

Pauli, Leonhard und ich!" Caro to Martius, 1 March 1904, DM NL93/10/3.

73. Caro to Graebe, 23 February 1904, DM NL93/10/3.
74. "... und ich kann mir wohl vorstellen, wie viel freundliche Erinnerungen an Ihr tatenreiches Leben Ihnen ... zugeströmt sind. Aber es ist davon auch einiges zurückgeströmt zu den zahlreichen Menschen, mit denen Sie nicht allein empfangend, sondern viel häufiger reichlich spendend in Ihrem langen Leben in Verbindung getreten sind.... Als ich vor fünfundzwanzig Jahren hilfesuchend zu Ihnen kam, stand ich nicht allein in dem empfänglichsten Lebensalter, sondern auch im ersten Beginn der wissenschaftlichen Laufbahn, wo von einem raschen Erfolge geradezu die Lebensziele beeinflusst werden. Sie haben mit Ihrer Anregung und materiellen Unterstützung damals meinen Versuchen einen grossen Vorschub geleistet und ich darf wohl sagen, dass ohne Ihre Hilfe die Fuchsinfrage von uns nicht gelöst worden wäre. Ich habe dann weiter bei Ihnen die geniale Art kennen gelernt, wie die Resultate der theoretischen Forschung in die lebenden Werte der Industrie umgesetzt werden können und dadurch eine viel bessere Meinung von dem Nutzen wissenschaftlicher Arbeit erhalten." Emil Fischer to Caro, 8 April 1904, DM NL93/10/3.
75. Perkin to Caro, 31 May 1906, DM HS 873.
76. Meldola, Green, and Cain, eds., *Jubilee of the Discovery of Mauve.*
77. For Caro's visit to England, and correspondence with the Sir William Perkin and (after his death) Lady Perkin, see the Caro Nachlass, and Simon Garfield, *Mauve* (Faber, 2000).
78. This follows the text of Amalie Caro in the "Erinnerungen," vol. 1, pp. 160-62. DM NL93/10/1. Heinrich Caro was not able to attend Victor Adolf's marriage on 30 April 1910 in Elberfeld because of ill health. Caro to Duisberg, 29 April 1910, Duisberg Papers, Bayer Archives.

Chapter 12

1. Ernest F. Ehrhardt, Reminiscences of Dr. Caro," *Chemistry and Industry* 43 (1924): 561-65, on 561.
2. Meldola to Caro, 17 February 1904, quoted in Ehrhardt, "Reminiscences of Dr. Caro," 564-65.
3. Caro (Mannheim) to Meldola, 2 March 1904, DM NL 93/10/3. An edited version is quoted by A. G. Green in Ehrhardt, "Reminiscences of Dr. Caro," 564.
4. For a recent discussion of the decline in the British dye industry during the 1860s, see Peter J. T. Morris and Anthony S. Travis, "The Chemical Society of London and the Dye Industry in the 1860s," *Ambix* 39 (1992): 117-26.
5. Raphael Meldola, "Review of Technical Chemists as 'Made in Germany,'" a review of Ferdinand Fischer, *Chemische Technologie an den Universitäten und technischen Hochschulen Deutschlands* (Braunschweig: Vieweg & Sohn, 1898), *Nature* 59 (1899): 361-63; "The Relations between Scientific Research and Chemical Industry" (lecture at the University Extension Meeting, Oxford, 3 August 1899), *Nature* 68 (1903): 398-404; "The Position and Prospects of Chemical Research in Great Britain," *Journal of the Chemical Society* 91 (1907): 626-58; and "President's Address. Education and Research in Applied Chemistry," *Journal of*

the Society of Chemical Industry 28 (1909): 554-78.

6. Henry E. Roscoe, "The Perkin Jubilee and Chemical Industries," *Nature* 73 (1906): 438; see also Henry L. Heathcote, "Birmingham Section. The University Training of Industrial Chemists," *Journal of the Society of Chemical Industry* 28 (1909): 171-77.
7. Michael Sanderson, "The English Universities and the 'Industrial Spirit', 1870-1914," *Historical Research* 61 (1988): 90-104, on 96-97.
8. For German responses, particularly by Emil Fischer, see Jeffrey A. Johnson, *The Kaiser's Chemists: Science and Modernization in Imperial Germany* (Chapel Hill: University of North Carolina Press, 1990). For the wartime reaction, see Timothy D. Moy, "Emil Fischer as 'Chemical Mediator': Science, Industry and Government in World War One," *Ambix* 36 (1989): 109-20.
9. John Fletcher Moulton, *The Manufacture of Aniline Dyes in England: An Address Delivered by Lord Moulton in the Town Hall, Manchester, on December 8th, 1914; the Lord Mayor of Manchester (Alderman McCabe) Presiding* (Manchester: Taylor, Garnett, Evans & Co., 1914). See also: "External Lectures and Addresses. The Manufacture of Aniline Dyes in England: Lord Moulton's Important Statement," *Journal of the Society of Dyers and Colourists* 31 (1915): 10-17; W. R. Ormandy, "Britain and Germany in Relation to the Chemical Trade," *Journal of the Society of Dyers and Colourists* 31 (1915): 17-18, reprinted from the *Journal of the Society of Arts*, 27 November 1914, 47; Sir W. A. Tilden, "The Supply of Chemicals to Britain and Her Dependencies," *Journal of the Society of Dyers and Colourists* 31 (1915): 19-20.
10. For Moulton's involvement, see W. J. Reader, *Imperial Chemical Industries: A History* Vol. 1 *The Forerunners 1870-1926* (London: Oxford University Press, 1970), 268-69, and for Moulton's career in science and law, see H. Fletcher Moulton, *The Life of Lord Moulton* (London: Nisbet, 1922).
11. Meldola was a member of the Board of Trade's Committee on the Supply of Chemical Products, set up late in August 1914.
12. Sir William Ramsay, *Nature*, 12 November 1914; quoted in Tilden, "The Supply of Chemicals to Britain and Her Dependencies," 19-20, and extracted from *Journal of the Society of Arts*, 27 November 1914, 26.
13. Raphael Meldola, "National Dye Industry," *Times*, 20 January 1915, 9.
14. Meldola's lobbying in public from the 1880s paralleled the pronouncements of other scientists in the columns of *Nature* and the *Times*, and in presidential and various prestigious addresses, as discussed by Frank M. Turner in "Public Science in Britain," *Isis* 71 (1980): 589-608.
15. There were "already grave doubts in the minds of many business men as to the ability of the new company to produce the necessary dyes of the right quality and at the right price." Quoted from "Aniline Dyes. Defects of the Government's Plan," *Times*, 15 January 1915, 5. This report had prompted Meldola's letter published five days later.
16. "British Dyes. Views of Two Eminent Chemists," *Times*, 10 March 1915; both letters were reprinted under the heading "British Dyes (Ltd.)." Sir William Ramsay, "Probable Causes of Failure," *Journal of the Society of Dyers and Colourists* 31

(1915): 104-05.

17. Henry E. Roscoe, "A Business for Chemists," *Times*, 10 March 1915; reprinted in *Journal of the Society of Dyers and Colourists* 31 (1915): 105-06; and, on 106, H. E. Armstrong's opinion in *Morning Post*, 13 March 1915. See also Roscoe's collection of related press cuttings from this time, pasted in one volume, John Rylands University Library of Manchester, Roscoe Papers.
18. Raphael Meldola, "Colouring Matters and Dyes. Manufacture of Aniline Dyestuffs in Great Britain," *Journal of the Society of Chemical Industry* 34 (1915): 73-75, on 74-75.
19. Raphael Meldola, "Colouring Matters and Dyes. British Manufacture of Aniline Dyes," *Journal of the Society of Chemical Industry* 34 (1915): 218-21, on 220-21; and Meldola, "The Supply of Dyewares," *Journal of the Society of Dyers and Colourists* 31 (1915): 102-04.
20. William H. Perkin, Junior, "The Position of the Organic Chemical Industry," *Journal of the Chemical Society, Transactions* 57 (1915): 557-78.
21. Walter M. Gardner, *The British Coal-Tar Industry: Its Origin, Development and Decline* (London: Williams & Norgate, 1915; reprinted New York: Arno, 1981). For the wider public science arguments during World War I, see Andrew Hull, "War of Words: The Public Science of the British Scientific Community and the Origins of the Department of Scientific and Industrial Research, 1914-16," *British Journal for the History of Science* 32 (1999): 461-81; and Turner, "Public Science in Britain."
22. Reader, *Imperial Chemical Industries*, vol. 1, quoting Robertson, 271.
23. Maurice Tordoff, *The Servant of Colour: A History of the Society of Dyers and Colourists 1884-1984* (Bradford: The Society of Dyers and Colourists, 1984), 107-13; Morris R. Fox, *Dye-Makers of Great Britain 1856-1976: A History of Chemists, Companies, Products and Changes* (Manchester: ICI, 1987), 85-90; "British Dyestuffs: The State as a Company Promoter 1914-1919," in Reader, *Imperial Chemical Industries*, vol.1, 266-73. See also F. Mollwo Perkin, "West Riding Section: The Future Prospects of the British Dye Industry," *Journal of the Society of Dyers and Colourists* 31 (1915): 234-41. For responses to shortages of German dyes in the United States, see Kathryn Steen, "Wartime Catalyst and Postwar Reaction: The Making of the United States Synthetic Organic Chemicals Industry, 1910-1930," (Ph.D. diss., University of Delaware, 1995).
24. See for example "Editorial," *Chemistry and Industry* 43 (1924): 110; and Gilbert T. Morgan, "The British and German Dyestuffs Industries," *Chemistry and Industry* 43 (1924): 168-69.
25. Herbert Levinstein, "Proceedings of the Society. West Riding Section. Some Thoughts on the British Dyestuffs Industry," *Journal of the Society of Dyers and Colourists* 40 (1924): 349-56, on 349, 351.
26. Ehrhardt, "Reminiscences of Dr. Caro," 561.
27. Ernest F. Ehrhardt, "Society of Chemical Industry. Manchester Section," *Chemistry and Industry* 43 (1924): 142.
28. Carl Glaser, "Erlebnisse und Erinnerungen nach meinem Eintritt in die Badische Anilin- & Soda-Fabrik im Jahre 1869," unpublished typescript, Heidelberg, 1921,

held at BASF Archives, W1 Glaser, 31.

29. Edmund Knecht, discussion following Ehrhardt, "Reminiscences of Dr. Caro," 565.

30. Caro to Duisberg, 20 October 1905, Duisberg Papers, Bayer Archives.

31. For cancer among dye workers see Ludwig Rehn "Blasengeschwuelste bei Fuchsin-Arbeitern," *Archiv für Klinische Chirurgie* 50 (1895): 588-600; Rehn, "Ueber Blasenerkrankungen bei Anilinarbeitern," *Verhandlungen der Deutschen Gesellschaft für Chirurgie* 35 (1906): 313-14; Isaac Berenblum, "Aniline Cancer," *Cancer Review*, August 1932, 337-55; T. S. Scott, "The Incidence of Bladder Tumours in a Dyestuffs Factory," *British Journal of Industrial Medicine* 9 (1952): 127-32; and David A. Hounshell and John K. Smith, *Science and Corporate Strategy: Du Pont R&D, 1902-1980* (Cambridge: Cambridge University Press, 1988), 555-72.

Bibliography

Books, monographs, major historical papers, and obituaries, reports, company histories, and dissertations dealing mainly with historical topics.

Abrahart, E. N. *The Clayton Aniline Company Limited, 1876-1976.* Manchester: Clayton Aniline Co. Ltd, 1976.

Andersen, Arne. *Historische Technikfolgenabschätzung am Beispiel des Metallhüttenwesens und der Chemieindustrie. 1850-1933.* Stuttgart: Steiner, 1996.

Anschütz, Richard. *August Kekulé*, 2 vols. Berlin: Verlag Chemie, 1929.

Baeyer, Adolf. *Adolf von Baeyer*'s *Gesammelte Werke*, 2 vols. Braunschweig: Vieweg, 1905.

Baines, Edward, Junior. *History of the Cotton Manufacture in Great Britain.* London: H. Fisher, R. Fisher & P. Jackson [1835].

Barclay, David E. *Frederick William IV and the Prussian Monarchy, 1840-1861.* Oxford: Oxford University Press, 1995.

Bäumer, Beatrix. *Von der physiologischen Chemie zur frühen biochemischen Arzneimittelforschung. Der Apotheker und Biochemiker Eugen Baumann (1846-1896) an den Universitäten Straßburg, Berlin, Freiburg und in der pharmazeutischen Industrie*. Stuttgart: Deutscher Apotheker Verlag, 1996.

Bäumler, Ernst. *Ein Jahrhundert Chemie*. Düsseldorf: Econ, 1963.

Beer, John J. "Coal Tar Dye Manufacture and the Origins of the Modern Industrial Research Laboratory." *Isis* 49 (1958): 123-31.

——. *The Emergence of the German Dye Industry.* Urbana: University of Illinois Press, 1959; reprinted New York: Arno, 1981

——. "Heinrich Caro." In *Dictionary of Scientific Biography*, ed. Charles Coulston Gillispie, 18 vols., vol. 3, pp. 84-85. New York: Charles Scribner's Sons, 1970-90.

Belt, Henk van den, and Arie Rip. "The Nelson-Winter-Dosi Model and Synthetic Dye Chemistry." In *The Social Construction of Technological Systems*, eds. Wiebe E. Bijker, Thomas P. Hughes, and Trevor Pinch, pp. 135-58. Cambridge, Mass.: MIT Press, 1987.

Benfey, O. Theodor, and Anthony S. Travis, "Carl Schorlemmer: The Red Chemist," *Chemistry and Industry*, 15 June 1992, pp. 441-44.

Bernthsen, August. "Heinrich Caro." *Berichte der Deutschen Chemischen Gesellschaft* 45 (1912): 1987-2042.

——. *50 Jahre Tätigkeit in chemischer Wissenschaft und Industrie. Einige Lebenserinnerungen.* Heidelberg, 1925.

Borscheid, Peter. *Naturwissenschaft, Staat und Industrie in Baden. 1848-1914.* Stuttgart: Klett, 1976.

Broad, D. W. *Centennial History of the Liverpool Section, Society of Chemical Industry, 1881-1981.* London: Society of Chemical Industry, 1981.

Brock, William H. *Justus von Liebig. The Chemical Gatekeeper.* Cambridge: Cambridge University Press, 1997.

Brunck, Heinrich. "Die Entwickelungsgeschichte der Indigo-Fabrication." *Berichte der Deutschen Chemischen Gesellschaft* 33, III (1900): lxxi-lxxxvi.

Bud, Robert F., and Gerrylynn K. Roberts. *Science versus Practice: Chemistry in Victorian Britain.* Manchester: Manchester University Press, 1984.

Bürgin, Alfred. *Geschichte des Geigy-Unternehmens von 1758 bis 1939. Ein Beitrag zur Basler Unternehmer– und Wirtschaftsgeschichte. Veröffentlichung zum 200jährigen Bestehen des Geigy-Unternehmens 1958.* Basel: Birkhäuser, 1958.

Caro, Amalie, ed. *Gesammelte Reden und Vorträge von Heinrich Caro.* Leipzig: Otto Spamer, 1913.

Caro, Heinrich. "Ueber die Entwickelung der Theerfarben-Industrie." *Berichte der Deutschen Chemischen Gesellschaft* 25 (1892): 955-1105.

——. "Über die Entwicklung der chemischen Industrie in Mannheim-Ludwigshafen a. Rh." *Zeitschrift für Angewandte Chemie* 17 (1904): 1343-62.

Cohen, J. M. *The Life of Ludwig Mond.* London: Methuen, 1956.

Crace Calvert, Frederick. *Lectures on Coal-Tar Colours, and on Recent Improvements in Dyeing and Calico Printing.* Manchester: Palmer & Howe [1863].

Craig, John E. *Scholarship and Nation Building. The Universities of Strasbourg and Alsatian Society 1870-1939.* Chicago: University of Chicago Press, 1984.

Crookes, William. *A Practical Handbook of Dyeing and Calico Printing*, 2 vols. London: Longmans, Green & Co., 1874.

Cutler, John, ed. *Reports of Patent Cases Decided by Courts of Law in the United Kingdom/Reports of Patent, Design and Trade Mark Cases Decided by Courts of Law in the United Kingdom.* London: The Patent Office, 1886, 1888, 1890.

Darmstaedter, Ernst. "Heinrich Caro." In *Das Buch der grossen Chemiker*, ed. Günther Bugge, 2 vols., vol. 2, pp. 298-309. Berlin: Chemie Verlag, 1929-30; reprinted Weinheim, 1965.

Deichmann, Ute. "Chemie–Innenansicht einer Wissenschaft, 1933-1945. Chemie und Biochemie an deutschen Universitäten und Kaiser Wilhelm-Instituten;

Entlassung und Exil jüdischer Chemiker und Biochemiker." Habilitationsschrift, Mathematisch-Naturwissenschaftliche Fakultät der Universität Köln, 1998.

Diem, Annemarie, and Otto P. Krätz. "Vom Alchimistenherd zur BASF. Die Lehrjahre Heinrich Caros." *Die BASF* 24 (1974): 3-10.

Duisberg, Carl. "Heinrich Caro," *Zeitschrift für Angewandte Chemie* 23 (1911): 1057-58.

Edgerton, David. *Science, Technology and British Industrial "Decline", 1870-1970.* Cambridge: Cambridge University Press, 1996.

Ehrhardt, Ernest F. "The Influence of Patent Law on Chemical Industry," Seventh International Congress of Applied Chemistry, London, May 1909, pp. 7-9.

——. "Society of Chemical Industry. Manchester Section." *Chemistry and Industry/Journal of the Society of Chemical Industry* 43 (1924): 142-43.

——. "Reminiscences of Dr. Caro." *Chemistry and Industry/Journal of the Society of Chemical Industry* 43 (1924): 561-65.

Engels, Friedrich. *Ludwig Feuerbach und der Ausgang der klassischen deutschen Philosophie*. Stuttgart: Dietz, 1888.

Farrar, Wilfred Vernon. "Edward Schunck, F.R.S.: A Pioneer of Natural Product Chemistry." *Notes and Records of the Royal Society of London* 31 (1977): 273-296.

Fischer, Emil: *Aus meinem Leben.* Berlin: Springer, 1922; reprinted 1987.

Fleischer, Arndt. *Patentgesetzgebung und chemisch-pharmazeutische Industrie im deutschen Kaiserreich. 1871-1918.* Stuttgart: Deutscher Apotheker Verlag, 1984.

Fletcher Moulton, H. *The Life of Lord Moulton*. London: Nisbet, 1922.

Fletcher Moulton, John. *The Manufacture of Aniline Dyes in England: An Address Delivered by Lord Moulton in the Town Hall, Manchester, on December 8th, 1914; the Lord Mayor of Manchester (Alderman McCabe) Presiding.* Manchester: Taylor, Garnett, Evans & Co., 1914.

Fox, Maurice R. *Dye-Makers of Great Britain, 1856-1976: A History of Chemists, Companies, Products and Changes.* Manchester: ICI, 1987.

Friedlaender, Paul. *Fortschritte der Theerfarbenfabrikation und verwandter Industriezweige*, 11 vols. Berlin: Springer, 1888-1915.

Fruton, Joseph S. *Contrasts in Scientific Style. Research Groups in the Chemical and Biochemical Sciences.* Philadelphia: American Philosophical Society, 1990.

Gardner, Walter M., ed. *The British Coal-Tar Industry: Its Origin, Development and Decline.* London: Williams & Norgate, 1915; reprinted New York: Arno, 1981.

Garfield, Simon. *Mauve*. London: Faber, 2000.

Gienapp, Ruth Anne. "Adolf von Baeyer." In *Dictionary of Scientific Biography*, ed. Charles Coulston Gillispie, 18 vols, vol. 1, pp. 389-91. New York: Charles Scribner's Sons, 1970-90.

Glaser, Carl. "Heinrich von Brunck." *Berichte der Deutschen Chemischen Gesellschaft* 46 (1913): 352-89.

——. "Erlebnisse und Erinnerungen nach meinem Eintritt in die Badische Anilin- & Soda-Fabrik im Jahre 1869." Unpublished, Heidelberg, 1921, held at BASF Archives.

Green, Arthur G. "The Reinstatement of the Dyestuff Industry in England." In "Science & Industry: The Organic Chemical Industry in England," supplement to *The Manchester Guardian*, 30 June 1917.

——. *Manchester Chemistry and Chemists in the Nineties. The Second Ivan Levinstein Memorial Lecture. Manchester Chemical Club, 22 November 1938.* Manchester: Manchester Chemical Club, 1938.

Grossmann, Hermann. "Peter Griess." In *Das Buch der großen Chemiker*, ed. Günther Bugge, 2 vols., vol. 2, pp. 217-28. Berlin: Verlag Chemie, 1929; reprinted Weinheim, 1965.

Haber, L. F. *The Chemical Industry During the Nineteenth Century. A Study of the Economic Aspect of Applied Chemistry in Europe and North America.* Oxford: Clarendon Press, 1958.

Hachtmann, Rüdiger. *Berlin 1848. Eine Politik- und Gesellschaftsgeschichte der Revolution.* Bonn: Dietz, 1997.

Hammond, P. W., and Harold Egan. *Weighed in the Balance: A History of the Laboratory of the Government Chemist.* London: HMSO, 1992.

Higgins, Sydney H. *Dyeing in Germany and America, With a Chapter on Colour Production.* Manchester: Manchester University Press, 1907.

Hoechst AG. *Dokumente aus Hoechster Archiven* Heft 3 *Neunzig Jahre Fuchsin in Hoechst.* Frankfurt: Hoechst, 1965.

——. *Dokumente aus Hoechster Archiven* Heft 26 *Dr. Sells Teerdestillation in Offenbach.* Höchst am Main: Hoechst, 1967.

Hofmann, August Wilhelm. "Colouring Derivatives of Organic Matter, Recent and Fossilised." In *Reports of the Juries, International Exhibition, London, 1862*, Class II, Section A, "Chemical and Pharmaceutical Products and Processes," eds. J. S. Iselin and P. Le Neve Foster, pp. 114-38. London: Society for the Encouragement of Arts, Manufactures and Commerce, 1863.

——, Emil Fischer, and Heinrich Caro. "Zur Erinnerung an Peter Griess." *Berichte der Deutschen Chemischen Gesellschaft* 24, Referate, Patente, Nekrologe (1891): 1007-78, and i-xxxviii (after p. 1078).

Homburg, Ernst. "The Influence of Demand on the Emergence of the Dye Industry. The Roles of Chemists and Colourists." *Journal of the Society of Dyers and Colourists* 99 (1983): 325-33.

——. "The Emergence of Research Laboratories in the Dyestuffs Industry." *British Journal for the History of Science* 25 (1992): 91-111.

——. *Van beroep 'Chemiker': De opkomst van de industriele chemicus en het polytechnische onderwijs in Duitsland. 1790-1850.* ("'Chemiker' by Occupation: The Rise of the Industrial Chemist and Polytechnic Education in Germany. 1790-1850.") Delft: Delftse Universitaire Pers, 1993.

——. "From Colour Maker to Chemist: Episodes from the Rise of the Colourist, 1670-1800." In *Natural Dyestuffs and Industrial Culture in Europe, 1750-1880*, eds. Robert Fox and Agustí Nieto-Galan, pp. 219-57. Canton, Mass.: Watson International/Science History Publications, 1999.

Hornix, Willem J. "August Wilhelm Hofmann and the Dyestuffs Industry." In *Die Allianz von Wissenschaft und Industrie. August Wilhelm Hofmann (1818-1892). Zeit, Werk, Wirkung*, eds. Christoph Meinel and Hartmut Scholz, pp. 151-65. Weinheim: VCH, 1992.

——. "From Process to Plant. Innovation in the Early Artificial Dye Industry." *British Journal for the History of* Science 25 (1992): 65-90.

Hounshell, David A., and John K. Smith, *Science and Corporate Strategy: Du Pont R&D, 1902-1980.* Cambridge: Cambridge University Press, 1988.

Hückstädt, Harald. "100 Jahre synthetisches Alizarin," *Unser Werk* 12 (1969): 20-25.

Hull, Andrew. "War of Words: The Public Science of the British Scientific Community and the Origins of the Department of Scientific and Industrial Research, 1914-16." *British Journal for the History of Science* 32 (1999): 461-81.

Ihde, Aaron. *The Development of Modern Chemistry.* New York: Harper and Row, 1964; reprinted, Dover, 1970.

Jacob, Gustaf. *Friedrich Engelhorn. Der Gründer der Badischen Anilin- & Soda-Fabrik.* Mannheim: Gesellschaft der Freunde Mannheims, 1959.

James, Frank A. J. L. *Chemistry and Theology in Mid-Victorian London: The Diary of Herbert McLeod, 1860-70.* London: Mansell, 1987.

Johnson, Jeffrey A. "Academic Self-Regulation and the Chemical Profession in Imperial Germany." *Minerva* 23 (1985): 241-71.

——. *The Kaiser's Chemists: Science and Modernization in Imperial Germany.* Chapel Hill: University of North Carolina Press, 1990.

——. "Academic, Proletarian, Professional? Shaping Professionalization for German Industrial Chemists, 1887-1920." In *German Professions 1800-1950*, eds. Geoffrey Cocks and Konrad H. Jarausch, pp. 123-42. New York: Oxford University Press, 1990.

——. "German Women in Chemistry 1895-1925," Part I, *N.T.M.* 6 (1998), 1-21 (preprint page numbers).

Kargon, Robert H. *Science in Victorian Manchester: Enterprise and Expertise.*

Baltimore: Johns Hopkins University Press, 1977.

Keas, Michael N. "Karl Aloys Schenzinger's Novel, *Anilin:* Chemistry and Chemical Technology in Nazi *Literaturpolitik.*" *Ambix* 39 (1992): 127-40.

Knecht, Edmund, Christopher Rawson, and Richard Loewenthal. *A Manual of Dyeing: For the Use of Practical Dyers, Manufacturers, Students, and All Interested in the Art of Dyeing*, 2 vols. London: Charles Griffin, 7th. ed., 1922.

Krätz, Otto P., and Annemarie Diem. "Heinrich Caro: Die Louisenthaler Actiengesellschaft in Mülheim an der Ruhr–eine kombinierte Naturfarbstoff-Fabrik und Färberei zur Zeit der ersten Anilinfarben." *Chemie, Experiment & Didaktik* 2 (1976): 179-86.

Levinstein, Herbert. "Proceedings of the Society. The First George Douglas Lecture: George Douglas, His Times, and Some Thoughts on the Future." *Journal of the Society of Dyers and Colourists* 65 (1949): 269-75.

Levinstein, Ivan. "The Development and Present State of the Alizarin Industry." *Journal of the Society of Chemical Industry* 2 (1883): 213-27.

——. "Observations and Suggestions on the Present Position of the British Chemical Industries with Special Reference to Coal-Tar Derivatives." *Journal of the Society of Chemical Industry* 5 (1886): 351-59.

——. "President's Address: Education and Legislation: The Influence of Trade and Industry." *Journal of the Society of Chemical Industry* 21 (1902): 893-99.

Lightfoot, John. *The Chemical History and Progress of Aniline Black.* Burnley, 1871.

Marsch, Ulrich. "Strategies for Success: Research Organization in German Chemical Companies and I.G. Farben Until 1936." *History and Technology* 12 (1995): 23-77.

Meinel, Christoph, and Hartmut Scholz, eds. *Die Allianz von Wissenschaft und Industrie: August Wilhelm Hofmann (1818-1892): Zeit, Werk, Wirkung.* Weinheim: VCH, 1992.

Meinzer, Lothar, Karl Dettke, Jutta Kissener, and Klaus-Jürgen Matz. *125 Jahre BASF. Stationen ihrer Geschichte. Katalog zur Ausstellung im Rathaus-Center Ludwigshafen, 28. April bis 29. Juni 1990.* Ludwigshafen: BASF, 1990.

Meldola, Raphael. "The Scientific Development of the Coal-Tar Colour Industry." Under "Abstracts from English and Foreign Journals. V. Coal-Tar Colours." *Journal of the Society of Dyers and Colourists* 2 (1886): 95-101.

——, Arthur G. Green, and John Cannell Cain, eds. *Jubilee of the Discovery of Mauve and of the Foundation of the Coal-Tar Colour Industry by Sir W. H. Perkin, F.R.S., D.Sc., LL.D., Ph.D., Dr. Ing.* London: Perkin Memorial

Committee, 1906.

Meyer, Richard. *Victor Meyer. Leben und Wirken eines deutschen Chemikers und Naturforschers. 1848-1897.* Leipzig: Akademische Verlagsgesellschaft, 1917.

Meyer, Rita. "Emil Erlenmeyer (1925-1909) als Chemietheoretiker und sein Beitrag zur Entwicklung der Strukturchemie." Ph.D. diss., University of Munich, 1984.

Meyer-Thurow, Georg. "The Industrialization of Invention: A Case Study from the German Chemical Industry." *Isis* 73 (1982): 363-81.

Morris, Peter J. T., and Colin A. Russell. *Archives of the British Chemical Industry 1750-1914: A Handlist*. British Society for the History of Science Monographs, no. 6. Faringdon, Oxfordshire: British Society for the History of Science, 1988.

——. "The Legacy of Ludwig Mond." *Endeavour* 13 (1989): 34-40.

——, and Anthony S. Travis. "The Chemical Society of London and the Dye Industry in the 1860s." *Ambix* 39 (1992): 117-26.

Moy, Timothy D. "Emil Fischer as 'Chemical Mediator': Science, Industry and Government in World War One." *Ambix* 36 (1989): 109-20.

Nagel, Alfred von. *Fuchsin, Alizarin, Indigo. Der Beginn eines Weltunternehmens*. Ludwigshafen: BASF, 1968.

Nipperdey, Thomas. *Deutsche Geschichte 1800-1866. Bürgerwelt und starker Staat*. Munich: Beck, 5th ed., 1991.

——. *Deutsche Geschichte 1866-1918. Arbeitswelt und Bürgergeist*. München: Beck, 2nd. ed., 1991.

Nottebohm, F. W. *Chronik der Königlichen Gewerbe-Akademie zu Berlin. Festschrift zur Feier des Fünfzigjährigen Bestehens der Anstalt.* Berlin, 1871.

O'Neill, Charles. *The Practice and Principles of Calico Printing, Bleaching, Dyeing, etc.*, 2 vols. Manchester: Palmer & Howe, 1878.

Partington, James Riddick. *A History of Chemistry*, 4 vols. London: Macmillan, 1961-70.

Perkin, William H. "The President's Address." *Journal of the Society of Chemical Industry* 4 (1885): 427-38

Perkin, William H., Junior. "The Position of the Organic Chemical Industry." *Journal of the Chemical Society, Transactions* 57 (1915): 557-78

Pfeiffer, Karl. "Carl Engler." In *Die Technische Hochschule Fridericiana Karlsruhe. Festschrift zur 125-Jahrfeier*, pp. 40-45. Karlsruhe, 1950.

Pieper, Wolfgang. "Seligmann Ladenburg als Finanzier der BASF." *Tradition* 12 (1967): 553-75

Pinnow, Hermann. *75 Jahre Werksgeschichte Hoechst. Zur Erinnerung an die 75. Wiederkehr des Gründungstages der Farbwerke vorm. Meister Lucius &*

Brüning. Munich: Bruckmann, 1938.

——. *Werksgeschichte der Gefolgschaft der Werke Leverkusen, Elberfeld und Dormagen zur Erinnerung an die 75. Wiederkehr des Gründungstages der Farbenfabriken vorm. Friedr. Bayer & Co.* Munich: Bruckmann, 1938.

Ploss, Emil. "Indigo. Die merkwürdige Geschichte eines Namens." *Die BASF* 10 (1960): 85-91.

Pohl, Hans, Ralf Schaumann, and Frauke Schönert-Röhlk. *Die chemische Industrie in den Rheinlanden während der industriellen Revolution*. Vol. 1. *Die Farbenindustrie*. Wiesbaden: Steiner, 1983.

Pollard, Sidney. *Britain's Prime and Britain's Decline. The British Economy, 1870-1914*. London: Arnold, 1989.

Prittwitz, Karl Ludwig von. *Berlin 1848. Das Erinnerungswerk des General-leutnants Karl Ludwig von Prittwitz und andere Quellen zur Berliner Märzrevolution und zur Geschichte Preußens um die Mitte des 19. Jahrhunderts*, ed. Gerd Heinrich. Berlin: Walter de Gruyter, 1985.

Ramsay, Sir William, and William Macnab, eds. *Seventh International Congress of Applied Chemistry, London, May 27th to June 2nd 1909. Section XI. Law, Political Economy, and Legislation Affecting Chemical Industry.* London: Partridge & Cooper, 1910.

Rassow, Berthold. *Geschichte des Vereins Deutscher Chemiker in den ersten 25 Jahren seines Bestehens.* Leipzig: Spamer, 1912.

Reader, William J. *Imperial Chemical Industries: A History*, 2 vols. London: Oxford University Press, 1970, 1975.

Reimann, Max. *On Aniline and its Derivatives: A Treatise Upon the Manufacture of Aniline and Aniline Colours*, trans. from the German, rev. and ed. by William Crookes. New York: John Wiley & Son, 1868.

Reinhardt, Carsten. "Die Farbe Blau: Indigo." In *Ein blaues Wunder. Blaudruck in Europa und Japan*, ed. Hartmut Walravens, pp. 14-24. Berlin: Akademie Verlag, 1993.

——. "Vom Alizarinblau zum Thallin, Pharmazeutisch-chemische Forschung der BASF in den achtziger Jahren des 19. Jahrhunderts." In *Brückenschläge. 25 Jahre Lehrstuhl für Geschichte der exakten Wissenschaften und der Technik an der Technischen Universität Berlin. 1969-1994*, eds. Hans-Werner Schütt and Burghard Weiss, pp. 253-76. Berlin: Engel, 1995.

——. *Forschung in der chemischen Industrie. Die Entwicklung synthetischer Farbstoffe bei BASF und Hoechst. 1863-1914.* Freiberg: Technische Universität Bergakademie Freiberg, 1997.

——. "An Instrument of Corporate Strategy: The Central Research Laboratory at BASF, 1868-1890." In *The Chemical Industry in Europe, 1850-1914: Industrial Growth, Pollution, and Professionalization*, eds. Ernst Homburg, Anthony S. Travis, and Harm G. Schröter, pp. 239-59. Dordrecht: Kluwer

1998.

——. "Basic Research in Industry: Two Case Studies at I. G. Farbenindustrie AG in the 1920s and 1930s." In *Determinants in the Evolution of the European Chemical Industry. 1900-1939. New Technologies, Political Frameworks, Markets and Companies*, eds. Anthony S. Travis, Harm G. Schröter, Ernst Homburg, and Peter J. T. Morris, pp. 67-88. Dordrecht: Kluwer, 1998.

——, and Anthony S. Travis. "The Introduction of Aniline Dyes to Paper Printing and Queen Victoria's Postage Stamps." *Ambix* 44 (1997): 11-18.

Remane, Horst. *Emil Fischer*. Leipzig: Teubner, 1984.

Riedl-Ehrenberg, Renate. *Alfred Kern (1850-1893), Edouard Sandoz (1853-1928). Gründer der Sandoz AG, Basel.* Schweizer Pioniere der Wirtschaft und Technik, vol. 44. Basel/Zurich: Verein für wirtschafts-historische Studien, 1986.

Rocke, Alan J. "Hypothesis and Experiment in the Early Development of Kekulé's Benzene Theory." *Annals of Science* 42 (1985): 355-81.

——. "Kekulé's Benzene Theory and the Appraisal of Scientific Theories." In *Scrutinizing Science. Empirical Studies of Scientific Change,* eds. Arthur Donovan, Larry Laudan, and Rachel Laudan, pp. 145-61. Dordrecht: Kluwer, 1988.

——. *The Quiet Revolution. Hermann Kolbe and the Science of Organic Chemistry.* Berkeley: University of California Press, 1993.

Rubinstein, W. D. *Capitalism, Culture, and Decline in Britain, 1750-1990.* London: Routledge, 1993.

Ruske, Walter. *100 Jahre Deutsche Chemische Gesellschaft*. Weinheim:Verlag Chemie, 1967.

——. "Zur Geschichte der technischen Chemie in Berlin." In *Wissenschaft und Gesellschaft. Beiträge zur Geschichte der Technischen Universität Berlin, 1879-1979*, ed. Reinhard Rürup, 2 vols, vol. 2, pp.153-76. Berlin: Springer, 1979.

Russell, Colin A. *The History of Valency.* Leicester: Leicester University Press, 1971.

Saftien, Karl. "Kekulé als Gutachter." *Die BASF* 15 (1965): 190-98.

Sanderson, Michael. "The English Universities and the 'Industrial Spirit', 1870-1914." *Historical Research* 61 (1988): 90-104.

Sandiford, A. V., and T. E. Ashworth, *The Forgotten Valley*. Bury: Bury and District Local History Society, 1981.

Scheinert, Wolfgang. "Joseph Wilhelm Weiler, Julius Weiler und das Anilin. Zur Entwicklungsgeschichte der deutschen Teerfarbenindustrie und der chemischen Technik vor dem Ersten Weltkrieg." *Zeitschrift für Unternehmensgeschichte* 33 (1988): 217-31.

Schenzinger, Karl Aloys. *Anilin.* Berlin: Zeitgeschichte-Verlag, Wilhelm

Andermann, 1936.

Schmorl, Karl. *Adolf von Baeyer.* Stuttgart: Wissenschaftliche Verlagsgesellschaft, 1952.

Schorlemmer, Carl A. *The Rise and Development of Organic Chemistry*, revised edition, ed. Arthur Smithells. Macmillan: London, 1894.

Schreier, Anna Elisabeth, and Manuela Wex. *Chronik der Hoechst AG. 1863-1988.* Frankfurt am Main: Hoechst, 1990.

Schröter, Hans. *Friedrich Engelhorn. Ein Unternehmer-Porträt des 19. Jahrhunderts.* Landau: Pfälzische Verlagsanstalt, 1991.

Schröter, Harm G., and Anthony S. Travis. "An Issue of Different Mentalities: National Approaches to the Development of the Chemical Industry in Britain and Germany before 1914." In *The Chemical Industry in Europe, 1850-1914: Industrial Growth, Pollution, and Professionalization*, eds. Ernst Homburg, Anthony S. Travis, and Harm G. Schröter, pp. 95-118. Dordrecht: Kluwer, 1998.

Schultz, Gustav. *Farbstofftabellen*, 2 vols. Leipzig: Akademische Verlagsgesellschaft, 7th. ed., 1931.

——, and Paul Julius. *Tabellarische Übersicht über die künstlichen organischen Farbstoffe.* Berlin: R. Gaertner's Verlagsbuchhandlung, 1888.

Schultze, Hermann. *Die Entwicklung der chemischen Industrie in Deutschland seit dem Jahre 1875. Eine volkswirtschaftliche Studie mit besonderer Berücksichtigung der Unternehmerverbände und der Rentabilität der Aktiengesellschaften.* Halle/Saale: Tausch & Grosse, 1908.

Schunck, [H.] Edward, R. Angus Smith, and Henry E. Roscoe. "On the Recent Progress and Present Condition of Manufacturing Chemistry in the South Lancashire District." In *Report of the Thirty-First Meeting of the British Association for the Advancement of Science (Manchester, 1861)*, pp. 109-28. London: John Murray, 1862.

Schuster, Curt. "Heinrich Caro." In *Ludwigshafener Chemiker*, ed. Kurt Oberdorffer, vol. 2, pp. 45-83. Düsseldorf: Econ-Verlag, 1960.

——. *Vom Farbenhandel zur Farbenindustrie. Die erste Fusion der BASF.* Ludwigshafen: BASF, 1973.

——. *Wissenschaft und Technik. Ihre Begegnung in der BASF während der ersten Jahrzehnte der Unternehmensgeschichte.* Ludwigshafen: BASF, 1976.

Schütt, Hans-Werner. "Der Wandel des Begriffes 'aromatisch' in der Chemie." In *Begriffswandel und Erkenntnisfortschritt in den Erfahrungswissenschaften*, eds. Friedrich Rapp and Hans-Werner Schütt, pp. 255-72. Berlin: Technical University of Berlin, 1987.

Steen, Kathryn. "Wartime Catalyst and Postwar Reaction: The Making of the United States Synthetic Organic Chemicals Industry, 1910-1930." Ph.D.

diss., University of Delaware, 1995.

Stern, Fritz. *Gold and Iron: Bismarck, Bleichröder, and the Building of the German Empire.* Peregrine/Penguin: Harmondsworth, 1987.

Swann, J. P. *Academic Scientists and the Pharmaceutical Industry. Cooperative Research in Twentieth-Century America.* Baltimore, 1988.

Tordoff, Maurice. *The Servant of Colour: A History of the Society of Dyers and Colourists, 1884-1984.* Bradford: The Society of Dyers and Colourists, 1984.

Travis, Anthony S. "Perkin's Mauve: Ancestor of the Organic Chemical Industry." *Technology & Culture* 31 (1990): 51-82.

——. "The Meeting of Practical Men." *Chemistry and Industry*, 19 July 1990, pp. 451-56.

——. "Heinrich Caro at Roberts, Dale & Co." *Ambix* 38 (1991): 113-34.

——. "Colour Makers and Consumers: Heinrich Caro's British Network." *Journal of the Society of Dyers and Colourists* 108 (1992): 311-16.

——. "Science's Powerful Companion: A. W. Hofmann's Investigation of Aniline Red and Its Derivatives." *British Journal for the History of Science* 25 (1992): 27-44.

——. "Science and Technology for an Empire: A.W. Hofmann and Heinrich Caro in England." In *Die Allianz von Wissenschaft und Industrie: August Wilhelm Hofmann (1818-1892): Zeit, Werk, Wirkung*, eds. Christoph Meinel and Hartmut Scholz, pp.119-32. Weinheim: VCH, 1992.

——. *The Rainbow Makers. The Origins of the Synthetic Dyestuffs Industry in Western Europe.* Bethlehem, Pa.: Lehigh University Press, 1993.

——. *From Turkey Red to Tyrian Purple: Textile Colours for the Industrial Revolution.* Jerusalem: Jewish National and University Library, 1993.

——. "Between Broken Root and Artificial Alizarin: The Textile Arts and Manufactures of Madder." *History and Technology* 11 (1994): 1-21.

——. "From Manchester to Massachusetts via Mulhouse: The Transatlantic Voyage of Aniline Black." *Technology and Culture* 35 (1994): 70-99.

——. "Artificial Dyes in John Lightfoot's Broad Oak Laboratory." *Ambix* 42 (1995): 10-27.

——. "Poisoned Groundwater and Contaminated Soil: The Tribulations and Trial of the First Major Manufacturer of Aniline Dyes in Basel." *Environmental History* 2 (1997): 343-65.

——. "Theory from Practice: Portraying the Constitutions of Aniline Dyes in the 1860s." In *The Invisible Industrialist*, eds. Ilana Löwy and Jean-Paul Gaudillière, pp. 122-42. Houndmills, Basingstoke: Macmillan, 1998.

——. "Heinrich Caro and Ivan Levinstein: Uniting the Colours of Ludwigshafen and Lancashire." In *The Chemical Industry in Europe, 1850-1914: Industrial Growth, Pollution, and Professionalization*, eds. Ernst Homburg,

Anthony S. Travis, and Harm G. Schröter, pp. 261-80. Dordrecht: Kluwer, 1998.

——. "High Pressure Industrial Chemistry: The First Steps, 1909-1913, and the Impact." In *Determinants in the Evolution of the European Chemical Industry. 1900-1939. New Technologies, Political Frameworks, Markets and Companies*, eds. Anthony S. Travis, Harm G. Schröter, Ernst Homburg, and Peter J. T. Morris, pp. 1-21. Dordrecht: Kluwer, 1998.

——. "'Ambitious and Glory Hunting ... Impractical and Fantastic': Heinrich Caro at BASF." *Technology and Culture* 39 (1998): 105-15.

——. "Heinrich Caro, Chemist and Calico Printer, and the Changeover from Natural to Artificial Dyes." In *Natural Dyestuffs and Industrial Culture in Europe, 1750-1880*, eds. Robert Fox and Agustí Nieto-Galan, pp. 285-307. Canton, Ma.: Watson International/Science History Publications, 1999.

——. "Surrogate Instruments: Industrial Chemical Reactors." In *Instrument–Experiment: Historische Studien*, ed. Christoph Meinel, pp. 201-16. Berlin: Diepholz, 2000.

Turner, Frank M. "Public Science in Britain, 1880-1919." *Isis* 71 (1980): 589-608.

Vaupel, Elisabeth. "Carl Graebe (1841-1927) – Leben, Werk und Wirken im Spiegel seines brieflichen Nachlasses," 2 vols. Ph.D. diss. University of Munich, 1987.

Verbong, Geert. "The Dutch Calico Printing Industry between 1870 and 1875." In *Natural Dyestuffs and Industrial Culture in Europe, 1750-1880*, eds. Robert Fox and Agustí Nieto-Galan, pp. 193-218. Canton, Mass.: Watson International/Science History Publications, 1999.

Verg, Erik, Gottfried Plumpe, and Heinz Schultheis. *Milestones: The Bayer Story. 1863-1988*. Leverkusen: Bayer, 1988.

Voelcker, Heinrich. *75 Jahre Kalle. Ein Beitrag zur Nassauischen Industriegeschichte. 1863-1938*. Wiesbaden-Biebrich: Kalle & Co., 1938.

Wetzel, Walter. *Naturwissenschaften und chemische Industrie in Deutschland. Voraussetzungen und Mechanismen ihres Aufstiegs im 19. Jahrhundert*. Stuttgart: Steiner, 1991.

Wiedenmann, Evelyn. "Die Konstruktion der richtigen Formel. Strukturaufklärung und Synthese des Indigblau, dargestellt an Hand des Briefwechsels Baeyer-Caro," 2 vols. Ph.D. diss. Technical University of Munich, 1978.

Wiener, M. J. *English Culture and the Decline of the Industrial Spirit, 1850-1980*. Cambridge: Cambridge University Press, 1981.

Willstätter, Richard. "Zur Geschichte der AGFA." *Berichte der Deutschen Chemischen Gesellschaft* 64 (1931): 140-49.

——. *Aus meinem Leben. Von Arbeit, Muße und Freunden*. Weinheim: Verlag

Chemie, 1949.

——. *From My Life: Memoirs of Richard Willstätter*, trans. from the German by Lilli S. Hornig; ed. in the original German by Arthur Stoll. New York: W. A. Benjamin, 1965.

Wimmer, Wolfgang. "*Wir haben fast immer was Neues.*" *Gesundheitswesen und Innovationen der Pharma-Industrie in Deutschland, 1880-1935*. Berlin: Duncker & Humblot, 1994.

Witt, Otto N. *Chemische Homologie und Isomerie in ihrem Einflusse auf Erfindungen aus dem Gebiete der organischen Chemie. Eine patentrechtliche Studie vom Standpunkte des Chemikers.* Berlin, 1889.

Wolf, Gerhart. *BASF. Development of a World-Wide Enterprise.* Ludwigshafen: BASF, 1970.

Wolff, Adolf. *Berliner Revolutionschronik. Darstellung der Berliner Bewegungen im Jahre 1848 nach politischen, sozialen und literarischen Beziehungen*, 3 vols. Berlin, 1851-54; reprinted, Leipzig,1979.

Wotiz, John H., ed. *The Kekulé Riddle. A Challenge for Chemists and Psychologists.* Clearwater, Fla.: Cache River Press, 1993.

Zimmermann, Paul A. *Patentwesen in der Chemie. Ursprünge, Anfänge, Entwicklung.* Ludwigshafen: BASF, 1965.

——. *Über die Grenzen hinaus. Notizen zur industriellen Entwicklung im 19. Jahrhundert.* Ludwigshafen: BASF, 1971.

Zubatsky, David S, and Irwin M. Bernet. *Sourcebook for Jewish Genealogies and Family Histories*. Teaneck, N.J.: Avotaynu, Inc., 1996.

Chapter Location of Major Dye Classes, Important Individual Dyes, Dye-Intermediates, and Raw Materials

Name Index

—N—

—O—

—P—

—R—

Index of Companies, Partnerships, Academic and Legal Institutions, and Trade and Professional Associations

GPSR Compliance

The European Union's (EU) General Product Safety Regulation (GPSR) is a set of rules that requires consumer products to be safe and our obligations to ensure this.

If you have any concerns about our products, you can contact us on ProductSafety@springernature.com

In case Publisher is established outside the EU, the EU authorized representative is:

Springer Nature Customer Service Center GmbH
Europaplatz 3
69115 Heidelberg, Germany

Batch number: 10809439

Printed by Printforce, the Netherlands